PRENTICE HALL

SCIENCE EXPLORER

Grade 6

Prentice
Hall

Needham, Massachusetts
Upper Saddle River, New Jersey
Glenview, Illinois

Grade 6

Program Resources

Student Edition
Annotated Teacher's Edition
Unit Resource Books, including:
- Chapter Project Support
- Lesson Plans
- Section Summaries
- Review and Reinforce Worksheets
- Enrich Worksheets
- Student Edition Lab Worksheets
- Answer Keys

Lesson Plans
Chapter and Unit Tests
Performance Assessments
Color Transparencies
Laboratory Manual, Student Edition
Laboratory Manual, Teacher's Edition
Guided Reading and Study Workbook
Guided Reading and Study Workbook, Teacher's Edition
Prentice Hall Assessment System

Program-Wide Components

Inquiry Skills Activity Book
Student-Centered Science Activity Book
   for the Southwest
Reading in the Content Area With
   Literature Connections
Probeware Laboratory Manual with
   CD-ROM
How to Assess Student Work
How to Manage Instruction in the Block
Teacher's ELL Handbook

Media/Technology

Science Explorer iText
Resource Pro CD-ROM
Science Explorer Web site
   at **www.phschool.com**
Computer Test Bank Book with CD-ROM
Student Edition on Audio CD
Student Edition on Audio CD—Spanish
Lab Activity Videotape Library
Science Explorer Videodiscs
Science Explorer Videotape Library
Science Explorer Videotape Library—Spanish

ISBN 0-13-053478-1
1 2 3 4 5 6 7 8 9 10   05 04 03 02 01

Astronaut Jerry Ross works outside the Space Shuttle *Endeavor* during a mission.

Program Authors

Michael J. Padilla, Ph.D.
Professor
Department of Science Education
University of Georgia
Athens, Georgia

Michael Padilla is a leader in middle school science education. He has served as an editor and elected officer for the National Science Teachers Association. He has been principal investigator of several National Science Foundation and Eisenhower grants and served as a writer of the National Science Education Standards.

As lead author of *Science Explorer*, Mike has inspired the team in developing a program that meets the needs of middle grades students, promotes science inquiry, and is aligned with the National Science Education Standards.

Ioannis Miaoulis, Ph.D.
Dean of Engineering
College of Engineering
Tufts University
Medford, Massachusetts

Martha Cyr, Ph.D.
Director, Engineering
    Educational Outreach
College of Engineering
Tufts University
Medford, Massachusetts

Science Explorer was created in collaboration with the College of Engineering at Tufts University. Tufts has an extensive engineering outreach program that uses engineering design and construction to excite and motivate students and teachers in science and technology education.

Faculty from Tufts University participated in the development of *Science Explorer* chapter projects, reviewed the student books for content accuracy, and helped coordinate field testing.

Book Authors

Elizabeth Coolidge-Stolz, M.D.
Medical Writer
North Reading, Massachusetts

Linda Cronin-Jones, Ph.D.
Professor, College of Education
University of Florida
Gainesville, Florida

Donald Cronkite, Ph.D.
Professor of Biology
Hope College
Holland, Michigan

Joseph D. Exline, M.A., Ed.D.
President
Exline Consulting Services, Inc.
Beaverdam, Virginia

David V. Frank, Ph.D.
Physical Science Department Head
Ferris State University
Big Rapids, Michigan

Fred Holtzclaw
Science Instructor
Oak Ridge High School
Oak Ridge, Tennessee

Jan Jenner, Ph.D.
Science Writer
Talladega, Alabama

Steve Miller
Science Writer
State College, Pennsylvania

Jay M. Pasachoff, Ph.D.
Professor of Astronomy
Williams College
Williamstown, Massachusetts

Barbara Brooks Simons
Science Writer
Boston, Massachusetts

Carole Garbuny Vogel, M.A.T.
Science Writer
Lexington, Massachusetts

Jonathan Gitlin, M.D.
School of Medicine
Washington University
St. Louis, Missouri

Dawn Graff-Haight, Ph.D.
Department of Health, Human
    Performance, and Athletics
Linfield College
McMinnville, Oregon

Deborah L. Gumucio, Ph.D.
Associate Professor
Department of Anatomy and
    Cell Biology
University of Michigan
Ann Arbor, Michigan

William S. Harwood, Ph.D.
Dean of University Division and
    Associate Professor of Education
Indiana University
Bloomington, Indiana

Cyndy Henzel, Ph.D.
Department of Geography
    and Regional Development
University of Arizona
Tucson, Arizona

Greg Hutton
Science and Health
    Curriculum Coordinator
School Board of Sarasota County
Sarasota, Florida

Susan K. Jacobson, Ph.D.
Department of Wildlife Ecology
    and Conservation
University of Florida
Gainesville, Florida

Judy Jernstedt, Ph.D.
Department of Agronomy and
    Range Science
University of California, Davis
Davis, California

John L. Kermond, Ph.D.
Office of Global Programs
National Oceanographic and
    Atmospheric Administration
Silver Spring, Maryland

David E. LaHart, Ph.D.
Institute of Science and
    Public Affairs
Florida State University
Tallahassee, Florida

Joe Leverich, Ph.D.
Department of Biology
St. Louis University
St. Louis, Missouri

Dennis K. Lieu, Ph.D.
Department of Mechanical
    Engineering
University of California
Berkeley, California

Desiree A. Jackson, Ph.D.
Department of Biology
Texas Southern University
Houston, Texas

Akhtar H. Mahmood, Ph.D.
Assistant Professor
University of Texas-Pan American
Edinburg, Texas

Cynthia J. Moore, Ph.D.
Science Outreach Coordinator
Washington University
St. Louis, Missouri

Joseph M. Moran, Ph.D.
Department of Earth Science
University of Wisconsin–Green Bay
Green Bay, Wisconsin

José L. Panero
Assistant Professor of Botany
University of Texas
Austin, Texas

Doris Rosenbaum, Ph.D.
Scholar in Residence, Physics
    Department
Southern Methodist University
Dallas, Texas

Ronald L. Sass, Ph.D.
Professor of Chemistry and Biology
Rice University
Houston, Texas

Eric S. Schmitt, Ph.D., M.S., C.G.C.
Genetic Counselor
Baylor College of Medicine
Houston, Texas

John M. Sharp, Jr., Ph.D.
Chevron Centennial Professor of
    Geology
University of Texas
Austin, Texas

Joseph Stukey, Ph.D.
Department of Biology
Hope College
Holland, Michigan

Seetha Subramanian
Lexington Community College
University of Kentucky
Lexington, Kentucky

Carl L. Thurman, Ph.D.
Department of Biology
University of Northern Iowa
Cedar Falls, Iowa

Edward D. Walton, Ph.D.
Department of Chemistry
California State Polytechnic
    University
Pomona, California

Susan D. Wiediger, Ph.D.
Research Associate
Department of Chemistry
Rice University
Houston, Texas

Aaron S. Yoshinobu, Ph.D.
Assistant Professor
Department of Geosciences
Texas Technical University
Lubbock, Texas

Robert S. Young, Ph.D.
Department of Geosciences and
    Natural Resource Management
Western Carolina University
Cullowhee, North Carolina

Edward J. Zalisko, Ph.D.
Department of Biology
Blackburn College
Carlinville, Illinois

Texas Consultants

Susan M. Cory, Senior Texas Consultant
Cypress Fairbanks ISD
Houston, Texas

Jill Bailer
Science Department Chairperson
Jane Long Middle School
Houston, Texas

Beverly Bowe
Comstock Middle School
Dallas ISD
Dallas, Texas

Sharon J. Delesbore
Olle Middle School
Alief ISD
Houston, Texas

Marcie Denton
Peterson Middle School
Peterson ISD
Kerrville, Texas

Cathy Harter
Mayde Creek Junior High
Katy ISD
Houston, Texas

David Hollis
Marsh Middle School
Dallas ISD
Dallas, Texas

Debra McCain
Science Department Chair
Bussey Middle School
Garland ISD
Garland, Texas

Candice Meyer
Hildebrandt Intermediate School
Klein ISD
Spring, Texas

Sharon Phillips-Watson
Rusk Middle School
Dallas ISD
Dallas, TX

Sarah Santos Montez
Science Specialist
Edgewood ISD
San Antonio, Texas

Paul Reyna
Lyles Middle School
Garland ISD
Garland, Texas

Eddie Rodriguez
Science Specialist
Edgewood ISD
San Antonio, Texas

C. Lorraine Thompson
Educator
Dallas ISD
Franklin Middle School
Dallas, Texas

Teacher Reviewers

José Luis Alvarez
Ysleta ISD
El Paso, Texas

Stephanie Anderson
Sierra Vista Junior High School
Canyon Country, California

John W. Anson
Mesa Intermediate School
Palmdale, California

Pamela Arline
Lake Taylor Middle School
Norfolk, Virginia

Lynn Beason
A & M Consolidated Middle School
College Station, Texas

Jennifer Becerra
Pease Middle School
San Antonio, Texas

Stacey L. Blair
Tivy Upper Elementary School
Kerrville, Texas

Richard Bothmer
Hollis School District
Hollis, New Hampshire

Jeffrey C. Callister
Newburgh Free Academy
Newburgh, New York

Judy D'Albert
Harvard Day School
Corona Del Mar, California

Betty Scott Dean
Guilford County Schools
McLeansville, North Carolina

Sarah C. Duff
Baltimore City Public Schools
Baltimore, Maryland

Patricia Durst
Handley Middle School
Fort Worth, Texas

Cecie Edwards
Sudan ISD
Sudan, Texas

Melody Law Ewey
Holmes Junior High School
Davis, California

Sherry L. Fisher
Lake Zurich Middle School North
Lake Zurich, Illinois

Melissa Gibbons
Dunbar Middle School
Fort Worth, Texas

Debra J. Goodding
Kraemer Middle School
Placentia, California

Jack Grande
Weber Middle School
Port Washington, New York

Carole W. Henry
Gus Garcia Middle School
San Antonio, Texas

Ross Ann Hill
Idalou Middle School
Idalou, Texas

Steve Hills
Riverside Middle School
Grand Rapids, Michigan

Sandra M. Justin
Swift Junior High School
Oakville, Connecticut

Rosie L. Leno
Krueger Middle School
San Antonio, Texas

Carol Ann Lionello
Kraemer Middle School
Placentia, California

Alison Minish-Ford
Ysleta Middle School
El Paso, Texas

Jaime A. Morales
Henry T. Gage Middle
School
Huntington Park,
California

Rebecca Morton
Wedgwood Sixth Grade
School
Fort Worth, Texas

Patsy Partin
Cameron Middle School
Fort Worth, Texas

Deedra H. Robinson
Newport News Public
Schools
Newport News, Virginia

Rick Robinson
Medina Valley Middle
School
San Antonio, Texas

Charles M. Sears
Belzer Middle School
Indianapolis, Indiana

Shirley Simon
South Park Middle
School
Beaumont, Texas

Barbara M. Strange
Ferndale Middle School
High Point, North
Carolina

Denzial Tittle
Thornton Middle
School
Katy, Texas

Kathy Usina
Belzer Middle School
Indianapolis, Indiana

Heidi M. von Oetinger
L'Anse Creuse Public
School
Harrison Township,
Michigan

Pam Watson
Hill Country Middle
School
Austin, Texas

Laurie Westphal
Thornton Middle School
Katy, Texas

Activity Field Testers

Nicki Bibbo
Russell Street School
Littleton, Massachusetts

Connie Boone
Fletcher Middle School
Jacksonville Beach,
Florida

Rose-Marie Botting
Broward County
School District
Fort Lauderdale, Florida

Colleen Campos
Laredo Middle School
Aurora, Colorado

Elizabeth Chait
W. L. Chenery Middle
School
Belmont, Massachusetts

Holly Estes
Hale Middle School
Stow, Massachusetts

Laura Hapgood
Plymouth Community
Intermediate School
Plymouth, Massachusetts

Sandra M. Harris
Winman Junior High
School
Warwick, Rhode Island

Jason Ho
Walter Reed Middle
School
Los Angeles, California

Joanne Jackson
Winman Junior High
School
Warwick, Rhode Island

Mary F. Lavin
Plymouth Community
Intermediate School
Plymouth, Massachusetts

James MacNeil, Ph.D.
Concord Public Schools
Concord, Massachusetts

Lauren Magruder
St. Michael's Country Day
School
Newport, Rhode Island

Warren Phillips
Plymouth Community
Intermediate School
Plymouth, Massachusetts

Carol Pirtle
Hale Middle School
Stow, Massachusetts

Kathleen M. Poe
Kirby-Smith Middle
School
Jacksonville, Florida

Cynthia B. Pope
Ruffner Middle School
Norfolk, Virginia

Anne Scammell
Geneva Middle School
Geneva, New York

Karen Riley Sievers
Callanan Middle School
Des Moines, Iowa

David M. Smith
Howard A. Eyer Middle
School
Macungie, Pennsylvania

Derek Strohschneider
Plymouth Community
Intermediate School
Plymouth, Massachusetts

Gene Vitale
Parkland Middle School
McHenry, Illinois

Zenovia Young
Meyer Levin Junior
High School (IS 285)
Brooklyn, New York

Contents

Grade 6

Unit 1 Properties of Physical Systems

Unit 2 Structure and Function in Living Systems

Unit 3 Matter and Energy in the Environment

Unit 4 Earth and Space Systems—Structure and Function

Reference Section

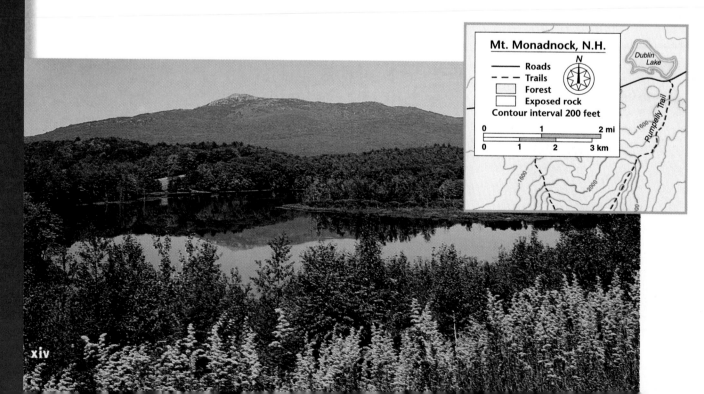

Mt. Monadnock, N.H.
— Roads
- - - Trails
  Forest
  Exposed rock
Contour interval 200 feet

0   1   2 mi
0 1 2 3 km

Dublin Lake

Pumpelly Trail

Activities

Inquiry Activities

CHAPTER PROJECT
Opportunities for long-term inquiry

DISCOVER
Exploration and inquiry before reading

PRENTICE HALL
SCIENCE EXPLORER

DISCOVER

Sharpen your *Skills*

Practice of specific science inquiry skills

TRY THIS
Reinforcement of key concepts

Skills Lab
In-depth practice of inquiry skills

Real-World Lab

Everyday application of science concepts

Science at Home

Family involvement in science exploration

Interdisciplinary Activities

Texas Essential Knowledge and Skills for Science

To Parents and Students:

The State of Texas has established standards describing science knowledge and skills for which all students are responsible. These standards are known as the Texas Essential Knowledge and Skills, or TEKS. State assessments of student achievement in science are based on these TEKS. The Grade 6 TEKS are listed below. The chapter references show where the content and skills are addressed in this textbook. A TEKS may be addressed in more than one chapter. Some chapters address only part of a TEKS.

To check for mastery of the content and process TEKS, students may use the Chapter Assessments at the end of each chapter and the *Science Explorer* iText at: **www.phschool.com**

(6.1) Scientific processes. The student conducts field and laboratory investigations using safe, environmentally appropriate, and ethical practices. *(Chapters 1–9, 11–16)*
The student is expected to:
(A) demonstrate safe practices during field and laboratory investigations; and
(B) make wise choices in the use and conservation of resources and the disposal or recycling of materials.

(6.2) Scientific processes. The student uses scientific inquiry methods during field and laboratory investigations. *(Chapters 1–5, 8–16)*
The student is expected to:
(A) plan and implement investigative procedures including asking questions, formulating testable hypotheses, and selecting and using equipment and technology;
(B) collect data by observing and measuring;
(C) analyze and interpret information to construct reasonable explanations from direct and indirect evidence;
(D) communicate valid conclusions; and
(E) construct graphs, tables, maps, and charts using tools, including computers to organize, examine, and evaluate data.

(6.3) Scientific processes. The student uses critical thinking and scientific problem solving to make informed decisions. *(Chapters 1–5, 7–16)*
The student is expected to:
(A) analyze, review, and critique scientific explanations, including hypotheses and theories, as to their strengths and weaknesses using scientific evidence and information;

(B) draw inferences based on data related to promotional materials for products and services;
(C) represent the natural world using models and identify their limitations;
(D) evaluate the impact of research on scientific thought, society, and the environment; and
(E) connect Grade 6 science concepts with the history of science and contributions of scientists.

(6.4) Scientific processes. The student knows how to use a variety of tools and methods to conduct science inquiry. *(Chapters 1–16)*
The student is expected to:
(A) collect, analyze, and record information using tools including beakers, petri dishes, meter sticks, graduated cylinders, weather instruments, timing devices, hot plates, test tubes, safety goggles, spring scales, magnets, balances, microscopes, telescopes, thermometers, calculators, field equipment, compasses, computers, and computer probes; and
(B) identify patterns in collected information using percent, average, range, and frequency.

(6.5) Science concepts. The student knows that systems may combine with other systems to form a larger system. *(Chapters 12, 16)*
The student is expected to:
(A) identify and describe a system that results from the combination of two or more systems such as, the solar system; and
(B) describe how the properties of a system are different from the properties of its parts.

(6.6) Science concepts. The student knows that there is a relationship between force and motion. *(Chapters 3, 11, 16)*
The student is expected to:
(A) identify and describe the changes in position, direction of motion, and speed of an object when it is acted upon by force;
(B) demonstrate that changes in motion can be measured and graphically represented; and
(C) identify forces that shape features of the Earth, including uplifting, movement of water, and volcanic activity.

(6.7) Science concepts. The student knows that substances have physical and chemical properties. *(Chapters 1, 2)*
The student is expected to:
(A) demonstrate that new substances can be made when two or more substances are chemically combined and compare the properties of the new substances to the original substances; and
(B) classify substances by their physical and chemical properties.

(6.8) Science concepts. The student knows that complex interactions occur between matter and energy. *(Chapters 1, 8, 12)*
The student is expected to:
(A) define matter and energy
(B) explain and illustrate the interactions between matter and energy in the water cycle and in the decay of biomass, such as in a compost bin; and
(C) describe energy flow in living systems, including food chains and food webs.

(6.9) Science concepts. The student knows that obtaining, transforming, and distributing energy affects the environment. *(Chapters 1, 9)*
The student is expected to:
(A) identify energy transformation occurring during the production of energy for human use, such as electrical energy to heat energy or heat energy to electrical energy;
(B) compare methods used for transforming energy in devices such as water heaters, cooling systems, or hydroelectric and wind power plants; and
(C) research and describe energy types from their source to their use and determine if the type is renewable, nonrenewable, or inexhaustible.

(6.10) Science concepts. The student knows the relationship between structure and function in living systems. *(Chapters 4–8)*
The student is expected to:
(A) differentiate between structure and function;
(B) determine that all organisms are composed of cells that carry on functions to sustain life; and
(C) identify how structure complements function at different levels of organization, including organs, organ systems, organisms, and populations.

(6.11) Science concepts. The student knows that traits of species can change through generations and that the instructions for traits are contained in the genetic material of the organisms. *(Chapters 4, 5, 6)*
The student is expected to:
(A) identify some changes in traits that can occur over several generations through natural occurrence and selective breeding;
(B) identify cells as structures containing genetic material; and
(C) interpret the role of genes in inheritance

(6.12) Science concepts. The student knows that the responses of organisms are caused by internal or external stimuli. *(Chapters 4–8)*
The student is expected to:
(A) identify responses in organisms to internal stimuli, such as hunger or thirst;
(B) identify responses in organisms to external stimuli, such as the presence or absence of heat or light; and
(C) identify components of an ecosystem to which organisms may respond.

(6.13) Science concepts. The student knows components of our solar system. *(Chapter 16)*
The student is expected to:
(A) identify characteristics of objects in our solar system, including the sun, planets, meteorites, comets, asteroids, and moons; and
(B) describe types of equipment and transportation needed for space travel.

(6.14) Science concepts. The student knows the structures and functions of Earth systems. *(Chapters 10, 12–15)*
The student is expected to:
(A) summarize the rock cycle;
(B) identify relationships between groundwater and surface water in a watershed; and
(C) describe components of the atmosphere, including oxygen, nitrogen, and water vapor; and identify the role of atmospheric movement in weather change.

TEXAS
Field Trip

IN THE PATH OF A HURRICANE

At dawn, it was raining. By noon, the wind was blowing across the island at more than 48 kilometers per hour. Cottages near the beach began washing out to sea. Many streets on the eastern and southern sides of the city were waist-deep in water. The bridge to the mainland was also flooded. It was too late to leave the island. By evening, the entire city was flooded. The water was 5 meters above street level. The wind was whipping at 190 kilometers per hour. It peeled tin roofs off houses and toppled telephone poles. Around midnight, the floodwaters finally began to recede, and the wind died down. The deadliest hurricane to ever strike the shores of the United States had passed, leaving the city of Galveston in ruins.

Scenes from Galveston after the hurricane of 1900.

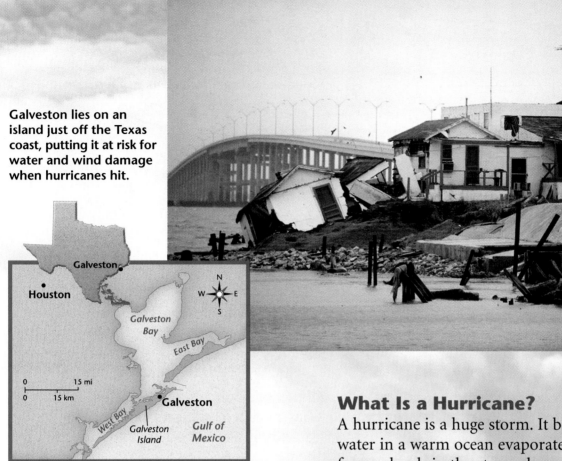

Galveston lies on an island just off the Texas coast, putting it at risk for water and wind damage when hurricanes hit.

Galveston

Houston

Galveston Bay

East Bay

West Bay

Galveston

Galveston Island

Gulf of Mexico

0   15 mi
0   15 km

N
W   E
S

A Record-Setting Hurricane

On September 8, 1900, a forceful hurricane pounded the city of Galveston, Texas. The destruction it left behind was astonishing. A mound of wreckage 5 kilometers long formed a semicircle around the city's business district. Outside this area, there was nothing—not a single home, not a single building, not a single tree. The bay was jammed with debris and dead bodies. The hurricane had destroyed more than 3,600 buildings and killed approximately 6,000 of the city's 37,000 residents.

The Galveston hurricane of 1900 is the deadliest hurricane that has ever hit the United States. No other hurricane since then has caused such terrible damage or loss of life. Were the later hurricanes less powerful? Not at all. The difference now is that people plan for hurricanes, predict their arrival, and get out of their way.

What Is a Hurricane?

A hurricane is a huge storm. It begins when water in a warm ocean evaporates and forms clouds in the atmosphere. Wind develops among the clouds. As the evaporation continues, the clouds become thicker. The wind speed increases, too. When the wind speed reaches 119 kilometers per hour, the storm is called a hurricane. It can take a week or more for a hurricane to develop.

A hurricane grows even stronger as it moves over warm water. When it reaches land, its powerful winds can devastate the shore. The wind blows down trees and telephone poles. It turns branches and pieces of metal into flying objects that crash into windows and cars. Sheets of rain can cause flooding.

The hurricane's wind pushes ocean water ahead of the storm, too. This action creates huge waves that crash onto the shore. Pounding waves can drag the land out from under buildings, causing them to collapse. The pieces of shattered buildings can then batter other buildings, causing even more damage.

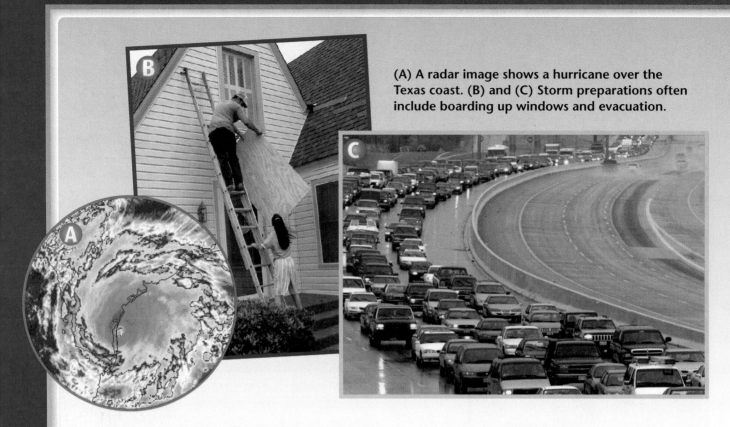

(A) A radar image shows a hurricane over the Texas coast. (B) and (C) Storm preparations often include boarding up windows and evacuation.

Protecting Lives and Property

The hurricane that hit Galveston in September of 1900 gained power as it stormed toward the city. Meanwhile, the people in Galveston didn't know that a storm was on its way.

Hurricane Warnings

In 1900, two changes signaled an approaching hurricane: the sky turning the color of "brick-dust," and a decrease in barometer readings. (A barometer is a device that measures air pressure.) Air pressure is lower before and during a storm than it is during clear weather. Unfortunately, the sky in Galveston never changed color before the storm hit that September. And, by the time the barometer started to drop, it was too late to get people out of the island city.

Today, technology helps meteorologists— scientists who study weather—locate and track storms that develop over the ocean. Radar and weather satellites provide data about the location and wind speed of a potential hurricane. Meteorologists at the National Hurricane Center begin tracking its motion. They use the data to predict the power and movement of the storm.

A Plan of Action

Cities facing a major hurricane usually receive an evacuation order. This notice means that everyone is supposed to move inland, away from the coast, where the winds are strongest and flooding is most likely. Cities plan in advance for evacuations. Certain roads are marked as evacuation routes, and people who live in the area know where these routes are. Emergency shelters are set up in safe places so that evacuated families have somewhere to go.

Preventing Damage

When a hurricane strikes, people can move to safer ground, but very little can be done to protect buildings from wind damage. Many people who live where a hurricane is likely to strike have sturdy shutters or pieces of plywood to cover windows.

Flood damage is hard to prevent. After the destruction from the storm in 1900,

The WEMITE tower is more than 10 meters high. Instruments on the tower collect wind data. A waterproof steel box protects the tower's computer from damage during storms.

the city of Galveston built a sea wall that would hold back the strong waves of a hurricane. The sea wall was tested in 1915, when an equally severe hurricane hit Galveston. Although the sea wall was battered and damaged, fewer than ten people died and there was very little property damage.

Wind Research at Texas Tech

In the past century, Texas was hit with more hurricanes than any other state except Florida. Because wind damage during a hurricane is a great concern, scientists at Texas Tech University at Lubbock are studying how buildings respond to the strong winds that come with hurricanes and tornadoes.

Among the university's research programs is the Wind Engineering Mobile Instrumented Tower Experiment (WEMITE). This project makes use of a tower that can be moved by trailer into the path of an approaching storm. Once in position, the tower can be operational in less than an hour. Amazingly, it can withstand wind forces of up to 240 kilometers per hour. Its battery-powered instruments can collect data on wind speed, air temperature, and pressure for at least 48 continuous hours. The goal of WEMITE is to provide data to wind engineering researchers. They use the information to design and test plans for buildings that will be able to withstand severe wind conditions.

TEXAS
Field Trip

SCIENCE ROUNDUP

Find out more about hurricanes and ways to prevent their damage.

Knowing what to do in advance can help keep you safe during an emergency situation. Discuss with your family what to do in case of a fire, hurricane, or tornado. Then write a plan your family can use for one of these emergencies.

Have you ever heard people talk about the "eye of a storm"? Do some research to find out what this phrase means, and how it applies to hurricanes.

Meteorologists give each hurricane a different name. Use library and other resources to find out more about how and why hurricanes are named. You may even be able to find out whether a hurricane will ever be named after you.

If you live in the Lubbock area, plan a visit to the Wind Research Center at Texas Tech University. At the center, you will be able to see wind research projects in progress and learn more about how hurricanes damage buildings.

REDUCING HURRICANE DAMAGE

▲ Kishor Mehta grew up in India, and moved to the United States to go to college. He remembers that his greatest challenge in learning English was learning how to think in a new language. After college, he received his Ph.D. in civil engineering from the University of Texas in Austin.

Hurricane winds roar through a coastal city, tearing off roof tiles and metal sidings from houses. An entire roof rips into the air. Flying tree limbs, street signs, and debris from broken houses crash into the windows and doors of other buildings, opening them to even more damage by wind and water. What can be done to change the fate of buildings in the path of heavy winds? At the Wind Engineering Research Center at Texas Tech University in Lubbock, people are trying to answer this question.

Kishor Mehta (KEE-shour MEH-tah) is the center's director and an expert on the effects of hurricane winds. "Hurricanes cause damage. We can't stop them, but we can learn to live with them. We can prevent them from disrupting the life of the community. That's our goal."

Studying the Wind

Kishor started his studies in the field of civil engineering—which focuses on the design and construction of public buildings, bridges, and other structures. He later became more interested in structural engineering—the branch of civil engineering that concentrates on design. A few years after arriving at Texas Tech, Kishor started to think about doing wind research. He thought that he and his colleagues might investigate wind power, but a tornado gave them an even better idea.

◀ High winds can rip apart buildings, leaving them battered or destroyed. The instrumented movable test building (shown below) at the Texas Tech Field Laboratory helps researchers study the effects of high winds on buildings.

Starting an Investigation

A devastating tornado had just torn through downtown Lubbock. "We began to study how structures perform under high wind conditions," explains Kishor. "At the time, very little research had been done in this area." Kishor and his team analyzed how the tornado had affected local buildings. Then they traveled to other towns and cities that had been struck by tornadoes or hurricanes to study damage that had happened in those places.

Their early data showed that the winds from tornadoes and hurricanes affect buildings in very similar ways. Once the engineers understood how and why damage was occurring, they began to think about ways to design buildings that could withstand high winds.

Broadening the Research

Lubbock is in a very windy part of Texas, so it is a good place to study how wind affects the structure of a building. Currently, under Kishor's leadership, students and teachers at the university's Wind Engineering Research Field Laboratory carry out a wide variety of wind experiments. In addition to the WEMITE tower described on page 5, the center has another instrumented tower that is used to measure weather conditions. Nearby, there is even a movable building! Depending on the direction of the wind, researchers can turn the building to orient the instruments in the direction of the wind and see how the roof and walls are affected.

Working in Teams

Kishor sometimes works with researchers from other fields. For example, he and a professor from Texas Tech's economics department conducted a study of property damage from hurricanes in Galveston. "I like working in teams," Kishor explains. "Each person brings a different set of skills, a different point of view. Keeping costs in mind, we can work together to decide where to put the most effort into design."

Designing buildings that resist severe weather is not a problem. Engineers know how, and they do just that for nuclear power plants. "But when it comes to building houses, the costs are too high" says Kishor "So what we do is sit down with a group of people—economists, architects, city planners—and decide how we can do the most good with the resources available."

Solving a Problem

While the Texas Tech researchers spend quite a bit of time in the field, they also use equipment and devices at the school's Wind Engineering Research Field Laboratory to solve specific problems.

A few years ago, the Texas Department of Transportation noticed something troubling about certain traffic lights. Some of the lights that were attached to horizontal poles hanging over the street would vibrate. State officials were concerned about the danger to cars passing under the lights. "They wanted to know what kind of wind was causing the problem and why it affected some poles but not others," says Kishor. Was there any way to reinforce the poles or the lights?

The school's field laboratory was set up to test how wind affects traffic light poles. Kishor and his colleagues discovered that serious

Kishor and another researcher watch as wind data from the instrumented tower and test building are recorded by computer. ▶

(A) A traffic light was erected at the field laboratory to test vibration of the pole in natural wind. (B) The solution to the problem was a metal plate above the traffic lights to prevent dangerous vibrations of the pole.

vibrations occur when the backs of the lights face into steady winds blowing from about 15 to 50 kilometers per hour. The team looked for a way to reduce the vibrations. They found that attaching a horizontal metal plate to the pole on top of the light eased the problem. Grateful for the suggestion, the state added the plates to the traffic lights. They also passed the study results on to other parts of the United States where high winds pose risks.

Reaching His Goals

Early in his career, Kishor realized that he enjoyed teaching. The opportunity to teach and do research led him to Texas Tech. In recent years, Kishor has spent more than half his time teaching.

He also continues to direct the overall research and management of the center, work with colleagues, and speak publicly about how wind affects buildings and other structures. As a result of the efforts of Kishor and his colleagues, the Texas Tech Wind Engineering Research Field Laboratory has become recognized as a place where people can find out how to live more safely.

In Your Journal

Kishor Mehta changed his plan for studying the wind when a tornado gave him another idea. Think about an example in your life when you switched to another plan for a project, trip, social event, or other activity. How did you feel about giving up your idea for a new one? What factors convinced you to change?

9

WHAT IS SCIENCE?

GUIDE FOR READING

◆ What skills do scientists use?

◆ How can you work safely in the laboratory?

Reading Tip Before you begin reading, make a list of the boldfaced terms. As you read, write the definition for each term.

Key Terms science
• scientific inquiry
• observation
• inference
• hypothesis
• variable
• manipulated variable
• responding variable
• controlled experiment
• data
• scientific law
• scientific theory

As a structural engineer, Kishor Mehta asks a lot of questions. Is the pole that holds up a traffic signal sturdy enough to stand up to strong winds? How can we design buildings so that they can withstand tornadoes and hurricanes? Asking questions is an important part of science.

Science is a way of learning about the natural world. Science also includes all the knowledge gained through the process of exploring the natural world. This body of knowledge is always growing and changing as scientists ask new questions and explore new ideas.

Another term for the many ways in which scientists study the world around them is **scientific inquiry.** Scientific inquiry is used every day by the engineers at the Wind Engineering Research Center at Texas Tech University.

You do not have to be a scientist to use scientific inquiry. In fact, you may not realize that you probably have used the process of scientific inquiry. If you have tried to find the best conditions for fish in a fish tank or the correct way to throw a curve ball, you have used scientific inquiry.

Figure 1 This student is using the skills of scientific inquiry as she monitors conditions in this fish tank. *Posing Questions What questions would you have about the conditions needed to keep fish alive and healthy in a fish tank?*

Thinking Like a Scientist

Kishor Mehta uses many skills as he investigates the effects of strong winds on buildings. You may have used some of these skills, while others will be new to you.

Some of the skills that scientists use are posing questions, making observations and inferences, developing hypotheses, designing experiments, collecting data and making measurements, interpreting data, and drawing conclusions. Sometimes scientists make models to help them understand the problem they are trying to solve. Scientists also must use the skill of communication in their work.

Posing Questions

In the 1800s, scientists used scientific inquiry to study glaciers. Glaciers are huge masses of ice. They are usually found on and around high mountains, such as the Alps in Switzerland.

Two hundred years ago, scientists knew very little about glaciers. Some scientists thought that glaciers could move. Others doubted that these huge masses of ice could move at all. So some scientists in Switzerland decided to investigate.

Scientists usually begin an investigation with a question about something that is unexplained. The Swiss scientists studying glaciers asked, "Do glaciers move?"

Making Observations and Inferences

Look at the glacier in Figure 2. What color is it? What does its surface look like? As you answer these questions, you are using a science skill. You are making observations. The skill of **observation** involves using one or more of your senses—sight, hearing, smell, and sometimes taste—to gather information. In this case, you used your sense of sight to gather information about glaciers.

You may have observed a dark band in the glacier. If you could travel to this glacier and make more-detailed observations, you would find that this dark band is due to rocks in the ice. Where did the rocks come from? You might think that they came from nearby mountains. This statement is an **inference,** an interpretation based on observations and prior knowledge.

✓ *Checkpoint* **What is the difference between an observation and an inference?**

Figure 2 The Gorner glacier winds down from high peaks in the Swiss Alps. The dark bands in the glacier are pieces of rock broken off and picked up by the moving ice.

Developing Hypotheses After posing a question, scientists often gather information or make observations. They then use this information to form a hypothesis. A **hypothesis** is a possible explanation for a set of observations or answer to a scientific question. In science, a hypothesis must be something that can be tested. A hypothesis can be tested by observation or experimentation. Scientists do not accept a hypothesis after just one test. Repeated tests must provide evidence that supports the hypothesis.

People in the Alps had long observed boulders in the valleys below glaciers. Did that mean that moving ice had carried the boulders? Such observations led scientists to propose the following hypothesis: *Glaciers move slowly over the land.*

Designing Controlled Experiments How do scientists test a hypothesis? In many cases, they carry out experiments. In setting up an experiment, scientists think about all the factors that could affect the outcome of the experiment. These factors are called **variables.** The scientists change one variable, called the **manipulated variable,** or independent variable. They then observe how this change affects another variable. The variable that changes as a result is called the **responding variable,** or dependent variable.

There can be many variables in an experiment. To be sure that changes in the manipulated variable alone are responsible for any changes in the responding variable, scientists must test only one variable at a time. They control all of the other variables so that they do not change. An experiment in which there is only one manipulated variable and all other variables are kept constant is called a **controlled experiment.**

Figure 3 shows an example of a controlled experiment. The student is investigating whether the shape of an ice block affects how quickly it melts. The manipulated variable in the experiment is the shape of the ice. The responding variable is the time it takes for the ice to melt. Notice that all other variables are kept constant. The two blocks of ice are exposed to identical sources of heat, contain the same volume of water, and are on identical surfaces. Because all other variables have been controlled, any difference in melting times must be due to the difference in shape.

Figure 3 In this controlled experiment, the shape of the ice block is the manipulated variable. The time it takes for melting to occur is the responding variable.
Developing Hypotheses What hypothesis is being investigated?

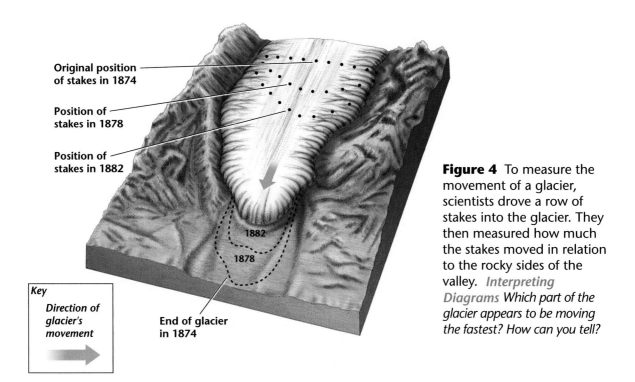

Original position of stakes in 1874

Position of stakes in 1878

Position of stakes in 1882

1882

1878

Key

Direction of glacier's movement

End of glacier in 1874

Figure 4 To measure the movement of a glacier, scientists drove a row of stakes into the glacier. They then measured how much the stakes moved in relation to the rocky sides of the valley. *Interpreting Diagrams Which part of the glacier appears to be moving the fastest? How can you tell?*

In the real world, conducting a controlled experiment can be difficult or impossible. The objects studied by some scientists can be very large. And some processes that scientists study can take millions of years. In cases like these, scientists test hypotheses through observation and measurement, as did the scientists who studied glaciers.

Figure 4 shows how the Swiss scientists investigated the movement of a glacier. They placed a row of stakes across the glacier, and went back over time to see if the stakes moved.

✓ *Checkpoint* *What is a variable?*

Collecting Data and Making Measurements The facts, figures, and other evidence collected in an experiment are called **data.** Scientists know that it is important to record all data carefully. That way they have a permanent account of what happened in an experiment.

Some data can be in the form of descriptions. For example, the scientists studying glaciers may have examined rocks and compared them with rocks from nearby mountains.

Much of the data collected in experiments is in the form of measurements. The scientists studying the glacier noted the original positions of the stakes in the glacier and then measured how far the stakes moved from these positions.

Scientists around the world all use the same system of measurement. This system is called the International System of Units. The name is abbreviated as SI, which comes from the French name for the system (*Système International d'Unités*).

SI is based on the metric system of measurements. If you have ever measured length in meters, you have used SI units. To learn about making measurements in science, see pages 582–583 in the Skills Handbook.

Interpreting Data After scientists collect their data, they then need to interpret, or find the meaning of, these data. Finding a way to display the data is part of interpreting it. One way to display data is in the form of a diagram, such as the one in Figure 4. Another way to display data is in data tables and graphs, as in Figure 5.

Interpreting data involves looking for patterns, or trends. The study of the Swiss glacier produced two sets of data. The positions of the stakes at three different times make up one set of data. Look back at Figure 4. What pattern do you see in these positions?

The other set of data is the three positions of the lower end of the glacier. There's a pattern here, too. How did the end of the glacier change over the years of the study?

Drawing Conclusions Once scientists have reviewed their data, they are ready to draw a conclusion. The data may support the hypothesis.

Or the data may show that the hypothesis was incorrect. Sometimes, no conclusion can be reached, and more data must be collected.

The Swiss scientists studying glaciers concluded that their data supported their hypothesis. But the data also revealed a surprise. As the glacier was moving downhill, it was also getting shorter at its lower end. A surprising find like this one can lead scientists to form new hypotheses and try new experiments. What hypothesis could you propose to explain the change at the lower end of the glacier?

In the example of the glacier, the evidence collected by the scientists supported their hypothesis. But what if it hadn't supported the hypothesis? Would that mean the experiment was a failure? Definitely not! Eliminating a false hypothesis is as important as supporting another hypothesis. And what may seem like a failure often turns out to be the first step on the path to a new discovery.

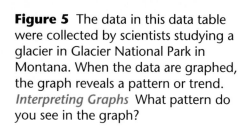

Change in Size of a Glacier Over Time

Year	Area of Glacier (hectares*)
1850	380
1900	370
1927	240
1945	160
1993	135

*1 hectare = 10,000 square meters

Figure 5 The data in this data table were collected by scientists studying a glacier in Glacier National Park in Montana. When the data are graphed, the graph reveals a pattern or trend. *Interpreting Graphs* What pattern do you see in the graph?

Figure 6 A weather map is a model of changing conditions in Earth's atmosphere. This map, based on satellite data, shows a storm over the eastern United States.

Making Models and Simulations

What would you do if you wanted to show your classmates what a glacier looks like? You can't take a glacier into your classroom, but you can use a model to show what the glacier looks like. The model could be a three-dimensional scale model. It could also be a diagram or a map. Many scientists today use computers to make models of complex objects or events.

Sometimes scientists use simulations to test a hypothesis. A simulation is a model that imitates a real-world situation.

Scientists working in modern laboratories have used simulations to study how glaciers move. The scientists studied samples of hot metal to see how the metal changes shape when under great pressure. The changes in the metal simulate the movement of the slowly flowing ice in a glacier. Using such simulations helps scientists develop new hypotheses and new ways of testing them.

Communicating Information

For scientists, communicating information is an important part of scientific inquiry. By sharing ideas and experimental findings, scientists learn from each other.

Scientists communicate with each other by writing articles for scientific journals. Scientists also go to scientific meetings. There they talk about their own research and listen to talks about the research of other scientists. Scientists also use the Internet to communicate with one another.

Scientific discoveries also are shared with the general public—people who are not scientists. In these communications, scientists must use simpler terms that can be easily understood by everyone. Communicating with nonscientists is especially important in areas that affect people's health and safety.

☑ *Checkpoint* **What are some ways in which scientists communicate information?**

Scientific Laws and Theories

Scientific inquiry often begins with observations. Scientists have noticed that some events in nature always happen the same way. What happens if you hold a ball in your hand and let go of it? Has this happened every time you've tried it? You have made the same observation over and over again—the ball falls to the ground.

When scientists have observed an event so often that they are sure it will always happen, they call the observation a scientific law. A **scientific law** is a statement that describes what scientists expect to happen every time under a particular set of conditions. In the case of the falling ball, the scientific law has to do with gravity.

Sometimes a large body of related information can be explained by a single major idea. If that idea is supported by many tests, it may develop into a scientific theory. A **scientific theory** is a well-tested scientific concept that explains a wide range of observations. An accepted scientific theory has withstood repeated tests. However, it is possible that additional tests could contradict the theory. If that happens, scientists will change the theory or abandon it.

Have you ever heard someone say, "Well, my theory is . . ."? In everyday language, people often use the word *theory* to refer to any explanation or personal opinion. Remember that, in science, a theory is an explanation that has been thoroughly tested. It is not merely a guess.

☑ *Checkpoint* **What is a scientific theory?**

Laboratory Safety

An important part of scientific inquiry is carrying out experiments. Scientists don't just go into a laboratory and start experimenting. They plan their steps carefully and make sure their procedures are safe.

As you use this textbook, you will conduct many experiments. As you do this, it is very important to think about safety. Always follow your teacher's instructions. Follow the steps you are given and use only the materials your teacher tells you to use. **Safe laboratory practices protect both you and your classmates from injury. In addition, your lab investigations will be more successful if you follow safety guidelines.**

Before conducting any experiments, review Appendix A on pages 597–599. Be sure that you understand the safety symbols and rules.

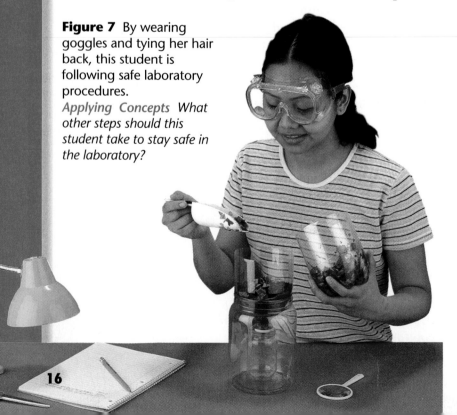

Figure 7 By wearing goggles and tying her hair back, this student is following safe laboratory procedures. *Applying Concepts What other steps should this student take to stay safe in the laboratory?*

Speeding Up Evaporation

Evaporation is the process by which water vapor enters Earth's atmosphere from the ocean and other surface waters. Rates of evaporation determine the amount of moisture in the atmosphere. Atmospheric moisture in turn affects the formation of clouds and helps to determine whether it will rain.

Problem

What factors increase the rate at which water evaporates?

Materials

water	plastic dropper
2 plastic petri dishes	1 petri dish cover
3 index cards	paper towels
stopwatch	lamp

Procedure

Part 1 Effect of Heat

1. How do you think heating a water sample will affect how fast it evaporates? Record your hypothesis.
2. Place each petri dish on an index card.
3. Add a single drop of water to each of the petri dishes. Try to make the two drops the same size.
4. Position the lamp over one of the dishes as a heat source. Turn on the light. Make sure the light does not shine on the other dish. **CAUTION:** *The light bulb will become very hot. Avoid touching the bulb or getting water on it.*
5. Observe the dishes every 3 minutes to see which sample evaporates faster. Record your result.

Part 2 Effect of Wind

6. How do you think fanning the water will affect how fast it evaporates? Record your hypothesis.
7. Dry both petri dishes and place them over the index cards. Add a drop of water to each dish as you did in Step 3.
8. Use an index card to fan one of the dishes for 5 minutes. Be careful not to fan the other dish.
9. Observe the dishes to see which sample evaporates faster. Record your result.

Analyze and Conclude

1. Did the evidence support both hypotheses? If not, which hypothesis was not supported?
2. Make a general statement about factors that increase the rate at which water evaporates.
3. **Think About It** What everyday experiences helped you make your hypotheses at the beginning of each experiment? Explain how hypotheses differ from guesses.

Design an Experiment

How do you think increasing the surface area of a water sample will affect how fast it evaporates? Write your hypothesis and then design an experiment to test it. Check your plan with your teacher before you begin.

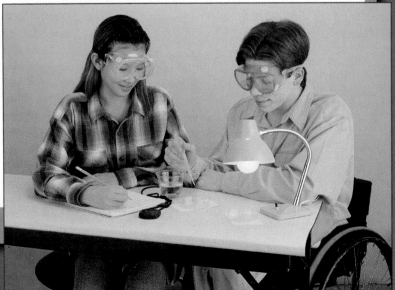

Branches of Science

There are four main branches of science—physical science, Earth science, life science, and environmental science. Physical science includes the study of motion, energy, sound, light, electricity, magnetism, and the tiny particles that make up everything around you.

Earth science is the study of Earth and its place in the universe. This includes studying landforms, oceans, rocks and minerals, weather, and the planets that make up the solar system.

Life science is the study of living things, including plants, animals, and microscopic life forms. Life scientists also study how living things interact with each other and with their surroundings.

Environmental science is the study of how human activities affect Earth's land, air, water, and living things. Environmental scientists try to find solutions for problems that result from the use of Earth's natural resources. Some problems that environmental scientists study are pollution and global warming.

The branches of science are not separate from one another. For example, Kishor Mehta and the other engineers he works with are mainly physical scientists. They study the effects of the force of wind on various objects. But to understand wind, they have to study weather, which is part of Earth science.

In Figure 8, you can see some of the work that scientists do. You may think of scientists as people who work in laboratories. But as you can see, scientists work in all kinds of places— from the bottom of the ocean to outer space. Scientists test water supplies to make sure the water is clean enough to drink. They design safer cars and buildings. They search the rain forests to find new plants and animals. Wherever people are asking questions and searching for answers, they are using the skills of scientific inquiry.

☑ *Checkpoint* *Which branch of science would be involved in studying volcanoes and earthquakes?*

Figure 8 Scientists seek answers to questions in a wide variety of places using diverse skills and tools.

Veterinarians ▶
Veterinarians are doctors that treat animals. They care for animals ranging from house pets to farm and zoo animals.

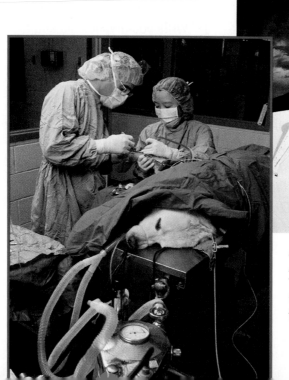

Astronomers ▲
Astronomers study the universe. These astronomers are using a radio telescope to detect radio signals from distant stars and galaxies.

Technology and the Internet

Today, many scientists use the latest technology in their research. From high-powered microscopes that can look at tiny viruses to huge telescopes that search the sky for faraway stars, scientists have many tools that they can use.

Most modern scientific instruments are connected to computers, which allow scientists to quickly record, store, and analyze the data they collect. You have already read how important computers are for creating models and simulations of scientific events.

Computers also help scientists communicate information to each other and to the public. You can find large amounts of information about current research and discoveries in science on the Internet. Many government agencies maintain Web sites that are excellent sources of scientific information. Hospitals and universities that have research centers often have Web sites, too. The publisher of this textbook maintains a Web site, **www.phschool.com**. This site includes links to other Web sites that may help you as you study science.

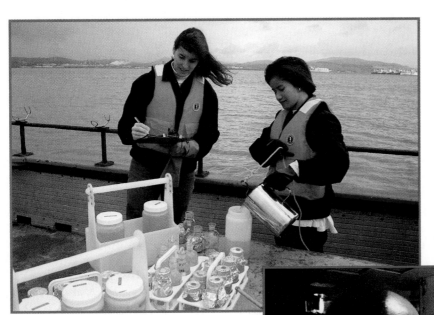

▼ Research chemists
Research chemists study the compositon and structure of matter as well as matter's physical and chemical properties. Their applied research is often aimed at developing new materials for a wide range of uses.

▲ Environmental scientists
Environmental scientists study how human activities affect Earth's natural resources. These scientists are testing water samples for evidence of pollution.

Study Guide

Key Ideas

◆ Science is both a way of learning about the natural world and the knowledge gained from that process.

◆ Scientific methods generally include posing questions, making observations and inferences, developing hypotheses, designing experiments, collecting data and making measurements, interpreting data, and drawing conclusions. Scientists also may make models and use the skill of communication in their work.

◆ The System of International Units (SI) is the standard system of measurement in science.

◆ A scientific law describes what scientists expect to happen every time under a particular set of conditions. A scientific theory is a well-tested scientific concept that explains a wide range of observations.

◆ In experiments and activities, it is very important to think about safety. Always follow your teacher's instructions on safety in the laboratory.

Key Terms

science	manipulated variable
scientific inquiry	responding variable
observation	controlled experiment
inference	scientific law
hypothesis	scientific theory
variable	

Reviewing Content

 Review key concepts online using iText at www.phschool.com

Multiple Choice

Choose the letter of the best answer.

1. Scientists seek to answer questions about the natural world in a process of
   a. modeling.   b. scientific inquiry.
   c. predicting.   d. developing hypotheses.

2. An explanation that can be tested by observation or experimentation is a(n)
   a. experiment.   b. scientific theory.
   c. scientific fact. d. hypothesis.

3. One of the factors that can change in an experiment is called a(n)
   a. variable.   b. theory.
   c. hypothesis.   d. observation.

4. One way in which scientists test a hypothesis is by
   a. asking questions.
   b. drawing conclusions.
   c. interpreting data.
   d. conducting a controlled experiment.

5. A scientist who studies weather and climate is a(n)
   a. life scientist.
   b. Earth scientist.
   c. physical scientist.
   d. environmental scientist.

True or False

If the statement is true, write true. If it is false, change the underlined word or words to make the statement true.

6. A <u>variable</u> is an interpretation of an observation.

7. The facts and figures that a scientist collects in an experiment are called <u>data</u>.

8. If an experiment fails to support a <u>scientific theory</u>, scientists will change the theory or abandon it.

9. A <u>hypothesis</u> is a model that imitates a real-world situation.

10. <u>Environmental scientists</u> study the effects of human activities on Earth's land, air, water, and living things.

Checking Concepts

11. In your own words, explain briefly what science is.
12. Why is it sometimes difficult to use controlled experiments to test hypotheses?
13. What is the difference between a hypothesis and a scientific theory?
14. Explain how a scientist would use the data gathered through a controlled experiment.
15. Explain the importance of following safety rules in laboratory experiments.
16. What are the four main branches of science? Briefly describe what each type of scientist studies.
17. **Writing to Learn** Give an example of an observation of the natural world that you have made. Then give an example of an inference that you made based on that observation. Explain.

Thinking Critically

18. **Problem Solving** You may have heard the saying, "Red sky at night/Sailor's delight." This expression is a hypothesis: A colorful red sunset means there will be fair weather the next day. Describe a scientific method of testing this hypothesis.
19. **Relating Cause and Effect** In a controlled experiment, why do scientists try to control all of the variables except one?
20. **Making Judgments** As a result of just one experiment, a scientist finds evidence that supports a hypothesis. Should other scientists around the world accept this hypothesis? Explain your answer.
21. **Classifying** Which branch of science would investigate the surface temperature of a star? Which branch would investigate the chemical makeup of a food?

Test Preparation

Use these questions to prepare for standardized tests.

Read the passage. Then answer Questions 22–25.

It may surprise you to learn that the climate in a large city can be different from the climate just outside the city. Climate is the average, year-to-year weather conditions in a region. Meteorologists have collected data on these climate differences. The data show that the climate in a city is often warmer and wetter than the climate in the nearby countryside. Cities are also less sunny and less windy than the country around them.

Why are cities warmer? One reason is that buildings and paved surfaces absorb and store more of the sun's energy than do grass, crops, and trees. Another reason is that cars, factories, heating, and air conditioning in cities all give off heat.

Scientists think several factors cause increased rainfall in cities. One hypothesis is that the built-up areas of a city form an obstacle to passing storms. As a result, the storms take longer to move over the city, allowing more rain to fall.

22. The best title for this reading selection is
    A Sunny Weather Ahead
    B Meteorologists at Work
    C City Climates
    D What Causes Storms?
23. Meteorologists found that the climate in a city differs from the climate in the country by
    F asking city residents.
    G collecting data.
    H observing clouds.
    J performing controlled experiments.
24. How would you predict a city could lower its outdoor temperature in the summer?
    A by building more factories
    B by having more parks with grass and trees
    C by putting more cars on the road
    D by adding more air conditioners
25. The idea that a city's buildings can increase rainfall by slowing down a passing storm is an example of a
    F variable.   G scientific theory.
    H determining factor. J hypothesis.

WEB ACTIVITY www.phschool.com

Comparing Brands X, Y, and Z

Before you get dressed, you probably spend time picking out clothes that go together. Clothes can come in a huge variety of colors. That's because researchers have developed many different dyes. Fibers, cloth, dyes, and water are just some examples of the materials that make up our world. The scientific name for these materials is matter. Every object in this photograph—actually, every object in the world—is an example of matter. Also, materials have different properties, such as color, shape, and hardness. It's the properties of a particular material that determine whether it is useful for a specific purpose.

Your Goal Compare a property of matter in three different brands of a consumer product.

To complete the project you will
◆ design a comparison test of a consumer-product property
◆ conduct the comparison test designed by a partner
◆ analyze the data you and a partner obtained
◆ follow the safety guidelines in Appendix A

Get Started As a class, brainstorm a list of different products to compare. For each product, write down several properties that could be compared, including those related to promotional claims of manufacturers. For example, paper towels may absorb different amounts of water. Review Designing an Experiment in the Skills Handbook.

Check Your Progress You'll be working on this project as you study this chapter. To keep your project on track, look for Check Your Progress boxes at the following points.
Section 1 Review, page 33: Design an experiment.
Section 3 Review, page 45: Perform the procedure.
Section 4 Review, page 50: Trade procedures with your partner.

Present Your Project At the end of the chapter (page 53), you and your second partner will try to repeat each other's procedures.

Dyes give fibers and other materials their distinctive colors.

TEKS

In addition to process TEKS, this chapter addresses these concept TEKS as they relate to the chapter's topics.

(6.7) The student knows that substances have physical and chemical properties. The student is expected to:
(A) demonstrate that new substances can be made when two or more substances are chemically combined and compare the properties of the new substances to the original substances; and
(B) classify substances by their physical and chemical properties.

(6.8) The student knows that complex interactions occur between matter and energy. The student is expected to:
(A) define matter and energy.

(6.9) The student knows that obtaining, transforming, and distributing energy affects the environment. The student is expected to:
(A) identify energy transformations occuring during the production of energy for human use such as electrical energy to heat energy or heat energy to electrical energy.

1 Describing Matter and Energy

DISCOVER · ACTIVITY · · · ·

What Is a Mixture?

1. Your teacher will give you a handful of objects, such as checkers, marbles, and paper clips of different sizes and colors.

2. Examine the objects. Then sort them into at least three groups. Each item should be grouped with other similar items.

3. Describe the differences between the unsorted handful and the sorted groups of objects. Then make a list of the characteristics of each sorted group.

Think It Over

Inferring The handful of objects represents a mixture. Your sorted groups represent substances. Using your observations, infer what the terms *mixture* and *substance* mean.

GUIDE FOR READING

◆ Why is it useful to know the physical and chemical properties of matter?

◆ What happens when elements combine?

◆ How do physical and chemical changes differ?

◆ How are energy and changes in matter related?

Reading Tip Before you read, use the headings to outline the section. As you read, add information to your outline.

Key Terms matter • energy
• chemistry • substance
• physical property
• chemical property • element
• compound • mixture
• physical change
• chemical change

You're watching a soccer game on an autumn afternoon. There's the whistle. The player kicks the ball, and it moves straight down the field into the net! You've just seen a goal. You've also just seen an example of the interaction of matter and energy. People use the words *matter* and *energy* in different ways. How often have you heard someone say, "As a matter of fact, . . ." or "Hey, what's the matter?" Maybe you've heard, "That team plays with a lot of energy!" Are these phrases familiar? What do the words mean in science?

Defining Matter and Energy

Scientists define **matter** as anything that has mass and takes up space. Mass is how much of something you have. As you learn more about matter and mass in this chapter, these terms will become more meaningful to you. Thinking about examples of matter is an easy way to get an idea of what matter is.

Examples of matter ▶

Figure 1 When the moving paddle wheel pushes against the water, energy is transferred to the boat, and the boat moves. *Applying Concepts What examples of matter are undergoing change in this photograph?*

Matter is the "stuff" that makes up everything in the universe. Fruit, softballs, tools, animals, rain, flowers—all these are examples of matter. Even air is matter. It may be invisible, but you know it is there when you feel a cool breeze on your face or watch bubbles rise in a fish tank.

Energy is the ability to do work or cause change. Change can sometimes mean motion, that is, moving matter from one place to another. When you pound a nail, energy moves the hammer that drives the nail into a board. Energy even moves your hand. Change can also mean a change in form. A kettle of water that goes from room temperature to boiling on the stove tells you something about energy. Energy is always involved when changes in matter occur. The study of the properties of matter and how matter changes is called **chemistry.**

Classifying Matter by Its Physical and Chemical Properties

In addition to having mass and taking up space, matter has a variety of characteristics, or properties, that can differ. For example, matter can be solid, liquid, or gas. In turn, solid matter can be hard or soft, rough or smooth, square or round. Some kinds of matter catch fire easily. Others don't. The properties of matter usually fall into two groups—physical properties and chemical properties. **Physical and chemical properties are used to identify, describe, and classify matter.** A single kind of matter that has distinct physical and chemical properties is called a **substance.**

Alike or Different?

1. Examine samples of powdered sugar, salt, cornstarch, and baking powder.

2. With a hand lens, look closely at each substance. Then rub a little of one substance between your fingers. Repeat with each of the other substances. Record your observations. Wash your hands.

3. Place one spoonful of each substance in a different plastic cup or test tube. Add two spoonfuls of water to each substance. Record any changes.

4. Repeat Step 3, using vinegar instead of water. Record any changes.

Classifying Make a list of properties for each of the substances. Based on your observations, can you group any of the substances together? Explain.

Physical Properties Have you ever smelled a bottle of vinegar? Whew! You can't miss its sharp odor. You wouldn't mistake its taste for the sweet taste of sugar, either. Odor and taste are physical properties. A **physical property** is a characteristic of a substance that can be observed without changing the substance into something else.

Other physical properties include hardness, texture, color, and the temperature at which a solid melts or a liquid boils. Every diamond, for example, is hard enough to scratch glass. Every sample of pure water boils at 100°C. Even when you describe a substance as a solid, a liquid, or a gas, you are stating one of its physical properties. Some types of matter can be easily classified based on their physical properties. Iron, copper, and aluminum may be different substances, but you know by looking at them that they are all metals.

Chemical Properties Some properties can't be determined just by looking at or touching a substance. Instead, you must change the substance to find out about such properties. A **chemical property** is a characteristic that is observed when a substance interacts with another substance. Like physical properties, chemical properties are used to classify substances. If you hold a toothpick and an iron rod in a candle flame, the toothpick will burn, but the rod will not. Burning, or flammability, is a chemical property of the substances in wood but is not a property of iron. Another chemical property involves rusting. Suppose you place an iron rod and a toothpick on a paper towel moistened with salt water. In a few days, the toothpick will remain unchanged, but the iron will react with water to form rust. Still other chemical properties determine whether a substance will explode like fireworks or tarnish like a piece of silverware.

✓ *Checkpoint* What is an example of a physical property of a candle? What is an example of a chemical property of a candle?

Figure 2 These medals are made of different substances but share many physical properties that classify them as metals.

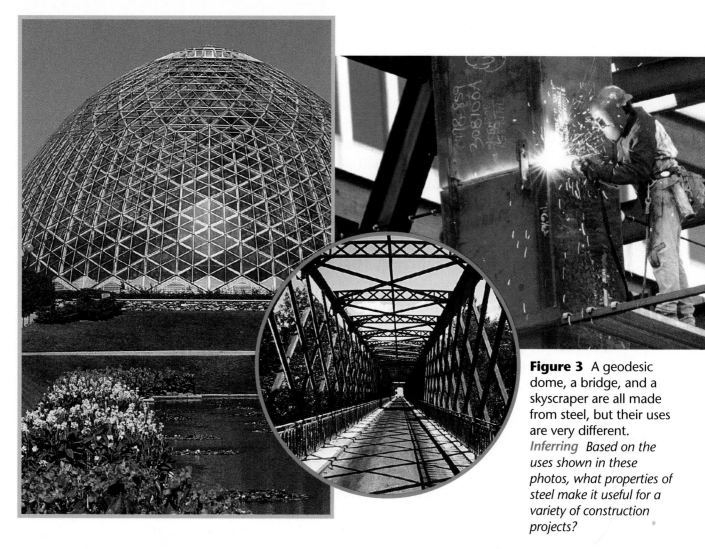

Figure 3 A geodesic dome, a bridge, and a skyscraper are all made from steel, but their uses are very different. *Inferring Based on the uses shown in these photos, what properties of steel make it useful for a variety of construction projects?*

Kinds of Matter

Take an imaginary walk through your city or town and notice all the buildings. Their shapes, sizes, and uses are very different. You would never confuse a doghouse with an airport terminal, or a gas station with a 50-story office tower. But they are all constructed of a few kinds of materials. Bricks, wood, glass, stone, concrete, and steel are some of the most common forms of matter used in building. Using these forms of matter, people have built many different structures.

Elements Just as many different buildings are made from a few kinds of materials, all the different kinds of matter in the universe are made from a few more than 100 different substances, called elements. An **element** is a substance that cannot be broken down into any other substances by chemical or physical means. Each element can be identified by its specific physical and chemical properties.

You have experience with some elements in the world around you. Examples include aluminum foil and copper coatings on pennies. Oxygen and nitrogen gases are two elements in the air you breathe.

Ratios

A ratio compares two numbers. It tells you how much you have of one item in comparison to how much you have of another. For example, a recipe for cookies calls for 2 cups of flour for every 1 cup of sugar. You can write the ratio of flour to sugar as:

2 to 1 or 2 : 1

The elements in a compound are present in a specific ratio. If two compounds contain the same elements in different ratios, such as CO and CO_2, they are different compounds.

Compounds Most elements are found in nature combined with other elements. A **compound** is a substance made of two or more elements chemically combined in a set ratio, or proportion. For example, the carbon dioxide gas you breathe out is a compound made of carbon and oxygen. Any sample of carbon dioxide will always be made of one part carbon to two parts oxygen (CO_2). Table salt (sodium chloride) is made of one part sodium to one part chlorine ($NaCl$).

You use many compounds every day. The fruit sugar that makes juice taste sweet, the water that you drink when you are thirsty, and the cavity-fighting ingredient in your toothpaste are all compounds made from different combinations of elements. Each compound has its own specific properties. Water at room temperature, for example, is a clear, colorless liquid.

When elements are combined to make a compound, the new substance has properties different from those of the original elements. Consider table sugar, for example. It is a compound made from three elements—carbon, oxygen, and hydrogen. The sugar crystals do not resemble the carbon you see in charcoal or the colorless gases oxygen and hydrogen.

Mixtures Most matter that you find in the environment occurs as mixtures. A **mixture** is made from two or more substances—elements, compounds, or both—that are in the same place but are not chemically combined. Mixtures differ from compounds in two ways. First, the substances in a mixture keep their individual properties. Second, the parts of a mixture are not necessarily present in set ratios.

Consider a handful of moist soil. If you look at the soil through a hand lens, you will find particles of sand, tiny bits of clay, maybe even pieces of decaying plants. If you squeeze the soil, you might force out a few drops of water. Another sample of soil won't necessarily contain the same amount of water or any other material. Soil from a flowerpot in your home may be very different from the soil in a nearby park.

☑ *Checkpoint* *Why is soil a mixture and not a compound?*

Figure 4 The element silver (above) is sometimes found in a wiry, tree-shaped form. The paints (right) are mixtures of several compounds. The compounds that give paints their colors are called pigments.

EXPLORING *Matter at the Beach*

You can find all sorts of matter at an ocean beach, including sand, seashells, grasses and other plants, and sea water. Many types of beach sand are made up of small rocks and other particles that are washed ashore by the ocean's waves.

Mixture
Some beach sand is a mixture of a substance called quartz and tiny fragments of seashells. Different types of shells cause different colors of beach sand.

Compounds
Seashells contain different calcium compounds, including calcium carbonate. Quartz is formed from a compound called silicon dioxide.

Calcium carbonate

Silicon dioxide

Elements
The compounds in beach sand are made mostly of four elements: silicon, oxygen, calcium, and carbon. Like most substances, beach sand shares few properties with the elements that make it up!

| *Silicon* | *Oxygen* | *Calcium* | *Carbon* |

Changes in Matter

Try to think of a world where nothing ever changes. Pretty boring, isn't it? Actually, you couldn't even survive in such a world because changes must occur inside your body if you are to remain alive. A sandwich that you eat for lunch must be changed by your body into muscle, blood, and other things you need. Chemists study both physical and chemical changes.

Physical Change Think of going to a costume party and seeing someone dressed as a clown. Could it be someone you know? How can you tell? Putting on a costume can make someone look quite different, but the person hasn't changed. So it is with some changes in matter. A change that alters the form or appearance of a material but does not make the material into another substance is called a **physical change.** Examples of physical changes include chopping wood, bending copper wire into new shapes, or molding clay.

As you probably know, matter has three principal states—solid, liquid, and gas. A change in state is another example of physical change. Matter can change from one state to another when the temperature changes. For example, ice cubes are made of solid (frozen) water. They will melt in a tray left on your kitchen table, forming liquid water. If you return the tray to the freezer, the water will become ice again. But if you leave the tray on the table overnight, some of the water will escape into the air as a gas. Water remains the same substance whether it's in the form of a solid, a liquid, or a gas. It is still made of two parts hydrogen and one part oxygen (H_2O).

☑ *Checkpoint Why is a change in state considered to be a physical change?*

Figure 5 Wood can be chopped into different shapes (above). The bubble below is a thin film of liquid that changes shape around a body of air.
Interpreting Photographs How can you tell that these changes are physical changes?

Figure 6 Unlike a physical change, a chemical change alters the identity of a substance. In a forest fire, wood is changed into gases and other substances, and energy is released.

Chemical Change A change in matter that produces new substances is called a **chemical change,** or a chemical reaction. In a chemical change, elements may combine to form compounds, or compounds may be broken down into elements, or compounds may change into other compounds. **Unlike a physical change, a chemical change produces new substances with properties different from the original substances.**

Some familiar examples of chemical changes include the souring of milk and the burning of wood. When wood burns, the compounds of the wood combine with oxygen in the air to make new substances. These new substances include carbon dioxide, water, and other compounds. The element carbon is left in the ashes. Each of these new substances can be identified by its properties, which are different from those of the original wood.

Energy and Matter

As you learned earlier, energy and changes in matter go hand-in-hand. Recall that energy may be defined as the ability to do work or cause change. Energy can have different forms, and it can be transformed from one form to another. The idea of energy becomes easier to understand if you remember that what you often observe is the *effects* of energy on matter. Soup boiling on a stove and the sound of clapping hands both result from energy affecting matter. You can detect the effects of energy when matter is moved, when it reacts, or when energy is transformed from one form to another. **Energy is always involved when physical and chemical changes occur in matter.** The following pages describe some forms of energy and its interactions with matter.

Sharpen your Skills

Inferring

ACTIVITY

1. Put a large spoonful of vinegar into a large resealable plastic bag. As instructed by your teacher, carefully smell the contents.

2. Add a drop of bromthymol blue indicator to the bag. (Bromthymol blue has a different color in different types of some water mixtures.)

3. Add an antacid tablet and seal the bag. Note any changes to the matter in the bag.

4. Based on the changes you observed, do you think there was a physical change to the matter in the bag? Explain.

Figure 7 A tornado strikes buildings in Pampa, Texas. *Interpreting Diagrams* Will the houses in the path of this tornado undergo a physical or a chemical change? Explain your answer.

Mechanical Energy Mechanical energy is related to the motion or position of matter. When you shoot a basketball, energy is transferred from your hands to the ball. If you transfer just the right amount of mechanical energy in just the right way, the ball flies into the basket. A skateboard rolling down a hill is another example of mechanical energy.

Thermal Energy One of the most familiar forms of energy is thermal energy, which you sense as heat. All matter is made of small particles that are constantly in motion. If thermal energy is added to matter, the particles move faster, and the matter feels warmer than it did before the energy was added. If thermal energy is lost, the particles move more slowly, and the matter feels cooler than before. Remember the ice cube tray mentioned earlier? To make ice, you would put liquid water into the tray and leave it in the freezer. Thermal energy is lost from the water to the surroundings, and the water freezes. On a hot day, thermal energy in your surroundings will quickly melt the ice if you take the tray out and forget to put it back.

Electromagnetic Energy A familiar form of electromagnetic energy is light. X-rays, microwaves, radio and TV signals, and ultraviolet rays are also forms of electromagnetic energy. When electromagnetic energy interacts with matter, it can produce physical or chemical changes. For example, a microwave oven can change a frozen block of spaghetti and tomato sauce into a piping hot meal—a physical change. This change occurs with the transformation of electromagnetic energy to thermal energy. A similar kind of transformation can produce chemical changes, too. Without sunblock, people at a beach who are exposed to electromagnetic energy from the sun can experience painful chemical changes to the matter that makes up their skin. You know this effect as sunburn.

Electrical Energy A moving electric charge produces electricity. The energy of these moving charges is electrical energy. Electrical energy becomes useful when it is transformed into other forms of energy. In factories, for example, electrical energy is transformed into mechanical energy that turns the large motors of manufacturing equipment. In a light bulb, electrical energy is transformed as it interacts with the metal wire in the bulb. With the flick of a switch, electrical energy is transformed into thermal energy and light.

Chemical Energy Matter itself contains energy known as chemical energy. Chemical energy is transformed to other forms of energy during a chemical reaction. When a candle burns, the chemical energy in candle wax becomes thermal and electromagnetic energy. You detect the change as heat and light.

 INTEGRATING LIFE SCIENCE One of the most important energy transformations on Earth involves chemical energy. Plants transform electromagnetic energy from the sun into chemical energy. These plants, and animals and other living things that eat plants, then transform this chemical energy once again. It becomes the mechanical, electrical, and thermal energy needed to carry out life activities. The potato you have for dinner might supply the energy you need to go for a walk or read this book!

Figure 8 Light can result from more than one kind of energy transformation. In glowsticks, chemical energy is changed to light by the reaction of two liquids. Electrical energy lights the bulbs on this ship's rigging.

Section 1 Review

1. Name several properties used to classify matter. Tell whether each is a physical property or a chemical property.
2. How are compounds formed?
3. Explain the difference between a physical change and a chemical change.
4. In what way are energy and matter related?
5. Describe a change in matter that you observed today. Tell what kind of energy change you think was involved.
6. **Thinking Critically Applying Concepts** You see a solid that looks like an ice cube, but it does not melt at room temperature. Can the solid be frozen water? Explain.

Check Your Progress   CHAPTER PROJECT
Choose which product and property you will test. Design a procedure to test the property you have selected. Decide which variables you will keep constant. Describe how you will measure and organize the data you collect. Discuss ideas for your procedure with a partner. Answer your partner's questions about the procedure, listen to any comments offered, and incorporate appropriate comments into your plan.

2 Measuring Matter

DISCOVER • ACTIVITY • • •

Which Has More Mass?

1. Your teacher will provide you with some small objects, such as a rock, a plastic cup, an aluminum can, and a pencil. Look at the objects, but do not touch them.

2. Predict which object is lightest, which is second lightest, and so on. Record your predictions.

3. Use a triple-beam balance to find the mass of each object.

4. Based on your results, list the objects from lightest to heaviest.

Think It Over

Drawing Conclusions How did your predictions compare to your results? Are bigger objects always heavier than smaller objects? Why or why not?

GUIDE FOR READING

◆ What is the difference between weight and mass?

◆ How is density calculated?

Reading Tip Before you read, define *mass, volume,* and *density* in your own words. Then revise your definitions as you read.

Key Terms weight • mass
• International System of Units
• volume • density

Figure 9 A spring scale measures the weight of an object.

H ere's a riddle for you: Which weighs more, a pound of feathers or a pound of bricks? If you answered "the pound of bricks," think again. Both weigh exactly the same—one pound!

There are all sorts of ways of measuring matter, and you use these measurements every day. Scientists rely on measurements as well. In fact, scientists work hard to make sure that their measurements are as accurate as possible.

Mass

A veterinarian wants an updated weight for a dog at its annual checkup. To find the weight, the owner steps on a spring scale, holding the dog. Their combined body weight presses down on springs inside the scale. The more the girl and her dog weigh, the more the springs compress, and the higher the reading. When the owner's weight is subtracted from the total, the vet has an answer.

A spring scale would not give the same result on the moon. If the girl and her dog were to step on a spring scale on the moon, the springs inside wouldn't compress as much as on Earth. The vet would record a lower weight.

Weight and Mass Your **weight** is a measure of the force of gravity on you. On Earth, all objects are attracted downward by Earth's gravity. On other planets, the force of gravity may be more or less. On the moon, the force of gravity is much weaker than on Earth. You would weigh less on the moon.

In everyday life, weight is a useful measurement of how much matter you have. But scientists rely on a property that is constant wherever the object may be. The **mass** of an object is the measurement of how much matter it contains. **Unlike weight, an object's mass will not change if the force of gravity on it changes. For this reason, mass is a useful physical property for describing and measuring matter.**

Units of Mass To measure the properties of matter, scientists use a system of units called the **International System of Units.** The system is abbreviated "SI," after its French name, Système International. For mass, the SI unit is the kilogram (kg). If you weigh 90 pounds on Earth, then your mass is approximately 40 kilograms.

Although you sometimes will see kilograms used in this textbook, usually you will see a smaller unit—the gram (g). There are exactly 1,000 grams in a kilogram. A nickel has a mass of about 5 grams, the mass of a baseball is about 150 grams, and the water in a medium-sized glass has a mass of about 200 grams.

☑ *Checkpoint* *What is the SI unit for mass?*

Volume

The amount of space that matter occupies is called its **volume.** It's easy to see the volume that solid and liquid objects take up. But gases have volume, too. Watch a balloon as you blow into it. You're actually increasing its volume with your breath.

3 cm ⟷ 3 cm

12 cm

Figure 10 Volume is measured in several units. Those that scientists commonly use include liters (L), milliliters (mL), and cubic centimeters (cm³).

INTEGRATING MATHEMATICS For rectangular objects such as a block of wood, the volume is found by multiplying the measurements of length, width, and height.

$$Volume = Length \times Width \times Height$$

When you multiply the three measurements, you must multiply the units as well as the numbers. So, just as $2 \times 2 \times 2 = 2^3$, $cm \times cm \times cm = cm^3$. If a block of wood has a length of 3 centimeters, a width of 3 centimeters, and a height of 12 centimeters, then the volume would equal the product of those values.

$$Volume = 3\ cm \times 3\ cm \times 12\ cm = 108\ cm^3$$

SCIENCE & History

Measurement Systems

Like so much else in science, systems of measurement developed gradually over time in different parts of the world.

1400 B.C.

Egypt

The ancient Egyptians developed the first known weighing instrument, a simple balance with a pointer. Earlier, they had been the first to standardize a measure of length. The length, called a cubit, was originally defined as the distance between the elbow and the tip of the middle finger.

1500 B.C.	1000 B.C.	500 B.C.	A.D. 1

640 B.C.

Lydia

Merchants in the Middle East and Mediterranean used units of weight to be sure that they received the correct amount of gold and silver in trade and to check the purity of the metal. A *talent* was about 25 kilograms and a *mina* about 500 grams. The Lydians minted the first true coins to have standard weight and value.

200 B.C.

China

Shih Huang Ti, the first emperor of China, set standards for weight, length, and volume. Even earlier, the Chinese were the first to use decimal notation, the number system based on 10 digits. This is the system most people use today.

The abbreviation "cm³" is read as *cubic centimeter(s)*, which is a common unit of volume. Other units of volume include the liter (L) and the milliliter (mL), both of which are often used to measure liquids. A milliliter is exactly 1 cubic centimeter. There are 1,000 milliliters in one liter.

How can you measure the volume of an object with an irregular shape, such as a piece of fruit or a rock? One way is to put the object in a graduated cylinder containing water and measure the change in the volume of the water.

✓ *Checkpoint* *How can you calculate the volume of a rectangular object like a shoe box?*

In Your Journal

Although scientists rely on SI units, people use other measurement units for many different purposes. Research the units used in diamond cutting, horse breeding, sailing, or other activities that interest you. Write a brief essay describing your findings.

A.D. 789
Central Europe

The foot of Charlemagne, emperor of most of central Europe, was set as the standard unit of length. The standard unit of weight was the *Karlspfund,* translated as "Charlemagne's pound."

A.D. 1714
Germany

Gabriel Fahrenheit invented the thermometer, a temperature-measuring device that relies on the expansion of mercury with heat. His name later came to be used as the name for a unit of temperature.

1831.—Fahrenheit's Thermometer.

A.D. 500   **A.D. 1000**   **A.D. 1500**   **A.D. 2000**

A.D. 700   **England**

During the reign of Ethelbert II in England, the term *acre* was in common use as a measurement of area. An acre was defined as the amount of land two oxen could plow in one day.

A.D. 1983
France

The International Bureau of Weights and Measures defines a single set of units that is the same everywhere. Scientists throughout the world use these units in their work.

Common Units and Conversions			
Quantity	**SI/Metric Units**	**Other Units**	**Conversions**
Mass	Kilogram (kg) Gram (g)		1 kilogram = 1,000 grams
Volume	Cubic meter (m^3) Liter (L) Milliliter (mL) Cubic centimeter (cm^3)	Quart Gallon	1 liter = 1,000 milliliters 1 milliliter = 1 cm^3
Distance	Meter (m) Kilometer (km) Centimeter (cm)	Foot Mile Inch	1 kilometer = 1,000 meters 1 centimeter = 0.01 meter

Density—A Physical Property of Matter

Different substances may have the same mass, but they don't necessarily fill the same volume. Remember the riddle about the bricks and the feathers? A kilogram of bricks takes up a much smaller volume than the same mass of feathers. This is because bricks and feathers have different densities—a very important property of matter. **Density** is a physical property that relates the mass and volume of an object or material. **To calculate the density of a sample, divide its mass by its volume.**

$$Density = \frac{Mass}{Volume}$$

A unit of density is always a unit of mass, such as grams, divided by a unit of volume, such as cubic centimeters. One typical unit of density is written as "g/cm^3," which is read as "grams per cubic centimeter." The word *per* means "for each," which in mathematics is the same as "divided by." For liquids, density is often stated in grams per milliliter, or g/mL. The density of water is 1.0 g/mL, which is the same as 1.0 g/cm^3.

Figure 12 An object sinks or floats in water depending, in part, on its density. This stone statue remains on the sea floor where it was placed. A statue of solid wood, with a density less than that of water, would float.

Sometimes you can compare the densities of substances just by observing them. For example, suppose you have a solid block of wood and a solid block of gold. When you drop each block into a tub of water, the wood floats and the gold sinks. You know the density of water is 1.0 g/cm^3. You can conclude that the density of wood is less than 1.0 g/cm^3. In contrast, the density of the gold is greater than 1.0 g/cm^3. In the same way, you can conclude that the density of the solid stone statue in Figure 12 is greater than the density of the water around it.

Sample Problem

A small block of wood floats on water. It has a volume of 25 cubic centimeters and a mass of 20 grams. What is the density of the wood?

Analyze.	You know the mass and the volume. You want to find the density.
Write the formula.	$\text{Density} = \dfrac{\text{Mass}}{\text{Volume}}$
Substitute and solve.	$\text{Density} = \dfrac{20\ g}{25\ cm^3}$
	$\text{Density} = 0.8\ g/cm^3$
Think about it.	The answer shows mass per unit volume.

Practice Problems

1. A sample of liquid has a mass of 24 grams and a volume of 16 milliliters. What is the density of the liquid?
2. A metal sample has a mass of 43.5 grams and a volume of 15 cubic centimeters. What is its density?

Watch a bottle of oil-and-vinegar salad dressing after it's been shaken. You will see oil droplets rise toward the top of the bottle. Eventually, the oil forms a separate layer above the other ingredients. What can you conclude? You're right if you said that the oil is less dense than the rest of the liquid dressing.

Density is a physical property that is the same for all samples of a substance. As a result, density can be used to help identify a substance. For example, all samples of pure gold have a density of 19.3 g/cm³. Finding the density of a shiny yellow material is one way to test whether or not that material is gold.

Section 2 Review

1. Why is mass more useful than weight for measuring matter?
2. What two quantities do you need to know in order to calculate density?
3. Describe how you could measure the volume of an object with an irregular shape.
4. **Thinking Critically Problem Solving** The density of aluminum is 2.7 g/cm³. A metal sample has a mass of 52.0 grams and a volume of 17.1 cubic centimeters. Could the sample be aluminum? Explain your answer.

Science at Home

Density Demonstration Label two cups A and B and place a cup of water in each. Stir 3 small spoonfuls of salt and several drops of food coloring into Cup B. Dip a clear straw into Cup A to a depth of about 2 cm. Place your finger on the end of the straw and transfer the straw into Cup B to a depth of about 4 cm. Remove your finger from the straw and then replace it. Remove the straw from the cup. Explain to your family what density has to do with the results.

MAKING SENSE OF DENSITY

In this lab you will find out if an object's density changes when its size changes.

Problem

Does the density of a substance change if it is broken into pieces?

Materials

balance   water   paper towels
wooden stick, approximately 6 cm long
ball of modeling clay, approximately 5 cm wide
crayon with paper covering removed
graduated cylinder, 100 mL
computer and spreadsheet program (optional)

Procedure

1. Use a balance to find the mass of the wooden stick. Record the mass in a data table like the one at the right or in a computer spreadsheet.
2. Add enough water to a graduated cylinder so that the stick can be completely submerged. Measure the initial volume of the water.
3. Place the stick in the graduated cylinder. Measure the new volume of the water.
4. The volume of the stick is the difference between the water levels in Steps 2 and 3. Calculate this volume and record it.
5. The density of the stick equals its mass divided by its volume. Calculate and record its density.
6. Thoroughly dry the stick with a paper towel. Then carefully break the stick into two pieces. Repeat Steps 1 through 5 to calculate the density of each of the two pieces.
7. Repeat Steps 1 through 6 using the clay rolled into a rope.
8. Repeat Steps 1–6 again using the crayon.

Analyze and Conclude

1. For each of the three objects you tested, compare the density of the whole object with the densities of the pieces of the object.
2. Use your results to explain how density can be used to identify a substance.
3. Why did you dry the objects in Step 6?
4. **Think About It** Predict the results of this experiment if you had used a pencil with an eraser on one end instead of a wooden stick. Explain your prediction.

More to Explore

Wrap the modeling clay around the wooden stick and predict the density of the object you created. Then measure mass and volume and calculate the density to see if your prediction was correct.

	DATA TABLE		
Object	Mass (g)	Volume Change (cm³)	Density (g/cm³)
Wooden Stick			
Whole			
Piece 1			
Piece 2			
Modeling Clay			
Whole			
Piece 1			
Piece 2			
Crayon			
Whole			
Piece 1			
Piece 2			

Particles of Matter

What's in the Box?

1. Your teacher will give you a sealed box that contains one or more objects. Without opening the box, try to find out as much as you can about the contents. Try tilting, turning, shaking, or tapping the box.

2. Ask yourself questions such as these: Are the objects inside round or flat? Do they slide or roll? How many objects are there?

3. Make a list of your observations about the objects in the box.

4. Trade boxes with another group of students and repeat the activity.

Think It Over

Inferring Try to imagine what familiar objects would fit your observations. Make a sketch showing what you think the contents look like. How is it possible to make an inference from indirect evidence?

lance at the painting below and you see people enjoying an afternoon in the park. Look again and notice that some people are in the sunlight and others are in the shade. How did the artist make your eyes see bright light, dark shadows, and shades in between? You can find the answer by looking closely at the circled detail of the painting. The artist used thousands of small spots of color.

Are you surprised that such a rich painting can be created from lots of small spots? Matter is like that too. The properties you can observe are produced by tiny objects and events that you cannot observe.

GUIDE FOR READING

◆ What did Dalton conclude about atoms?

◆ What are molecules made of?

Reading Tip As you read, take notes on the main points under each heading.

Key Terms atom
• chemical bond • molecule

◀ "Sunday Afternoon on the Island of La Grande Jatte," by Georges Seurat, at the Art Institute of Chicago

Figure 13 A drop of spilled mercury breaks into smaller droplets. (Don't do this at home. The element mercury is poisonous and can cause brain damage.) Although these droplets are small, they are not the smallest particles of mercury possible.
Applying Concepts What is the smallest particle of an element?

Early Ideas About Atoms

What's the smallest possible piece of an element? Think of tearing a sheet of aluminum foil in half, and then tearing the halves into quarters, and the quarters into eighths. Could you keep tearing forever, producing smaller and smaller pieces? Or would you eventually reach the smallest possible piece of aluminum? And if matter is made of such tiny pieces, what are those pieces like? How can they explain the properties of matter that you observe? Philosophers and scientists have asked these kind of questions for more than 2,000 years.

One of the first people known to have thought that matter is formed of small pieces was Democritus, a Greek philosopher who lived about 440 B.C. He thought that you could cut matter into ever smaller pieces until you got to its smallest piece, which couldn't be divided any further. Democritus called this smallest piece *atomos*, which is Greek for "uncuttable." Does that word look familiar? Of course! It's where the word *atom* comes from. An **atom** is the smallest particle of an element.

Dalton's Ideas About Atoms

A major step in understanding atoms occurred in 1802 when a British school teacher, John Dalton, proposed an atomic theory. No one knows how much Dalton was influenced by the ideas of Democritus. Unlike Democritus and the ancient Greeks, Dalton used experiments to test his ideas.

Based on evidence from experiments, Dalton inferred that atoms had certain characteristics. Here are his main conclusions.

◆ *Atoms can't be broken into smaller pieces.* **Dalton thought of atoms as similar to tiny marbles, or rigid spheres that are impossible to break.**

◆ *In any element, all the atoms are exactly alike.* This idea explains why an element always has the same properties.

◆ *Atoms of different elements are different.* This idea explains why different elements have their own set of properties.

◆ *Atoms of two or more elements can combine to form compounds.* Compounds can be broken down into elements, so Dalton concluded that compounds had to be made of atoms as well.

◆ *Atoms of each element have a unique mass.* Dalton and other scientists of his day were not actually able to measure the mass of individual atoms, however.

◆ *The masses of the elements in a compound are always in a constant ratio.* Water is made up of hydrogen atoms and oxygen atoms. In any two samples of pure water, the ratio of the mass of hydrogen to the mass of oxygen is always the same.

Today, scientists have identified some important exceptions to Dalton's statements. Even so, Dalton's ideas form the basis of our understanding of atoms.

☑ *Checkpoint* *What were two of Dalton's ideas about atoms?*

Math TOOLBOX

Constant Ratios

When two pairs of numbers produce the same ratio, the ratio is said to be constant. Suppose you wanted to increase the recipe in the Math Toolbox on page 28. To double the recipe, you would need 4 cups of flour and 2 cups of sugar. The ratio 4:2 reduces to 2:1 by dividing each number by 2.

$$\frac{4}{2} = \frac{2}{1}$$

To triple the recipe you would need 6 cups of flour and 3 cups of sugar. The ratio 6:3 reduces to 2:1 by dividing each number by 3.

$$\frac{6}{3} = \frac{2}{1}$$

The two ratios are constant because they both reduce to 2:1.

Similarly, for any quantity of a compound, the ratio of the masses of the elements in the compound is constant.

Figure 14 The compound calcium oxide is part of mortar, the "glue" that holds bricks together. In this compound, the ratio of the mass of calcium to the mass of oxygen is always 5 to 2.

Figure 15 Here you can see something scientists once thought no one would ever see—atoms! This image of silicon atoms was produced by a scanning tunneling microscope.

Ideas About Atoms Today

Atoms are so small that for many years no one expected to see them. Just how small are they? Compare the size of an atom to that of some everyday objects.

One grain of sand on a typical beach contains more atoms than there are grains of sand on the entire beach.

Newspaper pictures are made from tiny dots of ink. Each dot contains about a billion billion atoms! (That's a 1 followed by 18 zeros!)

There are 2,000,000,000,000,000,000,000 (that's 2,000 billion billion) atoms of oxygen in one drop of water—and twice as many atoms of hydrogen!

Despite their tiny size, there is now a tool that gives a glimpse of what atoms look like. A scanning tunneling microscope can magnify matter so much that it can actually capture images of atoms. Figure 15 shows an example of what this microscope can reveal.

Atoms and Molecules

An atom can frequently be linked with one or more other atoms. The force that holds two atoms together is a **chemical bond.** Two or more atoms that are bonded together form a particle called a **molecule.** Some molecules are made of atoms that are alike, as in the oxygen gas (O_2) that you breathe. **Most molecules are made of two or more different types of atoms bonded together.** Water molecules have 2 hydrogen atoms combined with 1 oxygen atom (H_2O). Acetic acid, the compound that gives vinegar its sharp odor and sour taste, has 2 carbon atoms, 4 hydrogen atoms, and 2 oxygen atoms ($C_2H_4O_2$). Molecules can be huge. Some molecules in your body contain millions of atoms.

Oxygen

Acetic acid

Water

Figure 16 Each diagram on the left is a model of a molecule made of atoms bonded together. The molecule on the right shows a small part of the DNA in living cells. (This computer image of DNA was made using a color code for atoms different from the code used in this book.) *Classifying Which one of these models shows a molecule of an element? How do you know?*

The Atom as a Model

Look at the atoms in Figure 15 again. From that image, you cannot really see what atoms look like or how they might work. Like a person trying to imagine what's in a box by shaking it, scientists studying atoms must make inferences about them based on observations.

In this way, atoms act as models. In science, a model may be a diagram, a mental picture, a mathematical statement, or an object that helps explain ideas about the natural world. Scientists use models to make and test predictions. In chemistry, models of atoms and molecules are often used to explain how matter behaves. Dalton's description of atoms was one of the first atomic models. Ideas about atoms have changed greatly since Dalton's time, but models continue to be valuable tools in science. You will see models many times in this book. In the next chapter, for example, simple models of atoms and molecules will be used to help explain the nature of solids, liquids, and gases.

Section 3 Review

1. What images did Dalton use to help describe atoms?
2. How are atoms and molecules related?
3. An ice cube consists of molecules of water (H_2O). Could you continue, forever, to break an ice cube into smaller and smaller pieces of ice? Explain your answer.
4. **Thinking Critically** **Interpreting Diagrams** Examine the model of acetic acid ($C_2H_4O_2$) in Figure 16. Which elements are represented by each of the three colors? How do you know? What does the model tell you about the way the different atoms are arranged?

CHAPTER PROJECT

Check Your Progress
Get your teacher's approval of your procedure for testing your product. Then obtain the materials you need and perform the test. If you alter the procedure, change the instructions to reflect your alterations. (*Hint:* A good experimental procedure should be reliable—repeatable. Test more than one sample to see if your results are repeated.)

SECTION 4 Elements From Earth

How Can You Separate Bolts From Sand?

1. Mix wet sand with a few small metal bolts and screws. Place the mixture in a tray or pie pan.

2. Think of a way to separate the sand from the bolts. You may not use a magnet, but you may use water, a bowl, paper towels, and other supplies available in your classroom.

3. With your teacher's permission, try your procedure.

Think It Over
Designing an Experiment What properties of matter did you use to separate the sand and the bolts? How successful was your procedure?

GUIDE FOR READING

◆ What physical property of gold allows it to be panned?

◆ What must be done to obtain an element from one of its compounds?

Reading Tip As you read, list the ways that people obtain elements from the forms in which they are found in nature.

Key Terms electrolysis
• electrode

Gold! In 1848, several gold nuggets were found in the American River in northern California near a mill owned by John Sutter. Thousands of people rushed to California with pans, pickaxes, and shovels. They searched the riverbanks and stream beds hoping to find more nuggets or even gold flakes.

Some people got rich, but many went home empty-handed. Perhaps the most disappointed of all were those who found pyrite, a substance that looks like gold. Pyrite is actually a compound of iron and sulfur. Can you tell why pyrite is also called "fool's gold"?

A miner pans for gold in ▶
northern California

Gold and Density

During the California gold rush, miners needed a way to remove the precious metal from a mixture that also contained dirt and sand. **Gold can be separated from other materials in a mixture because of its density.** As you read in Section 2, gold has a density of 19.3 g/cm^3. This density is much higher than that of most other materials, including fool's gold, which has a density of only 5.0 g/cm^3.

The miners used a technique called panning. They put the mixture of gold, dirt, and sand into a shallow pan and covered it with water. They then swirled the contents around and carefully poured off the water. The water carried the less dense dirt and sand with it. The more dense gold sank and was left behind. The miners repeated this process until only gold remained in the pan.

Today, gold mining is done on a much larger scale using machines called dredges. But the basic process of separating gold by its density is the same. The dredge scrapes up large amounts of dirt and sand, washes the mixture, and separates the gold in a way that's similar to panning.

☑ *Checkpoint* *What could you do to tell the difference between real gold and fool's gold?*

Figure 17 Gold nuggets contain only the element gold.

Copper and Electrolysis

In nature, finding an element that's not part of a compound is unusual. Most elements, including those that people use for industrial purposes in great amounts, are usually found as compounds. For example, copper compounds are most often found in a certain kind of ore. An ore is any rock that contains a metal or other economically useful material.

The process of obtaining copper from one of its compounds is more complicated than panning for gold. **To obtain an element from its compound, it is necessary to cause a chemical reaction to take place.** In that chemical change, the copper atoms must be separated from the other atoms in the compound.

Figure 18 Ores contain useful elements that are combined with other substances. **A.** Malachite contains copper. **B.** Iron pyrite contains iron.
Applying Concepts Why do ores have different properties from the elements that they contain?

A method that's commonly used to break down a copper compound is called **electrolysis,** which literally means "electric cutting." First, the copper compound is dissolved in water to form a mixture called a solution. Two metal strips called **electrodes** are placed in the copper compound solution. Each electrode is attached to a wire, and the wires are connected to a source of electric current such as a battery.

How It Works

Isolating Copper

In nature, copper is usually found in compounds with other elements. In this investigation, you will perform an electrolysis procedure to isolate copper from a compound called copper chloride.

Problem

How can copper be isolated from a compound by electrolysis?

Skills Focus

observing, inferring

Materials

glass jar, about 250 mL   6-volt battery
two paper clips   index card
wires with alligator clips or battery holder with
    wires
copper chloride solution (0.6 *M*), 100 mL

Procedure

1. Unbend a paper clip and make a hook shape. Push the long end through an index card until the hooked part touches the card.

2. Repeat Step 1 with another paper clip so that the clips are about 2–3 cm apart. The paper clips serve as your electrodes.

3. Pour enough copper chloride solution into a jar to cover at least half the length of the paper clips when the index card is set on top of the jar. **CAUTION:** *Copper chloride solution can be irritating to the skin and eyes. Do not touch it with your hands or get it in your mouth. The solution can stain your skin and clothes.*

4. Place the index card on top of the jar. If the straightened ends of the paper clips are not at least half-covered by the copper chloride solution, add more solution.

When the electric current is turned on, one electrode in the solution becomes coated with copper metal, which can be scraped off and used as needed. The other electrode attracts other materials in the solution. In a laboratory, electrolysis produces only small amounts of copper. In the copper industry, however, electrolysis is used on a huge scale to produce large amounts of copper metal.

Wire

Battery

Alligator clip

Metal paper clip

Index card

Copper chloride solution

5. Attach a wire to each pole of a battery. Attach the other ends of the wires to a separate paper clip. (See the drawing.) Prevent the paper clips from touching each other.

6. Predict what you think will happen if you allow the current to run for 2–3 minutes. (*Hint:* What elements are present in the copper chloride solution?)

7. Let the setup run for 2–3 minutes or until you see a deposit forming on one of the electrodes. Also look for bubbles.

8. Disconnect the wires. Remove the index card. Bring your face close to the jar and gently wave your hand toward your nose. Note any odor.

9. Note whether the color of the solution has changed since you began the procedure.

10. Note the color of the tips of the electrodes.

11. Discard the solution as directed by your teacher, and wash your hands.

Analyze and Conclude

1. Make a labeled diagram of your experimental setup. Indicate which electrode is connected to the positive side of the battery and which is connected to the negative side.

2. On which electrode was the copper produced? On which electrode was the chlorine produced?

3. If the color of the solution changed, how can you explain the change?

4. Compare the properties of copper, chlorine, and copper chloride solution.

5. Describe the changes in matter that you observed. Classify them as physical changes or chemical changes.

6. **Apply** Using your observations during this lab as evidence, explain why you think copper chloride is a compound, not a mixture.

More to Explore

Suppose you were to reconnect the wires with the positive and negative sides reversed. Predict how your results would differ under these conditions. With your teacher's permission, carry out the electrolysis with the connections reversed. Was your prediction correct?

Figure 19 Industry uses large-scale chemical reactions to produce useful materials. This blast furnace is used to make carbon react with iron ore to produce iron metal. The source of the carbon is coke, a substance produced from coal.

Iron and the Blast Furnace

Industry uses huge amounts of the element iron. Like copper, iron is usually found in an ore in the form of a compound. And also like copper, the element iron must be separated from its compounds by a chemical reaction.

Iron ores usually contain compounds formed of iron and oxygen. In order to release the iron, chunks of iron ore are placed in a hot fire along with coke, a source of carbon. In the intense heat of a blast furnace like the one in Figure 19, the carbon reacts with the oxygen. The element iron is left behind.

After leaving the blast furnace, iron is often used with other materials to produce mixtures having specific properties. For example, iron may be mixed with carbon and other metals to produce steel, which is stronger than iron alone. Adding chromium and nickel makes stainless steel, which resists rusting. Iron, copper, and gold are just three examples of useful elements that are extracted from Earth's surface.

Section 4 Review

1. Describe how panning for gold takes advantage of a specific property of gold.
2. What kind of change must take place to remove an element from its compound? Explain.
3. What happens to the elements in iron ore when the ore is mixed with carbon and heated?
4. **Thinking Critically Making Judgments** Planet Earth contains a limited supply of all metals. Predict whether programs to recycle aluminum, iron, and other metals will become more important in the future.

Check Your Progress CHAPTER PROJECT

Trade your written procedure and product samples with a new partner. Repeat this partner's procedure, following the directions as exactly as you can. Share your results with your new partner. Think of ways to improve both your procedure and your partner's procedure to make them clearer to follow.

SECTION 1 Describing Matter and Energy

Key Ideas

◆ Each specific substance has its own physical and chemical properties. These properties can be used to identify the substance.

◆ Matter is made up of elements. Elements can be chemically combined in compounds.

◆ Physical changes alter the form of a substance, but not its identity. Chemical changes result in one or more new substances.

◆ Energy is needed for both physical and chemical changes. There are different types of energy, which interact with matter in different ways.

Key Terms

matter	physical property	mixture
energy	chemical property	physical change
chemistry	element	chemical change
substance	compound	

 SECTION 2 Measuring Matter

Key Ideas

◆ Mass is a measurement of how much matter an object contains. If you move an object away from Earth, its weight changes, but its mass stays the same.

◆ The density of an object equals its mass divided by its volume. A unit of density is always a mass unit divided by a volume unit, such as grams per cubic centimeter (g/cm^3).

Key Terms

weight	volume
mass	density
International System of Units (SI)	

 SECTION 3 Particles of Matter

Key Ideas

◆ Atoms are the smallest particles of an element.

◆ Dalton stated that atoms are unbreakable, rigid spheres. He also said that atoms of different elements are different from one another.

◆ Atoms can be combined into molecules, which are held together by chemical bonds.

Key Terms

atom	chemical bond	molecule

 SECTION 4 Elements From Earth

INTEGRATING EARTH SCIENCE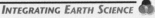

Key Ideas

◆ Gold, which is usually found in nature as an element, can be separated from other materials because of its density.

◆ Earth contains deposits of many elements in the form of compounds. A chemical reaction is needed to remove an element from its compound.

Key Terms

electrolysis	electrode

Organizing Information

Concept Map Copy the concept map about classifying matter onto a separate sheet of paper. Then complete the map and add a title. (For more on concept maps, see the Skills Handbook.)

Reviewing Content

 Review key concepts online using iText at www.phschool.com

Multiple Choice

Choose the letter of the answer that best completes the statement or answers the question.

1. Matter made of two or more substances is a(n)
   a. mixture.   b. element.
   c. compound.   d. property.
2. One form of electromagnetic energy is
   a. motion.   b. light.
   c. electricity.   d. energy in matter.
3. The density of an object equals
   a. the product of its length, width, and height.
   b. its volume divided by its mass.
   c. the product of the mass and volume.
   d. its mass divided by its volume.
4. Dalton imagined atoms to be
   a. rigid, unbreakable spheres.
   b. all exactly alike.
   c. always joined together in compounds.
   d. of equal mass.
5. A method used to release iron metal from its ore involves
   a. heating the ore and carbon together.
   b. cooling the ore in an ice bath.
   c. breaking the ore into small pieces.
   d. panning.

True or False

If the statement is true, write true. If it is false, change the underlined word to make it true.

6. <u>Compounds</u> are substances that cannot be broken down into other substances by any chemical means.
7. <u>Energy</u> is always involved when changes in matter occur.
8. If you move an object from place to place in the universe, the <u>weight</u> of the object will stay the same.
9. Grams per milliliter (g/mL) is an example of a unit of <u>volume</u>.
10. One of Dalton's principles is that each element is made of its own kind of <u>atom</u>.

Checking Concepts

11. When a piece of paper is torn into two pieces, has it undergone a chemical change or a physical change? Explain.
12. How could you find the volume of a small rock, using only a graduated cylinder and water?
13. What can you infer about the density of a substance if a block of that substance floats in water?
14. In terms of energy, describe what happens to water in a freezer.
15. **Writing to Learn** In a novel or short story, the author describes the properties of objects he or she is writing about. These details add interest to the story. Select at least six different kinds of objects. You might include objects from nature as well as objects made by people. List the properties of each object. Now use that list to write the first paragraph of a story.

Thinking Critically

16. **Problem Solving** How can you show that salt water is a mixture and not a compound? First compare the properties of the solution to the properties of the individual components. Then come up with a plan to separate the solution into its components.
17. **Comparing and Contrasting** Compare and contrast atoms and molecules. What do the two kinds of particles have in common? How are they related? Give an example that shows this relationship.
18. **Applying Concepts** How can you use Dalton's atomic theory to explain why every sample of a particular substance has the same properties?
19. **Inferring** Solid gold has a greater density than liquid gold. What must happen to the volume of a given mass of solid gold when it becomes a liquid? Explain.

Applying Skills

Use the table below to answer Questions 20–22. The table lists the mass and volume of six coins.

Coin	Mass (g)	Volume (cm³)
A	3.1	0.41
B	4.0	0.50
C	8.6	1.2
D	8.0	0.95
E	9.8	1.1
F	5.0	0.67

20. **Calculating** Based on the data in the table, calculate the density of Coins A–F.

21. **Interpreting Data** In Altrusia, all coins are made of a mixture of copper and zinc that has a density of 8.42 g/cm³. Which coins could be from Altrusia?

22. **Drawing Conclusions** The density of copper is 8.92 g/cm³ and the density of zinc is 7.14 g/cm³. If you assume that only copper and zinc were used to make the coins, can any of the coins be pure copper? Can any be pure zinc? Explain.

Performance CHAPTER PROJECT **Assessment**

Present Your Project Work with your second partner to show the data each of you collected. Present your data so that other students can see whether the procedure produced similar results each time. Briefly describe why or why not you think your data is reliable.

Reflect and Record In your journal, record the results of your experiment and describe why you think your conclusions are valid. Describe how your data compares with the advertising message promoted by the product's manufacturer.

Test Preparation

Use these questions to prepare for standardized tests.

Use the diagram to answer Questions 23–26.

Alexander found a solid block of an unknown material. He used a metric ruler to measure the size of the block. The measurements he recorded are shown in the diagram.

23. What is the volume of the block?
    A 9 cm
    B 24 cm²
    C 24 cm³
    D 60 cm³

24. Which measurement shown in the diagram was not needed to find the volume of the box?
    F length (4 cm)
    G height (2 cm)
    H width (3 cm)
    J diagonal (5 cm)

25. Alexander knows that the density of the material from which the block is made is 2 g/cm³. Knowing this, what is the mass of the block?
    A 4.8 g
    B 48 g
    C 480 g
    D 4,800 g

26. If the block could be molded into a flatter and longer shape, then the
    F mass, volume, and density all would change.
    G volume would change, but the mass and density would remain the same.
    H mass and volume would change, but the density would remain the same.
    J mass, volume, and density all would remain the same.

www.phschool.com
WEB ACTIVITY

A Story of Changes in Matter

Threw river is a story of changing matter. In winter, the surface of the river froze solid. Now it's spring, and the ice has begun melting. The ice around the rocks is the last to melt. The river water flows downstream, and plants, such as the green moss on the rocks, begin their spring growth.

If you could look very closely at ice, water, rock, and moss, you would be able to see that all matter is made up of small particles. In this chapter, you will learn how the behavior of these small particles explains the physical properties of solids, liquids, and gases. Your project is to model what happens to particles of matter as they change from a solid to a liquid to a gas.

Your Goal Create a skit or cartoon that demonstrates how particles of matter behave as they change from a solid to a liquid to a gas and then from a gas to a liquid to a solid.

To complete the project, you must

◆ describe what happens to the particles during each change of state
◆ outline your skit or cartoon in a storyboard format
◆ illustrate your cartoon or produce your skit

Get Started With a group of classmates, brainstorm a list of the physical properties of solids, liquids, and gases.

Check Your Progress You'll be working on this project as you study this chapter. To keep your project on track, look for Check Your Progress boxes at the following points.

Section 2 Review, page 67: Describe the particles in solids, liquids, and gases, and begin preparing a storyboard.

Section 4 Review, page 79: Finish your cartoon or skit.

Present Your Project At the end of the chapter (page 83), you will present your skit or cartoon to the class.

Ice formations on Bridal
Veil Creek, Columbia River
Gorge National Scenic
Area, Oregon

TEKS

In addition to process TEKS, this chapter addresses these concept TEKS as they relate to the chapter's topics.

(6.7) The student knows that substances have physical and chemical properties. The student is expected to:
(B) classify substances by their physical and chemical properties.

States of Matter

•••**ACTIVITY**••••

What Are Solids, Liquids, and Gases?

1. Break an antacid tablet (fizzing type) into three or four pieces. Place the pieces inside a large, uninflated balloon.

2. Fill a 1-liter plastic bottle about halfway with water. Stretch the mouth of the balloon over the top of the bottle, taking care to keep the pieces inside the balloon.

3. Jiggle the balloon so that the pieces fall into the bottle. Observe what happens for about two minutes.

4. Remove the balloon and examine its contents.

Think It Over

Classifying Identify examples of the different states of matter—solids, liquids, and gases—that you observed in this activity. Define each of the three states in your own words.

GUIDE FOR READING

◆ How do shape, volume, and particle motion help classify solids, liquids, and gases?

Reading Tip **Before you read, list properties that you think classify substances as solids, liquids, or gases. Revise your list as you read.**

Key Terms **solid**
• **crystalline solid**
• **melting point**
• **amorphous solid**
• **liquid • viscosity**
• **gas**

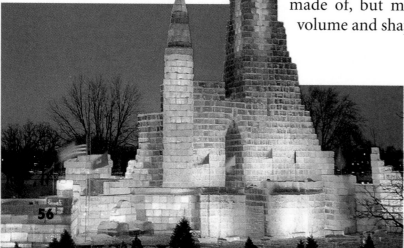

If you visit the annual Winter Carnival in St. Paul, Minnesota, you will see some unusual structures. To celebrate the cold winter weather, people carve huge sculptures out of ice. Over the years, the carnival has featured giant snow figures and ice palaces like the one shown here.

Even in Minnesota, anything made of snow and ice won't last beyond winter. When the temperature rises, snow figures and ice palaces melt into liquid water. And unlike frozen water, liquid water is a poor building material.

Your world is full of substances that can be classified as solids, liquids, or gases. Those substances may be elements, compounds, or mixtures. Gold is an element. Air is a mixture of gases. Water is a compound you've seen as both a solid and a liquid. The states of matter are not defined by what they are made of, but mainly by whether or not they hold their volume and shape.

Figure 1 Each year ice palaces like this one delight visitors to the Winter Carnival in St. Paul, Minnesota.

Figure 2 In the tanks on their backs, these scuba divers carry air to breathe. *Classifying* *Find an example of each state of matter in this photograph.*

Solids

What if you were to pick up a solid object, such as a pen or a comb, and move it from place to place around the room? What would you observe? Would the object ever change its size or shape as you moved it? Would a pen become larger if you put it in a bowl? Would a comb become flatter when you place it on a tabletop? Of course not. A **solid** has a definite volume and a definite shape. If your pen has a volume of 6 cm^3 and a cylindrical shape, then it will keep that volume and shape in any position and in any container.

Particles in a Solid The particles that make up a solid are packed very closely together, as shown in Figure 3A. In addition, each particle is tightly fixed in one position. This makes it hard to separate them. **Because the particles in a solid are packed tightly together and stay in fixed positions, a solid has a definite shape and volume.**

Are the particles in a solid completely motionless? No, not really. The particles vibrate, meaning they move back and forth slightly. This motion is similar to a person running in place. Or, you can think of the particles in a solid as something like a group of balls connected by tight springs. Like the balls in Figure 3B, the particles that make up a solid stay in about the same position. However, the individual pieces are still able to vibrate back and forth in their places.

Figure 3 The balls represent the particles in a solid. **A.** A solid keeps its own shape. It doesn't take the shape of a container. **B.** The particles vibrate back and forth within the solid.

Figure 4 When you heat an amorphous solid such as this butter, it softens before it melts.
Comparing and Contrasting How are the particles in an amorphous solid different from the particles in a crystalline solid?

Types of Solids In many solids, the particles form a regular, repeating pattern. These patterns create crystals. Solids that are made up of crystals are classified as **crystalline solids** (KRIS tuh lin). Salt, sugar, sand, and snow are examples of crystalline solids. When a crystalline solid such as snow is heated, it melts at a distinct temperature called its **melting point.**

In other solids the particles are not arranged in a regular pattern. These solids are classified as **amorphous solids** (uh MAWR fus). Plastics, rubber, and glass are amorphous solids. Unlike a crystalline solid, an amorphous solid does not have a distinct melting point. Instead, when it is heated it becomes softer and softer as its temperature rises. You have probably noticed this physical property in plastic items that have been out in the sun on a hot day. The plastic gradually melts. In fact, the word *plastic* means "able to be molded into many shapes."

✓ *Checkpoint* *How do crystalline and amorphous solids differ?*

Liquids

Unlike a solid, a **liquid** has no shape of its own. Instead, a liquid takes on the shape of its container. Without a container, a liquid spreads into a wide, shallow puddle.

However, liquids are like solids in that they do not easily compress or expand. If you gently squeezed on a water-filled plastic bag, for example, the water might change its shape, but its volume would not decrease or increase.

What if you have 100 mL of water? If you pour it into another container, the water still occupies 100 mL. It has the same volume no matter what shape its container has.

Figure 5 Although a liquid's volume does not change, it takes the shape of whatever container you pour it into.

Figure 6 You can think of the particles of a liquid as somewhat like the people in this train station. They remain near one another but move from place to place.

Particles in a Liquid The particles in a liquid are packed almost as closely as in a solid. However, the particles in a liquid move around one another freely. **Because its particles are free to move, a liquid has no definite shape. However, it does have a definite volume.** You can compare a liquid to the rush-hour crowd at a train station. Like particles in a liquid, the people in the crowd move around the platform that contains them, but they stay in close contact with one another.

Viscosity Because particles in a liquid are free to move around one another, a liquid can flow from place to place. Some liquids flow more easily than others. The resistance of a liquid to flowing is a physical property called **viscosity** (vis KAHS uh tee). Liquids with high viscosity flow slowly. For example, cold molasses has a particularly high viscosity. Liquids with low viscosity flow quickly. Water, rubbing alcohol, and vinegar have relatively low viscosities.

 INTEGRATING EARTH SCIENCE The viscosity of lava that erupts from a volcano helps classify the type of volcanic eruption. A volcano erupts quietly if it has thin, runny lava—that is, lava with low viscosity. High-viscosity lava, which is thick and sticky, is typical of a volcano that erupts explosively.

Gases

Gases can change volume more easily than either solids or liquids. If you put a gas in a sealed container, the gas particles will spread apart or squeeze together to fill that container. The volume and shape of a gas is the volume and shape of its container. To illustrate this principle, take a deep breath. Your chest expands. Can you feel the air coming through your nose and mouth? Air is a mixture of

---

TRY THIS

As Thick as Honey

Here's how you can compare the viscosity of two liquids.

ACTIVITY

1. Place on a table a clear plastic jar almost filled with honey and another clear plastic jar almost filled with vegetable oil. Make sure that the tops of both jars are tightly closed.

2. Turn the jars upside-down at the same time. Observe what happens.

3. Turn the two jars right-side up and again watch what happens.

Drawing Conclusions Which liquid has a greater viscosity? What evidence leads you to this conclusion?

Figure 7 The particles of a gas can be squeezed into a small volume (left). If allowed to, they will spread out without limit, somewhat like the flock of gulls on the right.

gases that acts as one gas. When you breathe in, air moves from your mouth to your windpipe to your lungs. In each place, the air changes shape and volume. When you breathe out, the changes happen in reverse. If you hold your hand in front of your mouth, you can feel the air move around and past your fingers.

If you could see the individual particles that make up a gas, you would see tiny particles flying at high speeds in all directions. **Gas particles spread apart, filling all the space available to them. Thus, a gas has neither definite shape nor volume.** You can compare a gas to the flock of gulls shown in Figure 7. Like gas particles, these gulls fly very quickly in different directions. They can spread out to "fill" any available space.

Section 1 Review

1. Describe properties you would use to classify a substance as a solid.
2. How does the movement of particles in a liquid help to explain the shape and volume of liquids?
3. Use what you know about the particles in a gas to explain why a gas has no definite shape and no definite volume.
4. **Thinking Critically** Relating Cause and **Effect** Glass is an amorphous solid. How can you use that information to help explain why a glassblower can bend and shape a piece of glass that has been heated?

Science at Home

What Gives? Show your family how liquids and gases differ. Completely fill the bulb and cylinder of a turkey baster with water. Hold it over the sink. While you seal the end with your finger, have a family member squeeze the bulb. Now let the water out of the turkey baster. Again, seal the end with your finger and have a family member squeeze the bulb. Was there a difference? Use what you know about liquids and gases to explain the observations.

2 Gas Behavior

DISCOVER ··· ACTIVITY····

How Can Air Keep Chalk From Breaking?

1. Standing on a chair or table, drop a piece of chalk onto a hard floor. Observe what happens to the chalk.

2. Wrap a second piece of chalk in wax paper or plastic food wrap. Drop the chalk from the same height used in Step 1. Observe the results.

3. Wrap a third piece of chalk in plastic bubble wrap. Drop the chalk from the same height used in Step 1. Observe the results.

Think It Over

Inferring Compare the results from Steps 1, 2, and 3. What properties of the air in the bubble wrap accounted for the results in Step 3?

Every Thanksgiving, the people of New York City gather to watch a big parade. Maybe you have seen this parade on television, or even in person. The parade is famous for its large, floating balloons, like the one shown on this page. The balloons float because they are filled with helium, a gas that is less dense than air.

If you were in charge of a parade balloon, you would be faced with many different questions. How large is the balloon? How much helium should you put inside the balloon? Does the balloon behave differently in warm weather than in cold weather? To answer these questions and others like them, you would need to understand the properties of gases.

GUIDE FOR READING

◆ How are the volume, temperature, and pressure of a gas related?

Reading Tip Before you read, change each heading into a question. Write a brief answer to each question as you read.

Key Terms temperature
• pressure • Boyle's Law
• Charles's Law

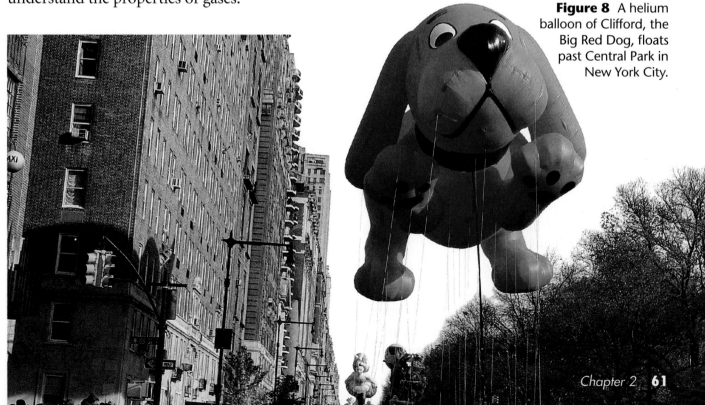

Figure 8 A helium balloon of Clifford, the Big Red Dog, floats past Central Park in New York City.

Figure 9 The helium gas in this tank is kept under high pressure within the volume set by the thick steel walls. *Predicting What happens to the helium atoms as they move into the balloons?*

Measuring Gases

How much helium is in the tank in Figure 9? You may think that measuring the volume of the tank will give you an answer. But gases easily contract or expand. To fill the tank, helium was compressed, or pressed together tightly. When the helium is used, it fills a total volume of inflated balloons much greater than the volume of the tank. The actual volume you get, however, depends on the temperature and air pressure that day. So what exactly do measurements of volume, pressure, and temperature mean?

Volume You know volume is the amount of space that matter fills. Volume is measured in cubic centimeters, milliliters, liters, and other units. Because gases fill the space available, the volume of a gas is the same as the volume of its container.

Temperature Hot soup, warm hands, cool breezes—you should be familiar with matter at different temperatures. But what exactly does temperature show? Recall that in any substance—solid, liquid, or gas—the particles are constantly moving. **Temperature** is a measure of the average energy of motion of the particles of a substance. The faster the particles are moving, the greater their energy and the higher the temperature. You might think of a thermometer as a speedometer for molecules.

Even at ordinary temperatures, the average speed of particles in a gas is very fast. At 20°C, which is about room temperature, the particles in a typical gas travel about 500 meters per second!

Pressure The motion of gas particles is related to the force, or push, of the particles against the walls of their container. Because gas particles are moving, they constantly collide with one another. They also collide with the walls of their container. As a result, the gas exerts an outward push on the walls of the container. The **pressure** of the gas is the force of its outward push divided by the area of the walls of the container. Pressure is measured in units of kilopascals (kPa).

$$Pressure = \frac{Force}{Area}$$

The firmness of an object inflated with a gas, such as a soccer ball, comes from the pressure of the gas. If the gas (in this case, air) leaks out of the ball, the pressure decreases, and the ball becomes softer. But why does an inflated ball leak when punctured? A gas flows from an area of high pressure to an area of low pressure. The air inside the ball is at a higher pressure than the air outside. Gas particles inside the ball hit the hole more often than gas particles outside the hole. Because more inside particles hit the hole, they have a better chance of getting out of the ball. Thus, many more particles go out than in. The pressure inside drops until it is equal to the pressure outside.

✓ *Checkpoint* *What are three properties of a gas that you can measure?*

Relating Pressure and Volume

Pressure is also related to the volume of a container. For example, imagine that you are operating a bicycle pump. By pressing down on the plunger, you force the gas inside the pump through the rubber tube and out the nozzle into the tire. What will happen if you close the nozzle and then push down on the plunger?

Figure 10 The gas particles are in constant motion, colliding with each other and with the walls of their container.

Figure 11 What will happen when this bicyclist operates the pump she is attaching? She will decrease the volume of air in the cylinder and increase its pressure. As a result, air will be forced into the bicycle tire and the tire will inflate.

Figure 12 As weights are added, the same number of gas particles occupies a smaller volume. The pressure of the gas increases. This relationship is called Boyle's law.

Balloon Test

What happens when you change the volume of a gas?

1. Hold the open end of a paper cup on the side of a partly inflated balloon.

2. Inflate the balloon until it presses against the cup and then let go of the cup. What happens?

Developing Hypotheses Use what you know about pressure and volume to write a hypothesis that explains the behavior of the cup after you let it go. How could you test your hypothesis?

The answer to this question comes from experiments with gases done by the English scientist Robert Boyle. In the 1600s, Boyle measured the volumes of gases at different pressures as he experimented with ways to improve air pumps. He saw that gases behave in a predictable way. **Boyle found that when the pressure of a gas is increased at constant temperature, the volume of the gas decreases. When the pressure is decreased, the volume increases.** This relationship between the pressure and volume of a gas is named **Boyle's law.**

INTEGRATING EARTH SCIENCE Boyle's law plays an important role in research done with some high-altitude balloons. These balloons are made from lightweight plastic. They are filled with only a small fraction of the helium they could hold. Why is that? As a balloon rises through the atmosphere, the air pressure around it decreases steadily. As the air pressure decreases, the helium inside the balloon expands, stretching the balloon to a greater and greater volume. If the balloon were fully filled at takeoff, it would burst before it got very high.

Boyle's law also applies to situations in which the *volume* of a gas is changed. Then the *pressure* changes in the opposite way. For example, if you squeeze an inflated balloon, you are decreasing its volume. You should be able to feel the increased pressure of the gas inside it. The bicycle pump described earlier is a similar case. As you push on the plunger, the volume of air inside the pump gets smaller and the pressure increases.

✓ *Checkpoint* *What is Boyle's law?*

Relating Pressure and Temperature

If you pour a bucket of sand onto your skin, it will not hurt at all. But suppose you are caught in a sandstorm. Because the sand grains are flying very fast, they will hurt a great deal! The faster the grains are traveling, the harder they will hit your skin.

Raising Temperature Raises Pressure

Although gas particles are much smaller and lighter than sand grains, a sandstorm is a good model for a gas. Like sand in a sandstorm, gas particles travel individually and at high speeds. Remember that pressure is a measure of how much gas particles push on the walls of a container. The greater the speed of the gas particles, the more collisions will occur. The more collisions there are, the greater the pressure will be.

Temperature is a measure of the average speed of the particles of a gas. The higher the temperature of a gas, the faster the gas particles are moving. Now you can state a relationship between temperature and pressure. **When the temperature of a gas at constant volume is increased, the pressure of the gas increases. When the temperature is decreased, the pressure of the gas decreases.** A constant volume means a closed, rigid container.

Figure 13 Particles of a heated gas are like the sand blown by the wind in this sandstorm. When a gas is heated, the particles move faster and collide more with one another and the sides of their container. *Relating Cause and Effect Why does the pressure of the gas increase when the number of collisions increases?*

Pressure and Temperature in Action Have you ever looked at the tires of an 18-wheel truck? Because these tires need to support a lot of weight, they are large, heavy, and stiff. The inside volume of these tires doesn't vary much.

On long trips, especially in the summer, a truck's tires can get very hot. As the temperature increases, so does the pressure of the air inside the tire. If the pressure becomes higher than the tire can hold, the tire will burst apart. For this reason, truck drivers need to monitor and adjust tire pressure on long trips.

Relating Volume and Temperature

If the temperature of the gas in a balloon is increased, its volume will change. Will the volume increase or decrease? If you answered "increase," you are right. Gases increase in volume when the temperature increases. On the other hand, as the temperature decreases, the gas volume decreases. People in charge of the large balloons used for parades need to understand the effect temperature has on volume so that the balloons can be inflated properly.

Charles's Law   In the late 1700s, a French scientist named Jacques Charles examined the relationship between the temperature and volume of a gas kept at a constant pressure. He measured the volume of a gas at various temperatures in a container whose volume could change. **Charles found that when the temperature of a gas is increased at constant pressure, its volume increases. When the temperature of a gas is decreased its volume decreases.** This principle is called **Charles's law.** Remember that at higher temperatures, the particles move faster. As a result, they collide more often with the walls around them. As long as the volume of the container can change, the pressure stays constant, and the total push of the collisions results in the gas taking up more space. The volume of the gas increases.

Charles's Law in Action   You can see Charles's law demonstrated using air contained in a party balloon. Look at Figure 15 on the next page. The left photograph shows the balloon in a beaker of water, resting on a tub of ice. (A smaller beaker of water keeps the balloon submerged in the larger beaker.) In the next photograph, the beaker has been heated on a hot plate. When you compare the photos, you should notice a change. The balloon in the right photograph is larger. This difference is the result of an increase in the volume of the air as it is heated.

Figure 14 If temperature is increased while pressure stays constant, the same number of particles of gas will occupy a greater volume. This relationship is called Charles's law.

−65°C   250°C

Figure 15 By heating a gas at constant pressure, you can increase its volume. A sample of air that is chilled (left) has a smaller volume than it does after it is heated (right). *Predicting What will happen to the balloon if the beaker is returned to an ice bath?*

In this example, pressure remains more or less constant because the expanding air is in a flexible container. But what would happen if heating were to continue, and the balloon reached its limit in size? You might guess it would pop, but can you figure out why? Think back to Boyle's law. When the balloon can no longer expand, the continued increase in temperature would cause an increase in pressure. Eventually, the pressure would be great enough to break the balloon.

Boyle, Charles, and others often described gas behavior two factors at a time. In the real world, however, gases can show changes in pressure, temperature, and volume all at once. Scientists, tire manufacturers, engineers, and others who work with gases must consider these combined effects.

Section 2 Review

1. Describe the relationship between the pressure and volume of a gas.
2. If you change the temperature of a gas but keep the volume the same, how does the pressure change?
3. What is Charles's law?
4. **Thinking Critically Applying Concepts** Suppose it is the night before Thanksgiving, and you are in charge of inflating a balloon for the Thanksgiving Day parade. You just learned that the temperature will rise 15°C by the time the parade starts. How will this information affect the way you inflate your balloon?

CHAPTER PROJECT

Check Your Progress
With the members of your group, write a description of how particles behave in each of the three states of matter. Next, think of different ways to model each state, using drawings and words. Decide whether you want to demonstrate a change of state as cartoon pictures or by acting out the motion of particles in a skit. (*Hint:* Prepare a storyboard. A storyboard is a series of simple drawings and captions that outline the action of a story.)

SECTION 3 Graphing Gas Behavior

DISCOVER ·· ACTIVITY····

What Does a Graph of Pressure and Temperature Show?

Temperature (°C)	Pressure (kPa)
0	8
5	11
10	14
15	17
20	20
25	23

1. In an experiment, the temperature was varied for a constant volume of gas. Gas pressure was measured after each 5°C change. You now need to graph the data in this table.

2. Show temperature on the horizontal axis with a scale from 0°C to 25°C. Show pressure on the vertical axis with a scale equally spaced from 0 kPa to 25 kPa.

3. For each pair of measurements, draw a point on the graph.

4. Draw a line to connect the points.

Think It Over

Graphing Use the graph to describe the relationship between the pressure and temperature of a gas.

GUIDE FOR READING

◆ What do graphs for Charles's law and Boyle's law look like?

Reading Tip As you read about the experiments in this section, refer to the graphs in Figures 19 and 21.

Key Terms graph
• directly proportional
• vary inversely

The population of a town is increasing. The schools are becoming more crowded, and the people need to decide whether to build more schools. Newspapers illustrate their articles about the problem with graphs.

How could a graph help tell this story? A **graph** is a diagram that tells how two variables, or factors, are related. Graphs show how changes in one variable result in changes in a second variable. You can use graphs to make predictions. For example, according to the graph in Figure 16, the town might have a population of 32,000 in 2020. That assumes, of course, that population continues to grow at the same rate. In this section, you will learn how to interpret graphs that relate properties of gases.

Figure 16 This graph shows that the population in the town is growing steadily. The dashed line predicts what the population would be if the current growth rate were to continue.

Cylinder

Piston

50 mL of gas

Ice bath at 0°C

Temperature		Volume
(°C)	(K)	(mL)
0	273	50
10	283	52
20	293	54
30	303	56
40	313	58
50	323	60
60	333	62
70	343	63
80	353	66
90	363	67
100	373	69

Figure 17 As the temperature of the water bath increases, the gas inside the cylinder is warmed by the water. The data from the experiment are recorded in the table. Celsius values can be converted to kelvins by adding 273 to the Celsius value.

Temperature and Volume

Recall from Section 2 that Charles's law relates the temperature and volume of a gas that is kept at a constant pressure. You can examine this relationship by doing an experiment in which you change the temperature of a gas and measure its volume. Then you can graph the data you have recorded and look for a relationship. Recall, also, that the motion of particles increases as their temperature increases.

Collecting Data As you can see from the cutaway view in Figure 17, the gas in the experiment is in a cylinder that has a movable piston. The piston moves up and down freely, which allows the gas to change volume and keep the same pressure. To control the temperature, the cylinder is placed in a water bath.

The experiment begins with an ice-water bath at 0°C and the gas volume at 50 mL. Then the water bath is slowly heated. Very gradually, the temperature increases from 0°C to 100°C. Each time the temperature increases by 10 degrees Celsius, the volume of the gas in the cylinder is recorded.

You'll notice a second set of temperatures listed in the table in Figure 17. Scientists often work with gas temperatures in units called kelvins. To convert from Celsius degrees to kelvins, you add 273. The kelvin temperatures will be used to graph the data.

Graphing the Results A graph consists of a grid set up by two lines—one horizontal and one vertical. Each line, or axis, is divided into equal units. The horizontal, or x-, axis shows the manipulated variable, in this case, temperature. The vertical,

Figure 18 The horizontal, or x-, axis and the vertical, or y-, axis are the "backbone" of a graph. *Interpreting Diagrams Which variable is placed on the x-axis?*

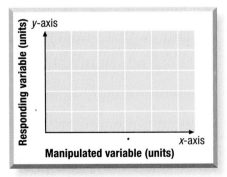

y-axis

Responding variable (units)

x-axis

Manipulated variable (units)

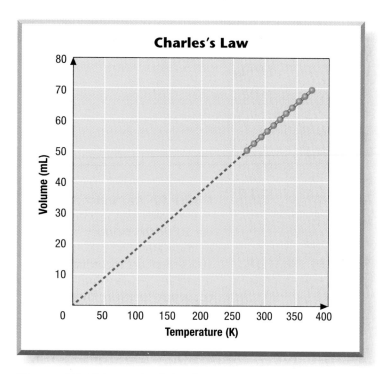

Charles's Law

Figure 19 This graph of the data from Figure 17 shows the linear relationship between temperature and volume known as Charles's law. The dotted line predicts how the graph would look if the gas could be cooled to lower temperatures.

or *y*-, axis shows the responding variable, in this case, volume. Each axis is labeled with the name of the variable, the units of measurement, and a range of values.

Look at the graph in Figure 19. It appears as if the line would continue downward if data could be collected for lower temperatures. Such a line would pass through the point (0, 0). When a graph of two variables is a straight line passing through the (0, 0) point, the relationship is linear, and the variables are said to be **directly proportional** to each other. **The graph of Charles's law shows that the volume of a gas is directly proportional to its kelvin temperature under constant pressure.**

☑ *Checkpoint* On which axis of a graph do you show the responding variable?

Pressure and Volume

You can perform another experiment to show how pressure and volume are related when temperature is kept constant. Recall that the relationship between pressure and volume is called Boyle's law.

Figure 20 By pushing on the top of the piston, you compress the gas and thereby increase the pressure of the gas inside the cylinder. The data from the experiment are recorded in the table.
Predicting What would happen if you pulled up on the piston?

Volume (mL)	Pressure (kPa)
100	60
90	67
80	75
70	86
60	100

Collecting Data The gas in this experiment is also contained in a cylinder with a movable piston. In this case, however, a pressure gauge indicates the pressure of the gas inside.

The experiment begins with the volume of the gas at 100 mL. The pressure of the gas is 60 kilopascals. Next, the piston is slowly pushed into the cylinder, compressing the gas, or shrinking its volume. The pressure of the gas is recorded after each 10-mL change in volume.

Graphing the Results To observe the relationship of the pressure and volume of a gas, it helps to display the data in another graph. In the pressure-volume experiment, the manipulated variable is volume. Volume is shown on the scale of the horizontal axis from 60 mL to 100 mL. The responding variable is pressure. Pressure is shown on the scale of the vertical axis from 60 kPa to 100 kPa.

As you can see in Figure 21, the points lie on a curve. Notice that the curve slopes downward from left to right. Also notice that the curve is steep close to the vertical axis and becomes less steep close to the horizontal axis. When a graph of two measurements forms this kind of curve, the relationship is nonlinear, and the measurements are said to **vary inversely** with each other. **The graph for Boyle's law shows that the pressure of a gas varies inversely with its volume at constant temperature.** In other words, the pressure of a gas decreases as its volume increases.

Figure 21 This graph of the data from Figure 20 shows the nonlinear relationship between pressure and volume known as Boyle's law. (The broken lines show gaps in the scales.)

 Section 3 Review

Science at Home

1. Describe a graph of Charles's law.
2. Describe a graph of Boyle's law.
3. How can you tell the difference between a graph in which one variable is directly proportional to another and a graph in which two variables vary inversely?
4. **Thinking Critically** **Interpreting Graphs** Suppose the temperature of the gas in the experiment illustrated in Figure 17 was increased to 400 K (127°C). Use Figure 19 to predict the new volume of the gas.

News Data Look for graphs in your newspaper or in newsmagazines. Point out to members of your family which variable is the manipulated variable and which is the responding variable for each graph. Then compare any line graphs you have found to the graphs in this section. Which of your graphs show two variables that are directly proportional to each other? Do any show variables that vary inversely?

It's a Gas

You can use a syringe as a model of an air pump. In this lab, you will determine how the pressure exerted on a syringe is related to the volume of the air inside it.

Problem

How does the volume of a gas change as the pressure you exert on it increases?

Materials

strong plastic syringe (with no needle), at least 35 cm^3 capacity
modeling clay
4 books of uniform weight
computer and graphing software (optional)

Procedure

1. Make a data table in your notebook like the one below.
2. Lift the plunger of the syringe as high as it will move without going off scale. The volume in the syringe will be as large as possible.
3. Seal the small opening of the syringe with a piece of clay. The seal must be airtight.

4. Hold the syringe upright with the clay end on the table. With the help of a partner, place a single book on top of the plunger. Balance the book carefully so it does not fall.
5. Read the volume indicated by the plunger and record it in your data table.
6. Predict what will happen as more books are placed on the syringe.
7. Place another book on top of the first book. Read the new volume and record it in your data table.

DATA TABLE

Adding Books		Removing Books	
Number of Books	Volume (cm^3)	Number of Books	Volume (cm^3)
0		4	
1		3	
2		2	
3		1	
4		0	

8. One by one, place each of the remaining books on top of the plunger. After you add each book, record the volume of the syringe in your data table.

9. Predict what will happen as books are removed from the plunger one by one.

10. Remove the books one at a time. After you remove each book, again record the volume of the syringe in your data table.

Analyze and Conclude

1. Why is this a good model of an air pump? What are the model's limitations?

2. Using a computer or graph paper, make a line graph of the data obtained from Steps 5, 7, and 8. Show volume in cubic centimeters (cm^3) on the vertical axis and number of books on the horizontal axis. Title this Graph 1.

3. Make a second line graph of the data obtained from Step 10. Title this Graph 2.

4. Did the results you obtained support your predictions in Steps 6 and 9? Explain.

5. Describe the shape of Graph 1. What does the graph tell you about the relationship between the volume and pressure of a gas?

6. Compare Graph 2 with Graph 1. How can you explain any differences in the two graphs?

7. **Think About It** Did the volume change between the addition of the first and second book? Did it change by the same amount between the addition of the second book and third book? Between the third and fourth book? What is happening to the gas particles in air that could explain this behavior?

Design an Experiment

How could you use ice and warm water to show how the temperature and volume of a gas are related? Design an experiment to test the effect of changing the temperature of a gas. With your teacher's approval, conduct this experiment.

SECTION 4 Changes in State

DISCOVER ●●● ACTIVITY ●●●●

What Happens When You Breathe on a Mirror?

1. Obtain a hand mirror. Clean it with a dry cloth. Describe the mirror's surface.

2. Hold the mirror about 15 cm away from your face. Try to breathe against the mirror's surface.

3. Reduce the distance until breathing on the mirror produces a visible change. Record what you observe.

Think It Over

Developing Hypotheses What did you observe when you breathed on the mirror held close to your mouth? How can you explain that observation? Why did you get different results when the mirror was at greater distances from your face?

GUIDE FOR READING

◆ When thermal energy is transferred, in what direction does it flow?

◆ How does the thermal energy of a substance change when it changes state?

Reading Tip As you read, make an outline that includes the headings and main ideas of the section.

Key Terms thermal energy
• melting • freezing
• vaporization
• evaporation
• boiling
• boiling point
• condensation
• sublimation

Think of what happens to an ice cream cone on a hot summer day. The ice cream quickly starts to drip onto your hand. You're not surprised. You know that ice cream melts if it's not kept cold.

Energy and Changes in State

If you turn on a faucet, the tap water is usually cold unless it comes through a heater. At a warmer temperature, the particles of substance have a higher average energy of motion than at a cooler temperature. The energy that the particles of a substance have is called **thermal energy.** The amount of thermal energy in a substance depends partly on its temperature and the way its particles are arranged.

Thermal energy is transferred from one substance to another as heat. **Thermal energy always flows from a warmer substance to a cooler substance.** When heat flows into a substance, its particles gain energy and move faster. When heat flows from a substance, its particles lose energy and move more slowly. So thermal energy is involved when a substance changes state.

74

Figure 22 A jeweler melts silver before pouring it into a mold. *Predicting What happens to the silver particles as the melted silver cools down?*

You saw that the arrangement and motion of the particles of a substance determine whether the substance is a solid, a liquid, or a gas. The particles of a solid have the least thermal energy. They simply vibrate in a fixed position. When the same substance becomes a liquid, the particles have more thermal energy. They move around freely, although they remain close to one another. The particles of the substance have even more thermal energy as a gas. They are separated from one another and move around in all directions at high speeds. **A substance changes state when its thermal energy increases or decreases by a sufficient amount.**

Changes Between Liquid and Solid

Each specific substance changes states at temperatures that are typical for that substance. But the overall pattern for the way substances change state is the same.

Melting The change in state from a solid to a liquid is called **melting.** In Section 1, you learned that a crystalline solid melts at a specific temperature, called the melting point. The melting point of a substance depends on how strongly its particles attract one another.

Think of an ice cube taken from the freezer. The energy to melt comes from the air in the room. At first, the added thermal energy makes the water molecules vibrate faster, raising their temperature. At 0°C, the water molecules are vibrating so fast that they break free from their positions in ice crystals. For a time, the temperature of the ice stops increasing. Instead, the added energy changes the arrangement of the water molecules from ice crystals into liquid water. This is the process you observe as melting.

☑ *Checkpoint* *What happens to the particles of a solid as it gains more and more thermal energy?*

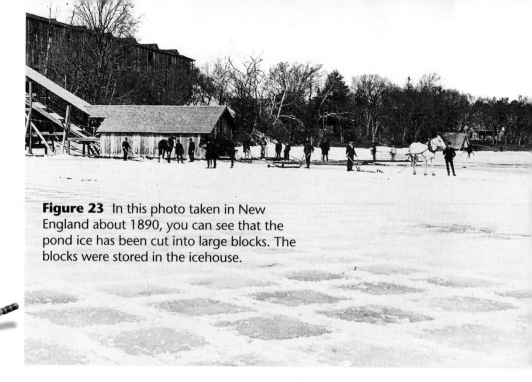

Figure 23 In this photo taken in New England about 1890, you can see that the pond ice has been cut into large blocks. The blocks were stored in the icehouse.

Freezing Now suppose you put the liquid water from the melted ice cube into a freezer. After a while, the water will freeze back into ice. **Freezing** is the change of state from liquid to solid—just the reverse of melting.

When you put liquid water into the freezer, the water loses energy to the cold air in the freezer. At first, the water molecules move more slowly. When the temperature reaches 0°C, the molecules are moving so slowly that they form regular patterns. These patterns are the crystals that form ice. When water freezes, the temperature stays at 0°C until freezing is complete. (This is the same temperature at which ice melts.)

Changes Between Liquid and Gas

Have you ever wondered how clouds form, or why rain falls from clouds? And why do puddles dry up after a rain shower? To answer these questions, you need to look at the ways that water changes between the liquid and gas states.

Vaporization The change from liquid water into water vapor is an example of **vaporization** (vay puhr ih ZAY shuhn). Vaporization occurs when a liquid gains enough energy to become a gas. There are two main types of vaporization.

The first kind, called **evaporation** (ee vap uh RAY shun), takes place only on the surface of a liquid. A drying puddle is an example. The water in the puddle gains energy from the ground, the air, or the sun. The energy enables the molecules on the surface of the puddle to escape into the air. Evaporation also occurs when you sweat. Sweat evaporates as it gains thermal energy from your skin, cooling you down on a hot day or when you exercise.

Figure 24 During evaporation, particles leave the surface of a liquid.

Figure 25 During boiling, groups of particles form bubbles of gas at many locations throughout the liquid. These bubbles rise to the surface, where the particles escape. *Applying Concepts What happens to the boiling point of water when the air pressure increases?*

The second kind of vaporization, called **boiling,** takes place inside a liquid as well as at the surface. Each liquid boils at a specific temperature called its **boiling point.** Like the melting point of a solid, the boiling point of a liquid depends on how strongly the particles of the substance are attracted to one another.

Boiling Point and Air Pressure The boiling point of a substance depends on the pressure of the air above a liquid. The lower the air pressure above the liquid, the less energy that liquid molecules need to escape into the air. As you go up in elevation, air pressure decreases. At the air pressure in places close to sea level, the boiling point of water is 100°C. In the mountains, however, air pressure is lower, and so is the boiling point of water.

INTEGRATING EARTH SCIENCE

For example, the city of Denver, Colorado, is 1,600 meters above sea level. At this elevation, the boiling point of water is 95°C. When a recipe calls for boiling water, cooks in Denver have to be careful. Food doesn't cook as quickly at 95°C as it does at 100°C.

Condensation The opposite of vaporization is called condensation. **Condensation** occurs when gas particles lose enough thermal energy to become a liquid. Clouds typically form when water vapor in the atmosphere condenses into liquid droplets. When the droplets get heavy enough, they fall to the ground as rain.

You can observe condensation by breathing onto a mirror. When warm water vapor in your breath reaches the cooler surface of the mirror, the water vapor condenses into liquid droplets. The droplets then evaporate into water vapor again.

Remember that when you observe clouds, mist, or steam from boiling water, you are not seeing water vapor, a gas that's impossible to see. What you see in those cases are tiny droplets of liquid water suspended in air.

☑ *Checkpoint* *How are vaporization and condensation related?*

Changes Between Solid and Gas

If you live where the winters are cold, you may have noticed that snow seems to disappear even when the temperature stays well below freezing. This happens because of sublimation. **Sublimation** occurs when the surface particles of a solid gain enough energy to become a gas. Particles do not pass through the liquid state at all. Some solids, such as naphthalene (moth balls), sublime more easily than others, such as table salt.

EXPLORING Changes of State

What changes occur as you slowly heat a beaker of ice from −10°C to 110°C?

A **Solid**
Below 0°C, water exists in its solid state—ice. Although the water molecules in ice crystals stay in fixed positions, they do vibrate. As the molecules are heated, they vibrate faster and the temperature rises.

B **Melting**
When more energy is added to ice at 0°C, the molecules overcome the forces that keep them in ice crystals. The ice melts, turning to liquid water. As ice melts, the molecules rearrange but do not move faster. Thus, the temperature of the ice stays at 0°C.

C **Liquid**
Water must be liquid before its temperature can rise above 0°C. As liquid water is heated, the molecules move faster and the temperature rises again.

D **Vaporization**
When more energy is added to liquid water at 100°C, molecules escape the liquid state and become a gas. This process is called vaporization. When water boils, the molecules overcome the forces that hold them together as liquids, but they do not move faster. Thus, the temperature stays at 100°C.

E **Gas**
Water must be in its gas state—called water vapor—before its temperature can rise above 100°C. As water vapor is heated, the molecules move faster, and the temperature rises again.

Figure 26 shows a common example of sublimation, the change in dry ice. "Dry ice" is the common name for solid carbon dioxide (CO_2). At ordinary air pressures, carbon dioxide cannot exist as a liquid. So instead of melting, solid carbon dioxide changes directly into a gas. As it changes state, it absorbs thermal energy, so it keeps materials near it cold and dry. For this reason, it's an excellent way to keep temperatures low when a refrigerator is not available. Recall that you cannot see the gas that dry ice forms. The fog around it results when water vapor from the nearby air cools and forms tiny droplets.

Figure 26 Dry ice is solid carbon dioxide. It changes directly to a gas in the process of sublimation. The energy absorbed in this change of state cools the water vapor in the air, creating fog. *Inferring Describe what happens to the carbon dioxide particles during sublimation.*

Identifying Substances Through Changes of State

Chemists sometimes face the problem of identifying unknown materials. In Chapter 1, you learned that the combination of properties a substance has can be used to identify it. To make such identification possible, chemists have built up a data bank of information about the properties of substances. As a result, comparing melting points and boiling points can be important steps in identifying an unknown material.

Suppose, for example, that chemists are trying to identify three clear, colorless liquids. One is water, another is chloroform (once used to cause sleep during surgery), and a third is ethanol (a type of alcohol). You already know the melting and boiling points of water. Chloroform melts at –64°C and boils at 61°C. Ethanol melts at –117°C and boils at 79°C. You can thus see how testing for these properties would help researchers identify them.

Section 4 Review

1. If an object at 50°C is placed in ice water, how will changes in thermal energy affect the temperature of the object?
2. In terms of energy and particle movement, what happens to a liquid as it changes into a gas?
3. What's the main difference between boiling and evaporation?
4. **Thinking Critically** **Applying Concepts** If you are stranded in a blizzard and are trying to stay warm, why should you melt snow and then drink it instead of just eating snow?

Check Your Progress CHAPTER PROJECT
Use the information you learned in this section to revise your storyboard, if necessary. Then if you are creating a cartoon, draw the cartoon and write the captions. If you are presenting a skit, write a script and stage directions. Rehearse the skit with the members of your group.

Measuring

MELTING ICE

In this experiment, you will measure temperature as you explore the melting of ice.

Problem

How does the temperature of the surroundings affect the rate at which ice melts?

Materials

thermometer or temperature probes and CBL
   procedure (optional)
stopwatch or timer
2 plastic cups, about 200 mL each
2 stirring rods, preferably plastic
ice cubes, about 2 cm on each side
warm water, about 40°C to 45°C
water at room temperature, about 20° C

Procedure

1. Read Steps 1–8. Based on your own experience, predict which ice cube will melt faster.
2. Make a data table like the one below.
3. Fill a cup halfway with warm water (about 40°C to 45°C). Fill a second cup to the same depth with water at room temperature.
4. Record the temperature of the water in each cup. If using a temperature probe, see your teacher for instructions.
5. Obtain two same-size ice cubes.
6. Place one piece of ice in each cup. Begin timing with a stopwatch. Gently stir each cup with a stirring rod.
7. Observe both ice cubes carefully. At the moment one of the ice cubes is completely melted, record the time and the temperature of the water in the cup.

8. Wait for the second ice cube to melt. Record its melting time and the water temperature.

Analyze and Conclude

1. Was your prediction in Step 1 supported by the results of the experiment? Explain why or why not.
2. In which cup did the water temperature change the most? Explain this result.
3. When the ice melted, its molecules gained enough energy to overcome the forces holding them together as solid ice. What is the source of that energy?
4. **Think About It** How well could you time the exact moment that each ice cube completely melted? How might errors in measurements affect your conclusions?

Design an Experiment

When a lake freezes in winter, only the top layer turns to ice. Design an experiment to model the melting of a frozen lake during the spring. With your teacher's approval, carry out your experiment. Be prepared to share your results with the class.

DATA TABLE

	Beginning Temperature (°C)	Time to Melt (s)	Final Temperature (°C)
Cup 1			
Cup 2			

SECTION 1 States of Matter

Key Ideas

◆ Solids have a definite shape and volume because the particles in a solid are packed tightly together and stay in fixed positions.

◆ Particles in a liquid move freely around one another. A liquid has no definite shape, but it does have a definite volume.

◆ The particles of a gas spread apart to fill all the space available to them. Thus, a gas has neither definite shape nor definite volume.

Key Terms

solid
crystalline solid
melting point
amorphous solid
liquid
viscosity
gas

SECTION 2 Gas Behavior

Key Ideas

◆ At constant temperature, when the volume of a gas decreases, its pressure increases.

◆ In a rigid container, raising the temperature of a gas increases its pressure.

◆ In a flexible container, raising the temperature of a gas increases its volume.

Key Terms

temperature
pressure
Boyle's law
Charles's law

SECTION 3 Graphing Gas Behavior

INTEGRATING **MATHEMATICS**

Key Ideas

◆ A graph shows that the volume of a gas and its kelvin temperature are directly proportional at constant pressure.

◆ A graph shows that the volume of a gas at constant temperature varies inversely with its pressure.

Key Terms

graph
directly proportional
vary inversely

SECTION 4 Changes in State

Key Ideas

◆ Thermal energy flows, in the form of heat, from a warmer substance to a cooler substance. The temperature of the warmer substance decreases, and the temperature of the cooler substance increases.

◆ Changes of state can occur when a substance gains or loses thermal energy.

Key Terms

thermal energy
melting
freezing
vaporization
evaporation
boiling
boiling point
condensation
sublimation

Organizing Information

Compare/Contrast Table Copy the compare/contrast table about the states of matter onto a separate sheet of paper. Then complete it and add a title. (For more on compare/contrast tables, see the Skills Handbook.)

State of Matter	Shape	Volume	Example (at room temperature)
a. _?_	Definite	b. _?_	Diamond
Liquid	c. _?_	Definite	d. _?_
Gas	e. _?_	Not definite	f. _?_

Reviewing Content

Review key concepts online using iText at www.phschool.com

Multiple Choice

Choose the letter of the answer that best completes each statement.

1. A substance whose particles are close together but move is classified as a(n)
   a. crystalline solid.   b. liquid.
   c. gas.   d. amorphous solid.
2. Unlike solids and liquids, a gas will
   a. keep its volume in different containers.
   b. keep its shape in different containers.
   c. expand to fill the space available to it.
   d. decrease in volume when the temperature rises.
3. Boyle's law states that the volume of a gas increases when its
   a. pressure increases.
   b. pressure decreases.
   c. temperature falls.
   d. temperature rises.
4. The vertical axis of a graph shows the
   a. responding variable.
   b. manipulated variable.
   c. constant factors.
   d. same variable as the *x*-axis.
5. When a liquid freezes, its particles
   a. move more rapidly.
   b. escape from its surface more quickly.
   c. vibrate faster.
   d. slow down and form patterns.

True or False

If the statement is true, write true. If it is false, change the underlined word or words to make it a true statement.

6. Rubber and glass become softer and softer over a wide range of temperatures. They are examples of <u>crystalline</u> solids.
7. The energy from the movement of particles is measured by the <u>temperature</u> of a substance.
8. If a gas is contained in a rigid container, raising its temperature will increase its <u>volume</u>.
9. Charles's law states that the volume of a gas varies <u>inversely</u> with its temperature.
10. The boiling point of a liquid is <u>lower</u> at sea level than on a mountain.

Checking Concepts

11. Describe the motion of particles in a solid.
12. Compare and contrast liquids with high and low viscosities.
13. How is the temperature of a substance related to the energy of movement of the particles in the substance?
14. What happens to the gas particles when the air in an inflated ball leaks out?
15. What happens during condensation?
16. What happens to water molecules when water is heated from 90°C to 110°C?
17. Compare the processes of melting and freezing.
18. **Writing to Learn** Imagine you are Robert Boyle or Jacques Charles at the time you described the law that came to be known by your name. Tell the story of your experiments and results as you think Boyle or Charles would if either one could talk to the students in your class today. Write down exactly what you would say.

Thinking Critically

19. **Relating Cause and Effect** Explain why placing a dented table tennis ball in boiling water is one way to remove a dent in the ball. Assume it has no holes.
20. **Comparing and Contrasting** Using diagrams, show the gas particles in an air mattress before you lie down on it and while you are lying on it.
21. **Applying Concepts** Describe what happens when an ice cube and solid carbon dioxide are each placed in a warm room. Why do you think the solid carbon dioxide is called "dry ice"?
22. **Inferring** When snow on the ground undergoes sublimation, where does the necessary energy come from?

Applying Skills

At each temperature, the mass of a compound dissolved in 100 mL of water was measured. Use this data to answer Questions 23–25.

Temperature (°C)	Mass of Compound Dissolved (g)
0	37
10	47
20	56
30	66
40	75

23. Graphing Graph the data for mass dissolved at each temperature. Label the horizontal axis from 0°C to 60°C and the vertical axis from 0 grams to 100 grams.

24. Interpreting Data What does the graph show about the effect of temperature on the amount of the compound that will dissolve in water?

25. Predicting Assume the amount of the compound dissolved continues to increase as the water is heated. Predict how many grams dissolve at 50°C.

Performance CHAPTER PROJECT Assessment

Present Your Project If you prepared a cartoon, read the captions to the class and discuss the illustrations. If you prepared a skit, perform the skit in front of the class. After you finish your presentation, invite the class to ask questions about your project. Be prepared to share the decisions you made in creating your presentation.

Reflect and Record In your journal, describe the strengths and weaknesses of the way you modeled changes of state. How successful was your model? How well did your classmates understand your cartoon or skit? Describe what you learned from observing the projects of your classmates.

Test Preparation

Use these questions to prepare for standardized tests.

Read the information below. Then answer Questions 26–29.

A scientist measured the pressure of a sample of a gas at various volumes. The temperature of the gas was kept constant. The data are shown below.

Volume (cm³)	Pressure (kPa)
15	222
21	159
31	108
50	67

26. At which volume was the pressure the highest?
   A 15 cm³   B 21 cm³
   C 31 cm³   D 50 cm³

27. If a measurement were taken when the volume was 25 cm³, the pressure would be
   F about 25 kPa.   G about 70 kPa.
   H about 130 kPa.   J about 240 kPa.

28. What would happen to the pressure if the volume were increased to 75 cm³?
   A The pressure will increase.
   B The pressure will decrease.
   C The pressure will remain the same.
   D There is no way to predict the pressure.

29. If you were to construct a graph with volume on the horizontal axis and pressure on the vertical axis, what would your graph look like?
   F a straight line slanting up from left to right
   G a curve slanting down from left to right
   H a straight horizontal line
   J a U-shaped curve

www.phschool.com

Speeds à la Carte

Suppose that you have traveled thousands of miles to visit the tropics of South America. Suddenly, vivid reds and blues brighten the green of the rain forest as a group of macaws swoop down and perch above you in a nut tree. They squawk at each other as they crack nuts with their powerful jaws and eat the meat. In a few minutes they spread their wings to take off, and vanish from sight. The macaws cracking nuts, flapping their wings, and flying through the forest are all examples of motion. Your plane flight to South America is another.

In this chapter, you will learn how to describe and measure motion. You will find examples of motion and describe how fast different objects move. You will measure the speeds of various common moving things.

Your Goal To identify several examples of motion and measure how fast each one moves. You will arrange your results from slowest to fastest.

Your project must

◆ include careful distance and time measurements
◆ use your data to calculate the speed of each example
◆ provide display cards that show data, diagrams, and calculations
◆ follow the safety guidelines in Appendix A

Get Started Brainstorm with a group of your classmates several examples of motion. For example, you might consider a feather falling, the water level rising in a bathtub, or the minute hand moving on a clock. Which examples will be easy to measure? Which will be more challenging?

Check Your Progress You'll be working on this project as you study this chapter. To keep your project on track, look for Check Your Progress boxes at the following points.
Section 1 Review, page 95: Create a data table.
Section 2 Review, page 105: Repeat measurements and make calculations.

Present Your Project At the end of the chapter (page 115), you will compare the speeds recorded by the class.

TEKS

In addition to process TEKS, this chapter addresses these concept TEKS as they relate to the chapter's topics.

(6.6) The student knows that there is a relationship between force and motion. The student is expected to:
(A) identify and describe the changes in position, direction of motion, and speed of an object when acted upon by force;
(B) demonstrate that changes in motion can be measured and graphically represented; and
(C) identify forces that shape features of the Earth including uplifting, movement of water, and volcanic activity.

Describing, Measuring, and Graphing Motion

How Fast and How Far?

1. Find out how long it takes you to walk 5 meters at a normal pace. Record your time.

2. Now find out how far you can walk in 5 seconds if you walk at a normal pace. Record your distance.

3. Repeat Steps 1 and 2, walking slower than your normal pace. Then repeat Steps 1 and 2, walking faster than your normal pace.

Think It Over

Inferring What is the relationship between the distance you walk, the time it takes you to walk, and your walking speed?

GUIDE FOR READING

◆ When is an object in motion?

◆ How can you find the speed and velocity of an object?

Reading Tip Before you read, rewrite the headings in the section as questions. As you read, look for answers.

Key Terms motion
• reference point • meter
• speed • velocity

It's three o'clock and school is over! You hurry out of class to enjoy the bright afternoon. A light breeze is blowing. A few clouds are lazily drifting across the sky, and colorful leaves float down from the trees. Two birds fly playfully over your head. A bunch of frisky squirrels chase one another up a tree. You spend a few minutes with some friends who are kicking a ball around. Then you head home.

Does anything strike you about this afternoon scene? It is filled with all kinds of motion: blowing, drifting, fluttering, flying, and chasing. There are simple motions and complicated motions, motions that are over in a moment, and motions that continue all afternoon.

Gray squirrels ▶

Figure 1 Whether or not an object is in motion depends on the reference point you choose. *Comparing and Contrasting Which people are moving if you compare them to the escalator? Which people are moving if you compare them to Earth?*

How else can you describe all of these examples of motion? There is actually a great deal to understand about how and why all these things move as they do. In this section, you will learn how scientists describe and measure motion.

Changing Position—Recognizing Motion

Deciding if an object is in motion isn't as easy as it sounds. For example, you are probably sitting as you read this paragraph. Are you moving? Other than your eyes blinking and your chest moving up and down, you would probably say that you (and this book) are not moving. An object is in **motion** when its distance from another object is changing. Since the distance between you and the walls of your room is not changing, you conclude that neither you nor the book is moving.

At the same time that you think you are sitting still, you are actually moving about 30 kilometers every second. At that speed, you could travel from New York City to Los Angeles in about 2 minutes! You are moving because you are on planet Earth, which is orbiting the sun. Earth moves about 30 kilometers every second, so you and everything else on Earth are moving at that speed as well.

Whether an object is moving or not depends on your point of view. If you compare the books on a desk to the floor beneath them, they are not moving.

Figure 2 Both the Hubble Space Telescope and the astronaut are actually moving rapidly through space. But compared to the Hubble Space Telescope, the astronaut is not moving, and he can therefore complete necessary repairs.

Sunrise, Sunset

Earth rotates as it moves around the sun. But to you, the sun appears to move.

1. Choose a spot from which you can observe the sky throughout one day.

2. From the same spot, observe the sun at 6 to 8 different times during the day. **CAUTION:** *Be careful not to look directly at the sun.* Describe its position by comparing it with things around you, such as trees and buildings.

3. Draw a diagram of the sun throughout the day.

Observing What reference point(s) did you use to study the sun? Did the sun appear to move when compared with those reference points? Did it really move?

But if you compare them to the sun, the books are moving quite rapidly. Earth and the sun are different reference points. A **reference point** is a place or object used for comparison to determine if something is in motion. **An object is in motion if it changes position relative to a reference point.** You assume that the reference point is stationary, or not moving.

If you have ever been on a slow-moving train, you know that you may not be able to tell the train is moving unless you look out the window. A nearby building is a good reference point, and a glance at it will tell you if you and the train are moving. But it is important to choose your reference point carefully. Have you ever been in a school bus stopped right next to another school bus? Suddenly, you think your bus is moving backward. When you look out the window on the other side, you find that your bus isn't moving at all. Actually, the other bus is moving forward! Your bus seemed to be moving backward because you used the other bus as a reference point. You assumed your reference point was stationary. But in fact, your reference point—the other bus—was really moving.

Describing Distance

INTEGRATING MATHEMATICS To describe motion further, you need to use units of measurement. Whether you realize it or not, you use units, or standard quantities, all the time. You might, for example, measure 2 cups of milk for a recipe, swim 100 yards after school, or buy 3 pounds of fruit at the store. Cups, yards, and pounds are all measurement units.

Scientists all over the world use the same system of measurement units so that they can communicate information clearly.

This system of measurement is called the International System of Units, or in French, Système International (SI). SI is a system based on the number ten. This makes calculations with the system relatively easy.

The basic SI unit of length is the **meter** (m). A meter is a little longer than a yard. The Eiffel Tower in Figure 3 is measured in meters. To measure the length of an object smaller than a meter, scientists use the metric unit called the centimeter (cm). The prefix *centi-* means "one hundredth." A centimeter is one hundredth of a meter, so there are 100 centimeters in a meter. The beautiful butterfly in Figure 3 is measured in centimeters. For even smaller lengths, the millimeter (mm) is used. The prefix *milli-* means "one thousandth," so there are 1,000 millimeters in a meter. In the International System, long distances are measured in kilometers (km). The prefix *kilo-* means "one thousand." There are 1,000 meters in a kilometer.

SI units are also used to describe quantities other than length. You can find more information about SI units in the Skills Handbook on page 582 of this textbook.

✓ *Checkpoint* *What unit would you use to describe the width of your thumb?*

Math TOOLBOX

Converting Units

When you convert one metric unit to another, you must move the decimal point.

1. How many millimeters are in 14.5 meters? You are converting from a larger unit to a smaller one, so you multiply. There are 1,000 millimeters in a meter. To multiply by 1,000, move the decimal to the right three places.
   14.500 m = 14,500. mm
   There are 14,500 mm in 14.5 m.

2. Convert 1,200 centimeters to meters. You are converting from a smaller unit to a larger one, so you divide (move the decimal to the left).
   1,200. cm = 12.00 m
   1,200 cm equals 12 m.

Figure 3 The Eiffel Tower is 300 meters tall, while this butterfly is 6.1 centimeters across. *Measuring What unit of length would you use to measure the distance between Paris and Rome?*

Speed affects the shape of cities. Because people want to travel quickly, they live close to major transportation routes—highways and railroads. Thus a city often looks like a hub with spokes coming out of it along the transportation routes.

In Your Journal

People prefer not to travel more than one hour from home to work. The table shows a city's travel routes.

Route	Average Speed
Highway 1	75 km/h
Highway 2	55 km/h
Blue Rail	60 km/h
Red Rail	75 km/h
Main Street	35 km/h

Along which two routes would you expect to find people living farther from the center of the city? Explain why. Draw a map of what you think this city might look like.

Calculating Speed

Scientists use SI units to describe the distance an object travels. A car, for example, might travel 90 kilometers. An ant might travel 2 centimeters. If you know the distance an object travels in a certain amount of time, you know the speed of the object. To be more exact, the **speed** of an object is the distance the object travels in one unit of time. Speed is a type of rate. A rate tells you the amount of something that occurs or changes in one unit of time.

To calculate the speed of an object, divide the distance the object travels by the amount of time it takes to travel that distance. This relationship can be written as follows.

$$\text{Speed} = \frac{\text{Distance}}{\text{Time}}$$

Speed measurements consist of a unit of distance divided by a unit of time. If you measure distance in meters and time in seconds, you express speed in meters per second (m/s). (The slash is read as "per.") If you measure distance in kilometers and time in hours, you express speed in kilometers per hour (km/h).

If a car travels 90 kilometers in one hour, the car is traveling at a speed of 90 km/h. An ant that moves 2 centimeters in one second is moving at a speed of 2 centimeters per second, or 2 cm/s. The ant is much slower than the car.

Constant Speed A ship traveling across the ocean may move at the same speed for several hours. Or a horse cantering across a field may keep a steady pace for several minutes. If so, the ship and the horse travel at constant speeds. If the speed of an object does not change, the object is traveling at a constant speed. When an object travels at a constant speed, you know that its speed is the same at all times during its motion.

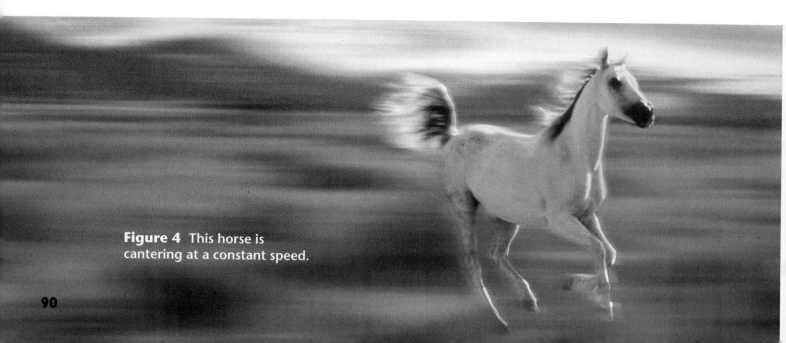

Figure 4 This horse is cantering at a constant speed.

Figure 5 The cyclists do not travel at a constant speed throughout this cross-country race. *Comparing and Contrasting* How does average speed differ from constant speed?

If you know the distance an object travels in a given amount of time, you can use the formula for speed to calculate the object's constant speed. Suppose, for example, that the horse in Figure 4 is moving at a constant speed. Find the horse's speed if it canters 21 meters in 3 seconds. Divide the distance traveled, 21 meters, by the time, 3 seconds, to find the horse's speed.

$$Speed = \frac{21 \, m}{3 \, s} = 7 \, m/s$$

The horse's speed is 7 meters per second, or 7 m/s.

Average Speed Most objects do not move at constant speeds for very long. The cyclists in Figure 5, for example, change their speeds many times during the race. They might glide along on level ground, move more slowly as they climb steep inclines, and dash down hills. Occasionally, they stop to fix a tire.

Unlike the horse described earlier, you cannot use any one speed to describe the motion of the cyclists at every point during the race. You can, however, find the average speed of a cyclist throughout the entire race. To find the average speed, divide the total distance traveled by the total time.

Suppose a cyclist travels 32 kilometers during the first two hours of riding, and 13 kilometers during the next hour. The average speed of the cyclist during the trip is the total distance divided by the total time.

$$Total \ distance = 32 \, km + 13 \, km$$

$$Total \ time = 2 \, h + 1 \, h$$

$$Average \ speed = \frac{45 \, km}{3 \, h} = 15 \, km/h$$

The average speed of the cyclist is 15 kilometers per hour.

Checkpoint How do you calculate average speed?

Describing Velocity

Knowing the speed at which something travels does not tell you everything about its motion. For example, if a weather forecaster announces that a severe storm is traveling at 25 km/h, would you prepare for the storm? Storms usually travel from west to east. If you live to the west of the storm and the storm is traveling to the east, you need not worry. But if you live to the east of the storm, take cover.

It is important to know not only the speed of the storm, but also its direction. **When you know both the speed and direction of an object's motion, you know the velocity of the object.**

The Speed of Transportation

The speed with which people can travel from one place to another has increased over the years.

1885
Benz Tricycle Car Introduced

This odd-looking vehicle was the first internal combustion (gasoline-powered) automobile sold to the public. Although it is an ancestor of the modern automobile, its top speed was only about 15 km/h—not much faster than a horse-drawn carriage.

1800   **1850**

1818
National Road Constructed

The speed of transportation has been limited largely by the quality of roadways. The U.S. government paid for the construction of a highway named the Cumberland Road. It ran from Cumberland, Maryland, to Wheeling, in present-day West Virginia. Travel by horse and carriage on the roadway was at a speed of about 11 km/h.

1869
Transcontinental Railroad

After more than six and a half years of work, railroad tracks from each side of the country met in Utah, just north of Great Salt Lake. Passengers could now travel across the United States by steam-powered trains. A cross-country trip took about a week at an average speed of 30 km/h.

Speed in a given direction is called **velocity**. If you know the velocity at which an object is moving, you know two different things about the object's motion—its speed and its direction. A weather forecaster may give the speed of the storm as 25 km/h, but you don't know its velocity unless you know that the storm is moving 25 km/h eastward.

Air traffic controllers must keep very close track of the velocities of all of the aircraft under their control. These velocities change more often than the velocities of storm systems. An error in determining a velocity, either in speed or in direction, could lead to a collision.

In Your Journal

The distance between Lufkin, Texas, and Lubbock, Texas, is about 786 kilometers. How many hours would it take to travel this distance for each of the vehicles in the time line if they each traveled at the speed shown? Record your results on a bar graph.

1908

Ford Model T Mass-Produced

Between 1908 and 1927, over 15 million of these automobiles were sold. The Model T had a top speed of 65 km/h.

1956

Inauguration of the Interstate Highway System

The passage of the Federal Aid Highway Act established the Highway Trust Fund. This act allowed the construction of the Interstate and Defense Highways. Nonstop transcontinental auto travel became possible. Speed limits in many parts of the system were more than 100 km/h.

1900　　　　　　　　**1950**　　　　　　　　**2000**

1936

Pioneer Zephyr Introduced

The first diesel passenger train in the United States was the *Pioneer Zephyr*. The *Zephyr* set a long-distance record, traveling from Chicago to Denver at an average speed of 125 km/h for more than 1,633 km.

1983

TGV in Motion

First introduced in 1983, this French high-speed train now has a top speed of 300 km/h. On its route from Paris to Lyon, it averages 152.6 km/h.

EXPLORING *Motion Graphs*

Motion graphs provide an opportunity to analyze changes in distance and time.

FIRST DAY

Start with enthusiasm.

The jogger travels at a constant speed of 170 m/min. The graph of constant speed is a slanted straight line. Notice that the speed is the same at every point on the graph. You can use the graph to analyze the jogger's motion. How far does the jogger run in 10 minutes? (1,700 m) How long does she run to travel 680 meters? (4 min)

The vertical or y-axis is used to show distance.

Divide the distance by the corresponding time to find speed.

$$Speed = \frac{850 \ m}{5 \ min} = 170 \ m/min$$

The horizontal or x-axis is used to show time.

SECOND DAY

Take a break.

The jogger again runs at a constant speed of 170 m/min, but she takes a break after running 850 m. The horizontal line shows that distance did not change during the break—thus there is no motion. What is the jogger's average speed if she ran a total distance of 1,190 m? (119 m/min)

THIRD DAY

Slow down.

As on the first day, the jogger runs at a constant speed, but this time she runs at a slower speed— 100 m/min. Notice that the slant, or slope, of the graph is smaller than it was on the first day. The slope is related to the speed. The faster the speed, the steeper the slope. How far does the jogger run in 10 minutes on this day? (1,000 m)

Figure 6 During a complicated maneuver, an airplane's direction changes continuously, along with its speed. Stunt pilots make spectacular use of their control over the velocity of their aircraft.

Graphing Motion

INTEGRATING MATHEMATICS You can show the motion of an object on a line graph in which you plot distance against time. Time is shown on the horizontal, or x-axis. It is represented by the first coordinate of the point—x. Distance is shown on the vertical, or y-axis. It is represented by the second coordinate of the point—y. A point (x, y) on the graph represents the location of an object at a particular time. To see examples of how graphs represent motion, read about the jogger in *Exploring Motion Graphs* on page 94.

Section 1 Review

1. Why do you need a reference point to know if an object is moving?
2. What is the difference between an object's speed and an object's velocity?
3. A bamboo plant grows 15 centimeters in 4 hours. At what average speed does the plant grow?
4. **Thinking Critically** **Problem Solving** The distance traveled by two crawling babies is shown in the table. Graph the information, and calculate each baby's speed.

Time (s)	Baby Sarah Distance (m)	Baby Scott Distance (m)
0	0	0
1	0.5	0.4
2	1	0.8
3	1.5	1.2
4	2	1.6

CHAPTER PROJECT

Check Your Progress
To measure each object's speed, you will need to know how far it moves in a certain amount of time. Create a data table to record your measurements and to show the speeds you calculate. Be sure to choose the best units for each speed measurement. To measure fast speeds, you may choose to measure distance in meters and time in seconds. For slower speeds you may choose to measure distance in centimeters or millimeters, and time in minutes or hours.

Inclined to Roll

In this lab, you will practice the skills of measuring time and distance to find the speed of a moving object.

Problem

How does the steepness of a ramp affect how fast an object moves across the floor?

Materials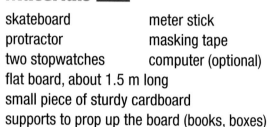

skateboard · meter stick
protractor · masking tape
two stopwatches · computer (optional)
flat board, about 1.5 m long
small piece of sturdy cardboard
supports to prop up the board (books, boxes)

Procedure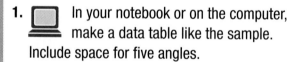

1. In your notebook or on the computer, make a data table like the sample. Include space for five angles.

2. Lay the board flat on the floor. Using masking tape, mark a starting line in the middle of the board. Mark a finish line on the floor 1.5 m beyond one end of the board.

3. Prop up the other end of the board. Use a protractor to measure the angle that the board makes with the ground. Record the angle.

4. Working in groups of three, have one person hold the skateboard so that its front wheels are even with the starting line. As the holder releases the skateboard, the other two students should start their stopwatches.

5. One timer should stop his or her stopwatch when the front wheels of the skateboard reach the end of the incline.

6. The second timer should stop his or her stopwatch when the front wheels reach the finish line. Record the times to the end of the ramp and the finish line in the columns labeled Time 1 and Time 2.

DATA TABLE							
Angle (degrees)	Trial Number	Time 1 (to bottom) (s)	Time 2 (to finish) (s)	Avg Time 1 (s)	Avg Time 2 (s)	Avg Time 2 − Avg Time 1 (s)	Avg Speed (m/s)
	1						
	2						
	3						
	1						
	2						
	3						
	1						
	2						

7. Repeat Steps 4–6 two more times. If your results for the three times aren't within 0.2 seconds of one another, carry out more trials.

8. Repeat Steps 3–7 four more times, making the ramp gradually steeper each time.

9. For each angle of the incline, complete the following calculations and record them in your data table.

   a. Find the average time the skateboard takes to get to the bottom of the ramp (Time 1).

   b. Find the average time the skateboard takes to get to the finish line (Time 2).

   c. Subtract the average Time 1 from the average Time 2.

Analyze and Conclude

1. How can you find the average speed of the skateboard across the floor for each angle of incline? Determine the average speed for each angle and record it in your data table.

2. Which is your manipulated variable and which is your responding variable in this experiment? Explain why. (For a discussion of manipulated and responding variables, see the Skills Handbook.)

3. On a graph, plot the speed of the skateboard (on the *y*-axis) against the angle of the ramp (on the *x*-axis). Connect the points on your graph.

4. What does the shape of your graph show about the relationship between the speed and the angle of the ramp?

5. **Think About It** Do you think your method of timing was accurate? Did the timers start and stop their stopwatches exactly at the appropriate points? How could the accuracy of the timing be improved?

Design an Experiment

A truck driver transporting new cars needs to roll the cars off the truck. You offer to design a ramp to help with the task. What measurements might you make that would be useful? Design an experiment to test your ideas.

DISCOVER

Will You Hurry Up?

1. Measure 10 meters in an area in which you can walk freely. Mark the distance with a piece of masking tape.

2. Walk the 10 meters in such a way that you keep moving faster throughout the entire distance. Have a partner time you.

3. Repeat Step 2, but try to walk the 10 meters in less time than you did before. Try it again, but this time walk it in twice the amount of time as the first. Remember that you must keep speeding up throughout the entire 10 meters.

Think It Over

Inferring How is the change in your speed related to the time you take to walk the 10-meter course?

GUIDE FOR READING

◆ How are forces related to motion?

◆ What happens to the motion of an object as it accelerates?

◆ How is acceleration calculated?

Reading Tip As you read, list the three different types of acceleration. Then give several examples of each.

Key Terms force • net force
• unbalanced force
• balanced force • friction
• acceleration • linear
• nonlinear

The pitcher winds up. She throws. The ball speeds to the batter and, *crack*—off the bat it goes. It's going, it's going, gone—a home run!

Before falling beyond the fence, the softball went through several changes in its motion. It started moving in the pitcher's hand, sped up, stopped moving at the bat, changed direction, and eventually slowed down. Most examples of motion involve similar changes. In fact, it is rare for any motion to stay the same for very long. What causes motion to change? A pitcher throwing a ball, a bat hitting a ball, and a catcher stopping a ball all have something in common—they all involve forces.

Forces and Motion

The next time you walk, pay attention to your feet and legs. You will discover that you move as a result of a combination of pushes and pulls. At first, you notice a pulling sensation as the muscles in your leg lift your foot. Then your other foot pushes against the floor, making your body move forward.

◀ The batter exerts a force on the ball with the bat.

A push or a pull on an object is called a **force**. When one object pushes or pulls another object, you say that the first object is exerting a force on the second object. **A force can cause an object to start or stop moving or change the way that an object is moving.** Think about some of the forces you exert each day. You exert a force to lift your books, write with a pen, or take out the trash.

Will a force always cause the motion of an object to change? The answer is no. Forces are described by how strong they are as well as the direction in which they act. When more than one force is acting on an object, the forces add together. So if two people push on a car stuck in the snow, the overall force on the car is the sum of their individual forces. Forces can be balanced or unbalanced.

Unbalanced Forces The overall force acting on an object is called the **net force**. When a net force changes an object's motion, the force is said to be an **unbalanced force**. An unbalanced force will result when multiple forces are exerted on an object in the same direction, as in the case of the car in the snow. An unbalanced force may also result when two forces act in different directions on the same object. In this case, the net force is the difference between the two forces. If one force is greater than the other, the net force is in the direction of the greater force. Forces are usually represented by arrows, as shown in Figure 7. In this book, the stronger the force, the wider the arrow. The strength of a force can be measured using a spring scale or a force probe.

Figure 7 The child exerts a force in one direction, while the wagon exerts a force in the other direction. *Relating Cause and Effect* What will happen to the wagon if the child exerts an unbalanced force on it?

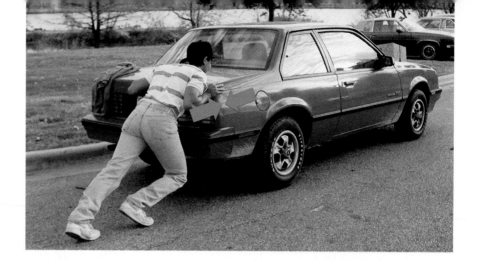

Figure 8 The man in the photograph exerts a contact force to push the car. *Applying Concepts Suppose the man is able to move the car. Would the overall force exerted by the man on the car be balanced or unbalanced, and why?*

Balanced Forces What happens if two forces acting on an object are equal in strength but acting in opposite directions? Equal forces acting on one object in opposite directions are called **balanced forces.** In this case, the forces cancel out. Balanced forces do not result in a net force. **An unbalanced force will change an object's motion whereas balanced forces will not.** You know this if you have ever played tug-of-war. When the forces pulling on each end of the rope are balanced, the rope does not move. But when one force becomes greater than the other, an unbalanced force results. This force might be great enough to pull one team into the mud.

Types of Forces

There are several kinds of force acting on you and the things around you all the time. You are probably familiar with forces such as friction. Other forces are gravitational force, magnetic force, and electrical force.

Contact Forces Two objects that touch each other are said to be in contact with one another. When two objects are in contact, each object exerts a force on the other that pushes it away. This force is called a contact force. When you push a child on a swing, the contact force of your push makes her move away. When a bulldozer pushes a large pile of dirt, it is using contact force as well. Sometimes a contact force is not obvious. Right now, the chair you are sitting on is exerting a contact force that pushes you up.

Friction Why does a kicked soccer ball eventually stop rolling across the grass? The answer is friction. **Friction** is the force that one substance exerts on another when the two rub against each other. For example, it helps you walk and run. The surfaces of water skis and snowboards are made to reduce friction, so skiers move quickly. Friction slows down moving objects, too. In addition to the soccer ball, it slows automobiles, bicycles, and trains.

Gravitational Force If you drop a quarter, it falls to the floor because Earth exerts a force that pulls you and everything near Earth's surface toward Earth's center. This force is known as the gravitational force. The gravitational force acts between all objects in the universe. In fact, the gravitational force is responsible for holding the planets in orbit around the sun. The gravitational force is also responsible for giving you your weight. Weight is a measure of the force of gravity on a mass.

Magnetic Force When you put a magnet on your refrigerator, it doesn't fall down. The reason is that a magnet is a material that attracts certain metals, such as iron, to itself. This attraction is known as the magnetic force. A magnet has two regions, known as poles, where its magnetism is strongest. One pole is called a north pole, and the other is called a south pole. When you arrange magnets so that the north pole of one is near the south pole of the other, the magnets attract one another. If, however, you arrange them so that like poles are near each other, the magnets repel each other. These pushes and pulls are due to the magnetic force.

Electrical Force You have experienced the results of an electrical force if you have ever found your socks stuck to your sweater in the clothes dryer. The electrical force results from the charged parts of the clothing's atoms. When charges are brought near each other, they either exert a pull or a push on each other. Charges that are the same repel each other, and charges that are different attract each other. When objects acquire more of one type of charge than another, they are said to be charged. Like charged particles, charged objects repel or attract one another. A negatively charged shirt attracts a positively charged sock in the clothes dryer, which explains why your clothes stick together.

☑ *Checkpoint* *What kinds of forces are exerted on a leaf that has just fallen from a tree?*

Over the Edge

Objects experience forces all the time. In this activity you will consider some of those forces.

1. Place a coin on your desk so that half of it hangs over the edge.
2. Predict what will happen if you move it so that more of the coin hangs over the edge. Test your prediction.
3. Draw a diagram that uses arrows to show the forces acting on the coin in Steps 1 and 2. Label each type of force involved.

Inferring How do the forces explain your observations in this activity?

Figure 9 Some forces act on objects without making contact with them. **(A)** This girl is experiencing the force of static electricity. **(B)** A metal needle in a compass is moved by Earth's magnetic forces.

Acceleration

Any type of unbalanced force can change the motion of an object. In other words, an unbalanced force can cause an object to accelerate. **Acceleration** is the rate at which velocity changes. Recall that velocity has two components (speed and direction). Acceleration involves a change in either of these components. **In science, acceleration refers to increasing speed, decreasing speed, or changing direction.**

Increasing Speed Any time an unbalanced force causes the speed of an object to increase, the object experiences acceleration. Can you think of examples of acceleration? A softball accelerates when the pitcher throws it, and again when the batter hits it with the bat. A car that begins to move from a stopped position or speeds up to pass another car is accelerating. The runners in Figure 10 accelerate to sprint down the track. You accelerate as you speed up to catch the bus for school.

Decreasing Speed Just as objects can speed up, they can also slow down. Motion in which speed decreases is also acceleration. This change in speed is sometimes called deceleration. Can you think of examples of deceleration? A ball decelerates as it rolls to a stop. A car decelerates when it comes to a stop at a red light. The diver in Figure 10 decelerates when she enters the water.

Changing Direction A car on a highway may be traveling at constant speed. Thus you may be tempted to conclude that it is not accelerating. Recall, however, that velocity involves *both* speed and direction.

Figure 10 The diver, the skaters, and the runners are all accelerating. *Classifying Can you identify the change in motion in each example?*

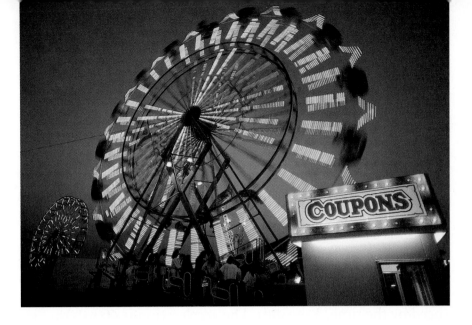

Figure 11 The Ferris wheel accelerates as it changes direction. *Making Generalizations* *What path does the Ferris wheel follow?*

Therefore, an object can be accelerating even if its speed is constant. The car, for example, will be accelerating if it follows a gentle curve in the road or changes lanes. The skaters in Figure 10 accelerate as they round the turns on the track.

Many objects continuously change direction without changing speed. An example of this type of motion is circular motion, or motion along a circular path. The seats on the Ferris wheel in Figure 11 accelerate continuously, because they move in a circle. **INTEGRATING SPACE SCIENCE** The moon also accelerates continuously, because it is always changing direction. Just as Earth revolves around the sun, the moon revolves around Earth. Satellites that orbit Earth continuously accelerate, also.

☑ *Checkpoint* *How is it possible for a car to be accelerating if its speed is a steady 65 km/h?*

Calculating Acceleration

Acceleration describes the rate at which velocity changes. **To determine the acceleration of an object, you must calculate the change in velocity during each unit of time.** This is summarized by the following formula.

$$Acceleration = \frac{Final\ velocity - Initial\ velocity}{Time}$$

If velocity is measured in meters per second, and time is measured in seconds, the unit of acceleration is meters per second per second. This unit is written as m/s^2. This unit may sound peculiar at first. But acceleration is the change in velocity per unit of time, and velocity is the change in distance per unit of time. Therefore, acceleration has two units of time. Suppose velocity is measured in kilometers per hour, and time is measured in hours. Then the unit of acceleration becomes kilometers per hour per hour, or km/h^2.

Change in Speed Over Time	
Time (s)	Speed (m/s)
0	0
1	8
2	16
3	24
4	32
5	40

Figure 12 The speed of the airplane increases by the same amount each second.

If the object's speed changes by the same amount during each unit of time, the acceleration at any time during its motion is the same. If, however, the acceleration varies, you can describe only the average acceleration.

For an object moving without changing direction, the acceleration of the object is the change in its speed during one unit of time. Consider, for example, a small airplane moving on a runway. The speed of the airplane at the end of each of the first 5 seconds of its motion is shown in Figure 12.

To calculate the acceleration of the airplane, you must first subtract the initial speed (0 m/s) from the final speed (40 m/s). This gives the change in speed, 40 m/s. Then divide the change in speed by the time, 5 seconds. The acceleration is 40 m/s divided by 5 seconds, which is 8 m/s^2. The acceleration tells you how the speed of the airplane in Figure 12 changes during each second.

Sample Problem

A roller coaster car rapidly picks up speed as it rolls down a slope. As it starts down the slope, its speed is 4 m/s. But 3 seconds later, at the bottom of the slope, its speed is 22 m/s. What is its average acceleration?

Analyze.
You know the initial velocity and final velocity of the car, and the length of time during which its velocity changed. You are looking for its acceleration.

Write the formula.
$$\text{Acceleration} = \frac{\text{Final velocity} - \text{Initial velocity}}{\text{Time}}$$

Substitute and solve.
$$\text{Acceleration} = \frac{22 \text{ m/s} - 4 \text{ m/s}}{3 \text{ s}}$$

$$\text{Acceleration} = \frac{18 \text{ m/s}}{3 \text{ s}}$$

$$\text{Acceleration} = 6 \text{ m/s}^2$$

Think about it.
The answer is reasonable. If the car's velocity increases by 6 m/s each second, its velocity will be 10 m/s after one second, 16 m/s after two seconds, and 22 m/s after three seconds.

Practice Problem

1. A car advertisement states that a certain car can accelerate from rest to 90 km/h in 9 seconds. Find the car's average acceleration.

2. An eagle accelerates from 15 m/s to 22 m/s in 4 seconds. What is the eagle's average acceleration?

Changes in Speed and Distance Over Time		
Time (s)	Speed (m/s)	Distance (m)
0	0	0
1	10	5
2	20	20
3	30	45
4	40	80
5	50	125

Notice that after each interval of one second, the speed of the airplane is 8 m/s greater than during the previous interval. So after one second, its speed is 8 m/s. After two seconds, its speed is 8 m/s + 8 m/s, or 16 m/s, and so on. Since the acceleration of the airplane does not change during the 5 seconds, you can use this formula for any time interval during the five seconds. Try it.

Figure 13 These graphs plot the motion of an accelerating object. *Predicting How would the slant, or slope, of the speed and time graph change if the object were accelerating more rapidly? More slowly? What do you think the graph of a decelerating object would look like?*

Graphing Acceleration

You can use a graph to analyze the motion of an object that is accelerating. Figure 13 shows the data for an object that is accelerating at 10 m/s^2. The graph showing speed versus time is a slanted straight line. The straight line shows that acceleration is constant. For every increase of one second, the speed increases by 10 m/s. Thus the graphed line rises the same amount each second and shows a **linear** relationship. If the object accelerated by a different amount each second, the graph would not be a straight line.

The graph of distance versus time is a curved line and shows a **nonlinear** relationship. This tells you that the distance traveled by the accelerating object varies each second. As the speed increases, the graph curves upward.

Section 2 Review

1. Do all forces cause a change in motion? Explain.
2. What three kinds of change in motion are called acceleration? Give an example of each.
3. What formula is used to calculate acceleration?
4. **Thinking Critically Problem Solving** A car is creeping down a deserted highway at 1 m/s. Sometime later, its speed is 25 m/s. This could have happened if the car accelerated at 3 m/s^2 for 8 seconds. Is this the only way the increase in speed could have happened? Explain.

Check Your Progress
CHAPTER PROJECT

You can improve the accuracy of your speed estimations by repeating measurements and by using averaged data. Make all your calculations in an organized, step-by-step manner. Prepare display cards that show how you calculated each speed.

Stopping on a Dime

T he school has decided to put a new basketball court in a small area between two buildings. Safety is an important consideration in the design of the court. You and your friends volunteer to find out experimentally how close the out-of-bounds lines can be to the buildings and still allow players to stop without running into a wall.

Problem

What distance is necessary between the out-of-bounds line and a wall so that a player can stop before hitting the wall?

Skills Focus

measuring, calculating, inferring

Materials

wooden meter stick   tape measure
2 stopwatches or watches with second hands

Procedure

Part I Reaction Time

1. Have your partner suspend a wooden meter stick between your thumb and index finger, as shown. Your thumb and index finger should be about three centimeters apart.
2. Your partner will drop the meter stick without giving you any warning. You will try to grab it with two fingers.
3. Note the level at which you grabbed the meter stick and use the chart shown to determine your reaction time. Record the time in the class data table.
4. Reverse roles with your partner and repeat Steps 1 through 3.

Reaction Time

Distance (cm)	Time (s)	Distance (cm)	Time (s)
15	0.175	25	0.226
16	0.181	26	0.230
17	0.186	27	0.235
18	0.192	28	0.239
19	0.197	29	0.243
20	0.202	30	0.247
21	0.207	31	0.252
22	0.212	32	0.256
23	0.217	33	0.260
24	0.221	34	0.263

CLASS DATA TABLE

Student Name	Reaction Time (s)	Running Time (s)	Stopping Distance (m)

Part II Stopping Distance

5. On the school field or in the gymnasium, mark off a distance of 25 m.
6. Have your partner time how long it takes you to run the course at full speed. **CAUTION:** *Be sure to remove any obstacles from the course.* After you pass the 25-m mark, come to a stop as quickly as possible and remain standing. You must not slow down before the mark.
7. Have your partner measure the distance from the 25-m mark to your final position. This is the distance you need to come to a complete stop. Enter your time and distance into the class data table.
8. Reverse roles with your partner. Enter your partner's time and distance into the class data table.

Analyze and Conclude

1. How can you calculate the average speed of the student who ran the 25-m course the fastest? Find this speed.
2. Multiply the speed of the fastest student (calculated in Question 1) by the slowest reaction time listed in the class data table. Why would you be interested in this product?
3. Add the distance calculated in Question 2 to the longest stopping distance in the class data table. What does this total distance represent?
4. Explain why it is important to use the fastest speed, the slowest reaction time, and the longest stopping distance in your calculations.

5. What other factors should you take into account to get results that apply to a real basketball court?
6. **Apply** Suppose the distance between the out-of-bounds line and the wall in a playground or gymnasium is, according to your calculations, too short for safety. Suggest some strategies that could be used (other than moving the wall) for making that playground safer.

Getting Involved

Visit a local playground and examine it from the viewpoint of safety. Use what you learned about stopping distance as one of your guidelines, but also try to identify other potentially unsafe conditions. Write a letter to the department of parks or to the officials of your town informing them of your findings.

SECTION
3 Water in Motion

What Affects How Water Moves?

1. Cover the bottom of a pan with a mixture of sand and pebbles.

2. Press a small piece of porcelain tile onto the sand mixture to represent pavement. In another area of the pan, press a clump of soil and grass into the sand.

3. Prop up one end of the pan so it slopes gently.

4. Using a watering can, sprinkle "rain" onto the pan's contents.

5. Observe how the water moves when it falls on the sand mixture, on the tile, and on the grass.

6. Wash your hands when you are finished with this activity.

Think It Over

Predicting How would the movement of the water change if you poured the water all at once? If you tilted the pan more steeply?

GUIDE FOR READING

◆ How does moving water shape the land around it?

◆ How does a flood affect the land near a river?

Reading Tip Before you read, use the section headings to make an outline. Leave space to take notes as you read.

Key Terms erosion
• deposition • sediment
• headwaters • flood plain
• meander • oxbow lake
• mouth • delta • flood
• levee

The next time it rains, watch the rainwater flow along the side of a road. Notice how the water picks up leaves and twigs and carries them away. Bits of paper and small pebbles bounce and swirl along in the flow. Even a tiny stream has the power to move objects.

Rivers Shape the Land

Now picture a large river, and think about how its running water can cause erosion. **Erosion** is the process by which fragments of soil and rock are broken off from the ground surface and carried away. Moving water carries these fragments along. Eventually, they are dropped or deposited in a new place. **Deposition** is the process by which soil and rock are dropped in a new location. **The force of moving water shapes many features of Earth's surface.** Rivers, for example, wear away landforms through erosion and build new landforms through deposition. The particles of rock and soil picked up and moved by erosion and deposition are called **sediment.** The river deposits heavier sediment particles first, then lighter ones.

The speed of moving water affects its ability to wear away the land. The faster water flows, the more energy it has. A river traveling at a speed of 1 kilometer per hour can move pebbles along. At 18 kilometers per hour, it can move a boulder the size of an armchair! When a river slows, its energy decreases.

Three factors affect how fast a river flows. One factor is the steepness of its slope. Water flows faster down a mountainside than over a flat plain. A second factor is the volume of water in the river. The more water in a river, the faster the river flows. A third factor is the slope of the channel through which it flows. The river water rubbing against the sides and bottom of the channel creates friction. This friction slows the water's movement. In a shallow narrow channel, almost all the water contacts the sides or bottom, and it moves slowly. In a broad, deep channel, most of the water does not contact the sides, so the river flows faster.

Profile of a River

Follow this rafting trip along a river's entire length to see how the river changes. You can follow the journey in *Exploring a River* on the next page.

The Headwaters Your trip starts near the river's beginning, or source, in the mountains. The many small streams that come together at the source of the river are called the **headwaters**. Your ride through the headwaters is quite bumpy. Your raft bounces through rapids and drops suddenly over a small waterfall. You notice how the fast-flowing water breaks off clumps of soil from the riverbanks and carries them along. This erosion wears away the sides and cuts into the bottom of its channel. The channel gradually widens and deepens.

Downriver As you continue downriver, your ride smoothes out. The land around the river is less steep than it was near the headwaters. Some smaller streams have joined the river, increasing the volume of water. With less water contacting the sides, there is less friction. As a result, although the slope is gentler, the river flows fairly swiftly.

The Flood Plain Next you travel through the middle of a wide valley. The river created this valley over time by eroding the land along its banks. The broad, flat valley through which the river flows is called the **flood plain.**

Figure 14 A hiker carefully avoids the collapsed edge of this dirt road, evidence of moving water's power to erode soil.

EXPLORING a River

As you follow this river from its headwaters to its mouth, notice how its speed, volume, and shape change. Each part of the river forms different features on Earth's surface.

A Headwaters
The steep slope of the land causes the river to flow quickly. The fast-moving water cuts a narrow channel.

Tributary

Oxbow lake

Meander

B Downriver
The slope of the land is less steep. Tributaries increase the river's volume. The river erodes its channel, making it wider and deeper.

C Flood plain
The river meanders through the middle of its flood plain. There, the river's speed is determined by its volume.

D Mouth
At its mouth, the river slows down. It deposits the sediments it carries.

Delta

Ocean

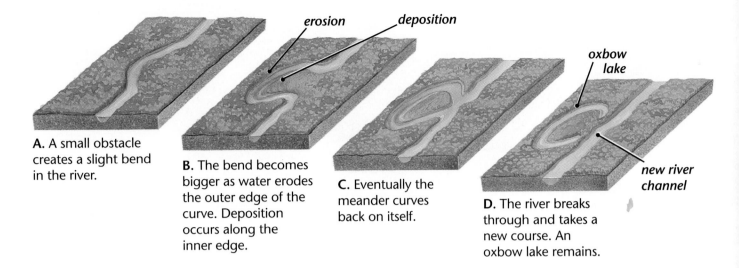

A. A small obstacle creates a slight bend in the river.

erosion   deposition

B. The bend becomes bigger as water erodes the outer edge of the curve. Deposition occurs along the inner edge.

C. Eventually the meander curves back on itself.

D. The river breaks through and takes a new course. An oxbow lake remains.

oxbow lake

new river channel

Figure 15 A river changes its course over time, forming winding meanders. *Predicting The oxbow lake is cut off from the river. What will the oxbow lake look like in the future?*

In places, small obstacles in the river's channel cause the water to flow slightly to one side or the other. This movement creates a bend in the river. As Figure 15 shows, the water erodes the outer edge of the curve, where it flows faster. The river deposits sediments along the inner edge, where it flows slower. This process gradually forms looping curves in the river called **meanders.** Eventually, the river may break through the ends of the meander, carving a new channel. The crescent-shaped, cutoff body of water that remains is called an **oxbow lake.**

The Mouth Your raft trip is nearly over as you approach the river's mouth. The **mouth** is the point where a river flows into another body of water—a larger river, a lake, or an ocean. When the fast-moving waters of a river hit the slower waters of a lake or ocean, the river suddenly slows down. As it slows, the river deposits most of its sediment. These deposits at the river's mouth build up, forming an area called a **delta.** The sediment deposits are rich in nutrients and minerals. As a result, the soil in delta areas is very fertile for farming.

☑ *Checkpoint* What are some land features shaped by the movement of water?

Rivers and Floods

A **flood** occurs when the volume of water in a river increases so much that the river overflows its channel. As rain or melting snow adds more water to a river, the river gains in speed and strength. Recall that as the speed of a river increases, so does the amount of energy it has. Floods greatly increase a river's ability to erode sediment and change land features. **A flooding river can erode and deposit huge amounts of soil, sand, and gravel. Floods can uproot trees and pluck boulders from the ground.**

Figure 16 A flood can be disastrous for nearby residents, such as the owners of this house. *Making Generalizations Explain how floods can be both harmful and helpful to people.*

As a river overflows onto its flood plain, it slows down, depositing heavier sediment alongside the channel. Sediment deposits actually build a natural defense against floods. These deposits that build up over time into long ridges that parallel the river are called **levees**. These natural levees help keep the river inside its banks. People sometimes build up the natural levees with sandbags or stone and concrete to provide further protection against floods.

Throughout history, people have both feared and welcomed floods. Ancient Egyptians, for instance, called their fertile cropland "the gift of the Nile." Deposition from regular floods left a layer of rich soil on each side of the river, creating a green strip of good land in the middle of the desert. But floods can also wash away bridges and destroy farms, towns, and crops.

Section 3 Review

1. Name and describe the two major processes by which a river moves sediments, thereby shaping the land around it.
2. Describe the effects of a flooding river on the land near the river.
3. What is a meander and how does it form?
4. **Thinking Critically** Relating Cause and Effect During a flood, the volume and speed of the water in a river increases. What effect does this have on a river's ability to cause erosion? Explain.

Science at Home

Muddying the Waters With a family member, fill a clear plastic jar half full of dirt and half full of water. Cover the jar tightly. Hold the jar firmly, and shake it. Allow the dirt to settle. Without disturbing the dirt, pour off the water into another jar. Use a spoon to scoop off different layers of dirt onto a paper towel. Observe the dirt layers, and tell your family members how the layers are like those a river deposits.

SECTION 1 — Describing, Measuring, and Graphing Motion

Key Ideas
◆ The motion of an object is determined by its change of position relative to a reference point.
◆ Speed is the distance an object travels in one unit of time. If an object moves at constant speed, its speed can be determined by dividing the distance it travels by the time taken. If an object's speed varies, then dividing distance by time gives you the object's average speed.
◆ When you state both the speed of an object and the direction in which it is moving, you are describing the object's velocity.

Key Terms
motion
reference point
meter

speed
velocity

SECTION 2 — Force and Acceleration

Key Ideas
◆ A force is a push or pull. Two or more forces acting on an object combine.
◆ Equal and opposite forces are called balanced forces. Uneven forces are called unbalanced forces. Unbalanced forces cause objects to accelerate.
◆ Contact forces, like friction, are exerted by direct contact. Gravitational, electrical, and magnetic forces are exerted without direct contact.
◆ Acceleration is the rate at which velocity changes. It involves increasing speed, decreasing speed, or changing direction.
◆ Acceleration can be calculated by dividing the change in velocity by the amount of time it took that change to occur.

Key Terms
force
net force
unbalanced force
balanced force

friction
acceleration
linear
nonlinear

SECTION 3 — Water in Motion

INTEGRATING **EARTH SCIENCE**

Key Ideas
◆ Moving water, like rivers, can wear away and create landforms through erosion and deposition of sediments.
◆ Water travels from the headwaters of a river, downriver through flood plains. Sediments collected along the way are deposited in a delta at the mouth of the river.
◆ Floods occur when a river overflows its channel. Erosion and deposition of sediments are greatly increased by flooding.
◆ Artificial flood-control levees, like naturally occurring ones, can help harness a river's energy for beneficial purposes.

Key Terms
erosion
deposition
sediment
headwaters

flood plain
meander
oxbow lake
mouth

delta
flood
levee

Organizing Information

Concept Map Copy the concept map about motion onto a separate sheet of paper. Then complete it and add a title. (For more on concept maps, see the Skills Handbook.)

Reviewing Content

 Review key concepts online using iText at www.phschool.com

Multiple Choice

Choose the letter of the best answer.

1. A change in position with respect to a reference point is
   a. acceleration.   b. velocity.
   c. direction.   d. motion.

2. To find the average speed of an object,
   a. add together its different speeds and divide by the number of speeds.
   b. divide the distance it travels by the time taken to travel that distance.
   c. divide the time it takes to travel a distance by the distance traveled.
   d. multiply the acceleration by the time.

3. If you know a car travels 30 km in 20 minutes, you can find its
   a. acceleration.   b. average speed.
   c. direction.   d. graph

4. If you divide the increase in an object's speed by the time taken for that increase, you are determining the object's
   a. acceleration.   b. constant speed.
   c. average speed.   d. velocity.

5. Which of the following features is most typical of the headwaters of a river?
   a. broad, flat valley
   b. waterfalls and rapids
   c. winding meanders
   d. muddy, slow-moving water

True or False

If the statement is true, write true. If it is false, change the underlined word or words to make the statement true.

6. In a moving elevator, you are not moving from the reference point of the <u>elevator</u>.

7. The graph of distance versus time for an object moving at constant speed is a <u>curve</u>.

8. Acceleration is a change in speed or <u>direction</u>.

9. The distance an object travels in one unit of time is called <u>acceleration</u>.

10. Soil and rock are dropped in a new location during <u>deposition</u>.

Checking Concepts

11. Which has a greater speed, a hawk that travels 600 meters in 60 seconds or a tiny warbler that travels 60 meters in 5 seconds? Explain.

12. An insect is on a compact disc that is put into a compact disc player. The disc spins around, and the insect hangs on. Is the insect accelerating? Explain why or why not.

13. How do erosion and deposition change as a river flows from the headwaters to the mouth?

14. How do floods move sediment in such a way that might prevent future floods?

15. **Writing to Learn** Suppose that one day some of the things that usually move very slowly start to go faster, while some things that usually move quickly slow to a snail's pace. Write a description of some events that might occur during such a day. Include a few actual speeds as part of your description.

Thinking Critically

16. **Making Generalizations** Suppose you make two measurements. One is the time that a car takes to travel a city block. The other is the time the car takes to travel the next city block. From these measurements, explain how you decide if the car is moving at a steady speed or if it is accelerating.

17. **Problem Solving** Two drivers start at the same time to make a 100-km trip. Driver 1 takes 2 hours to complete the trip. Driver 2 takes 3 hours, but stops for an hour at the halfway point. Which driver had a greater average speed for the whole trip? Explain.

18. **Applying Concepts** A family takes a car trip. They travel for an hour at 80 km/h and then for 2 hours at 40 km/h. Find the average speed. (*Hint:* Remember to consider the total distance and the total amount of time.)

19. **Inferring** Natural and artificial levees are used for flood control along many rivers. How could levees affect the agricultural regions of a river's flood plain?

Applying Skills

Use the illustration of the motion of a ladybug to answer Questions 20–22.

A — Start   B   C — Finish

20. **Measuring** Measure the distance from the starting line to line B, and from line B to the finish line. Measure to the nearest tenth of a centimeter.

21. **Calculating** Starting at rest, the ladybug accelerated to line B and then moved at constant speed until it reached the finish line. If it took 2.5 seconds to move from line B to the finish line, calculate its constant speed during that time.

22. **Interpreting Data** The speed you calculated in Question 21 is also the speed the ladybug had at line B (at the end of its acceleration). If it took 2 seconds to accelerate from the start line to line B, what is its acceleration during that time?

Test Preparation
Use these questions to prepare for standardized tests.

Study the graph. Then answer Questions 23–27.

23. What would be the best title for this graph?
    A Train at Rest
    B Train Moving at Constant Acceleration
    C Train Moving at Constant Speed
    D Train Slowing to a Stop

24. During each 15-minute interval, the train travels a distance of
    F 9 kilometers.   G 18 kilometers.
    H 36 kilometers.   J 45 kilometers.

25. According to the graph, how long does it take for the train to travel 27 kilometers?
    A 15 minutes   B 30 minutes
    C 45 minutes   D 1 hour

26. What is the train's speed?
    F 9 km/h   G 18 km/h
    H 36 km/h   J 72 km/h

27. After 75 minutes, the train stops for 5 minutes to pick up passengers. How would the graph look during this period?
    A The line would slant downward.
    B The line would be horizontal.
    C The line would be broken.
    D The line would stop at a point and continue from the same point once the train begins to move again.

UNDERSTANDING NATURE'S DESIGNS

**Engineer and Scientist
Ioannis Miaoulis**

Dr. Miaoulis was born in Greece and grew up there. He then came to the United States to study. He is now a professor of mechanical engineering and Dean of the School of Engineering at Tufts University in Medford, Massachusetts.

Fish in a tank glide under the watchful eye of a video camera. Inside a glass box, spiders spin webs in the wind from a powerful fan. "This is a biomechanics laboratory," says Professor Ioannis Miaoulis (YAHN is my OW lis). "What we study is how animals and plants use energy, motion, and forces."

Miaoulis walks over to a network of earthen tunnels built between two panes of glass. The structure looks like a toy ant farm, but it has a tube for blowing air over the top. Miaoulis explains:

"This is a cross section of a prairie-dog burrow. There are two entrance holes. One hole is flat, while the other one is built up and rounded. Biologists were wondering why. They thought the prairie dogs wanted a good view, but then why not make both holes high and rounded and get a good view from both?"

TALKING WITH IOANNIS MIAOULIS

Miaoulis and his students are learning the likely reason. Wind blowing over a flat surface moves more slowly, because it doesn't have to travel as far as the same breeze going over a rounded surface. "Slow air means high pressure across here" — Miaoulis points to the flat hole. "Fast air going over the rounded hole means low pressure. High pressure here, low pressure there. The holes' shape moves air through the burrow—in the flat hole and out the rounded one. It's prairie-dog air conditioning."

Q *How did you get started in science?*

A I grew up in Athens, Greece. It's a congested and polluted city, but my school was in the woods and I could do things outdoors. I got to love

nature. I dug out anthills to see how they were inside. I found the places where turtles laid their eggs. In the summers, we lived near the ocean and every day I'd go fishing and snorkeling. I got to know each rock underwater. I didn't even know what a scientist was then, but I was observing and thinking through things because I wanted to catch more fish. If the flow of water was in this direction, where would be a good place for the fish to hang out? I was observing flow patterns to see where, how, and why fish build their nests. I still do it, in part to catch them, because I still like fishing. But now I do it to observe them, to figure them out. I was always curious.

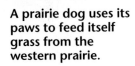

A prairie dog uses its paws to feed itself grass from the western prairie.

Air moves through a prairie dog hole that can be more than four meters deep. Side pockets are for nesting and food storage.

How Prairie-Dog Air Conditioning Works

1 Air moves over the flat hole.

2 Air moves faster over the rounded hole. Fast-moving air creates a large pressure drop.

Air flows from an area of high pressure to an area of low pressure. The difference in pressure between the two holes pushes air through the prairie dogs' burrow, creating a breeze.

Butterfly wings are studied under bright lights to learn how evenly they absorb heat.

A microscopic view of a butterfly wing shows the many thin, overlapping layers that collect heat from the sun.

Q *You teach engineering. Is that different from science?*

A Well, I enjoyed doing things with my hands, taking things apart and seeing how they worked, building things and making them work. I found that what I enjoyed about studying was learning science and then doing something with it. And that's engineering. I try to discover something about an animal that nobody ever understood before. Then I'll use that information to design something that will make people's lives easier.

Q *How have you used nature in your engineering designs?*

A Here's an example. I got interested in how heat travels in the chips that make computers work.

> **What we study is how animals and plants use energy, motion, and forces.**

They're made in very thin layers or films, thinner than one-hundredth the thickness of your hair. Sometimes, if chips don't heat evenly, they fall apart when you try to make them. I wondered if any plants or animals had solved that problem—using thin films to control how heat was absorbed or reflected. We looked for animals that bask or lie in the sun, or for animals and insects that depend on the warmth of the sun.

Why is a maple seed shaped as it is?

A seed tends to detach when the wind is blowing.

Because of its winglike shape, the seed spirals slowly to the ground. So, in the wind, it travels away from the tree.

A seed that falls away from the roots and shade of the parent tree has a better chance to grow.

If you touch a butterfly, you get a dust on your fingers. When I was little I used to catch butterflies and didn't really understand what the dust was. If you slice those "dust" particles, you find that they are made of many layers. These thin films are little solar collectors. Butterflies can change the amount of heat they catch. They just change the angle at which they hold the thin films on their wings up to the sun. Large areas of butterfly wings heat evenly. So we're looking at the layers on butterfly wings to learn how to make computer chips that will transfer heat more evenly.

Q *How do you come up with the questions you ask?*

A It depends. Sometimes it's simply by observing things. If you see a maple seed with wings falling in a fancy way, you might not even think twice about it. But if you start observing and appreciating nature, you start asking questions about how things work. Why would it help the tree to have a seed that could be blown by the wind? I can combine my love of nature from when I was small with what I've learned of science and engineering.

Maple seeds can fall to the ground any time from May to early fall.

In Your Journal

Do you, too, have "a questioning eye"? Miaoulis carefully observes plants and animals and asks himself questions about them. Quietly observe some animals in your environment (pets, insects, birds) for 15 or 20 minutes. Then write down four "how" or "why" questions about the movement and speed of the animals. For example, why does a frog have a stop-and-start movement?

Cells: The Building Blocks of Life

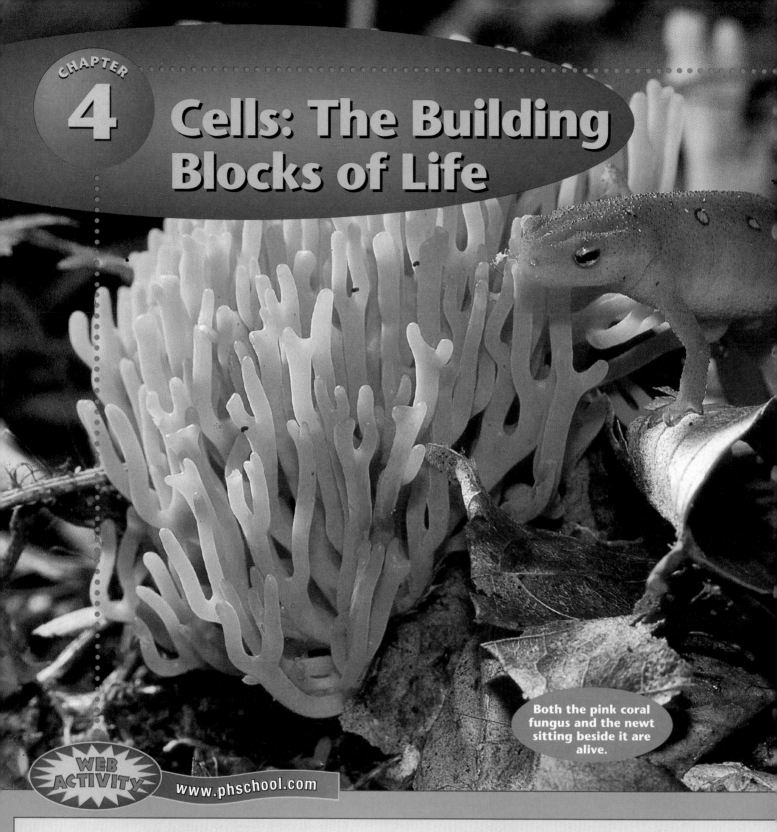

Both the pink coral fungus and the newt sitting beside it are alive.

WEB ACTIVITY
www.phschool.com

Mystery Object

Suppose that you visited a location like the one in this scene. Imagine yourself standing perfectly still, all your senses alert to the things around you. You wonder which of the things around you are alive. The newt clearly is, but what about the rest? Is the pink thing alive? Are the other things living or nonliving? In this chapter, you will learn that it is not always easy to determine whether something is alive. This is because living things share some characteristics with nonliving things. To explore this idea firsthand, you will be given a mystery object to observe. How can you determine if your object is a living thing? What signs of life will you look for?

Your Goal To study an object for several days to determine whether or not it is alive.

To complete this project successfully, you must

◆ care for your object following your teacher's instructions
◆ observe your object each day, and record your data
◆ determine whether your object is alive
◆ follow the safety guidelines in Appendix A

Get Started With a few classmates, brainstorm a list of characteristics that living things share. Can you think of any nonliving things that share some of these characteristics? Which characteristics on your list can help you conclude whether or not your mystery object is alive?

Check Your Progress You'll be working on this project as you study this chapter. To keep your project on track, look for Check Your Progress boxes at the following points.

Section 1 Review, page 129: Carry out your tests.
Section 2 Review, page 137: Record your observations daily.
Section 4 Review, page 152: Classify the object as living or nonliving.

Present Your Project At the end of the chapter (page 155), you will display your object and present evidence for whether or not it is alive. Be prepared to answer questions from your classmates.

TEKS

In addition to process TEKS, this chapter addresses these concept TEKS as they relate to the chapter's topics.

(6.10) The student knows the relationship between structure and function in living systems. The student is expected to:
(A) Differentiate between structure and function;
(B) determine that all organisms are composed of cells that carry on functions to sustain life; and
(C) identify how structure complements function at different levels of organization including organs, organ systems, organisms, and populations.

(6.11) The student knows that traits of species can change through generations and that the instructions for traits are contained in the genetic material of the organisms. The student is expected to:

(A) identify some changes in traits that can occur over several generations through natural occurrence and selective breeding;
(B) identify cells as structures containing genetic material; and
(C) interpret the role of genes in inheritance.

(6.12) The student knows that the responses of organisms are caused by external and internal stimuli. The student is expected to:
(A) identify responses of organisms to internal stimuli such as hunger or thirst;
(B) identify responses in organisms to external stimuli such as the presence or absence of heat or light.

1 What Is Life?

Is It Living or Nonliving?

1. Your teacher will give you and a partner a wind-up toy.

2. With your partner, decide who will find evidence that the toy is alive and who will find evidence that the toy is not alive.

3. Observe the wind-up toy. Record the characteristics of the toy that support your position about whether or not the toy is alive.

4. Share your lists of living and nonliving characteristics with your classmates.

Think It Over

Forming Operational Definitions Based on what you learned from the activity, create a list of characteristics that living things share.

GUIDE FOR READING

◆ **What characteristics do all living things share?**

◆ **What are structure and function?**

◆ **What do living things need to survive?**

Reading Tip As you read, use the headings to make an outline of the characteristics and needs of living things.

Key Terms organism
• cell • structure
• function • stimulus
• external stimulus
• internal stimulus
• response • reproduce
• spontaneous generation
• autotroph • heterotroph
• homeostasis

Looking like the slimy creatures in horror movies, "blobs" appeared in towns near Dallas, Texas, in the summer of 1973. Jellylike masses overran yards and porches all over the towns. People around Dallas were worried until biologists, scientists who study living things, put their minds at ease. The blobs were slime molds—living things usually found on damp, decaying material on a forest floor. The unusually wet weather around Dallas that year provided ideal conditions for the slime molds to grow in people's yards.

The Characteristics of Living Things

If you were asked to name some living things, or **organisms,** you might name yourself, a pet, and maybe some insects or plants. But you would probably not mention a moss growing in a shady spot, the mildew on bathroom tiles, or the slime molds that oozed across the lawns in towns near Dallas. But all of these things are also organisms that share six important characteristics with all other living things. **All living things are made of cells, contain similar chemicals, use energy, grow and develop, respond to their surroundings, and can reproduce.**

Figure 1 Slime molds similar to these grew in yards and porches in towns near Dallas, Texas.

◀ Animal cells

◀ Plant cells

Figure 2 Like all living things, the butterfly and the leaf are made of cells. Although the cells of different organisms are not identical, they share important characteristics. *Making Generalizations In what ways are cells similar?*

Cellular Organization All organisms are made of cells, which carry on the functions necessary to sustain life. A **cell** is the basic unit of **structure** and **function** in an organism. **An organism's structure is the way it is made. The function of a part of an organism is the job it performs.** An organism's structure includes what its parts are like and how they are put together. In an organism, structure and function are usually closely related. For example, your hand has a thumb that can touch all your other fingers. This structure enables your hand to perform the function of grasping objects.

Organisms may be composed of only one cell or of many cells. Unicellular, or single-celled, organisms include bacteria (bak TEER ee uh), the most numerous organisms on Earth. A bacterial cell carries out all of the functions necessary for the organism to stay alive. Multicellular organisms are composed of many cells. The cells of many multicellular organisms are specialized to do certain tasks. For example, you are made of trillions of cells. Specialized cells in your body, such as muscle and nerve cells, work together to keep you alive. Nerve cells carry messages from your surroundings to your brain. Other nerve cells then carry messages to your muscle cells, making your body move.

The Chemicals of Life The cells of all living things are composed of chemicals. The most abundant chemical in cells is water. Other chemicals called carbohydrates (kahr boh HY draytz) are a cell's main energy source. Two other chemicals, proteins (PROH teenz) and lipids (LIP idz), are the building materials of cells, much like wood and bricks are the building materials of houses. Finally, nucleic (noo KLEE ik) acids are the genetic material—the chemical instructions that direct the cell's activities.

Figure 3 Over time, a tiny acorn develops into a giant oak tree. A great deal of energy is needed to produce the trillions of cells that make up the body of an oak tree.
Comparing and Contrasting In what way does the structure of the seedling resemble that of the oak tree? In what ways is it different?

Acorn   Seedling   Oak tree

React!

ACTIVITY

In this activity, you will test your responses to three different stimuli.

1. Have a partner clap his or her hands together about six inches in front of your face. Describe how you react.

2. Look at one of your eyes in a mirror. Cover the eye with your hand for a minute. While looking in the mirror, remove your hand. Observe how the size of your pupil changes.

3. Bring a slice of lemon close to your nose and mouth. Describe what happens.

Classifying For each action performed, name the stimulus and the response. Identify whether the stimulus was external or internal.

Energy Use The cells of organisms use energy to do what living things must do, such as grow and repair injured parts. An organism's cells are always hard at work. For example, as you read this paragraph, your eye and brain cells are busy. The cells of your stomach and intestine are digesting food. Your blood cells are moving chemicals around your body. If you've hurt yourself, some of your cells are repairing the damage.

Growth and Development Living things grow and develop. Growth is the process of becoming larger. Development is the process of change that occurs during an organism's life to produce a more complex organism. For example, as multicellular organisms develop, their cells become specialized. To grow and develop, organisms use energy to create new cells.

You may argue that some nonliving things grow and change as they age. For example, a pickup truck rusts as it ages. Icicles grow longer as more water freezes on their tips. But pickup trucks and icicles do not use energy to change and grow. They also don't become more complex over time.

Response to Surroundings If you've ever seen a plant in a sunny window, you may have observed that the plant's stems have bent so that the leaves face the sun. Like a plant bending toward the light, all organisms react to changes in their environment. A change in an organism's surroundings that causes the organism to react is called a **stimulus** (plural *stimuli*). **External stimuli** come from outside the organism. External stimuli include things such as light, sound, and the temperature of the environment. **Internal stimuli** come from within the organism—for example, hunger and thirst.

An organism reacts to a stimulus with a **response**—an action or change in behavior. For example, has someone ever leapt out at you from behind a door? If so, it's likely that you jumped or screamed. Your friend's sudden motion was the external stimulus that caused your startled response. Your response to the internal stimulus of thirst might be to drink a glass of water. Nonliving things, such as rocks, do not react to stimuli as living things do.

Reproduction Another characteristic of organisms is the ability to **reproduce,** or produce offspring that are similar to the parents. Robins lay eggs that develop into young robins that closely resemble their parents. Sunflowers produce seeds that develop into sunflower plants, which in turn make more seeds. Bacteria produce other bacteria exactly like themselves.

☑ *Checkpoint* *How do growth and development differ?*

Life Comes From Life

Today, people know that all organisms are the result of reproduction by living things. Four hundred years ago, however, people believed that life could sometimes appear from nonliving material. For example, when people saw flies swarming around decaying meat, they concluded that flies could arise from rotting meat. When frogs appeared in muddy puddles after heavy rains, people concluded that frogs could sprout from the mud in ponds. The mistaken idea that living things arise from nonliving sources is called **spontaneous generation.**

It took hundreds of years of experiments to convince people that spontaneous generation does not occur. One scientist who did some of these experiments was an Italian doctor, Francesco Redi. In the mid-1600s, Redi designed a controlled experiment to show that flies do not spontaneously arise from decaying meat. In a controlled experiment, a scientist carries out two tests that are identical in every respect except for one factor. The one factor that the scientist changes is called the variable. The scientist can conclude that any differences in the results of the two tests must be due to the variable.

Figure 4 All organisms respond to changes in their surroundings. This willow ptarmigan's feathers have turned white in response to its snowy surroundings. This Alaskan bird's white plumage will help protect the bird from animals that feed on it.

Even after Redi's work, many people continued to believe that bacteria could be produced by spontaneous generation. In the mid-1800s, however, the French chemist Louis Pasteur designed some controlled experiments that finally proved spontaneous generation does not happen. The controlled experiments of Francesco Redi and Louis Pasteur helped to convince people that living things do not arise from nonliving material. Look at *Exploring the Experiments of Redi and Pasteur* to learn more about the experiments they performed.

☑ *Checkpoint* *In a controlled experiment, what is the term for the one factor that scientists change?*

EXPLORING the Experiments of Redi and Pasteur

Redi designed one of the first controlled experiments. By Pasteur's time, controlled experiments were standard procedure. As you explore, identify the variable in each experiment.

FRANCESCO REDI

REDI'S EXPERIMENT

① Redi placed meat in two identical jars. He left one jar uncovered. He covered the other jar with a cloth that let in air.

② After a few days, Redi saw maggots (young flies) on the decaying meat in the open jar. There were no maggots on the meat in the covered jar.

③ Redi reasoned that flies had laid eggs on the meat in the open jar. The eggs hatched into maggots. Because flies could not lay eggs on the meat in the covered jar, there were no maggots there. Therefore, Redi concluded that the decaying meat did not produce maggots.

The Needs of Living Things

Imagine yourself biking through a park on a warm spring day. As you ride by a tree, you see a squirrel running up the tree trunk. Although it may seem that squirrels and trees do not have the same basic needs as you, they do. All organisms need four things to stay alive. **Living things must satisfy their basic needs for energy, water, living space, and stable internal conditions.**

Energy You read earlier that organisms need a source of energy to live. They use food as their energy source. Organisms differ in the ways they obtain their energy. Some organisms, such as plants, use the sun's energy along with carbon dioxide, a gas found in Earth's atmosphere, and water to make their own food.

PASTEUR'S EXPERIMENT

LOUIS PASTEUR

1 In one experiment, Pasteur put clear broth into two flasks with curved necks. The necks would let in oxygen but keep out bacteria from the air. Pasteur boiled the broth in one flask to kill any bacteria in the broth. He did not boil the broth in the other flask.

2 In a few days, the unboiled broth became cloudy, showing that new bacteria were growing. The boiled broth remained clear. Pasteur concluded that bacteria do not spontaneously arise from the broth. New bacteria appeared only when living bacteria were already present.

Later, Pasteur took the curve-necked flask containing the broth that had remained clear and broke its long neck. Bacteria from the air could now enter the flask. In a few days, the broth became cloudy. This evidence confirmed Pasteur's conclusion that new bacteria appear only when they are produced by existing bacteria.

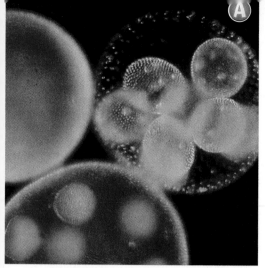

Figure 5 All organisms need a source of energy to live.
(A) *Volvox* is an autotroph that uses the sun's energy to make its own food. **(B)** This American lobster, a heterotroph, is feeding on a herring. *Applying Concepts How do heterotrophs depend on autotrophs for energy?*

Organisms that make their own food are called **autotrophs** (AW tuh trawfs). *Auto-* means "self" and *-troph* means "feeder." Autotrophs use the food they make as an energy source to carry out their life functions.

Organisms that cannot make their own food are called **heterotrophs** (HET uh roh trawfs). *Hetero-* means "other." A heterotroph's energy source is also the sun—but in an indirect way. Heterotrophs either eat autotrophs and obtain the energy in the autotroph's stored food, or they consume other heterotrophs that eat autotrophs. Animals, mushrooms, and slime molds are examples of heterotrophs.

Water All living things need water to survive—in fact, most organisms can live for only a few days without water. Organisms need water to do things such as obtain chemicals from their surroundings, break down food, grow, move substances within their bodies, and reproduce.

INTEGRATING CHEMISTRY One important property of water that is vital to living things is its ability to dissolve more chemicals than any other substance on Earth. In your body, for example, water makes up 92 percent of the liquid part of your blood. The food that your cells need dissolves in the blood and is transported throughout your body. Waste from cells also dissolve in the blood and are carried away. Your body's cells also provide a watery environment in which chemicals are dissolved. In a sense, you can think of yourself as a person-shaped sack of water in which other substances are dissolved. Fortunately, your body contains some substances that do not dissolve in water, so you hold your shape.

Living Space All organisms need a place to live—a place to get food and water and find shelter. Because there is a limited amount of living space on Earth, some organisms may compete for space. Plants, for example, occupy a fixed living space. Above the ground, their branches and leaves compete for living space with those of other plants. Below ground, their roots compete for water and minerals. Unlike plants, organisms such as animals move around. They may either share living space with others or compete for living space.

Stable Internal Conditions Because conditions in their surroundings can change significantly, organisms must be able to keep the conditions inside their bodies constant. The maintenance of stable internal conditions despite changes in the surroundings is called **homeostasis** (hoh mee oh STAY sis). You know that when you are healthy your body temperature stays constant despite temperature changes in your surroundings. Your body's regulation of temperature is an example of homeostasis.

Other organisms have different mechanisms for maintaining homeostasis. For example, imagine that you are a barnacle attached to a rock at the edge of the ocean. At high tide, the ocean water covers you. At low tide, however, your watery surroundings disappear, and you are exposed to hours of sun and wind. Without a way to keep water in your cells, you'd die. Fortunately, a barnacle can close up its hard outer plates, trapping droplets of water inside. In this way, the barnacle can keep its body moist until the next high tide.

Figure 6 A tree trunk provides these mushrooms with food, water, and shelter.

Section 1 Review

1. Name six characteristics that you have in common with a tree.
2. What is meant by the terms *structure* and *function?*
3. List the four things that all organisms need.
4. How did Pasteur's experiment show that bacteria do not arise spontaneously in broth?
5. **Thinking Critically Applying Concepts** Critically analyze Redi's experiment. First decide what Redi's hypothesis probably was. Then decide whether the results of the experiment supported that hypothesis. Explain your reasoning.

CHAPTER PROJECT

Check Your Progress
At this point, you should be ready to carry out your tests for signs of life following your teacher's directions. Before you start, examine your mystery object carefully, and record your observations. Also, decide whether you need to revise the list of life characteristics you prepared earlier. *(Hint:* Do not be fooled by the object's appearance— some organisms appear dead during certain stages of their lives.)

Please Pass the Bread!

In this lab, you will control variables in an investigation into the needs of living things.

Problem

What factors are necessary for bread molds to grow?

Materials

paper plates
plastic dropper
bread without preservatives
sealable plastic bags

tap water
packing tape
computer (optional)

Procedure

1. Predict which factors might affect the growth of bread mold. Record your ideas.
2. To test the effect of moisture on bread mold growth, place two slices of bread of the same size and thickness on separate, clean plates.
3. Add drops of tap water to one bread slice until the whole slice is moist. Keep the other slice dry. Expose both slices to the air for 1 hour.
4. Put each slice into its own bag. Press the outside of each bag to remove the air. Seal the bags. Then use packing tape to seal the bags again. Store the bags in a warm, dark place.
5. Use a paper and pencil or the computer to copy the data table. Use the table to organize, examine, and evaluate your data.

6. Every day for at least 5 days, briefly remove the sealed bags from their storage place. Record whether any mold has grown. Estimate the area of the bread where mold is present. **CAUTION:** *Do not unseal the bags. At the end of the experiment, give the sealed bags to your teacher.*
7. Choose another factor that may affect mold growth, such as temperature or the amount of light. Set up an experiment to test the factor you choose. Remember to keep all conditions the same except for the one you are testing.

Analyze and Conclude

1. What conclusions can you draw from each of your experiments?
2. What was the variable in the first experiment? In the second experiment?
3. What basic needs of living things were demonstrated in this lab? Explain.
4. **Think About It** What is meant by "controlling variables"? Why is it necessary to control variables in an experiment?

Design an Experiment

Suppose that you lived in Redi's time. A friend tells you that molds just suddenly appear on bread. Design an experiment to show that the new mold comes from existing mold. Consult your teacher before performing the experiment.

DATA TABLE

	Moistened Bread Slice		Unmoistened Bread Slice	
	Mold Present?	Area with Mold	Mold Present?	Area with Mold
Day 1				
Day 2				

SECTION 2 Discovering Cells

DISCOVER •• ACTIVITY•••••

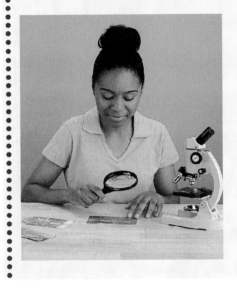

Is Seeing Believing?

1. ✂ Cut a black-and-white photograph out of a page in a newspaper. With your eyes alone, closely examine the photo. Record your observations.

2. Examine the same photo with a hand lens. Record your observations.

3. Place the photo on the stage of a microscope. Use the clips to hold the photo in place. Shine a light on the photo. Focus the microscope on part of the photo. (To learn how to use the microscope, see Appendix B.) Record your observations.

4. Think of a way to reuse or recycle the newspapers.

Think It Over

Observing What did you see in the photo with the hand lens and the microscope that you could not see with your eyes alone?

A majestic oak tree shades you on a sunny day at the park. A lumbering rhinoceros wanders over to look at you at the zoo. After a rain storm, mushrooms sprout in the damp woods. An oak tree, a rhinoceros, and a mushroom are all living things. What makes all of these living things alike? If you said that they are made of cells, you are correct.

Cells are the basic units of structure and function in living things. Just as bricks are the building blocks of a house or school, cells are the building blocks of living things. Since you are alive, you are made of cells. Look closely at the skin on your arm.

GUIDE FOR READING

◆ How did the invention of the microscope contribute to scientists' understanding of living things?

◆ What is the cell theory?

◆ How does a microscope lens magnify an object?

Reading Tip As you read, make a flowchart showing how the contributions of several scientists led to the development of the cell theory.

Key Terms microscope
• compound microscope
• cell theory • magnification
• resolution

Figure 7 This building is made up of individual bricks. Similarly, all living things are made up of individual cells.

No matter how hard you look with your eyes alone, you won't be able to see individual skin cells. The reason is that cells are very small. In fact, one square centimeter of your skin's surface contains over 100,000 cells.

First Sightings of Cells

Until the late 1500s there was no way to see cells. No one even knew that cells existed. Around 1590, the invention of the microscope enabled people to look at very small objects. **The invention of the microscope made it possible for people to discover and learn about cells.**

A **microscope** is an instrument that makes small objects look larger. Some microscopes do this by using lenses to focus light. The lenses used in light microscopes are similar to the clear curved pieces of glass used in eyeglasses. A simple microscope contains only one lens. A hand lens is an example of a simple microscope. A light microscope that has more than one lens is called a **compound microscope.**

Robert Hooke One of the first people to observe cells was the English scientist and inventor Robert Hooke. In 1663, Hooke observed the structure of a thin slice of cork using a compound microscope he had built himself. Cork, the bark of the cork oak tree, is made up of cells that are no longer alive. To Hooke, the cork looked like tiny rectangular rooms, which he called *cells.* Hooke described his observations this way: "These pores, or cells, were not very deep...." You can see Hooke's drawings of cork cells in Figure 8. What most amazed Hooke was how many cells the cork contained. He calculated that in a cubic inch there were about 1.2 billion cells—a number he described as "most incredible."

Figure 8 Robert Hooke made this drawing of dead cork cells that he saw through his microscope. Hooke called these structures *cells* because they reminded him of tiny rooms. *Comparing and Contrasting How are cells similar to the bricks in a building? How are they different?*

Fig.II. p.93.

Fig.I. p.93.

Fig.VII. p.96.

Fig.VI. p.96.

Fig.III. p.94.

Figure 9 Microscopes allow people to look at very small objects. **(A)** Anton van Leeuwenhoek made these drawings of organisms in the late 1600s after looking through a simple microscope. **(B)** This is a hydra, a tiny water organism, as seen through a modern microscope. Compare this hydra to the one Leeuwenhoek drew, which is labeled Fig. III.

Anton van Leeuwenhoek   At about the same time that Robert Hooke made his discovery, Anton van Leeuwenhoek (LAY vun hook) also began to observe tiny objects with microscopes. Leeuwenhoek was a Dutch businessman and amateur scientist who made his own lenses. He then used the lenses to construct simple microscopes.

One of the things Leeuwenhoek looked at was water from a pond. He was surprised to see one-celled organisms, which he called *animalcules* (an uh MAL kyoolz), meaning "little animals."

Leeuwenhoek looked at many other specimens, including scrapings from teeth. Leeuwenhoek was the first person to see the tiny single-celled organisms that are now called bacteria. Leeuwenhoek's many discoveries caught the attention of other researchers. Many other people began to use microscopes to see what secrets they could uncover about cells.

Matthias Schleiden and Theodor Schwann   Over the years, scientists have continued to use and improve the microscope. They have discovered that all kinds of living things are made up of cells. In 1838, a German scientist named Matthias Schleiden (SHLY dun) concluded that all plants are made of cells. He based this conclusion on his own research and on the research of others before him. The next year, another German scientist, Theodor Schwann, concluded that all animals are also made up of cells. Thus, stated Schwann, all living things are made up of cells.

Schleiden and Schwann had made an important discovery about living things. However, they didn't understand where cells came from. Until their time, most people thought that living things could come from nonliving matter. In 1855, a German doctor, Rudolf Virchow (FUR koh) proposed that new cells are formed only from existing cells. "All cells come from cells," wrote Virchow.

☑ *Checkpoint* *What did Schleiden and Schwann conclude about cells?*

The Cell Theory

The observations of Hooke, Leeuwenhoek, Schleiden, Schwann, Virchow, and others led to the development of the **cell theory.** The cell theory is an explanation of the relationship between cells and living things. **The cell theory states:**

- ◆ **All living things are composed of cells.**
- ◆ **Cells are the basic unit of structure and function in living things.**
- ◆ **All cells are produced from other cells.**

The Microscope— Improvements Over Time

The discovery of cells would not have been possible without the microscope. Microscopes have been improved in many ways over the last 400 years.

1660

Hooke's Compound Microscope

Robert Hooke improved the compound microscope. The stand at the right holds oil for a flame, which shines light on the specimen under the microscope.

1600   **1750**

1590

First Compound Microscope

Hans Janssen and his son Zacharias, Dutch eyeglass makers, made one of the first compound microscopes. Their microscope was simply a tube with a lens at each end.

1683

Leeuwenhoek's Simple Microscope

Although Leeuwenhoek's simple microscope used only one tiny lens, it could magnify a specimen up to 266 times. Leeuwenhoek was the first person to see many one-celled organisms, including bacteria.

The cell theory holds true for all living things, no matter how big or small, or how simple or complex. Since cells are common to all living things, they can provide information about all life. And because all cells come from other cells, scientists can study cells to learn about growth, reproduction, and all other functions that living things perform. By learning about cells and how they function, you can learn about all types of living things.

☑ *Checkpoint* *Which scientists contributed to the development of the cell theory?*

In Your Journal

Choose one of the microscopes. Write an advertisement for it that might appear in a popular science magazine. Be creative. Emphasize the microscope's usefulness or describe the wonders that can be seen with it.

1933
Transmission Electron Microscope (TEM)

The German physicist Ernst Ruska created the first electron microscope. TEMs make images by sending electrons through a very thinly sliced specimen. They can only examine dead specimens, but are very useful for viewing internal cell structures. TEMs can magnify a specimen up to 500,000 times.

1981
Scanning Tunneling Microscope (STM)

A STM measures electrons that leak, or "tunnel," from the surface of a specimen. With a STM, scientists can see individual molecules on the outer layer of a cell. STMs can magnify a specimen up to 1,000,000 times.

1900   **2050**

1886
Modern Compound Light Microscope

German scientists Ernst Abbé and Carl Zeiss made a compound light microscope similar to this one. The horseshoe stand helps keep the microscope steady. The mirror at the bottom focuses light up through the specimen. Modern compound light microscopes can magnify a specimen up to 1,000 times.

1965
Scanning Electron Microscope (SEM)

The first commercial SEM is produced. This microscope sends a beam of electrons over the surface of a specimen, rather than through it. The result is a detailed three-dimensional image of the specimen's surface. SEMs can magnify a specimen up to 150,000 times.

Sharpen your Skills

1. Place a prepared slide of a thin slice of cork on the stage of a microscope.

2. Observe the slide under low power. Draw what you see.

3. Put a small, very thin piece of tomato, onion, or lettuce on a slide. Repeat Step 2.

4. Place a few drops of pond water on another slide and cover it with a coverslip. Repeat Step 2.

5. Wash your hands after handling pond water.

Observing How does your drawing in Step 2 compare to Hooke's drawing in Figure 8 on page 132? Based on your observations in Step 4, why did Leeuwenhoek call the organisms he saw "little animals"?

How a Light Microscope Works

INTEGRATING PHYSICS Microscopes use lenses to make small objects look larger. But simply enlarging a small object is not useful unless you can see the details clearly. For a microscope to be useful to a scientist, it must combine two important properties—magnification and resolution.

Magnification The first property, **magnification,** is the ability to make things look larger than they are. **The lens or lenses in a light microscope magnify an object by bending the light that passes through them.** If you examine a hand lens, you will see that the glass lens is curved, not flat. The center of the lens is thicker than the edges. A lens with this curved shape is called a convex lens. Look at Figure 10 to see how light is bent by a convex lens. The light passing through the sides of the lens bends inward. When this light hits the eye, the eye sees the object as larger than it really is.

Because a compound microscope uses more than one lens, it can magnify an object even more. Light passes through a specimen and then through two lenses. Figure 10 also shows the path that light takes through a compound microscope. The first lens near the specimen magnifies the object. Then a second lens near the eye further magnifies the enlarged image. The total magnification of the microscope is equal to the magnifications of the two lenses multiplied together. For example, if the first lens has a magnification of 10 and the second lens has a magnification of 40, then the total magnification of the microscope is 400.

Figure 10 Microscopes use lenses to make objects look larger. A compound microscope has two convex lenses. Each convex lens bends light, making the image larger. *Calculating If one lens had a magnification of 10, and the other lens had a magnification of 50, what would the total magnification be?*

Convex lens

Convex lens

Mirror

Light rays

Light rays

Convex lens

136

Resolution To create a useful image, a microscope must also help you see individual parts clearly. The ability to clearly distinguish the individual parts of an object is called **resolution.** Resolution is another term for the sharpness of an image.

For example, when you use your eyes to look at a photo printed in a newspaper, it looks like a complete picture from one side to the other. That picture, however, is really made up of a collection of small dots. To the unaided eye, two tiny dots close together appear as one. If you put the photo under a microscope, however, you can see the dots. You see the dots not only because they are magnified but also because the microscope improves resolution. Good resolution—being able to see fine detail—is not needed when you are reading the newspaper. But it is just what you need when you study cells.

Figure 11 This head louse, shown clinging to a human hair, was photographed through a scanning electron microscope. It has been magnified to about 80 times its actual size.

Electron Microscopes

The microscopes used by Hooke, Leeuwenhoek, and other early researchers were all light microscopes. Since the 1930s, scientists have developed a different type of microscope called an electron microscope. Electron microscopes use a beam of electrons instead of light to examine a specimen. Electrons are tiny particles that are smaller than atoms. The resolution of electron microscopes is much higher than the resolution of light microscopes. As the technology of microscopes keeps improving, scientists will continue to learn more about the structure and function of cells.

Section 2 Review

1. How did the invention of the microscope affect scientists' understanding of living things?
2. Explain the three main ideas of the cell theory.
3. How does a compound microscope use lenses to magnify an object?
4. Explain why both magnification and resolution are important when viewing a small object with a microscope.
5. **Thinking Critically Applying Concepts**
   Why do scientists learn more about cells each time the microscope is improved?

Check Your Progress
CHAPTER PROJECT
Observe your object at least once a day. Record your observations in a data table. Draw accurate diagrams. *(Hint:* Measuring provides important information. Take measurements of your object regularly. If you cannot measure it directly, make estimates.)

DISCOVER

ACTIVITY

How Large Are Cells?

1. Look at the organism in the photo. The organism is an ameba, a large single-celled organism. This type of ameba is about 1 millimeter (mm) long.

2. Multiply your height in meters by 1,000 to get your height in millimeters. How many amebas would you have to stack end-to-end to equal your height?

3. Many of the cells in your body are about 0.01 mm long—one hundredth the size of an ameba. How many body cells would you have to stack end-to-end to equal your height?

Think It Over

Inferring Look at a metric ruler to see how small 1 mm is. Now imagine a distance one-hundredth as long, or 0.01 mm. Why can't you see your body's cells without the aid of a microscope?

GUIDE FOR READING

◆ What functions do the cell membrane, nucleus, and other organelles perform?

◆ What levels of organization do organisms exhibit?

Reading Tip Preview *Exploring Plant and Animal Cells* on pages 142–143. List any unfamiliar terms. As you read, write a definition for each.

Key Terms organelle
• cell wall • cell membrane
• nucleus • chromosome
• cytoplasm • mitochondria
• endoplasmic reticulum
• ribosome • Golgi body
• chloroplast • vacuole
• lysosome • prokaryote
• eukaryote • tissue • organ
• organ system • population

Imagine you're in California standing next to a giant redwood tree. You have to bend your head way back to see the top of the tree. Some of these trees are over 110 meters tall and more than 10 meters in circumference! How do redwoods grow so large? How do they carry out all the functions necessary to stay alive?

To answer these questions, and to learn many other things about living things, you are about to take an imaginary journey. It will be quite an unusual trip. You will be traveling inside a living redwood tree, visiting its tiny cells. On your trip you will observe some of the structures found in plant cells. You will also learn about some of the differences between plant and animal cells.

◀ A giant redwood tree

Figure 12 All cells have cell membranes, but not all cells have cell walls. The cell membrane of this single-celled paramecium **(A)** controls what substances enter and leave the cell. The cell walls of these onion root cells **(B)** have been stained green so you can see them clearly. Cell walls protect and support plant cells.

As you will discover on your journey, cells themselves contain even smaller structures. These tiny cell structures, called **organelles,** carry out specific functions within the cell. Just as your stomach, lungs, and heart have different functions in your body, each organelle has a different function within the cell. The cell is a system, and the organelles and other cell structures are its parts. You can see the organelles found in plant and animal cells in *Exploring Plant and Animal Cells* on pages 142 and 143. Now it's time to hop aboard your imaginary ship and prepare to enter a typical plant cell.

Cell Wall

Entering a plant's cell is a bit difficult. First you must pass through the cell wall. The **cell wall** is a rigid layer of nonliving material that surrounds the cells of plants and some other organisms. The cell wall is made of a tough, yet flexible, material called cellulose. If you think of a wooden desk, you will have a good idea of what cellulose is. Wood contains a lot of cellulose.

The cells of plants and some other organisms have cell walls. In contrast, the cells of animals and some other organisms lack cell walls. A plant's cell wall functions to protect and support the cell. In woody plants, the cell walls are very rigid. This is why giant redwood trees can stand so tall. Each cell wall in the tree adds strength to the tree. Although the cell wall is stiff, many materials, including water and oxygen, can pass through the cell wall quite easily. So sail on through the cell wall and enter the cell.

✓ *Checkpoint* What is the function of the cell wall?

Cell Membrane

After you pass through the cell wall, the next structure you encounter is the **cell membrane.** All cells have cell membranes. In cells with cell walls, the cell membrane is located just inside the cell wall. In other cells, the cell membrane forms the outside boundary that separates the cell from its environment.

Writers often use analogies to help readers understand unfamiliar ideas. In an analogy, a writer explains something by comparing it to something similar with which the reader is more familiar. For example, the author of this textbook describes the cell membrane by making an analogy to a window screen. This analogy helps the readers understand that the cell membrane is a boundary that separates the cell from the outside environment.

In Your Journal

Identify other analogies used by the author. Then choose two cell parts from this section. Write an analogy for each part that helps explain its structure or function.

As your ship nears the edge of the cell membrane, you notice that there are tiny openings, or pores, in the cell membrane. You steer toward an opening. Suddenly, your ship narrowly misses being struck by a chunk of waste material passing out of the cell. **You have discovered one of the cell membrane's main functions: the cell membrane controls what substances come into and out of a cell.**

Everything the cell needs—from food to oxygen—enters the cell through the cell membrane. Harmful waste products leave the cell through the cell membrane. For a cell to survive, the cell membrane must allow these materials to pass into and out of the cell. In a sense, the cell membrane is like a window screen. The screen keeps insects out of a room. But holes in the screen allow air to enter and leave the room.

Nucleus

As you sail inside the cell, a large, oval structure comes into view. This structure, called the **nucleus** (NOO klee us), acts as the "brain" of the cell. **You can think of the nucleus as the cell's control center, directing all of the cell's activities.**

Nuclear Membrane Notice in Figure 13 that the nucleus is surrounded by a nuclear membrane. Just as the cell membrane protects the cell, the nuclear membrane protects the nucleus. Materials pass in and out of the nucleus through small openings, or pores, in the nuclear membrane. So aim for that pore just ahead and carefully glide into the nucleus.

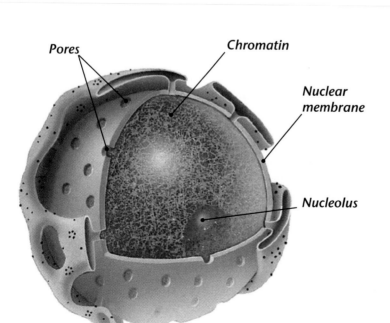

Pores

Chromatin

Nuclear membrane

Nucleolus

Figure 13 The nucleus is the cell's control center. The chromatin in the nucleus contains instructions for carrying out the cell's activities.

Chromosomes The nucleus contains thin strands called chromatin. Chromatin contains the genetic material, the instructions that direct the functions of a cell. For example, the instructions in the chromatin ensure that leaf cells grow and divide to form more leaf cells. When cells begin to divide, the chromatin strands coil and condense to form structures called **chromosomes.** When an existing cell divides, a copy of its genetic material is passed on to each new cell. You'll learn more about how cells divide in Chapter 5.

Nucleolus As you prepare to leave the nucleus, you spot a small object floating by. This structure, the nucleolus, is where ribosomes are made. Ribosomes are the organelles where proteins are produced.

☑ *Checkpoint* *Where in the nucleus is genetic material found?*

Organelles in the Cytoplasm

As you leave the nucleus, you find yourself in the **cytoplasm,** the region between the cell membrane and the nucleus. Your ship floats in a clear, thick, gel-like fluid. The fluid in the cytoplasm is constantly moving, so your ship does not need to propel itself. Many cell organelles are found in the cytoplasm. **The organelles in a cell function to produce energy, build and transport needed materials, and store and recycle wastes.**

Mitochondria As you pass into the cytoplasm, you see rod-shaped organelles called **mitochondria** (my tuh KAHN dree uh) (singular *mitochondrion*). Mitochondria are called the "powerhouses" of the cell because they produce most of the energy the cell needs to carry out its functions. Muscle cells and other very active cells have large numbers of mitochondria.

Figure 14 The mitochondria produce most of the cell's energy. *Predicting In what types of cells would you expect to find a lot of mitochondria?*

EXPLORING Plant and Animal Cells

On these pages, you can compare structures found in two kinds of cells: plant cells and animal cells. As you study these cells, remember that they are generalized cells. In living organisms, cells vary somewhat in shape and structure.

PLANT CELL

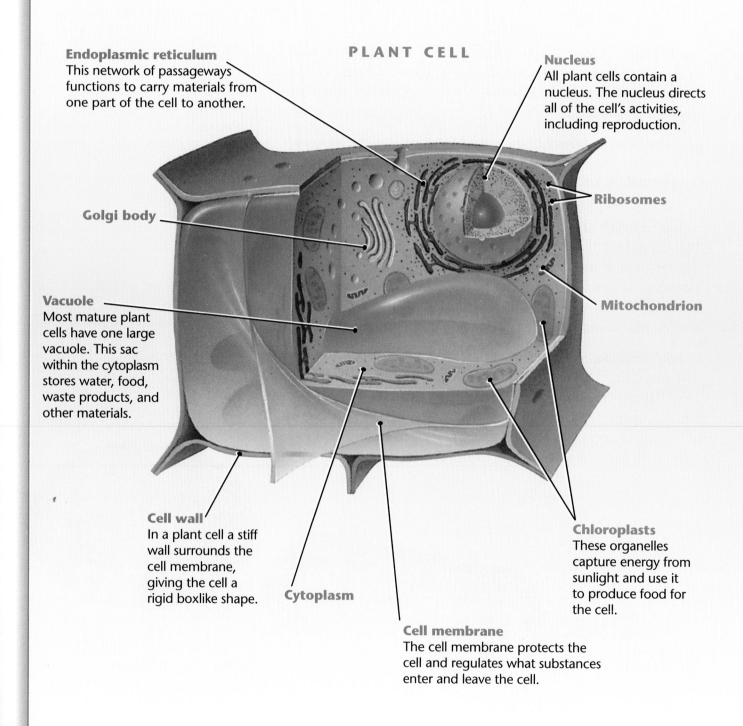

Endoplasmic reticulum
This network of passageways functions to carry materials from one part of the cell to another.

Nucleus
All plant cells contain a nucleus. The nucleus directs all of the cell's activities, including reproduction.

Golgi body

Ribosomes

Mitochondrion

Vacuole
Most mature plant cells have one large vacuole. This sac within the cytoplasm stores water, food, waste products, and other materials.

Cell wall
In a plant cell a stiff wall surrounds the cell membrane, giving the cell a rigid boxlike shape.

Cytoplasm

Chloroplasts
These organelles capture energy from sunlight and use it to produce food for the cell.

Cell membrane
The cell membrane protects the cell and regulates what substances enter and leave the cell.

Vacuole
Some animal cells have vacuoles that store food, water, wastes, and other materials.

ANIMAL CELL

Golgi body
The Golgi bodies receive materials from the endoplasmic reticulum and send them to other parts of the cell. They also release materials outside the cell.

Ribosomes
These small structures function as factories to produce proteins. Ribosomes may be attached to the outer surfaces of the endoplasmic reticulum, or they may float free in the cytoplasm.

Cytoplasm
The cytoplasm is the area between the cell membrane and the nucleus. It contains a gel-like fluid in which many different organelles are found.

Endoplasmic reticulum

Nucleus
Almost all animal cells contain a nucleus. The nucleus directs all of the cell's activities, including reproduction.

Mitochondria
Most of the cell's energy is produced within these rod-shaped organelles.

Cell membrane
Since an animal cell does not have a cell wall, the cell membrane forms a barrier between the cytoplasm and the environment outside the cell.

Lysosomes
These small organelles found in many animal cells contain chemicals that function to break down food particles and worn-out cell parts.

Figure 15 The endoplasmic reticulum is a passageway through which proteins and other materials move within the cell. The spots on the outside of the endoplasmic reticulum are ribosomes, structures that produce proteins.

Gelatin Cell

Make your own model of a cell.

1. Dissolve a packet of colorless gelatin in warm water. Pour the gelatin into a rectangular pan (for a plant cell) or a round pan (for an animal cell).

2. Choose different materials that resemble each of the cell structures found in the cell you are modeling. Insert these materials into the gelatin before it begins to solidify.

Making Models On a sheet of paper, develop a key that identifies each cell structure in your model. Describe the function of each structure.

Endoplasmic Reticulum As you sail farther into the cytoplasm, you find yourself in a maze of passageways called the **endoplasmic reticulum** (en duh PLAZ mik rih TIK yuh lum) or ER. These passageways carry proteins and other materials from one part of the cell to another.

Ribosomes Attached to the outer surface of the endoplasmic reticulum are small grainlike bodies called **ribosomes.** Other ribosomes are found floating in the cytoplasm. Ribosomes function as factories to produce proteins. The attached ribosomes pass the proteins to the endoplasmic reticulum. From the interior of the endoplasmic reticulum, the proteins will be transported to the Golgi bodies.

Golgi Bodies As you move through the endoplasmic reticulum, you see structures that look like a flattened collection of sacs and tubes. These structures, called **Golgi bodies,** can be thought of as the cell's mailroom. The Golgi bodies receive proteins and other newly formed materials from the endoplasmic reticulum, package them, and distribute them to other parts of the cell. The Golgi bodies also release materials outside the cell.

Chloroplasts Have you noticed the many large green structures floating in the cytoplasm? Only the cells of plants and some other organisms have these structures. These organelles, called **chloroplasts,** capture energy from sunlight and use it to produce food for the cell. It is the chloroplasts that give plants their green color. You will learn more about chloroplasts in Chapter 6.

Vacuoles Steer past the chloroplasts and head for that large, round, water-filled sac floating in the cytoplasm. This sac, called a **vacuole** (VAK yoo ohl), is the storage area of the cell. Most plant cells have one large vacuole. Some animal cells do not have vacuoles; others do.

Vacuoles store food and other materials needed by the cell. Vacuoles can also store waste products. Most of the water in plant cells is stored in vacuoles. When the vacuoles are full of water, they make the cell plump and firm. Without much water in the vacuoles, the plant wilts.

Lysosomes Your journey through the cell is almost over. Before you leave, take another look around you. If you carefully swing your ship around the vacuole, you may be lucky enough to see a lysosome. **Lysosomes** (LY suh sohmz) are small round structures that contain chemicals that break down large food particles into smaller ones. Lysosomes also break down old cell parts and release the substances so they can be used again. In this sense, you can think of the lysosomes as the cell's cleanup crew. Lysosomes are found in both animal cells and plant cells.

Although lysosomes contain powerful chemicals, you need not worry about your ship's safety. The membrane around a lysosome keeps these harsh chemicals from escaping and breaking down the rest of the cell.

Bacterial Cells

The plant and animal cells that you just learned about are very different from the bacterial cell you see in Figure 16. First, bacterial cells are usually smaller than plant or animal cells. A human skin cell, for example, is about 10 times as large as an average bacterial cell.

There are several other ways in which bacterial cells are different from plant and animal cells. **While a bacterial cell does have a cell wall and a cell membrane, it does not contain a nucleus.** Organisms whose cells lack a nucleus are called **prokaryotes** (proh KAR ee ohtz). The bacterial cell's genetic material, which looks like a thick, tangled string, is found in the cytoplasm. Bacterial cells contain ribosomes, but none of the other organelles found in plant or animal cells. Organisms whose cells contain a nucleus and many of the organelles you just read about are called **eukaryotes** (yoo KAR ee ohtz).

Figure 16 This single-celled organism is a type of bacteria. Bacterial cells lack a nucleus and some other organelles.
Applying Concepts *Where is the genetic material in a bacterial cell found?*

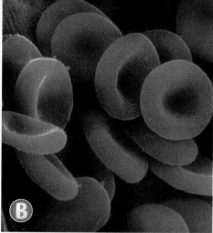

Figure 17 Your body contains a variety of different types of cells. **(A)** Nerve cells have long projections through which messages are sent throughout the body. **(B)** Red blood cells are thin and flexible, which allows them to fit through tiny blood vessels.

Structure and Function in Cells

Unlike bacteria and other single-celled organisms, plants, animals, and other complex organisms contain many cells. Cells in many complex organisms are specialized—that is, different kinds of cells perform different functions. Many plants, for example have root cells that are specialized to absorb water from soil. In animals, one kind of specialized cells—muscle cells—enables movement. Nerve cells are specialized to carry messages that enable the animal to respond to external and internal stimuli.

The structure of specialized cells enables them to perform their functions. For example, red blood cells, such as those shown in Figure 17, carry oxygen throughout the body. Their thin, flexible structure helps them squeeze through tiny blood vessels. Nerve cells have long, threadlike projections that act something like telephone wires. These "wires" carry messages throughout your body.

Levels of Organization

Cells in complex organisms interact with other cells to perform their functions. This can happen because cells are grouped together. **The bodies of many multicellular organisms have four levels of organization—cells, tissues, organs, and organ systems.**

A group of cells that performs a specialized function is called a **tissue.** Your body contains tissues specialized for functions such as absorbing materials, transporting materials, and support. Bone tissue demonstrates how structure relates to function at the tissue level of organization. The cells in bone tissue produce a hard, strong material that supports the body.

The next level of organization is the **organ,** which is a group of tissues that perform a specific function. The stomach, heart, and bones in your body are organs. Like cells and tissues, organs have structures that help them perform their function. Bones, which support the body, are hard and sturdy because of the tissues of which they are composed. In addition, bones come together in joints. Joints give your body flexibility and enable movement.

146

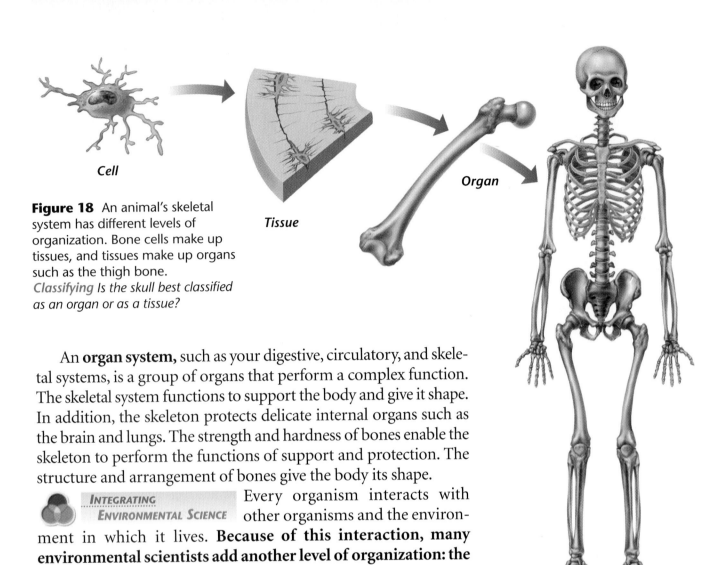

Cell

Tissue

Organ

Organ system

Figure 18 An animal's skeletal system has different levels of organization. Bone cells make up tissues, and tissues make up organs such as the thigh bone.
Classifying Is the skull best classified as an organ or as a tissue?

An **organ system,** such as your digestive, circulatory, and skeletal systems, is a group of organs that perform a complex function. The skeletal system functions to support the body and give it shape. In addition, the skeleton protects delicate internal organs such as the brain and lungs. The strength and hardness of bones enable the skeleton to perform the functions of support and protection. The structure and arrangement of bones give the body its shape.

INTEGRATING ENVIRONMENTAL SCIENCE Every organism interacts with other organisms and the environment in which it lives. **Because of this interaction, many environmental scientists add another level of organization: the population.** A **population** is all the members of one kind of organism in a particular area. So you can think of the levels of organization in living things this way: cells, tissues, organs, organ systems, organisms, and populations.

Section 3 Review

1. What is the function of the cell membrane?
2. Why is the nucleus sometimes called the control center of the cell?
3. Name two plant cell parts that are not found in animal cells. What is the function of each part?
4. Describe the levels of organization that complex organisms exhibit.
5. **Thinking Critically** **Inferring** How might a cell wall be an advantage to a bacterial cell? (*Hint:* Think of the functions of the cell wall in plant cells.)

Science at Home

Building Blocks Ask family members to help you find five items in your house that are made of smaller things. Make a list of the items and identify as many of their building blocks as you can. Be sure to look at prepared foods, furniture, and books. Discuss with your family how these building blocks come together to make up the larger objects. Do these objects or their building blocks possess any characteristics of living things?

A Magnified View of Life

In this lab, you will use your observation skills to compare plant and animal cells.

Problem

How are plant and animal cells alike and different?

Materials

plastic dropper
water
microscope slide
microscope
colored pencils
prepared slide of animal cells

Elodea leaf
forceps
coverslip

Procedure

1. Before you start this lab, read *Using the Microscope* (Appendix B) on pages 596–597. Be sure you know how to use a microscope correctly and safely.

Part 1 Observing Plant Cells

2. Use a plastic dropper to place a drop of water in the center of a slide. **CAUTION:** *Slides and coverslips are fragile. Handle them carefully. Do not touch broken glass.*

3. With forceps, remove a leaf from an *Elodea* plant. Place the leaf in the drop of water on the slide. Make sure that the leaf is flat. If it is folded, straighten it with the forceps.

4. Holding a coverslip by its edges, slowly lower it onto the drop of water and *Elodea* leaf. If any air bubbles form, tap the slide gently to get rid of them.

5. Use a microscope to examine the *Elodea* leaf under low power. Then, carefully switch to high power.

6. Observe the cells of the *Elodea* leaf. Draw and label what you see, including the colors of the cell parts. Record the magnification.

7. Discard the *Elodea* leaf as directed by your teacher. Carefully clean and dry your slide and coverslip. Wash your hands thoroughly.

Part 2 Observing Animal Cells

8. Obtain a prepared slide of animal cells. The cells on the slide have been stained with an artificial color.

9. Observe the animal cells with a microscope under both low and high power. Draw and label the cell parts that you see. Record the magnification.

Analyze and Conclude

1. How are plant and animal cells alike?
2. How are plant and animal cells different?
3. What natural color appeared in the plant cells? What structures give the plant cells this color?
4. **Think About It** Why is it important to record your observations while you are examining a specimen?

More to Explore

Observe other prepared slides of animal cells. Look for ways that animal cells differ from each other. Obtain your teacher's permission before carrying out these observations.

4 Introduction to Genetics

DISCOVER

Can You Identify the Mother?

1. Look at the photograph of the girl. Carefully observe the characteristics of her face.

2. Now look at the photographs of each of the three women. Observe their characteristics.

3. One of the women is the girl's mother. Decide which woman is the mother.

Think It Over

Observing What characteristics did you use to make your decision?

Y ou have probably noticed that offspring tend to resemble their parents. Maybe you see that your cousin's hair is the same color as his mother's. If you save seeds from sunflowers in the fall and then plant them the next spring, the flowers that grow look like sunflowers. They don't look like tulips or lilies. The new sunflowers resemble the flowers of the plants that produced the seeds.

Offspring resemble parents because organisms inherit characteristics from their parents. The physical characteristics that an organism can pass on to its offspring are called **traits.** Human traits include such characteristics as eye color and whether hair is straight or curly. Some traits of sunflowers are the color and shape of the petals, the shape of the leaves, and the way leaves are arranged on the stem.

Parents to Offspring

In Section 3, you learned that chromatin in the nucleus of the cell contains genetic material that directs the cell's activities. This genetic material also plays a role in **heredity,** or the process by which traits pass from parents to offspring. **Organisms resemble their parents because they inherit genetic material from their parents. Genetic material is contained in cells.** The scientific study of heredity is called genetics.

GUIDE FOR READING

◆ What determines the characteristics that an organism inherits?

◆ What is selective breeding?

Reading Tip As you read, make an outline of this section. Use the main headings as the main topics for your outline.

Key Terms trait • heredity
• DNA • gene
• asexual reproduction
• sexual reproduction
• sperm • egg
• selective breeding

Figure 19 The wood duck (top) and the mallard (bottom) are similar in some ways but different in others. Their similarities and differences are determined by genes.

The Role of Genes in Inheritance

Chromosomes are partly composed of long-chain molecules called deoxyribonucleic acid (dee ahk see ry boh noo KLEE ic), or DNA. **DNA** is the genetic material that carries information about an organism that is passed from parents to offspring.

Some of the DNA in chromosomes consists of genes. A **gene** is a section of DNA that controls a trait that an organism inherits. For example, a gene determines whether or not you have dimples when you smile. The structure of a grasshopper's wing and the shape of a maple leaf are both determined by genes. Genes are like recipes. Just as a recipe contains instructions for preparing food, genes contain instructions for building and running cells. Each chromosome contains a large number of genes.

Asexual and Sexual Reproduction

Genetic material is passed from parents to offspring during reproduction. Some organisms, such as bacteria, usually reproduce asexually. **Asexual reproduction** is a reproductive process that involves only one parent, not two. The offspring of asexual reproduction have genes that are identical to those of the parent organism. A bacterial cell, for example, usually reproduces asexually by dividing into two new cells. The genes in the new cells are exactly like the genes in the parent cell. Therefore, the two new bacterial cells will have the same traits, and these traits will be the same as those of the parent cell.

Many organisms, including most animals and many plants, reproduce sexually. In **sexual reproduction,** new organisms result from the combination of genetic material from two parent organisms. New organisms are usually produced by the joining of sperm and eggs, which are cells that are specialized for reproduction. A **sperm** is the male sex cell, and an **egg** is the female sex cell. Both the sperm and the egg contain genetic material. The traits of the new organism are determined by genetic material from both the male and the female parents.

Figure 20 This bacterial cell (left) is reproducing asexually, by dividing into two new cells that will be identical to the original cell. In contrast, dogs reproduce sexually. The puppies (right) are not identical to either of their parents.

Figure 21 Many garden flowers, such as these zinnias, are the result of selective breeding.
Inferring What traits would be desirable in garden flowers?

Sexual Reproduction and Change

The offspring of sexually reproducing organisms, such as humans, inherit genetic material from both parents. Therefore, while children may resemble their parents, they are not exactly like either their mother or their father. Children usually look even less like their grandparents. And there may be very little resemblance between great-grandchildren and their great-grandparents. Sexually reproducing organisms change from generation to generation. That happens because the genetic material is re-sorted, over and over, each time reproduction occurs.

☑ *Checkpoint* Why aren't the offspring of sexually reproducing organisms identical to either of their parents?

Changing Traits by Selective Breeding

Since the beginning of agriculture, farmers have tried to improve the quality of crops and farm animals. **Selective breeding** is a technique used to improve the quality of organisms by selecting, or choosing, certain organisms for reproduction. **In selective breeding, organisms that have certain desired traits are mated to produce offspring with the desired traits of both parents. The desired traits are produced by the combination of genetic material that the offspring inherit from both of their parents.** The process of selective breeding may take many generations to produce organisms with the desired combination of traits. Selective breeding has produced prize-winning racehorses, cotton plants that yield strong fibers, and large, juicy tomatoes.

Santa Gertrudis cattle, which originated on the King Ranch in southeastern Texas, were produced by selective breeding. Around 1910, breeders on the King Ranch began mating Brahman cattle with shorthorn cattle, hoping to produce cattle with the desired traits of both breeds. Shorthorn cattle have tender and tasty beef but do not do well in the hot environment of the King Ranch. In contrast, hardy Brahman cattle thrive in the heat, but the beef they produce is not as good as the shorthorns' beef.

Sharpen your Skills

Observing

ACTIVITY

Use reference materials to learn more about different breeds of cats. Consult books, encyclopedias, and multimedia resources. You can also contact local veterinarians and cat breeders.

Choose cats from two breeds and observe their photographs carefully. Read the text descriptions of each cat's traits. Create a compare/contrast table that compares three traits in these breeds, such as eye color, length of hair, and shape of head and face.

Figure 22 Santa Gertrudis cattle were bred on the King Ranch in Texas.

Eventually, several generations of selective breeding produced heat-resistant cattle with tender, flavorful beef. This new breed of cattle was named Santa Gertrudis. The genes of Santa Gertrudis cattle come from both shorthorn and Brahman cattle. Now, generation after generation, Santa Gertrudis cattle pass the desirable characteristics on to their offspring.

☑ *Checkpoint* *What is selective breeding?*

Changing Traits in Nature

Selective breeding is planned and carried out by farmers and breeders. But the traits of organisms can also change over generations naturally. The changes that occur in organisms often help those organisms survive better in their environments.

Consider, for example, what often happens when chemicals called pesticides are used to kill harmful insects. When a pesticide is first used on a field, it kills almost all the insects in the field. But a few insects survive because they have naturally occurring changes in some genes that help them resist the pesticide. The surviving insects reproduce. When those insects reproduce, some of their offspring inherit genes that enable the offspring to survive the pesticide. This process happens over and over, generation after generation. In each generation, the only insects that survive are those that are resistant to the harmful effects of the pesticide. After many years, most of the insects in the field will be resistant to the pesticide. The pesticide has lost its effectiveness, because it can no longer kill most of the harmful insects.

Section 4 Review

1. What determines the traits that an organism inherits from its parents?
2. What is the name for the process that produced Santa Gertrudis cattle?
3. What is the difference between asexual reproduction and sexual reproduction?
4. **Thinking Critically Inferring** Do you think that all of an organism's characteristics are determined by genes? Explain your answer.

Check Your Progress CHAPTER PROJECT

Now that you have completed your observations, analyze your data. Arrange your data in a chart or diagram. Find another object that is familiar to you and similar to your mystery object. Compare the two objects. Conclude whether your object is alive.

SECTION 1 What Is Life?

Key Ideas

◆ All living things are made of cells, contain similar chemicals, use energy, grow and develop, respond to their surroundings, and reproduce.

◆ An organism's structure is the way it is made. The function of a part of an organism is the job it performs.

◆ All living things need energy, water, living space, and stable internal conditions.

Key Terms

organism	response	autotroph
cell	reproduce	heterotroph
stimulus	spontaneous	homeostasis
external stimulus	generation	
internal stimulus		

SECTION 2 Discovering Cells

INTEGRATING TECHNOLOGY

Key Ideas

◆ The microscope enabled the discovery of cells.

◆ Cells make up all living things, are the basic units of structure and function in living things, and are produced from other cells.

Key Terms

microscope	magnification
compound microscope	resolution
cell theory	

SECTION 3 Looking Inside Cells

Key Ideas

◆ Levels of organization in complex organisms include cells, tissues, organs, and organ systems.

Key Terms

organelle	endoplasmic	prokaryote
cell wall	reticulum	eukaryote
cell membrane	ribosome	tissue
nucleus	Golgi body	organ
chromosome	chloroplast	organ system
cytoplasm	vacuole	population
mitochondria	lysosome	

SECTION 4 Introduction to Genetics

Key Ideas

◆ Organisms resemble their parents because they inherit genetic material from their parents. Genetic material is contained in DNA in cells.

◆ In selective breeding, organisms that have certain traits are mated to produce the desired traits in their offspring. The desired traits are produced by the combination of genes that the offspring inherit from both their parents.

Key Terms

trait	sexual reproduction
heredity	sperm
DNA	egg
gene	selective breeding
asexual reproduction	

Organizing Information

Concept Map Copy the concept map about the needs of organisms onto a separate sheet of paper. Then complete it and add a title. (For more on concept maps, see the Skills Handbook.)

Reviewing Content

Review key concepts online using iText at www.phschool.com

Multiple Choice

Choose the letter of the best answer.

1. The idea that life could spring from nonliving matter is called
   a. development.
   b. spontaneous generation.
   c. homeostasis.
   d. evolution.

2. The ability of microscopes to distinguish fine details is called
   a. resolution.
   b. bending.
   c. magnification.
   d. active transport.

3. In plant and animal cells, the control center of the cell is the
   a. chloroplast.
   b. ribosome.
   c. nucleus.
   d. Golgi body.

4. All of one kind of organism in an area make up a(n)
   a. chromosome.
   b. population.
   c. tissue.
   d. organ.

5. Genetic material is contained in
   a. vacuoles   b. cell walls
   c. lysosomes   d. DNA

True or False

If the statement is true, write true. If it is false, change the underlined word or words to make the statement true.

6. The heart is an example of <u>an organ system</u>.

7. Cells were discovered using <u>electron</u> microscopes.

8. <u>Vacuoles</u> are the "powerhouses" of the cell.

9. Bacterial cells differ from the cells of plants and animals in that they lack a <u>nucleus</u>.

10. Organisms that make their own food are called <u>heterotrophs</u>.

Checking Concepts

11. Your friend thinks that plants are not alive because they do not move. How would you respond to your friend?

12. Explain how the structure of the skeletal system is related to its function.

13. What role did the microscope play in the development of the cell theory?

14. What is selective breeding?

15. Give an example of an external stimulus and describe how an organism might respond to this stimulus.

16. **Writing to Learn** Suppose you had been a reporter assigned to cover early scientists' discoveries about cells. Write a brief article for your daily newspaper that explains one scientist's discoveries. Be sure to explain both how the discoveries were made and why they are important.

Thinking Critically

17. **Classifying** How do you know that a robot is not alive?

18. **Relating Cause and Effect** When people believed that spontaneous generation occurred, there was a recipe for making mice: Place a dirty shirt and a few wheat grains in an open pot; wait three weeks. List the reasons why this recipe might have worked. How could you demonstrate that spontaneous generation was not responsible for the appearance of mice?

19. **Applying Concepts** Explain how the cell theory applies to a dog.

20. **Predicting** Could a cell survive without a cell membrane? Give reasons to support your answer.

21. **Comparing and Contrasting** How are plant and animal cells similar? How are they different? To answer these questions, make a list of the different organelles in each cell. Explain how each organelle is vital to the life and function of a plant or animal.

Applying Skills

A student designed an experiment to test how light affects the growth of plants. Refer to the illustrations below to answer Questions 22–25.

22. **Controlling Variables** Is this a controlled experiment? If not, why not? If so, identify the manipulated variable.
23. **Developing Hypotheses** What hypothesis might this experiment be testing?
24. **Predicting** Based on what you know about plants, predict how each plant will have changed after two weeks.
25. **Designing Experiments** Design a controlled experiment to determine whether the amount of water that a plant receives affects its growth.

Performance ▽ Assessment
CHAPTER PROJECT

Present Your Project Prepare a display presenting your conclusion about your mystery object. Describe the observations that helped you reach your conclusion. Compare your ideas with those of other students. If necessary, defend your work.

Reflect and Record Make a list of the characteristics of life that you observed in your mystery object. Which were hard to study? Explain in your journal why some characteristics were hard to investigate.

Test Preparation
Use these questions to prepare for standardized tests.

Study the table. Then answer Questions 26–30.

Cell	Nucleus	Cell Wall	Cell Membrane
Cell A	Yes	Yes	Yes
Cell B	Yes	No	Yes
Cell C	No	Yes	Yes

26. Which cell is probably an animal cell?
    A cell A   B cell B
    C cell C   D none of the above
27. Which cell is probably a plant cell?
    F cell A   G cell B
    H cell C   J none of the above
28. Which cell is a prokaryote?
    A cell A   B cell B
    C cell C   D none of the above
29. In Cell B, where would the genetic material be found?
    F in the mitochondria
    G in the vacuoles
    H in the nucleus
    J in the cell membrane
30. Which cell(s) would most likely contain chloroplasts?
    A cell A   B cell B
    C cell C   D cell B and cell C

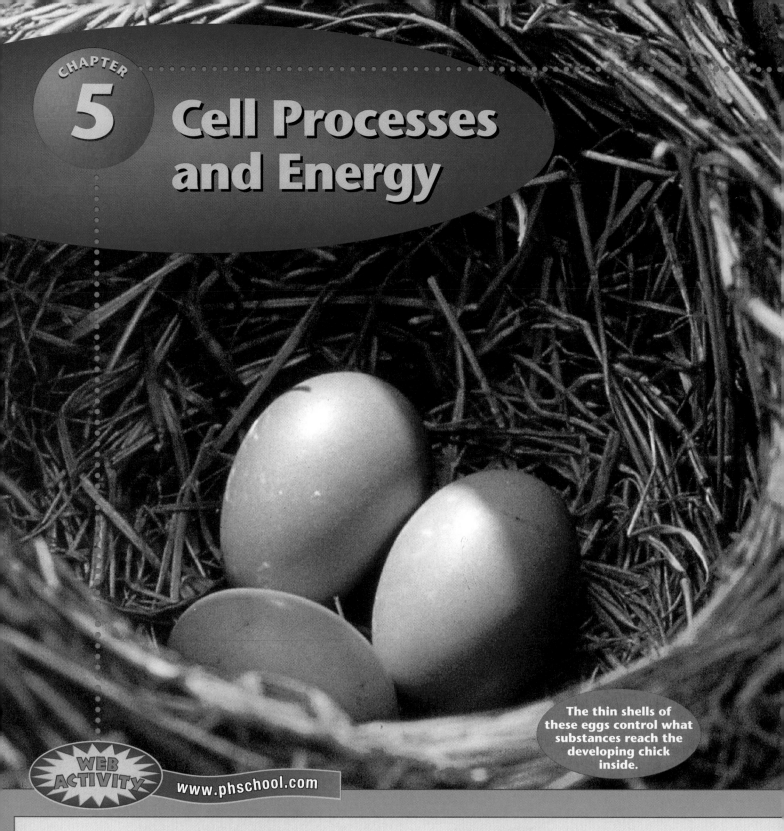

CHAPTER

5 Cell Processes and Energy

The thin shells of these eggs control what substances reach the developing chick inside.

WEB ACTIVITY
www.phschool.com

Egg-speriment With a Cell

Did you ever wonder how a baby chick can breathe when it's still inside the egg? The structure of an egg's shell allows air to reach the developing chick inside, while it keeps most other substances outside. Just as an egg needs to control which substances can enter it, so too does every cell in your body.

In this chapter, you'll learn more about cells and how they carry out the essential functions of life. You'll learn how cells make and use energy and how they grow and divide. You can start your discoveries right away by studying an everyday object that can serve as a model of a cell: an uncooked egg.

Your Goal To observe how various materials enter or leave a cell, using an egg as a model of the cell.

To complete this project, you will

◆ observe what happens when you soak an uncooked egg in vinegar, then in water, food coloring, salt water, and finally in a liquid of your choice
◆ measure the circumference of the egg every day, and graph your results
◆ explain the changes that your egg underwent
◆ follow the safety guidelines in Appendix A

Get Started Predict what might happen when you put an uncooked egg in vinegar for two days. How might other liquids affect an egg? Find a place where you can leave your egg undisturbed. Then begin your egg-speriment!

Check Your Progress You will be working on this project as you study this chapter. To keep your project on track, look for Check Your Progress boxes at the following points.

Section 1 Review, page 162: Make measurements and record data.
Section 2 Review, page 168: Experiment with different liquids.
Section 3 Review, page 177: Graph your data and draw conclusions.

Present Your Project At the end of the chapter (page 181), you will display your egg and share your results.

TEKS

In addition to process TEKS, this chapter addresses these concept TEKS as they relate to the chapter's topics.

(6.10) The student knows the relationship between structure and function in living systems. The student is expected to:
(A) differentiate between structure and function;
(B) determine that all organisms are composed of cells that carry on functions to sustain life.

(6.11) The student knows that traits of species can change through generations and that the instructions for traits are contained in the genetic material of the organisms. The student is expected to:
(B) identify cells as structures containing genetic material.

1 The Cell in Its Environment

DISCOVER .... ACTIVITY ....

How Do Molecules Move?

1. With your classmates, stand so that you are evenly spaced throughout the classroom.

2. Your teacher will spray an air freshener into the room. When you first begin to smell the air freshener, raise your hand.

3. Note how long it takes for other students in the classroom to smell the scent.

Think It Over

Developing Hypotheses How was each student's distance from the teacher related to when he or she smelled the air freshener? Develop a hypothesis about why this pattern occurred.

GUIDE FOR READING

◆ How does the structure of the cell membrane relate to its function?

◆ What is the difference between passive transport and active transport?

Reading Tip Before you read, use the headings to make an outline about how materials move into and out of cells. As you read, make notes about each process.

Key Terms diffusion
• selectively permeable
• osmosis • passive transport
• active transport

▼ The *Mir* space station

How is a cell like a space station? The walls of a space station protect the astronauts inside from the airless vacuum of space. Food, water, and other supplies must be brought to the space station by shuttles from Earth. In addition, the space station needs to be able to get rid of wastes. The doors of the space station allow the astronauts to bring materials in and move wastes out into the shuttle to be returned to Earth.

Like space stations, cells have structures that protect them from the outside environment. As you learned, all cells are surrounded by a cell membrane that separates the cell from the outside environment. Just like the space station, the cell has to take in needed materials and get rid of wastes. It is the cell membrane that controls what materials move into and out of the cell.

The Cell Membrane as Gatekeeper

The cell membrane has a structure that makes it **selectively permeable,** which means that some substances can pass through it while others cannot. **The selectively permeable structure of the cell membrane enables it to regulate the materials that enter and leave the cell.** You can think of the cell membrane as being like a gatekeeper at an ancient castle. It was the gatekeeper's job to decide when to open the gate to allow people to pass into and out of the castle. The gatekeeper made the castle wall "selectively permeable"—it was permeable to friendly folks but not to enemies.

A cell membrane is usually permeable to substances such as oxygen, water, and carbon dioxide. On the other hand, the cell membrane is usually not permeable to some large molecules and salts. Substances that can move into and out of a cell do so by one of three methods: diffusion, osmosis, or active transport.

Diffusion—Molecules in Motion

The main method by which small molecules move into and out of cells is diffusion. **Diffusion** (dih FYOO zhun) is the process by which molecules tend to move from an area of higher concentration to an area of lower concentration. The concentration of a substance is the amount of the substance in a given volume.

If you did the Discover activity, you observed diffusion in action. The area where the air freshener was sprayed had many molecules of freshener. The molecules gradually moved from this area of higher concentration to the other parts of the classroom, where there were few molecules of freshener, and thus a lower concentration.

What Causes Diffusion? Molecules are always moving. As they move, the molecules bump into one another. The more molecules there are in an area, the more collisions there will be. Collisions cause molecules to push away from one another. Over time, the molecules of a substance will continue to spread out. Eventually they will be spread evenly throughout the area.

Diffusion in Cells Have you ever used a microscope to observe one-celled organisms in pond water? These organisms obtain the oxygen they need to survive from the water around them. There are many more molecules of oxygen in the water outside the cell than there are inside the cell. In other words, there is a higher concentration of oxygen molecules in the water than inside the cell. Remember that the structure of the cell membrane is permeable to oxygen molecules. The oxygen molecules diffuse from the area of higher concentration—the pond water—through the cell membrane to the area of lower concentration—the inside of the cell.

Figure 1 Molecules move by diffusion from an area of higher concentration to an area of lower concentration. **(A)** There is a higher concentration of molecules outside the cell than inside. **(B)** The molecules diffuse into the cell. Eventually, there is an equal concentration of molecules inside and outside the cell.
Predicting What would happen if the concentration of the molecules outside the cell was lower than the concentration inside?

Osmosis—The Diffusion of Water Molecules

Like oxygen, water passes easily into and out of cells through the cell membrane. The diffusion of water molecules through a selectively permeable membrane is called **osmosis.** Osmosis is important to sustain life because cells cannot function properly without adequate water.

Remember that molecules tend to move from an area of higher concentration to an area of lower concentration. In osmosis, water molecules move by diffusion from an area where they are highly concentrated through the cell membrane to an area where they are less concentrated. This can have important consequences for the cell.

Look at Figure 2 to see the effect of osmosis on cells. In Figure 2A, red blood cells are bathed in a solution in which the concentration of water is the same as it is inside the cells. This is the normal shape of a red blood cell.

Now look at Figure 2B. The red blood cells are floating in water that contains a lot of salt. The concentration of water molecules outside the cells is lower than the concentration of water molecules inside the cells. This is because the salt takes up space in the salt water, so there are fewer water molecules. As a result, water moves out of the cells by osmosis, and the cells shrink.

Finally, consider Figure 2C. The red blood cells are floating in water that contains a very small amount of salt. The water inside the cells contains more salt than the solution they are floating in. Thus, the concentration of water outside the cell is greater than it is inside the cell. The water moves into the cell, causing it to swell.

☑ *Checkpoint* **How is osmosis related to diffusion?**

Figure 2 Osmosis is the diffusion of water molecules through a selectively permeable membrane.

(A) This is the normal shape of a red blood cell.

(B) This cell has shrunk because water moved out of it by osmosis.

(C) This cell is swollen with water that has moved into it by osmosis.

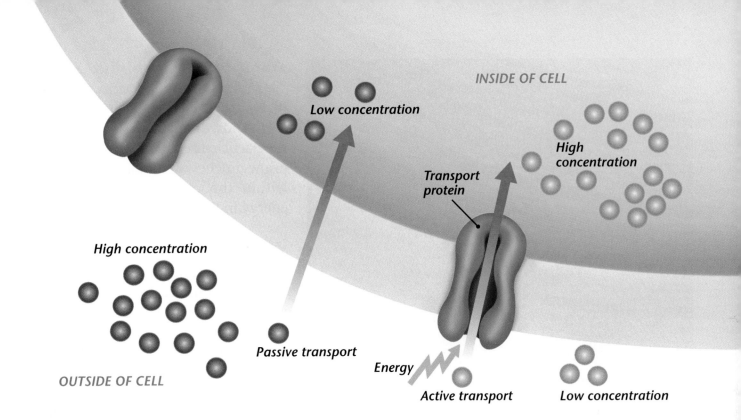

INSIDE OF CELL

Low concentration

High concentration

Transport protein

High concentration

OUTSIDE OF CELL

Passive transport

Energy

Active transport

Low concentration

Active Transport

If you have ever ridden a bicycle down a long hill, you know that it doesn't take any of your energy to go fast. But pedaling back up the hill does take energy. For a cell, moving materials through the cell membrane by diffusion and osmosis is like cycling downhill. These processes do not require the cell to use any energy. The movement of materials through a cell membrane without using energy is called **passive transport.**

What if a cell needs to take in a substance that is in higher concentration inside the cell than outside? The cell would have to move the molecules in the opposite direction than they naturally move by diffusion. Cells can do this, but they have to use energy—just as you would use energy to pedal back up the hill. **Active transport** is the movement of materials through a cell membrane using energy. **The main difference between passive transport and active transport is that active transport requires the cell to use energy while passive transport does not.**

Transport Proteins A cell has several ways of moving materials by active transport. In one method, transport proteins in the cell membrane function to "pick up" molecules outside the cell and carry them in, using energy in the process. Transport proteins also carry molecules out of cells in a similar way. Some substances that are carried into and out of cells in this way include calcium, potassium, and sodium.

Figure 3 Diffusion and osmosis are forms of passive transport. These processes do not require the cell to use any energy. Active transport, on the other hand, requires the use of energy. *Interpreting Diagrams How are passive and active transport related to the concentrations of the molecules inside and outside the cell?*

Figure 4 A cell can move some materials into itself by engulfing them. This single-celled ameba is engulfing a smaller single-celled organism. *Applying Concepts How does this process differ from passive transport?*

Transport by Engulfing You can see another method of active transport in Figure 4. First the cell membrane surrounds, or engulfs, a particle. Once the particle is engulfed, the cell membrane pinches off and forms a vacuole within the cell. The cell must use energy in this process.

Why Are Cells Small?

As you know, most cells are so small that you cannot see them without a microscope. Have you ever wondered why cells are so small? One reason is related to how materials move into and out of cells.

As a cell's size increases, more of its cytoplasm is located farther from the cell membrane. Once a molecule enters a cell, it is carried to its destination by a stream of moving cytoplasm, somewhat like the way currents of water in the ocean move a raft. But in a very large cell, the streams of cytoplasm must travel farther to bring materials to all parts of the cell. It would take much longer for a molecule to reach the center of a very large cell than it would in a small cell. Likewise, it would take a long time for wastes to be removed. If a cell grew too large, it could not function well enough to survive. When a cell reaches a certain size, it divides into two new cells. You will learn more about cell division later in this chapter.

Section 1 Review

1. Describe the structure of the cell membrane. Then explain three methods by which substances can move into and out of cells.
2. How are passive transport and active transport similar? How do they differ?
3. Why is small size an advantage to a cell?
4. **Thinking Critically** **Predicting** A single-celled organism is transferred from a tank of fresh water into a tank of salt water. How will the cell change? Explain.

Check Your Progress
CHAPTER PROJECT
By now you should have started your "egg-speriment" by soaking an uncooked egg in vinegar. Leave your egg in the vinegar for at least two days. Each day, rinse your egg in water and measure its circumference. Record all of your observations. (*Hint:* Handle the egg gently. If your egg breaks, don't give up or throw away your data. Simply start again with another egg and keep investigating.)

SECTION 2 The Cell and Energy

DISCOVER • ACTIVITY • • •

Where Does the Energy Come From?

1. Obtain a solar-powered calculator that does not use batteries. Place the calculator in direct light.

2. Cover the solar cells with your finger. Note how your action affects the number display.

3. Uncover the solar cells. What happens to the number display?

4. Now cover all but one of the solar cells. How does that affect the number display?

Think It Over

Inferring From your observations, what can you infer about the energy that powers the calculator?

It's a beautiful summer afternoon—a perfect day for spending time in the park. Dogs play together under a nearby tree. Blue jays swoop down from the tree's branches, hunting for food. "Let's go for a bike ride," suggests your cousin. "Great idea," you say, and you ride off down the path.

Dogs playing, birds flying, people biking—all of these activities require energy. Where do you think this energy comes from? Believe it or not, the energy comes from the sun. In fact, the sun is the source of almost all the energy used by living things on Earth.

What Is Photosynthesis?

All living things need energy. Their cells need energy to carry out functions that sustain life such as transporting substances into and out of cells. You and other heterotrophs eat food to supply your cells with energy. But plants and some other organisms are autotrophs that use the sun's energy to make their own food.

The process by which a cell of an autotroph captures the energy in sunlight and uses it to make food is called **photosynthesis** (foh toh SIN thuh sis). Chloroplasts contain chemicals that absorb light. One of these is **chlorophyll,** which gives chloroplasts their green color. Chlorophyll and other light-absorbing chemicals capture light energy and use it to power photosynthesis. In plants, it occurs in their cells' chloroplasts.

GUIDE FOR READING

◆ What happens during the process of photosynthesis?

◆ What events occur during respiration?

◆ How are photosynthesis and respiration related?

Reading Tip Before you read, write definitions of *photosynthesis* and *respiration*. After reading this section, revise your definitions.

Key Terms photosynthesis • chlorophyll • respiration • fermentation

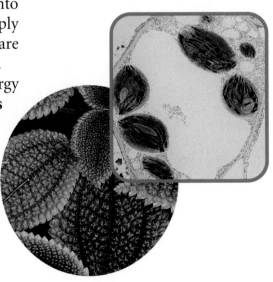

Figure 5 Photosynthesis occurs inside chloroplasts in the cells of plants and some other organisms.
Applying Concepts What is the source of energy in photosynthesis?

The Events of Photosynthesis

Photosynthesis is a complex process that results in chemical change. Recall from Chapter 1 that, during a chemical change, substances may combine to form new substances. **During photosynthesis, cells capture energy from sunlight and use it to change carbon dioxide gas and water into oxygen and sugars, such as glucose.** Some of the sun's energy is stored as chemical energy in the sugar molecules made during photosynthesis.

The events of photosynthesis can be summed up by the following chemical equation:

$$6\,CO_2 \;+\; 6\,H_2O \;\xrightarrow{\text{light energy}}\; C_6H_{12}O_6 \;+\; 6\,O_2$$

carbon dioxide   water   glucose   oxygen

Notice that the raw materials—6 molecules of carbon dioxide and 6 molecules of water—are on the left side of the equation. The products—1 molecule of glucose and 6 molecules of oxygen—are on the right side of the equation. An arrow, which is read as "yields," connects the raw materials to the products. Light energy , which is necessary for the chemical reaction to occur, appears above the arrow.

☑ *Checkpoint* *What two substances are produced during the process of photosynthesis?*

Figure 6 During photosynthesis, chlorophyll and other light-absorbing chemicals capture energy from sunlight. The cells then use this energy, along with water and carbon dioxide, to produce sugars and oxygen. *Applying Concepts What is the chemical equation for photosynthesis?*

Figure 7 Both the caterpillar and the western bluebird obtain their energy indirectly from the sun.

Storing and Releasing the Energy in Food

What happens to the products of photosynthesis? Plant cells use some of the glucose for food. Their cells break down the glucose molecules to release the chemical energy the molecules contain. This energy is then used to carry out the plant's functions. Other glucose molecules are converted to cellulose, a chemical that plays an important role in the structure of the cell walls of plants. When heterotrophs, such as the ones in Figure 7, eat food from plants or animals that have eaten plants, they take in the plant's stored food.

The other product of photosynthesis is oxygen. Most of the oxygen passes out of the plant and into the atmosphere. Today, Earth's atmosphere is about 21 percent oxygen. Autotrophs have produced almost all of this oxygen through photosynthesis. The oxygen in Earth's atmosphere is important because most living things need oxygen to survive. Why? Most living things use oxygen in the cells of their bodies to release the energy in food.

To understand how cells store and use energy, think about how you might save money. You would probably put it in a savings account at a bank. When you wanted to buy an item, you would withdraw some money. Cells store and use energy in a similar way. For example, during photosynthesis, plants capture energy from sunlight and "save" it in the form of substances such as sugars. When their cells need energy, plants "withdraw" it by breaking down the sugars and releasing energy from their sugars. Similarly, when you eat, you add to your body's energy savings account. When your cells need energy, they make a withdrawal and break down the food to release its energy. Read on to discover how your cells break down food.

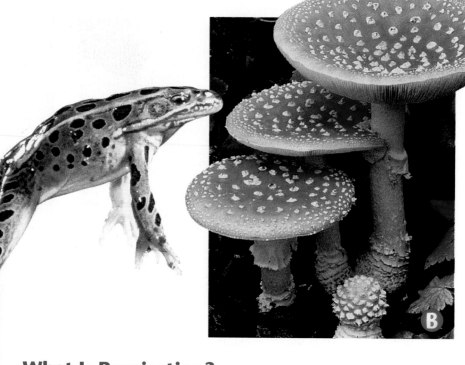

Figure 8 All organisms need energy to live. **(A)** Although these mushrooms don't move, they still need a continuous supply of energy to grow and reproduce. **(B)** This leopard frog uses the energy stored in carbohydrates to leap great distances.
Applying Concepts What is the name of the process by which cells obtain the energy they need?

What Is Respiration?

After you eat a meal, your body converts the food into the sugar glucose. When cells need energy, they obtain that energy from glucose in a process called **respiration. During respiration, cells break down simple food molecules such as glucose and release the energy they contain.** Because living things need an ongoing supply of energy, the cells of all living things carry out respiration continuously.

The term *respiration* might be confusing. You have probably used it to mean breathing, which is the moving of air in and out of your lungs. To avoid confusion, the respiration process that occurs in cells can be called cellular respiration. However, the double use of the term *respiration* points out an important connection. Breathing brings oxygen into your lungs, and most cells need oxygen for cellular respiration.

Cellular respiration occurs in the mitochondria of an organism's cells. The overall process of cellular respiration is summarized in the following equation:

$$C_6H_{12}O_6 \; + \; 6\,O_2 \; \longrightarrow \; 6\,CO_2 \; + \; 6\,H_2O \; + \; energy$$

glucose   oxygen   carbon dioxide   water

Notice that the raw materials for cellular respiration are glucose and oxygen. Plants and other organisms that undergo photosynthesis make their own glucose. The glucose in the cells of animals and other organisms comes from the food they consume. The oxygen comes from the air or water surrounding the organism.

✓ *Checkpoint* *What substance is broken down during respiration?*

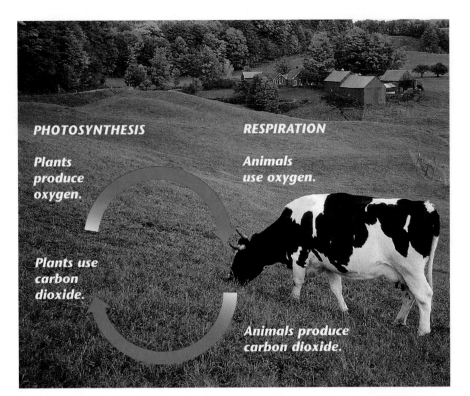

Figure 9 Photosynthesis and respiration can be thought of as opposite processes. All organisms, including plants, undergo respiration. *Interpreting Photographs How do these two processes keep the levels of oxygen and carbon dioxide in the atmosphere fairly constant?*

PHOTOSYNTHESIS

Plants produce oxygen.

Plants use carbon dioxide.

RESPIRATION

Animals use oxygen.

Animals produce carbon dioxide.

Comparing Photosynthesis and Respiration

Do you notice anything familiar about the equation for respiration? You are right if you said it is the opposite of the equation for photosynthesis. During photosynthesis, carbon dioxide and water are used to produce sugars and oxygen. During respiration, sugars and oxygen are used to produce carbon dioxide and water. **Photosynthesis and respiration can be thought of as opposite processes.** Together, they form a cycle that keeps the levels of oxygen and carbon dioxide fairly constant in Earth's atmosphere. Living things use both gases over and over again.

Fermentation

Some cells are able to obtain energy from food without using oxygen. For example, some single-celled organisms live where there is no oxygen, such as in the mud of lakes or swamps. These organisms obtain their energy through **fermentation,** an energy-releasing process that does not require oxygen. The amount of energy released from each sugar molecule during fermentation, however, is much lower than the amount released during respiration.

Alcoholic Fermentation One type of fermentation occurs in yeast and some other single-celled organisms. This process is sometimes called alcoholic fermentation because alcohol is one of the products made when these organisms break down sugars. The other products are carbon dioxide and a small amount of energy.

Yeast Feast

1. Fill two test tubes half full of warm water. Add 5 milliliters of sugar to one of the test tubes.
2. Add 0.5 milliliters of yeast (unicellular organisms) to each tube. Stir the contents of each tube. Put a stopper in each tube.
3. Observe any changes that occur in the test tubes over the next 10 to 15 minutes.

Inferring Describe what occurred in each test tube. Use your knowledge to explain any energy-related processes you observed.

The products of alcoholic fermentation are important to bakers and brewers. The carbon dioxide produced by yeast causes dough to rise, and it creates the air pockets you see in bread. Carbon dioxide is also the source of bubbles in alcoholic drinks such as beer and sparkling wine.

Lactic-Acid Fermentation Another type of fermentation takes place at times in your body, and you've probably felt its effects. Think of a time when you've run as fast as you could for as long as you could. Your leg muscles were pushing hard against the pavement, and you were breathing quickly. Eventually, however, your legs became tired and you couldn't run any more.

No matter how hard you breathed, your muscle cells used up the oxygen faster than it could be replaced. Because your cells lacked oxygen, they used the process of fermentation to produce energy. One by-product of this type of fermentation is a substance known as lactic acid. When lactic acid builds up, your muscles feel weak, tired, and sore.

Figure 10 When an athlete's muscles run out of oxygen, lactic-acid fermentation occurs. The athlete's muscles feel tired and sore. *Inferring Which muscles in this runner were producing the most lactic acid?*

Section 2 Review

1. What are the raw materials needed for photosynthesis? What are the products?
2. What happens during respiration?
3. Explain the relationship between photosynthesis and respiration.
4. What raw material used in respiration is *not* needed for fermentation to occur?
5. **Thinking Critically** Applying Concepts Do plant cells need to carry out respiration? Explain.

> **CHAPTER PROJECT**
>
> **Check Your Progress**
> At this point, you should soak your egg for one or two days in water, then in water with food coloring, then in salt water, and finally in another liquid of your choice. Continue to rinse your egg and measure and record its circumference every day. Your egg should be going through some amazing changes in appearance.
>
>

Gases in Balance

Problem

How are photosynthesis and respiration related?

Skills Focus

controlling variables, interpreting data

Materials

marking pens
2 *Elodea* plants
plastic graduated cylinder, 100-mL
bromthymol blue solution
3 flasks with stoppers, 250-mL

straws
light source

DATA TABLE		
	Color of Solution	
Flask	Day 1	Day 2
L (light)		
D (dark)		
C (control)		

Procedure

1. Bromthymol blue can be used to test for carbon dioxide. To see how this dye works, pour 100 mL of bromthymol blue solution into a flask. Record its color. **CAUTION:** *Bromthymol blue can stain skin and clothing. Avoid spilling or splashing it on yourself.*

2. Provide a supply of carbon dioxide by gently blowing into the solution through a straw until the dye changes color. Record the new color. **CAUTION:** *Do not suck any of the solution through the straw.*

3. Copy the data table into your notebook. Add 100 mL of bromthymol blue to the other flasks. Then blow through clean straws into each solution until the color changes.

4. Now you will test to see what gas is used by a plant in the presence of light. Obtain two *Elodea* plants of about the same size.

5. Place one plant into the first flask. Label the flask "L" for light. Place the other plant in the second flask. Label the flask "D" for darkness. Label the third flask "C" for control. Put stoppers in all three flasks.

6. Record the colors of the three solutions under Day 1 in your data table.

7. Place the flasks labeled L and C in a lighted location as directed by your teacher. Place the flask labeled D in a dark location as directed by your teacher. Wash your hands thoroughly when you have finished.

8. On Day 2, examine the flasks and record the colors of the solutions in your data table. Follow your teacher's instructions for disposing of all materials.

Analyze and Conclude

1. Explain why the color of each solution did or did not change from Day 1 to Day 2.

2. Why was it important to include the flask labeled C as part of this experiment?

3. Predict what would happen if you blew into the flask labeled L after you completed Step 8. Explain your prediction.

4. **Apply** How does this lab show that photosynthesis and respiration are opposite processes?

More to Explore

Suppose you were to put an *Elodea* plant and a small fish in a stoppered flask. Predict what would happen to the levels of oxygen and carbon dioxide in the flask. Explain your prediction.

What Are the Cells Doing?

1. Use a plastic dropper to transfer some yeast cells from a yeast culture to a microscope slide. Your teacher has prepared the slide by drying methylene blue stain onto it. Add a coverslip and place the slide under a microscope.

2. Examine the cells on the slide. Use low power first, then high power. Look for what appears to be two cells attached to each other. One cell may be larger than the other. Draw what you see.

Think It Over

Developing Hypotheses What process do you think the "double cells" are undergoing? Develop a hypothesis that might explain what you see.

GUIDE FOR READING

◆ What events take place during the three stages of the cell cycle?

◆ What is the role of DNA replication?

Reading Tip Before you read, use the headings to outline the process of cell division. As you read, draw pictures to help you understand the process.

Key Terms cell cycle
• interphase • replication
• mitosis • chromatid
• cytokinesis

In the early autumn, many local fairs run pumpkin contests. Proud growers enter their largest pumpkins, hoping to win a prize. If you've never seen these prize-winning pumpkins, you would be amazed. Some have masses close to 400 kilograms and can be as big as a doghouse. What's even more amazing is that these giant pumpkins began as small flowers on pumpkin plants. How did the pumpkins grow so big?

A pumpkin grows in size by increasing both the size and the number of its cells. A single cell divides, forming two cells. Then two cells divide, forming four, and so on. This process of cell division does not occur only in pumpkins, though. In fact, many cells in your body are undergoing cell division as you read this page.

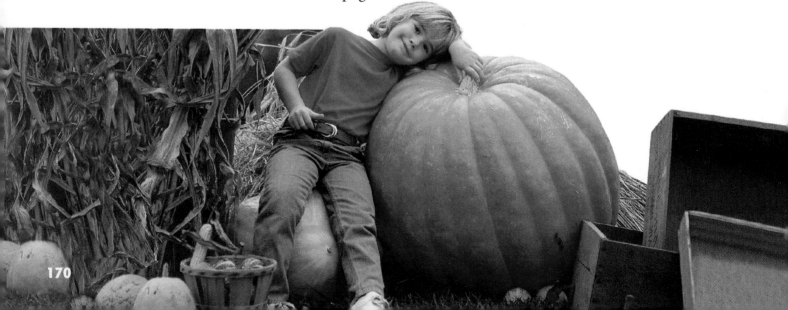

The Cell Cycle

Think about the cells you learned about in Chapter 4. Each cell contains many different structures, including a cell membrane, a nucleus, mitochondria, and ribosomes. To divide into two equal parts, the cell would need to either duplicate the structures or divide them equally between the two new cells. Both cells would then contain everything they need in order to function.

The regular sequence of growth and division that cells undergo is known as the **cell cycle.** You can see details of the cell cycle in *Exploring the Cell Cycle* on pages 174 and 175. Notice that the cell cycle is divided into three main stages. As you read about each stage, follow the events that occur as one "parent" cell divides to form two identical "daughter" cells.

Figure 11 The cells that make up this young monkey are the same size as those that make up its mother. However, the adult has many more cells in its body. *Applying Concepts What is the name of the regular sequence of growth and division that a cell undergoes?*

Stage 1: Interphase

The first stage of the cell cycle is called **interphase.** Interphase is the period before cell division occurs. Even though it is not dividing, the cell is quite active during this stage. **During interphase, the cell grows to its mature size, makes a copy of its DNA, and prepares to divide into two cells.**

Growth During the first part of interphase, the cell doubles in size and produces all the structures needed to carry out its functions. For example, the cell enlarges its endoplasmic reticulum, makes new ribosomes, and produces enzymes. Both mitochondria and chloroplasts make copies of themselves. The cell's structure matures, and it grows to its full size.

DNA Replication After a cell has grown to its mature size, the next part of interphase begins. The cell makes a copy of the DNA in its nucleus in a process called **replication.** Recall that DNA is a nucleic acid found in the chromatin in a cell's nucleus. DNA is the genetic material that holds all the information that the cell needs to carry out its functions. The replication of a cell's DNA is very important, since each daughter cell must have a complete set of DNA to survive. At the end of DNA replication, the cell contains two identical sets of DNA. One set will be distributed to each daughter cell. You will learn the details of DNA replication later in this section.

Figure 12 During mitosis, the chromatin condenses to form rodlike chromosomes. Each chromosome consists of two identical strands, or chromatids. *Interpreting Diagrams What is the name of the structure that holds the chromatids together?*

Centromere

Chromatids

Modeling Mitosis

Refer to *Exploring the Cell Cycle* as you carry out this activity.

1. Construct a model of a cell that has three chromosomes. Use a piece of construction paper to represent the cell. Use different-colored pipe cleaners to represent the chromosomes. Make sure that the chromosomes look like double rods.

2. Position the chromosomes in the cell where they would be during prophase.

3. Repeat Step 2 for metaphase, anaphase, and telophase.

Making Models How did the model help you understand the events of mitosis? In what ways was the model unlike the actual process of mitosis?

Preparation for Division Once the cell's DNA has replicated, preparation for cell division begins. The cell produces structures that it will use to divide during the rest of the cell cycle. At the end of interphase, the cell is ready to divide.

Stage 2: Mitosis

Once interphase is complete, the second stage of the cell cycle begins. **Mitosis** (my TOH sis) is the stage during which the cell's nucleus divides into two new nuclei. **During mitosis, one copy of the DNA is distributed into each of the two daughter cells.**

Scientists divide mitosis into four parts, or phases: prophase, metaphase, anaphase, and telophase. During prophase, the threadlike chromatin in the cell's nucleus begins to condense and coil, like fishing line wrapping around a ball. Under a light microscope, the condensed chromatin looks like tiny rods, as you can see in Figure 12. Since the cell's DNA has replicated, each rod has doubled. Each is an exact copy of the other. Scientists call each doubled rod of condensed chromatin a chromosome. Each identical rod, or strand, of the chromosome is called a **chromatid.** The two strands are held together by a structure called a centromere.

As the cell progresses through metaphase, anaphase, and telophase, the chromatids separate from each other and move to opposite ends of the cell. Then two nuclei form around the chromatids at the two ends of the cell. You can follow this process in *Exploring the Cell Cycle.*

☑ *Checkpoint During which stage of mitosis does the chromatin condense to form rodlike structures?*

Stage 3: Cytokinesis

After mitosis, the final stage of the cell cycle, called **cytokinesis** (sy toh kih NEE sis), completes the process of cell division. **During cytokinesis, the cytoplasm divides, distributing the organelles into each of the two new cells.** Cytokinesis usually starts at about the same time as telophase.

During cytokinesis in animal cells, the cell membrane squeezes together around the middle of the cell. The cytoplasm pinches into two cells with about half of the organelles in each daughter cell.

Cytokinesis is somewhat different in plant cells. A plant cell's rigid cell wall cannot squeeze together in the same way that a cell membrane can. Instead, a structure called a cell plate forms across the middle of the cell. The cell plate gradually develops into new cell membranes between the two daughter cells. New cell walls then form around the cell membranes.

There are many variations of the basic pattern of cytokinesis. For example, yeast cells divide, though not equally. A small daughter cell, or bud, pinches off of the parent cell. The bud then grows into a full-sized yeast cell.

Cytokinesis marks the end of the cell cycle. Two new cells have formed. Each daughter cell has the same number of chromosomes as the original parent cell. At the end of cytokinesis, each cell enters interphase, and the cycle begins again.

✓ *Checkpoint* *When in the cell cycle does cytokinesis begin?*

Length of the Cell Cycle

How long does it take for a cell to go through one cell cycle? The answer depends on the type of cell. In a young sea urchin, for example, one cell cycle takes about 2 hours. In contrast, a human liver cell completes one cell cycle in about 22 hours, as shown in Figure 13. The length of each stage in the cell cycle also varies greatly from cell to cell. Some cells, such as human brain cells, never divide—they remain in the first part of interphase for as long as they live.

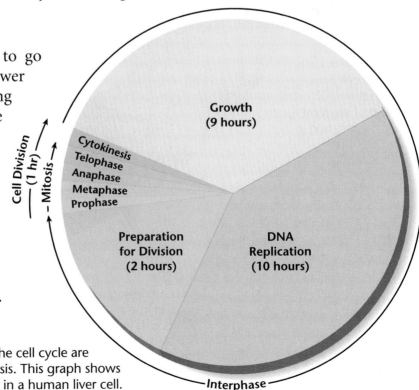

Figure 13 The main stages of the cell cycle are interphase, mitosis, and cytokinesis. This graph shows the average length of each stage in a human liver cell.

EXPLORING *the* Cell Cycle

Cells undergo an orderly sequence of events as they grow and divide. The sequence shown here is a typical cell cycle in an animal cell. Plant cells have somewhat different cell cycles.

1 INTERPHASE
The cell grows to its mature size, makes a copy of its DNA, and prepares to divide into two cells.

3 CYTOKINESIS
The cell membrane pinches in around the middle of the cell. Eventually, the cell pinches in two. Each daughter cell ends up with the same number of identical chromosomes and about half the organelles and cytoplasm.

2D MITOSIS: Telophase
The chromosomes begin to stretch out and lose their rodlike appearance. This occurs in the two regions at the ends of the cell. A new nuclear membrane forms around each region of chromosomes.

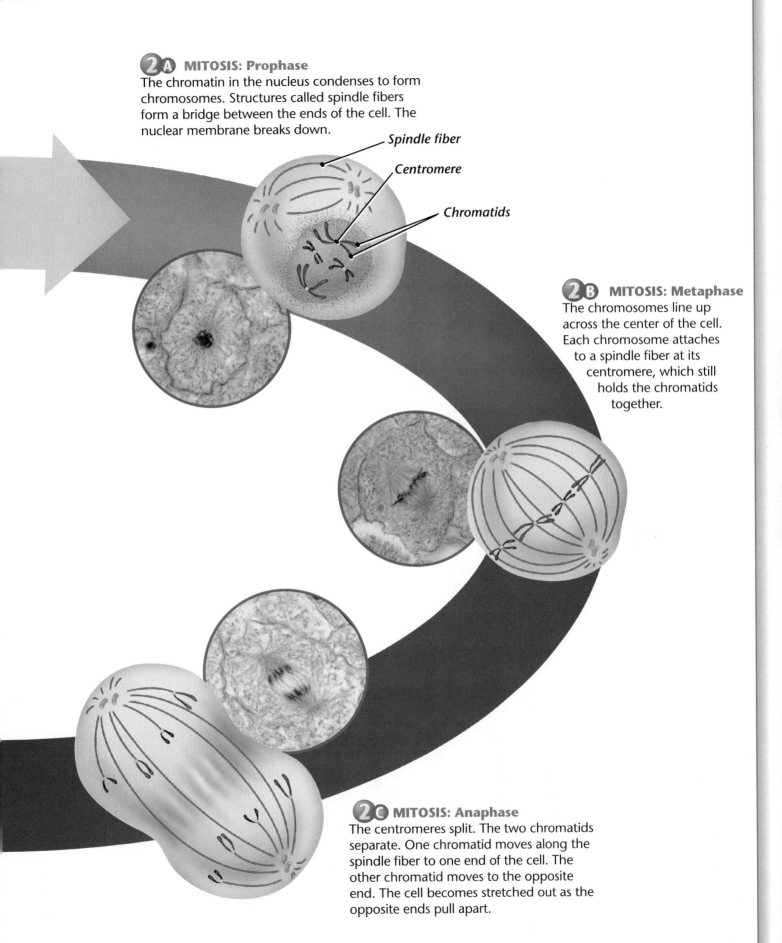

②Ⓐ MITOSIS: Prophase
The chromatin in the nucleus condenses to form chromosomes. Structures called spindle fibers form a bridge between the ends of the cell. The nuclear membrane breaks down.

Spindle fiber

Centromere

Chromatids

②Ⓑ MITOSIS: Metaphase
The chromosomes line up across the center of the cell. Each chromosome attaches to a spindle fiber at its centromere, which still holds the chromatids together.

②Ⓒ MITOSIS: Anaphase
The centromeres split. The two chromatids separate. One chromatid moves along the spindle fiber to one end of the cell. The other chromatid moves to the opposite end. The cell becomes stretched out as the opposite ends pull apart.

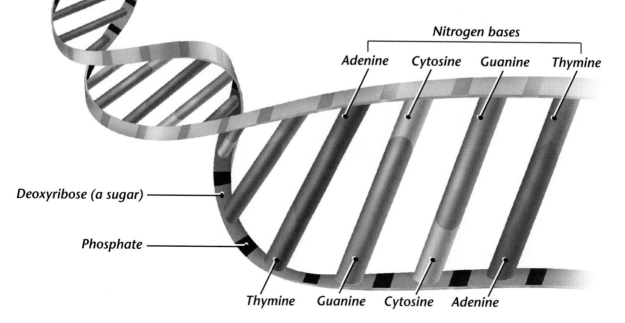

Figure 14 A DNA molecule is shaped like a twisted ladder. The sides are made up of sugar and phosphate molecules. The rungs are formed by pairs of nitrogen bases. *Classifying Which base always pairs with adenine?*

DNA Replication

A cell makes a copy of its DNA before mitosis takes place. **DNA replication ensures that each daughter cell will have all of the genetic information it needs to carry out its activities.**

Only in the last 50 years have scientists understood the importance of DNA. By the early 1950s, the work of several scientists showed that DNA carries all of the cell's instructions. They also learned that DNA is passed from a parent cell to its daughter cells. In 1953, two scientists, James Watson and Francis Crick, figured out the structure of DNA. Their discovery revealed important information about how DNA copies itself.

The Structure of DNA Notice in Figure 14 that a DNA molecule looks like a twisted ladder, or spiral staircase. Because of its shape, a DNA molecule is often called a "double helix." A helix is a shape that twists like the threads of a screw.

The two sides of the DNA ladder are made up of molecules of a sugar called deoxyribose, alternating with molecules known as phosphates. Each rung of the DNA ladder is made up of a pair of molecules called nitrogen bases. Nitrogen bases are molecules that combine the element nitrogen with other elements. There are four kinds of nitrogen bases: adenine (AD uh neen), thymine (THY meen), guanine (GWAH neen), and cytosine (SY tuh seen). The capital letters A, T, G, and C are used to represent the four bases.

Look closely at Figure 14. Notice that the bases on one side of the ladder match up in a specific way with the bases on the other side. Adenine (A) only pairs with thymine (T), while guanine (G) only pairs with cytosine (C). This pairing structure is the key to understanding how DNA replication functions.

Nitrogen bases

Adenine   Cytosine   Guanine   Thymine

Deoxyribose (a sugar)

Phosphate

Thymine   Guanine   Cytosine   Adenine

176

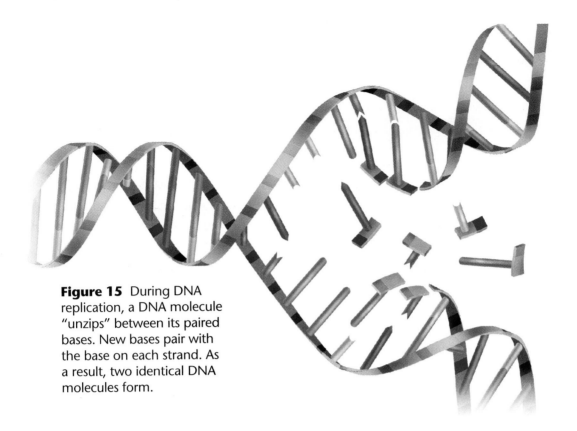

Figure 15 During DNA replication, a DNA molecule "unzips" between its paired bases. New bases pair with the base on each strand. As a result, two identical DNA molecules form.

The Replication Process DNA replication begins when the two sides of the DNA molecule unwind and separate, like a zipper unzipping. As you can see in Figure 15, the molecule separates between the paired nitrogen bases on each rung. Next, nitrogen bases that are floating in the nucleus pair up with the bases on each half of the DNA molecule. Remember that the pairing of bases follows definite rules: A always pairs with T, while G always pairs with C. Once the new bases are attached, two new DNA molecules are formed. The order of the bases in each new DNA molecule will exactly match the order in the original DNA molecule.

 Section 3 Review

1. What are the three main stages of the cell cycle? Briefly describe the events that occur at each stage.
2. Why must the DNA in a cell replicate before the cell divides?
3. How does cytokinesis differ in plant and animal cells?
4. **Thinking Critically** **Predicting** Suppose that during anaphase, the centromeres did not split, and the chromatids did not separate. Predict the results.

Check Your Progress

CHAPTER PROJECT

Begin to think about why the egg changed as it did at each stage of the project. Consider how each of the different substances affected your egg. (*Hint:* Water plays a crucial role in the activities of a cell. How has water been involved in your investigation?) Organize your results into a report and make a graph of your egg's changing circumference. You may want to include diagrams to explain the processes that took place.

Skills Lab

Multiplying by Dividing

Problem

How long do the stages of the cell cycle take?

Materials

microscope
colored pencils
calculator or computer (optional)
prepared slides of onion root tip cells
    undergoing cell division

Procedure

1. Place the slide on the stage of a microscope. Use low power to locate a cell in interphase. Then switch to high power, and make a labeled drawing of the cell. **CAUTION:** *Slides and coverslips break easily. Do not allow the objective to touch the slide.*

2. Repeat Step 1 to find cells in prophase, metaphase, anaphase, and telophase. Then use pencil and paper or the computer to copy the data table.

3. Return to low power. Find an area with many cells dividing. Switch to the magnification that lets you see about 50 cells (for example, 100×).

4. Examine the cells row by row, and count the cells that are in interphase. Record that number in the data table under *First Sample.*

5. Examine the cells row-by-row four more times to count the cells in prophase, metaphase, anaphase, and telophase. Record the results.

6. Move to a new area on the slide. Repeat Steps 3–5 and record your counts in the column labeled *Second Sample.*

7. Fill in the column labeled *Total Number* by adding the numbers across each row.

8. Add the totals for the five stages to find the total number of cells counted.

Analyze and Conclude

1. Which stage of the cell cycle did you observe most often?

2. The cell cycle for onion root tips takes about 720 minutes (12 hours). Use your data and the formula below to find the number of minutes each stage takes. Do your calculations with a pencil and paper, a calculator, or a computer.

$$\text{Time for each stage} = \frac{\text{Number of cells at each stage}}{\text{Total number of cells counted}} \times 720 \text{ min}$$

3. **Think About It** Compare the amount of time spent in mitosis with the total time for the whole cell cycle.

More to Explore

Examine prepared slides of animal cells undergoing cell division. Use drawings and descriptions to compare plant and animal mitosis.

DATA TABLE

Stage of Cell Cycle	First Sample	Second Sample	Total Number
Interphase			
Mitosis: Prophase			
Metaphase			
Anaphase			
Telophase			
Total number of cells counted			

SECTION 1 — The Cell in Its Environment

Key Ideas

◆ The cell membrane is selectively permeable. This structure enables it to perform the function of regulating the materials that enter and leave the cell.

◆ Substances move into and out of a cell by one of three methods: diffusion, osmosis, or active transport.

◆ The main method by which substances move into and out of cells is diffusion. Diffusion is the process by which molecules tend to move from an area of higher concentration to an area of lower concentration.

◆ Water molecules pass into and out of a cell through osmosis, which is the diffusion of water molecules through a selectively permeable membrane.

◆ Active transport requires the cell to use energy, while passive transport does not.

Key Terms

selectively permeable
diffusion
osmosis
passive transport
active transport

SECTION 2 — The Cell and Energy

INTEGRATING CHEMISTRY

Key Ideas

◆ During photosynthesis, cells capture energy from sunlight and use it to change carbon dioxide gas and water into oxygen and sugars, such as glucose.

◆ During respiration, cells break down simple food molecules such as glucose and release the energy they contain.

◆ Photosynthesis and respiration can be thought of as opposite processes.

Key Terms

photosynthesis   respiration
chlorophyll   fermentation

SECTION 3 — Cell Division

Key Ideas

◆ The cell cycle is the regular sequence of growth and division that cells undergo.

◆ During interphase, the cell grows to its mature size, makes a copy of its DNA, and prepares to divide into two cells.

◆ Mitosis is the stage during which the cell's nucleus divides into two new nuclei. During mitosis, one copy of the DNA is distributed to each of the two daughter cells.

◆ During cytokinesis, the cytoplasm divides, distributing the organelles into each of the two new cells.

◆ DNA replication, which occurs before mitosis, ensures that each daughter cell will have all of the genetic information it needs to carry out its activities.

Key Terms

cell cycle   mitosis
interphase   chromatid
replication   cytokinesis

Organizing Information

Cycle Diagram Copy the cycle diagram about the cell cycle onto a separate sheet of paper. Then complete it and add a title. (For more on cycle diagrams, see the Skills Handbook.)

Reviewing Content

 Review key concepts online using iText at **www.phschool.com**

Multiple Choice

Choose the letter of the best answer.

1. The process by which water moves across a cell membrane is called
   a. osmosis.
   b. active transport.
   c. diffusion.
   d. resolution.

2. The movement of materials through a cell membrane without using energy is called
   a. active transport.
   b. passive transport.
   c. selective permeability.
   d. metaphase.

3. What process is responsible for producing most of Earth's oxygen?
   a. photosynthesis
   b. replication
   c. mutation
   d. reproduction

4. The process in which a cell makes an exact copy of its DNA is called
   a. fermentation.
   b. respiration.
   c. replication.
   d. reproduction.

5. Chromatids are held together by a
   a. spindle.
   b. chloroplast.
   c. centromere.
   d. cell membrane.

True or False

If the statement is true, write true. If it is false, change the underlined word or words to make the statement true.

6. The <u>cell membrane</u> is selectively permeable.

7. Transport proteins are involved in <u>passive transport</u>.

8. The process of respiration takes place mainly in the <u>mitochondria</u>.

9. An energy-releasing process that does not require oxygen is <u>replication</u>.

10. The stage of the cell cycle when DNA replication occurs is <u>telophase</u>.

Checking Concepts

11. Explain how the selectively permeable structure of the cell membrane relates to one of the functions of the cell membrane.

12. What is diffusion? What role does diffusion play in the cell?

13. Briefly explain what happens to energy from the sun during photosynthesis.

14. Explain how heterotrophs depend on the sun for energy.

15. Why do organisms need to carry out the process of respiration?

16. How do the events of the cell cycle ensure that the daughter cells will be identical to the parent cell?

17. **Writing to Learn** Write a paragraph comparing and contrasting photosynthesis and respiration. Be sure to discuss how the two processes maintain the oxygen and carbon dioxide balance in the atmosphere.

Thinking Critically

18. **Comparing and Contrasting** Compare and contrast the processes of alcoholic fermentation and lactic acid fermentation. Explain how the two processes are alike and different.

19. **Predicting** Suppose a volcano spewed so much ash into the air that it blocked most of the sunlight that usually strikes Earth. How might this affect the ability of animals to obtain the energy they need to live?

20. **Applying Concepts** Explain the relationship between the processes of breathing and respiration.

21. **Inferring** Suppose one strand of a DNA molecule contained the following bases: A C G T C T G. What would the bases on the other strand be?

22. **Problem Solving** Explain why it is important that the cell cycle results in daughter cells that are identical to the parent cell.

Applying Skills

Use the table below to answer Questions 23–25.

Percentages of Nitrogen Bases In the DNA of Various Organisms

Nitrogen Base	Human	Wheat	E. coli bacterium
Adenine	30%	27%	24%
Guanine	20%	23%	26%
Thymine	30%	27%	24%
Cytosine	20%	23%	26%

23. Graphing For each organism, draw a bar graph to show the percentages of each nitrogen base in its DNA.

24. Interpreting Data What is the relationship between the amounts of adenine and thymine in the DNA of each organism? Between the amounts of guanine and cytosine?

25. Inferring Based on your answer to Question 24, what can you infer about the structure of DNA in these three organisms?

Performance CHAPTER PROJECT **Assessment**

Present Your Project Bring in your egg, your graph, and any diagrams you made. As a class or in groups, discuss your results and conclusions. Then, as a group, try to agree on answers to these questions: What happened to the eggshell? What process took place at each stage of the experiment?

Reflect and Record In your notebook, describe what you learned from doing this "egg-speriment." Which part of the project was the most surprising? Why? When did you begin to understand what was happening to the egg? If you did the project again, what would you do differently? Why?

Test Preparation

Use these questions to prepare for standardized tests.

Study the equations. Then answer Questions 26–28.

Photosynthesis

$$6\,CO_2 + 6\,H_2O \xrightarrow{\text{light energy}} C_6H_{12}O_6 + 6\,O_2$$

Respiration

$$C_6H_{12}O_6 + 6\,O_2 \rightarrow 6\,CO_2 + 6\,H_2O + \text{energy}$$

26. What products are produced during photosynthesis?
A carbon dioxide and water
B light energy and carbon dioxide
C carbon dioxide and sugar
D sugar and oxygen

27. What raw materials are needed for respiration to occur?
F energy and water
G carbon dioxide, water, and energy
H sugar and oxygen
J sugar and carbon dioxide

28. Why are the words "light energy" written above the arrow in the photosynthesis equation?
A Light energy is necessary for the reaction to occur.
B Light energy is produced during the reaction.
C Oxygen can exist only in the presence of light.
D Sugar can exist only in the presence of light.

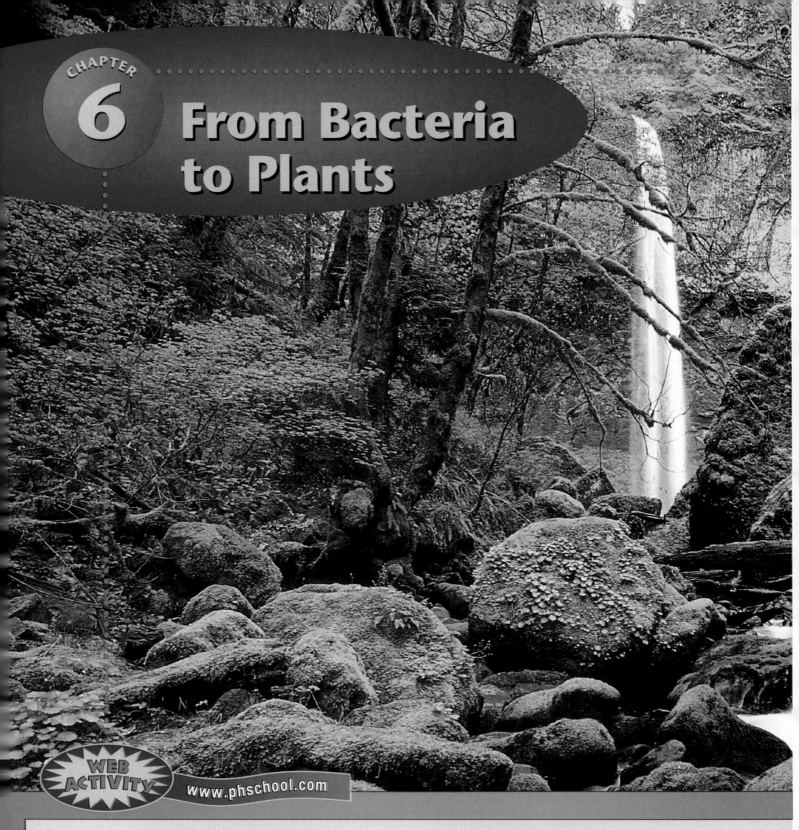

Cycle of a Lifetime

In a shady valley, tiny mosses cover the banks of a stream. Overhead, tall trees stretch their branches to the light. Can organisms that seem so different have anything in common? In this chapter, you'll find out. And in this chapter's project, you'll learn how some of these organisms reproduce. You'll grow some seeds, then care for the plants until they, in turn, produce their own seeds.

Your Goal To care for and observe a plant throughout its life cycle. To complete this project successfully you must

◆ grow a plant from a seed
◆ observe and describe key parts of your plant's life cycle, such as seed germination and pollination
◆ harvest and plant the seeds that your growing plant produces
◆ follow the safety guidelines in Appendix A

Get Started Observe the seeds that your teacher gives you. In a small group, discuss what conditions the seeds might need to grow. What should you look for after you plant the seeds? What kinds of measurements could you make? Will it help to make drawings? When you are ready, plant your seeds.

Check Your Progress You'll be working on this project as you study this chapter. To keep your project on track, look for Check Your Progress boxes at the following points.
Section 1 Review, page 189: Observe the developing seedlings.
Section 3 Review, page 203: Pollinate your flowers.
Section 4 Review, page 211: Collect the seeds from your plant and plant some of them.

Present Your Project At the end of the chapter (page 215), you'll present an exhibit showing the plant's life cycle.

Mosses carpet the rocks along this stream in Pennsylvania's Pocono Mountains.

TEKS

In addition to process TEKS, this chapter addresses these concept TEKS as they relate to the chapter's topic

(6.10) The student knows the relationship between structure and function in living systems. The student is expected to:
(A) differentiate between structure and function;
(B) determine that all organisms are composed of cells that carry on functions to sustain life; and
(C) identify how structure complements function at different levels of organization including organs, organ systems, organisms, and populations.

(6.11) The student knows that traits of species can change through generations and that the instructions for traits are contained in the genetic material of the organisms. The student is expected to:
(B) identify cells as structures containing genetic material.

(6.12) The student knows that the responses of organisms are caused by internal or external stimuli. The student is expected to:
(A) identify responses in organisms to internal stimuli such as hunger or thirst;
(B) identify responses in organisms to external stimuli such as the presence or absence of heat or light.

Classifying Living Things

Can You Organize a Junk Drawer?

1. Your teacher will give you some items that you might find in the junk drawer of a desk. Your job is to organize the items.

2. Examine the objects and decide on three groups into which you can sort them.

3. Place each object into one of the groups based on how the item's features match the characteristics of the group.

4. Compare your grouping system with those of your classmates.

Think It Over

Classifying Explain which grouping system seemed most useful.

GUIDE FOR READING

◆ What characteristics do scientists consider when they classify an organism?

◆ What are the six kingdoms into which all organisms are grouped?

Reading Tip Before you read, look at the list of the boldfaced vocabulary terms. As you read, write the meaning of each term in your own words.

Key Terms classification
• taxonomy
• binomial nomenclature
• genus • species

Suppose you had only ten minutes to run into a supermarket to get what you need—milk and tomatoes. In most supermarkets this would be easy. First, you'd go to the dairy aisle for the milk. Then you'd go to the produce aisle and find the tomatoes.

Now imagine shopping for these items in a market where the shelves are not organized. To find what you need, you'd have to search through shelves in which apples, boxes of cereal, cans of tuna, and many more items were all mixed together. You could be there for a long time!

Why Do Scientists Classify Organisms?

Just as shopping can be a problem in a disorganized store, learning about organisms could also be a problem without organization. Scientists have identified at least 1.7 million kinds of organisms on Earth. This number includes all forms of life, from bacteria to plants and animals. It is important for biologists to have these living things organized into groups. **Classification** is the process of grouping things based on their shared traits. Biologists use classification to organize living things into groups so that the organisms are easier to study.

◀ Vegetables organized by type

Figure 1 These animals belong to the genus *Felis*. (A) The species of the puma is *Felis concolor*. (B) The ocelot belongs to the species *Felis pardalis*. (C) The species name of the house cat is *Felis domesticus*. *Classifying* List one characteristic that distinguishes *Felis pardalis* from the other two species.

The scientific study of how living things are classified is called **taxonomy** (tak SAHN uh mee). Living things that are classified together have similar characteristics. Taxonomy is useful because after an organism is classified, a scientist knows a lot about the organism's structures and its relationships to other organisms. For example, crows are classified as birds. This classification lets you know that crows, like all birds, have wings, feathers, and beaks. In addition, you know that a crow shares more characteristics with other birds than it does with other kinds of animals, such as fishes or insects.

☑ *Checkpoint* What is classification?

The Classification System of Linnaeus

Modern taxonomy has its roots in a classification system developed in the 1750s by a Swedish scientist named Carolus Linnaeus. Linnaeus observed many organisms. He placed organisms in groups based on their observable features.

Linnaeus also used his observations to devise a naming system for organisms. In Linnaeus's naming system, called **binomial nomenclature** (by NOH mee ul NOH men clay chur), each organism is given a two-part name.

The first part of an organism's scientific name is its genus. A **genus** (JEE nus) (plural *genera*) is a classification grouping that contains similar, closely related organisms. For example, pumas, ocelots, and house cats are all classified in the genus *Felis*. Organisms that are classified in the genus *Felis* share features such as sharp, retractable claws and behaviors such as hunting.

The second part of an organism's scientific name identifies its species. A **species** (SPEE sheez) is a group of similar organisms that can mate and produce fertile offspring. A species name sets one species in a genus apart from the other species in the genus. The species name often describes a distinctive feature of an organism, such as where it lives or its color. For example, the species name of a housecat is *Felis domesticus*. The Latin word *domesticus* means "of the house" in Latin.

You don't have to understand Latin to know that you should avoid an organism named *Ursus horribilis*. *Ursus horribilis* is commonly known as a grizzly bear. The Latin word *ursus* means "bear" and *horribilis* means "horrible or feared."

A species name describes an organism like an adjective describes the noun it modifies. Some names describe a specific trait; others tell who discovered the organism. Other names tell you where the organism lives. Guess where you'd find the plant *Viola missouriensis*.

In Your Journal

Look up the meanings of these species names: *Musca domestica*, *Hirudo medicinalis*, and *Cornus florida*. Then find some English words derived from the Latin terms.

Classification Today

Like Linnaeus, biologists today classify organisms on the basis of observable characteristics. **When biologists classify an organism, they look at its structure. They also look at the way it develops, or changes, during its life. Biologists also examine the organism's DNA.** As you learned in Chapter 4, DNA is a molecule in cells that determines an organism's inherited characteristics. The more similar two organisms are in their DNA and other characteristics, the more closely they are probably related.

The Seven Levels of Classification Today's classification system uses several levels to classify organisms. Organisms are grouped into seven major levels by shared characteristics. The more characteristics that organisms have in common, the more classification levels they share.

The broadest level of classification is a kingdom. Within each kingdom, there are more specific levels called phyla (FY luh) (singular *phylum*). Within each phylum are levels called classes. Each class is divided into orders. Each order contains families, and each family contains at least one genus. Finally, within a genus, there are species.

To help you understand a classification system made up of several levels, imagine a room filled with everybody in your state. First, the people who live in your *town* raise their hands. Next, those people who live in your *neighborhood* raise their hands. Then those who live on your *street* raise their hands. Finally, those people who live in your *house* raise their hands. Each time, fewer people raise their hands. But you would be in all of the groups.

In the classification system just described, the most general level is the state. The most specific level is the house. Similarly, in the classification of organisms, the most general level is the kingdom. The most specific level is the species.

Classifying an Owl Take a close look at Figure 2 to see how the levels of classification apply to the great horned owl, a member of the animal kingdom. Look at the top row of the figure. As you can see, a wide variety of organisms also belong to the animal kingdom. Now, look at the other levels. Notice that as you move down the levels, there are fewer kinds of organisms in each group. More importantly, the organisms in each level share more characteristics. For example, the class Aves includes all birds, while the order Strigiformes includes only owls. Different species of owl have more in common with each other than with other birds.

☑ *Checkpoint* *List the seven major levels of classification from the broadest to the most specific.*

Kingdom Animalia

Phylum Chordata

Class Aves

Order Strigiformes

Family Strigidae

Genus *Bubo*

Species *Bubo virginianus*

Figure 2 Scientists use seven levels to classify organisms such as the great horned owl. Notice that, as you move down the levels, the number of organisms decreases. The organisms at lower levels share more characteristics.
Interpreting Diagrams How many levels do a robin and the great horned owl share?

Figure 3 Heat-loving archaebacteria thrive in this hot spring in Yellowstone National Park.

Six Kingdoms

Today, scientists classify all organisms into six kingdoms. **The six kingdoms of organisms are archaebacteria, eubacteria, protists, fungi, plants, and animals.** An organism is classified into a particular kingdom based on specific characteristics. They include the type of cells found in the organism, whether the organism is unicellular or multicellular, and how the organism obtains food. While the organisms within a kingdom vary greatly, members of a kingdom share those characteristics.

Archaebacteria In 1983, scientists took a water sample from a spot deep in the Pacific Ocean where hot gases and molten rock boiled into the ocean from Earth's interior. To their surprise, they discovered unicellular organisms in the water sample. Today, scientists classify these tiny organisms in a kingdom called archaebacteria (ahr kee bak TEER ee uh).

Archaebacteria are prokaryotes. Recall that prokaryotes are organisms whose cells lack a nucleus. Archaebacteria can be either autotrophic or heterotrophic.

Eubacteria What do the bacteria that produce yogurt have in common with the bacteria that give you strep throat? They both belong to the kingdom known as eubacteria (yoo bac TEER ee uh). Like archaebacteria, eubacteria are unicellular prokaryotes. And like archaebacteria, some eubacteria are autotrophs while others are heterotrophs. Eubacteria are classified in their own kingdom, however, because their chemical makeup is different from that of archaebacteria.

Figure 4 Both *Staphylococcus aureus* **(A)** and *Escherichia coli* **(B)** are eubacteria. *Staphylococcus aureus* bacteria make up about 30 percent of the bacteria on your skin. *Escherichia coli* bacteria are found in your digestive tract.

Protists Protists are sometimes called the "odds and ends" kingdom because the members of this kingdom are so different from one another. Some protists are unicellular and some are multicellular. Some are heterotrophs and some are autotrophs. However, all protists are eukaryotes, which are organisms whose cells contain nuclei.

Fungi Fungi include organisms such as yeasts, mushrooms, and molds. Like protists, fungi are eukaryotes. Most fungi are many-celled organisms, but a few, such as yeasts, are unicellular. Fungi are found almost everywhere on land, but only a few live in water. All fungi are heterotrophs. Most fungi feed on dead or decaying organisms.

Plants Dandelions on a lawn, mosses in a forest, and tomatoes in a garden are some familiar kinds of plants. All plants are multicellular eukaryotes. In addition, plants are autotrophs. Some plants produce flowers, while other plants do not.

Animals A dog, a flea on the dog's ear, and a rabbit the dog chases are all animals. Animals are multicellular eukaryotes that are heterotrophs. At some point in their lives, most animals can move from one place to another. You will learn more about animals in Chapter 7.

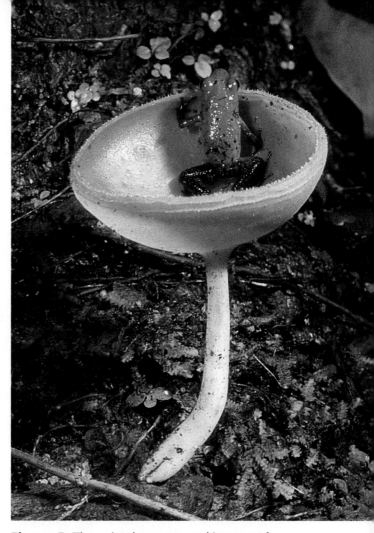

Figure 5 The animal you see peeking out of this cuplike fungus is a poison arrow frog. These organisms live in the forests of Central America. *Interpreting Photographs Which organisms in the photograph are heterotrophs?*

Section 1 Review

1. What is taxonomy? What characteristics do taxonomists use to classify organisms?
2. List the six kingdoms into which all organisms are classified.
3. Explain how organisms are named.
4. **Thinking Critically Classifying** In a rain forest, you see an unfamiliar green organism. As you watch, an ant walks onto one of its cuplike leaves. The leaf closes and traps the ant. Do you have enough information to classify this organism into a kingdom? Why or why not?

Check Your Progress

CHAPTER PROJECT

If your seeds haven't germinated yet, they soon will. For the next few days keep a close watch on your young plants to see how they grow. How do they change in height? How do the leaves appear and grow? (*Hint:* Consider using drawings or photographs as part of your record keeping.)

SECTION 2 Bacteria

DISCOVER .... ACTIVITY....

How Fast Do Bacteria Multiply?

1. Your teacher will give you some beans and paper cups. Number the cups 1 through 8. Each bean will represent a bacterial cell.

2. Put one bean into cup 1 to represent the first generation of bacteria. Approximately every 20 minutes, a bacterial cell reproduces by dividing into two cells. Put two beans into cup 2 to represent the second generation of bacteria.

3. Calculate how many bacterial cells there would be in the third generation if each cell in cup 2 divided into two cells. Place the correct number of beans in cup 3.

4. Repeat Step 3 for each of the remaining cups. All the cups should now contain beans. How many cells would be in the eighth generation? How much time would have elapsed since the first generation?

Think It Over

Inferring Based on this activity, explain why the number of bacteria can increase rapidly in a short time.

GUIDE FOR READING

◆ How are the cells of bacteria different from those of all other organisms?

◆ Why are bacteria important to you?

Reading Tip Before you read, write a paragraph stating what you know about bacteria. As you read, add information to your paragraph.

Key Terms flagellum
• binary fission • conjugation
• endospore • decomposer

You may not know it, but seconds after your birth, tiny organisms invaded your body. Today millions of these unicellular organisms coat your skin. They swarm inside your nose, throat, and mouth. In fact, there are more of these organisms living in your mouth than there are people living on Earth. They are found nearly everywhere—in soil, rocks, volcanoes, Arctic ice, and all living things. These organisms are bacteria.

The Bacterial Cell

As you read in Chapter 4, the cells of bacteria differ from the cells of other organisms in important ways. **Bacteria are prokaryotes. The genetic material in their cells is not contained in a nucleus.** In addition to lacking a nucleus, the cells of prokaryotes lack many other structures, such as mitochondria, that are found in the cells of eukaryotes.

Cell Shape The cells of bacteria have three basic shapes: spherical, rodlike, or spiral. The shape of a bacterial cell helps scientists identify the bacterium. The chemical makeup of the bacterium's outermost structure, its rigid cell wall, determines the cell's shape.

◄ Bacteria on the surface of a human tooth

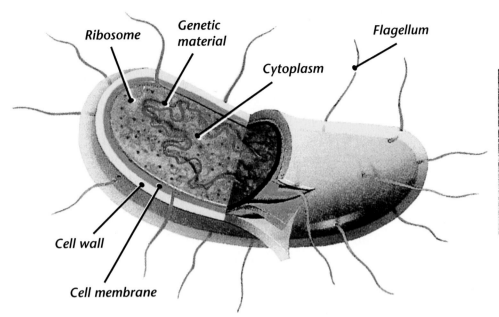

Ribosome
Genetic material
Cytoplasm
Flagellum
Cell wall
Cell membrane

Figure 6 The diagram shows the structures found in a typical bacterial cell. *Interpreting Photographs Which structures can you locate in the photograph of the bacterium? What roles do these structures play?*

Cell Structures and Functions Inside the cell wall is the cell membrane, which controls the movement of materials into and out of the cell. In the gel-like material of the cytoplasm are ribosomes, the sites where proteins are made. The genetic material, which looks like a thick, tangled string, is also located in the cytoplasm. If the genetic material were untangled, it would be circular.

You can see the cell wall, ribosomes, and genetic material of a bacterial cell in Figure 6. You also see **flagella** (fluh JEL uh) (singular *flagellum*), which extend from the cell membrane and pass out through the cell wall. A bacterial cell may have one or many flagella. The long, whiplike structure of a flagellum enables it to perform its function of moving the bacterial cell from one place to another. A flagellum moves the cell by spinning in place like a propeller.

Checkpoint List four structures found in bacterial cells.

Energy Needs

Like all organisms, bacteria must obtain food. Some bacteria are autotrophs that capture and use the sun's energy to make their own food, much as plants do. Other bacteria, such as those that live deep in the ocean, are autotrophs that use the energy from chemical substances in their environment to make their food. Still other bacteria are heterotrophs that consume autotrophs or other heterotrophs as food.

Bacteria use their food to supply the energy they need. Most bacteria use oxygen to break down food and release its energy. However, some bacteria do not need oxygen for respiration. In fact, they die if oxygen is present in their surroundings.

Bacteria for Breakfast

In this activity, you will observe helpful bacteria in a common food.

1. Put on your apron. Add water to plain yogurt to make a thin mixture.

2. 🔬 With a plastic dropper, place a drop of the mixture on a glass slide.

3. Use another plastic dropper to add one drop of methylene blue dye to the slide. **CAUTION:** *This dye can stain your skin.*

4. Put a coverslip on the slide.

5. Observe the slide under both the low and high power lenses of a microscope.

6. Dispose of the materials as your teacher instructs.

Observing Draw a diagram of what you see under high power. Label any cell structures that you see.

Reproduction

In Figure 7A you see bacteria reproducing by **binary fission,** a process in which one cell divides to form two identical cells. Binary fission is a form of asexual reproduction. In binary fission, the cell first duplicates its genetic material. Then it divides into two cells that contain the same genetic material.

Some bacteria, such as those in Figure 7B, sometimes undergo a form of sexual reproduction called conjugation. During **conjugation** (kahn juh GAY shun), one cell transfers some of its genetic material into another cell through a thread-like bridge between the cells. After the transfer, the cells separate. These bacteria can then reproduce by binary fission. Conjugation results in bacteria that differ genetically from their parents.

☑ *Checkpoint* **What is conjugation?**

Survival Needs

Sometimes conditions in the environment become unfavorable for the growth of bacteria. For example, food sources can disappear or wastes can build up. Some bacteria respond to an unfavorable environment by forming endospores that survive these conditions. An **endospore** is a small, thick-walled, resting cell that forms inside a bacterial cell. It contains the cell's genetic material and some of the gel-like material in its cytoplasm. Endospores can survive for many years because they resist freezing, heating, and drying. When conditions are suitable, they can open and grow again.

Figure 7 Bacteria reproduce either by binary fission (**A**) or conjugation (**B**). In binary fission, a cell divides to form two new cells. In conjugation, one bacterium transfers genetic material into another.

Figure 8 Scientists use bacteria such as these *Ochrobactrum anthropi* to help clean up oil spills. *Applying Concepts How do bacteria clean up spilled oil?*

Bacteria and the Living World

When you think about bacteria, you might think first of strep throat or ear infections. The bacteria that cause these diseases are eubacteria. **Although some bacteria do cause diseases, most bacteria interact with you and other organisms in harmless or positive ways.**

Bacteria play positive roles in fuel and food production as well as in environmental recycling and cleanup. For example, archaebacteria that died millions of years ago produced methane gas. Today, this methane gas is the major component in about 20 percent of Earth's deposits of natural gas, a fuel that heats many homes. Some eubacteria that grow in milk produce dairy products such as buttermilk, yogurt, and cheeses.

Some bacteria living in Earth's soil are **decomposers,** organisms that break down large molecules in dead organisms into smaller molecules. Decomposers recycle Earth's matter by returning basic chemicals to the environment for other organisms to reuse. Other recycling bacteria live in the roots of plants such as peanuts and soybeans. They use the nitrogen in air to form compounds the plants need to grow. Finally, some bacteria help clean up oil spills on land and water. These bacteria convert the dangerous chemicals in oil into harmless substances.

Section 2 Review

1. How is a bacterial cell different from the cells of other kinds of organisms?
2. List four ways in which bacteria are important to you.
3. Describe three ways that bacteria may obtain food.
4. **Thinking Critically Comparing and Contrasting** How are binary fission and conjugation alike? How do they differ?

Science at Home

Helpful Bacteria With a family member, look around your kitchen for foods that are made using bacteria. Read the labels on the foods to see if the role of bacteria in the food's production is mentioned. Discuss with your family member the helpful roles that bacteria play in people's lives.

Do Disinfectants Work?

When your family goes shopping, you may buy disinfectants that kill micro-organisms such as bacteria. You will compare the effects of two disinfectants.

Problem

How well do disinfectants control the growth of bacteria?

Skills Focus

observing, inferring, drawing conclusions

Materials

clock
2 plastic droppers
2 household disinfectants
3 plastic petri dishes with sterile nutrient agar
3 sealable plastic bags
computer (optional)

wax pencil
transparent tape

Procedure

1. With a computer or a pencil and paper, make a data chart to organize your observations.

2. Work with a partner. Obtain 3 petri dishes containing sterile agar. Without opening them, use a wax pencil to label the bottoms "A," "B," and "C." Write your initials beside each letter.

3. Wash your hands thoroughly with soap, then run a fingertip across the surface of your worktable. Your partner should hold open the cover of petri dish A while you run that fingertip gently across the agar in a zig-zag motion. Close the dish immediately.

4. Repeat Step 3 for dishes B and C.

5. Use a plastic dropper to transfer 2 drops of one disinfectant to the center of petri dish A. Open the cover just long enough to add the disinfectant to the dish. Close the cover immediately. Record the name of the disinfectant in your data chart. **CAUTION:** *Do not inhale vapors from the disinfectant.*

6. Repeat Step 5 for dish B but add 2 drops of the second disinfectant. **CAUTION:** *Do not mix any disinfectants together.*

7. Do not add any disinfectant to dish C.

8. Tape down the covers of all 3 petri dishes so that they will remain tightly closed. Then carefully slide each petri dish into a plastic bag. Seal the bags and tape them closed. Allow the 3 dishes to sit upright on your work surface for at least 5 minutes. **CAUTION:** *Do not open the bags or petri dishes again.* Wash your hands with soap and water.

9. As directed by your teacher, store the petri dishes in a warm, dark place where they can remain for at least 3 days. Remove them only to make a brief examination each day.

DATA CHART

Petri Dish	Disinfectant	Day 1	Day 2	Day 3
A				
B				
C				

10. After one day, observe the contents of each dish without removing the bags or covers. Estimate the percentage of the agar surface that shows any changes. Record your observations. Return the dishes to their storage place when you have finished observing. Wash your hands with soap.

11. Repeat Step 10 after the second day and again after the third day.

12. After you and your partner have made your last observations, return the petri dishes to your teacher unopened.

Analyze and Conclude

1. Use the information in your data chart to examine and evaluate your observations. How did the appearance of dish C change during the lab?

2. How did the appearance of dishes A and B compare with dish C? Explain any similarities or differences.

3. How did the appearance of dishes A and B compare with each other? How can you account for any differences?

4. Why was it important to set aside one petri dish that did not contain any disinfectant?

5. **Apply** Based on the results of this lab, what recommendation would you make to your family about the use of disinfectants? Where in the house do you think these products would be needed most?

Design an Experiment

Go to a store and look at soap products that claim to be "antibacterial" soaps. How do their ingredients differ from other soaps? How do their prices compare? Design an experiment to test how well these products control the growth of bacteria.

DISCOVER ....ACTIVITY....

What Lives in a Drop of Water?

1. Use a plastic dropper to place a drop of pond water on a microscope slide.
2. Put the slide under your microscope's low-power lens. Focus on the objects you see.
3. Find at least three different objects that you think might be organisms. Observe them for a few minutes.
4. Draw the three organisms in your notebook. Below each sketch, describe the movements or behaviors of the organism. Work with your teacher to devise a plan for disposing of the materials. Wash your hands thoroughly when you have finished.

Think It Over

Observing What characteristics did you observe that made you think that each organism was alive?

GUIDE FOR READING

◆ What are the characteristics of animal-like, plantlike, and fungus-like protists?

◆ What characteristics do fungi share?

Reading Tip Before you read, preview the headings. Record them in outline form, leaving space for writing notes as you read.

Key Terms protozoan
• pseudopod • cilia • parasite
• host • algae • spore
• hyphae • budding

Look at the objects in Figure 9. What do they look like? Jewels? Crystal ornaments? You might be surprised to learn that these beautiful structures are the walls of unicellular protists called diatoms. Believe it or not, diatoms provide food for many organisms that live in the ocean.

The Protist Kingdom

Diatoms are only one type of organism classified in the protist kingdom. The protist kingdom is sometimes referred to as the "junk drawer" kingdom. A "junk drawer" is filled with odds and ends, such as pencils, ticket stubs, and postcards. The protist kingdom is filled with organisms that don't fit easily into other kingdoms. However, these organisms do share some characteristics. They are all eukaryotes, or organisms that have cells with nuclei. In addition, almost all protists live in moist areas.

Despite these common characteristics, the word that best describes the protist kingdom is *diversity*. For example, many protists are unicellular organisms. But some protists are multicellular. In fact, the protists known as giant kelps can be over 100 meters long. Protists also vary in how they obtain food.

Figure 9 These delicate-looking diatoms are classified in the protist kingdom.

Some protists are heterotrophs, some are autotrophs, and others are both. Some protists cannot move, while others zoom around in their surroundings.

Because protists vary greatly, scientists have proposed different ways of grouping these organisms. One useful way of grouping protists is to divide them into three categories: animal-like protists, plantlike protists, and fungus-like protists.

☑ *Checkpoint* *What characteristics do all protists share?*

Animal-like Protists

What image pops into your head when you think of an animal? A tiger chasing prey? A snake slithering onto a rock? Most people associate animals with movement. **Like animals, animal-like protists have structures that enable them to move around. And these organisms, like animals, are heterotrophs.** Unlike animals, however, animal-like protists, which are also called **protozoans** (proh tuh ZOH unz), are unicellular.

When an organism moves, it is usually responding to a stimulus. Protozoans move in response to a variety of external stimuli. For example, protozoans move toward food, such as bacteria. Protozoans may move away from harmful chemicals. Some protozoans respond to the stimulus of light by moving toward it. Others move away from light.

Protozoans With Pseudopods One group of protozoans use structures called pseudopods (SOO doh pahdz) to move and obtain food. **Pseudopods** are temporary bulges of the cell membrane. The cytoplasm flows into the bulge and the rest of the organism follows. Amebas are protozoans that form pseudopods. Amebas use pseudopods to respond to external stimuli. Amebas move away from bright light and toward food.

Figure 10 The protist kingdom includes animal-like, plantlike, and fungus-like organisms. **(A)** These shells contained unicellular, animal-like protists called foraminifera. **(B)** This red alga is a multicellular, plantlike protist that lives on ocean floors. **(C)** This yellow slime mold is a fungus-like protist.
Comparing and Contrasting In what way are animal-like protists similar to animals? How do they differ?

Protozoans With Cilia Members of a second group of protozoans have structures called cilia that they use to move and obtain food. **Cilia** (SIL ee uh) are hairlike projections from cells that move with a wavelike pattern. Cilia move an organism by acting something like tiny oars. Their movement also sweeps food into the organism. One type of protozoan with cilia is a paramecium. Look at *Exploring Protozoans* to compare the structures of an ameba and a paramecium and to learn about the functions of each structure. Notice that the cell of a paramecium has a greater variety of structures than that of an ameba.

Protozoans With Flagella Members of a third group of protozoans use flagella to move. These organisms often live inside the bodies of other organisms. For example, protozoans with flagella

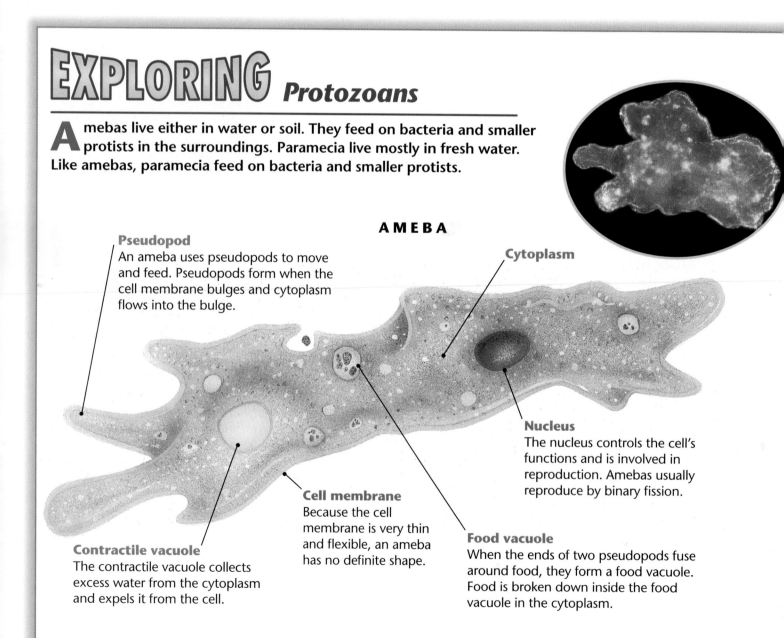

EXPLORING *Protozoans*

Amebas live either in water or soil. They feed on bacteria and smaller protists in the surroundings. Paramecia live mostly in fresh water. Like amebas, paramecia feed on bacteria and smaller protists.

AMEBA

Pseudopod
An ameba uses pseudopods to move and feed. Pseudopods form when the cell membrane bulges and cytoplasm flows into the bulge.

Cytoplasm

Nucleus
The nucleus controls the cell's functions and is involved in reproduction. Amebas usually reproduce by binary fission.

Cell membrane
Because the cell membrane is very thin and flexible, an ameba has no definite shape.

Contractile vacuole
The contractile vacuole collects excess water from the cytoplasm and expels it from the cell.

Food vacuole
When the ends of two pseudopods fuse around food, they form a food vacuole. Food is broken down inside the food vacuole in the cytoplasm.

live in the intestines of termites. These protozoans digest the wood that the termites eat, producing sugars for themselves and for the termites.

Other Protozoans A fourth group of protozoans, called sporozoans, are characterized more by the way they live than by the way they move. Sporozoans are **parasites,** organisms that live on or in another organism, the **host,** and harm that organism. Sporozoans feed on the cells and body fluids of their hosts. Some sporozoans use flagella to move, and others depend on hosts for transport. One sporozoan even slides from place to place on a layer of slime that it produces. A sporozoan called *Plasmodium* causes the disease malaria in people.

☑ *Checkpoint* *What is the function of a pseudopod?*

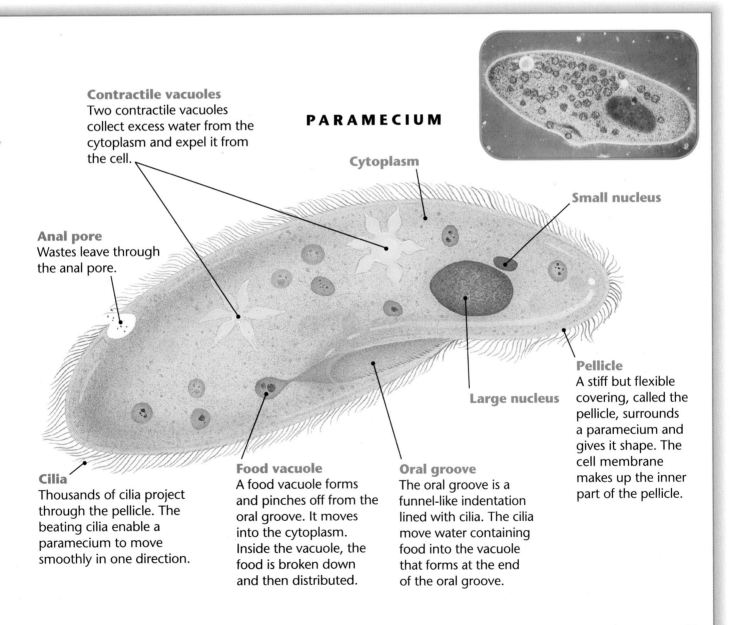

PARAMECIUM

Contractile vacuoles
Two contractile vacuoles collect excess water from the cytoplasm and expel it from the cell.

Cytoplasm

Small nucleus

Anal pore
Wastes leave through the anal pore.

Pellicle
A stiff but flexible covering, called the pellicle, surrounds a paramecium and gives it shape. The cell membrane makes up the inner part of the pellicle.

Large nucleus

Cilia
Thousands of cilia project through the pellicle. The beating cilia enable a paramecium to move smoothly in one direction.

Food vacuole
A food vacuole forms and pinches off from the oral groove. It moves into the cytoplasm. Inside the vacuole, the food is broken down and then distributed.

Oral groove
The oral groove is a funnel-like indentation lined with cilia. The cilia move water containing food into the vacuole that forms at the end of the oral groove.

Figure 11 Euglenas are unicellular algae that live in fresh water. In sunlight, euglenas make their own food. Without sunlight, they obtain food from their environment.

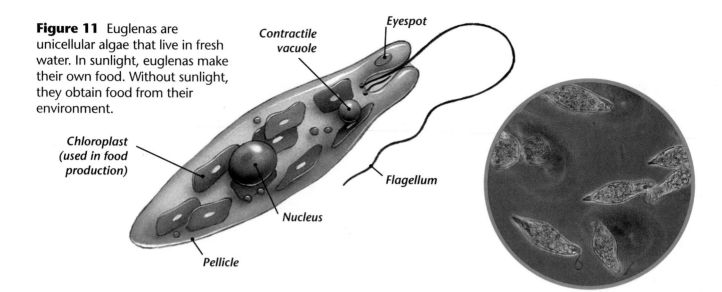

Eyespot

Contractile vacuole

Chloroplast (used in food production)

Flagellum

Nucleus

Pellicle

Feeding Paramecia

ACTIVITY

In this activity you will feed *Chlorella*, a plantlike protist, to paramecia.

1. Use a plastic dropper to place one drop of paramecium culture on a micrscope slide. Add some cotton fibers to slow down the paramecia.

2. Use the microscope's low-power objective to find some paramecia.

3. Add one drop of *Chlorella* to the paramecium culture on your slide.

4. Switch to high power and locate a paramecium. Observe what happens. Then wash your hands.

Inferring What evidence do you have that paramecia are heterotrophs? That *Chlorella* are autotrophs?

Plantlike Protists

If you've ever seen seaweed at a beach, then you are familiar with a type of plantlike protist. Plantlike protists, which are commonly called **algae** (AL jee), are even more varied than animal-like protists. **The one characteristic that all algae share is that, like plants, they are autotrophs.**

Some algae live in the soil, others live on the barks of trees, and still others live in fresh water or salt water. Algae that live on the surface of ponds, lakes, and oceans are an important food source for other organisms in the water. In addition, most of the oxygen in Earth's atmosphere is made by these algae.

Algae range greatly in size. Some algae, such as diatoms and euglenas, are unicellular. Recall from Chapter 4 that a unicellular organism carries out all the functions necessary for life. Unlike other algae, euglenas like the ones shown in Figure 11 can be heterotrophs under certain conditions. Euglenas are green and use flagella to move. In contrast, diatoms move on slime that oozes out of slits in their cell walls.

Other algae are groups of unicellular organisms that live together in colonies. Unlike true multicellular organisms, an algae colony contains few or no cells that are specialized to perform specific functions. Like unicellular organisms, most cells in a colony carry out all the life processes.

Still other algae, such as seaweeds, are multicellular organisms. Multicellular algae contain cells that are specialized to perform specific tasks. For example, giant kelps, which are a kind of seaweed, have many plantlike tissues and organs. Holdfasts anchor the alga to rocks. Stalks support the leaflike blades. Brown algae also have gas-filled sacs called bladders that allow the algae to float upright in the water.

Fungus-like Protists

A third group of protists are the fungus-like protists. **Fungus-like protists are heterotrophs, have cell walls, and use spores to reproduce.** A **spore** is a tiny cell that is able to grow into a new organism. All fungus-like protists are able to move at some point in their lives. In Figure 12, you can see a type of fungus-like protist called a water mold.

☑ *Checkpoint* *What is a spore?*

The Fungi Kingdom

Like the fungus-like protists, fungi use spores to reproduce. The cricket-killing fungus in Figure 13 began as a spore that fell on a living cricket. Tiny threads from the spore began to grow into the cricket's body. The threads released chemicals that dissolved the cricket's tissue. Then some threads thickened, forming the stalks with knobs at their ends that grew out of the cricket's body. When the knobs break open, they will release thousands of spores, which the wind may carry to new victims.

Although you may not have heard of a cricket-killing fungus before, you are probably familiar with other kinds of fungi. For example, the molds that grow on stale bread or decaying fruit are all fungi. The mushrooms that sprout in forests or yards are fungi. Unicellular yeasts that make bread rise are also fungi.

Most fungi share three important characteristics: They are eukaryotes, use spores to reproduce, and are heterotrophs that feed in a similar way. In addition, fungi need moist, warm places in which to grow. They thrive on moist foods, damp tree bark, lawns coated with dew, damp forest floors, and even wet bathroom tiles.

Figure 12 The threadlike water mold is a protozoan parasite that grows on fish. The water mold eventually kills the fish. *Applying Concepts* *What is a parasite?*

Figure 13 A bush cricket has been attacked by a killer fungus.

Cell Structure of Fungi

Yeasts are unicellular fungi, but other fungi are multicellular. The cells of multicellular fungi are arranged in structures called hyphae. **Hyphae** (HY fee) (singular *hypha*) are branching, thread-like tubes that make up the bodies of multicellular fungi.

The appearance of a fungus depends on how its hyphae are arranged. In some fungi, such as fuzzy-looking molds, the hyphae are loosely tangled. In other fungi, hyphae are packed tightly together. For example, the stalks and caps of the mushrooms in Figure 14 are made of hyphae packed so tightly that they appear solid. Underground, however, the hyphae of these mushrooms form a loose, threadlike maze.

How Do Fungi Obtain Food?

Some fungi feed on the remains of dead organisms. Other fungi are parasites that break down the chemicals in living organisms. For example, athlete's foot is a disease caused by a fungus that feeds on chemicals in a person's skin.

Fungi absorb food through hyphae that grow into the food source. First, the fungus grows hyphae into a food source. Then digestive chemicals ooze from the hyphae into the food. The chemicals break down the food into small molecules that the hyphae can absorb. Imagine yourself sinking your fingers into a chocolate cake and dripping digestive chemicals out of your fingertips. Then imagine your fingers absorbing the digested particles of the cake. That's how a fungus feeds.

Hyphae are a good example of how structure is related to function in organisms. The long, threadlike structure of a fungus's hyphae provide a large surface area for absorbing food. The larger the surface area, the greater the amount of food that can be absorbed.

Cap

Gills

Stalk

Hyphae

Underground hyphae

Figure 14 The hyphae in the stalk and cap of a mushroom are packed tightly to form very firm structures. Underground hyphae, on the other hand, are arranged loosely. *Inferring What function do the underground hyphae perform?*

Figure 15 Budding is a form of asexual reproduction that occurs in yeast. The small yeast cell that grows from the body of a parent cell is identical to the parent.

Reproduction in Fungi

Like it or not, fungi are everywhere. The way they reproduce guarantees that they survive and spread. Fungi usually reproduce by means of spores that are lightweight and have protective coverings. They travel easily through air or water to new sites.

Asexual Reproduction Most fungi reproduce both asexually and sexually. When there is adequate moisture and food, most fungi reproduce asexually by growing spore-producing reproductive hyphae. Fungi produce thousands of spores. However, only a few of them fall where conditions are right for them to grow into new organisms.

Unicellular yeast cells undergo a form of asexual reproduction called **budding.** In budding, no spores are produced. Instead, a small yeast cell grows from the body of a large parent cell in a way that might remind you of a bud forming on a tree branch. The new cell then breaks away and lives on its own.

Sexual Reproduction When growing conditions become unfavorable, fungi may reproduce sexually. In sexual reproduction, the hyphae of two fungi grow together. Then a new spore-producing structure grows from the joined hyphae. These spores develop into fungi that have a combination of the genetic material of both parents.

Section 3 Review

1. List the characteristics of animal-like protists, plantlike protists, and fungus-like protists.
2. List three characteristics that fungi share.
3. Explain how the threadlike structure of a fungus's hyphae enables the fungus to obtain a large amount of food.
4. How do fungi reproduce?
5. **Thinking Critically Classifying** Explain why mushrooms are classified as fungi rather than plants.

Check Your Progress

CHAPTER PROJECT

Your plants should now have, or will soon have, flowers. Make a diagram of the flower's structure. When the flowers open, you'll have to pollinate them. This work is usually done by insects or birds. After pollination, watch how the flower changes. (*Hint:* Pollination is explained on pages 209–210. Discuss with your teacher and classmates how to pollinate the flowers.)

SECTION 4 The Plant Kingdom

What Do Leaves Reveal About Plants?

1. Your teacher will give you two leaves from plants that grow in two very different environments: a desert and an area with average rainfall.

2. Carefully observe the color, size, shape, and texture of the leaves. Touch the surfaces of each leaf. Examine each leaf with a hand lens. Record your observations in your notebook.

3. When you have finished, wash your hands thoroughly with soap and water.

Think It Over

Inferring Use your observations to determine which plant lives in the desert and which does not. Give at least one reason to support your inference.

GUIDE FOR READING

◆ What are the characteristics of plants?

◆ What is the structure of a seed?

◆ How do plants respond to their surroundings?

Reading Tip Before you read, write at least three characteristics of plants that you already know. As you read, add to your list.

Key Terms vascular tissue
• stomata • fertilization
• zygote • embryo
• seed • cotyledon
• pollen • ovule
• flower • stamen
• pistil • fruit
• tropism
• hormone

Imagine a forest where a thick mat of fungi, mosses, and ferns carpets the floor. Because there is no bare soil, seedlings start their lives on fallen logs. Ferns hang like curtains from the limbs of giant hemlock trees. Douglas fir trees grow taller than 20-story buildings. Other plants with strange names—vanilla leaf, self-heal, and licorice fern—also grow in the forest.

Such a forest exists on the western slopes of the Olympic Mountains in the state of Washington. Native Americans named the forest Hoh, which means "fast white water," after a river there. In parts of the forest, over 300 centimeters of rain fall each year. Many plants thrive in this moist environment.

The Hoh rain forest ▶

204

Cell with chloroplasts

Vascular tissue

Stoma

Figure 16 The structure of a leaf helps the plant to perform photosynthesis. *Inferring* What kind of substance does vascular tissue carry away from a leaf to cells throughout the plant?

What Is a Plant?

Members of the plant kingdom share important characteristics. **Plants are multicellular eukaryotes that produce their food through photosynthesis. In addition, many plants have vascular tissue, leaves, roots, and stems.**

Vascular Tissue Most plants have vascular tissue to transport needed materials to their cells. **Vascular tissue** is an internal system of tubelike structures that carry water, minerals, and food. Materials move quickly through vascular tissue. In addition, vascular tissue supports the bodies of plants, enabling them to grow large. Plants with vascular tissue are called vascular plants.

Nonvascular plants, such as mosses, do not have vascular tissue. Nonvascular plants can only pass materials from one cell to the next. Therefore, materials do not travel very far or very quickly. Also, nonvascular plants lack the support that vascular tissue provides. Without vascular tissue, these plants cannot grow very wide or tall. *Exploring Plant Groups* on the next two pages shows examples of nonvascular and vascular plants.

Leaves In vascular plants, leaves are organs that carry out photosynthesis. Nonvascular plants, on the other hand, have leaflike structures where photosynthesis occurs. The structure of a leaf is ideal for photosynthesis. For example, photosynthesis takes place in chloroplasts. Notice in Figure 16 that the cells with the most chloroplasts are near the leaf's upper surface, where they are exposed to the sun. Vascular tissue carries the water needed for photosynthesis to the leaf. Plants also need carbon dioxide for photosynthesis. Carbon dioxide enters a leaf through tiny pores called **stomata** (STOH muh tuh) (singular *stoma*), which control the movement of gases into and out of the leaf. When stomata are open, carbon dioxide enters the leaf while oxygen and water vapor move out.

TRY THIS

What Stomata?

In this activity, you will use a microscope to observe stomata in leaf tissue.

1. Carefully break a lettuce leaf so that a thin, transparent layer on the underside separates from the rest of the leaf.

2. Cut a small section of this transparent layer and put it on a slide. Add one or two drops of water and add a coverslip.

3. Find and observe some stomata under low power and then high power.

4. Count the number of stomata that you see under high power. Compare that number to the number observed by other students.

Observing A range is the lowest number and highest number of items in a sample. What was the lowest number of stomata counted? The highest number?

EXPLORING *Plant Groups*

Plants can be classified according to the presence or absence of vascular tissue and how they reproduce.

NONVASCULAR PLANTS

Plants in this group lack vascular tissue and use spores for reproduction. These plants do not have true roots, stems or leaves. Nonvascular plants are low-growing plants that live in moist areas.

▲ Mosses

This is a closeup view of a moss. The spores with which the moss reproduces are produced in a capsule at the top of the stalklike structures.

Liverworts ▲

Liverworts, such as the one shown here, are nonvascular plants. They are named for the shape of the plant's body, which looks somewhat like a human liver.

VASCULAR PLANTS: SEEDLESS

In addition to vascular tissue, these plants have roots, stems, and leaves. These plants reproduce by means of spores and must live in moist areas.

▲ Club mosses

Because club mosses have vascular tissue, they are not really mosses. This club moss looks something like a small pine tree.

▲ Ferns

Ferns like this one have underground roots and stems. The fern's leaves are called fronds.

VASCULAR PLANTS: SEEDS

These plants have vascular tissues and produce seeds. Seed plants have roots, stems, and leaves. There are two kinds of seed plants: gymnosperms and angiosperms. The seeds of gymnosperms are "naked"; that is, they do not develop within any protective covering. Angiosperms are flowering plants. They produce seeds in structures that develop into fruits.

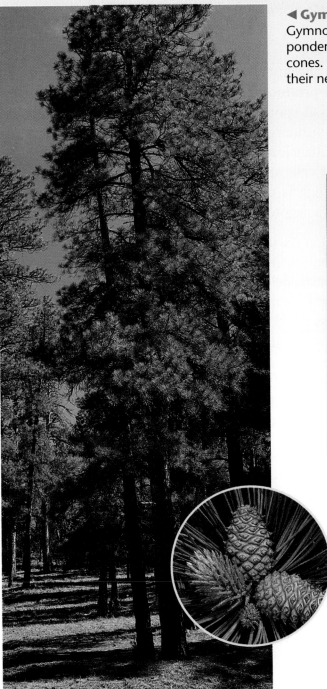

◀ Gymnosperms

Gymnosperms include conifers, such as this ponderosa pine. Conifers produce seeds in cones. Most conifers are evergreens that keep their needles year-round.

▲ Angiosperms

Grasses and apple trees are both angiosperms. Like all angiosperms, grasses produce seeds that are enclosed in fruits. Apple trees produce flowers in the spring. The seeds develop inside apples, which are fruits.

The In-Seed Story

1. Your teacher **ACTIVITY** will give you a hand lens and two different seeds that have been soaked in water.

2. Carefully observe the outside of each seed. Draw what you see.

3. Gently remove the coverings of the seeds. Then carefully separate the parts of each seed. Use a hand lens to examine the inside of each seed. Draw what you see.

Observing Based on your observations and the diagrams below, label the parts of each seed. Then describe the function of each part next to its label.

Roots and Stems Vascular plants have roots and stems. Roots are organs that anchor plants in the ground and absorb water and nutrients from soil. Stems carry substances back and forth between the roots and leaves. They also support plants and hold up leaves to the sun. Nonvascular plants do not have true roots or stems. However, they have structures that are similar to roots and stems and perform the same functions.

☑ *Checkpoint* **What is the function of roots?**

Reproduction

The life cycles of plants have two stages, or generations. In one stage, the plant produces spores, the tiny cells that can grow into new organisms. A spore develops into the plant's other stage, in which the plant undergoes sexual reproduction that involves fertilization. **Fertilization** occurs when a sperm cell unites with an egg cell. Sperm cells and egg cells contain genetic information. The fertilized egg is called a **zygote.** A young organism that develops from a zygote is called an **embryo.**

Seeds In seed plants, including gymnosperms and angiosperms, an embryo develops inside a seed. A **seed** is a structure that contains a young plant inside a protective covering. **A seed has three important parts—an embryo, stored food, and a seed coat.** The embryo has the beginnings of roots, stems, and leaves. The embryo uses food stored in the seed until it can make its own food. In some plants, food is stored inside one or two seed leaves, or **cotyledons** (kaht uh LEED unz). The outer covering of a seed is called the seed coat. The seed coat protects the embryo and its food and keeps them from drying out.

Figure 17 The structures of three different seeds are shown in this diagram.

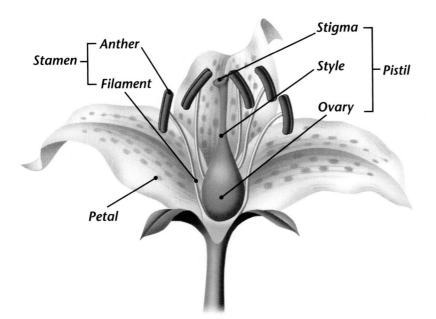

Stamen — Anther
        — Filament

Stigma —
Style — Pistil
Ovary —

Petal

Figure 18 Like most flowers, this lily contains both male and female reproductive structures.
Interpreting Photographs What structures in the diagram can you find in the photograph?

After seeds have formed, they are usually scattered, or dispersed, sometimes far from where they were produced. Seeds are dispersed in several ways. Wind carries some seeds from one place to another. Animals may eat seeds, and then deposit them elsewhere in wastes. Seeds may stick to an animal's fur and hitch a ride to a new place. When seeds land in a suitable area, they can germinate, or begin to grow. To develop into a new plant, a seed needs light, water, and nutrients.

Cones Gymnosperms usually have reproductive structures called cones. Most gymnosperms have two types of cones: male cones and female cones. Male cones produce tiny grains of pollen. **Pollen** contains the microscopic cells that will later become sperm cells. Female cones produce ovules. An **ovule** (OH vyool) is a structure that contains an egg cell. During reproduction, pollen from a male cone reaches a female cone. Fertilization occurs when a sperm cell and an egg cell join together in an ovule on the female cone. After fertilization occurs, the zygote develops into the embryo part of the seed.

Flowers Most of the plants that you see around you are angiosperms. In these plants, the seeds are produced in **flowers,** which are the reproductive organs of some kinds of seed plants. Look at Figure 18 to see the parts of a typical flower. Within the petals are the flower's male and female reproductive organs. **Stamens** (STAY munz) are the male reproductive parts. Pollen is produced in the knobby structure, or anther, at the top of the stamen. Each of the female parts, or **pistils,** has a hollow organ called an ovary. In the ovary are the ovules that contain egg cells.

Figure 19 The face of this sunflower turns on its stalk throughout the day so that it always faces the sun.
Making Generalizations How does a positive phototropism help a plant survive?

A flower is pollinated when a grain of pollen falls on the top of a pistil, called the stigma. Because the stigma is sticky, pollen adheres to it. In time, the sperm cell fertilizes the egg cell in the ovule. The zygote develops into the embryo part of the seed. As the seed develops, the ovary changes into a **fruit,** which is a ripened ovary and other structures that enclose one or more seeds. Apples and cherries are fruits. So are many foods you usually call vegetables, such as tomatoes and squash.

Plant Responses and Growth

As you learned in Chapter 4, all living things respond to stimuli in their surroundings. Animals usually respond to stimuli by moving. **Unlike animals, plants commonly respond to stimuli by growing either toward or away from a stimulus.**

Tropisms A plant's growth response toward or away from a stimulus is called a **tropism** (TROH pihz uhm). If a plant grows toward the stimulus, it shows a positive tropism. If a plant grows away from a stimulus, it shows a negative tropism.

Plants respond to three important external stimuli: touch, light, and gravity. For example, the stems of many vines, such as grapes and morning glories, respond positively to touch. They coil around any object they touch. All plants grow toward light, which is a positive tropism. The parts of plants respond differently to gravity. Roots grow downward, which is a positive tropism. However, stems grow upward, which is a negative tropism to gravity.

Hormones Plants are able to respond to touch, light, and gravity because they produce hormones. A **hormone** is a chemical produced inside an organism that affects the organism's body processes, such as growth and development. Hormones act as internal stimuli that cause an organism's cells, tissues, and organs to respond in specific ways. In addition to tropisms, plant hormones also control the formation of flowers, stems, and leaves, the shedding of leaves, and the development and ripening of fruit.

Figure 20 A flowering plant is classified as an annual, biennial, or perennial depending on the length of its life cycle. **(A)** These morning glories are annuals. **(B)** This foxglove, *Digitalis purpurea*, is a biennial. **(C)** This peony, a perennial, will bloom year after year.

Life Spans of Flowering Plants If you've ever planted a garden, you know that many flowering plants grow, flower, and die in one year. Flowering plants that live for only one growing season are called annuals. Marigolds, petunias, and pansies are all annuals. Wheat, tomatoes, and cucumbers are also annuals.

Flowering plants that live for two years are called biennials (by EN ee ulz). In the first year, biennials grow roots, very short stems, and leaves. During their second year, they grow new stems and leaves, produce flowers and seeds, and then die. Parsley, celery, and most kinds of foxglove are biennials.

Flowering plants that live any longer than two years are called perennials. Some perennials, such as peonies and asparagus, have leaves and above-ground stems that die each winter. These perennials produce new leaves and stems each spring. Most perennials, however, have woody stems that do not die each winter. Bristlecone pines, oak trees, and honeysuckle are examples of woody-stemmed perennials.

Section 4 Review

1. List the characteristics that all plants share.
2. What is the function of a seed coat?
3. How do plants respond to stimuli?
4. Describe the functions of roots, stems, and leaves.
5. **Thinking Critically Classifying** Is the grass that grows in most lawns an annual, biennial, or perennial? Explain.

Check Your Progress
Your plants should be near the end of their growth cycle. Continue to observe them. Harvest the seeds carefully, observe them, and compare them with the original seeds. If you have time, plant a few of these new seeds to begin the life cycle again.

CHAPTER PROJECT

Developing Hypotheses

Which Way Is Up?

In this lab, you will develop and test a hypothesis about how seedlings respond to gravity.

Problem

How is the growth of a seed affected by gravity?

Materials

4 corn seeds	plastic petri dish
paper towels	scissors
water	masking tape
marking pencil	clay

Masking tape

Arrow points directly up

Clay

Procedure

1. Read over the entire procedure. Then, with your group, develop a hypothesis about the direction in which the seedlings will grow in response to gravity.
2. Arrange four seeds that have been soaked in water for 24 hours in a petri dish. The pointed ends of the seeds should face the center of the dish, as shown in the illustration.
3. Place a circle cut from a paper towel over the seeds. Moisten one or more paper towels with water so that they are wet but not dripping. Pack them in the dish to hold the seeds firmly in place. Cover the dish, and seal it with tape.
4. Lay the dish upside-down so the seeds show. Use a marking pencil to draw a small, outward-facing arrow over one of the seeds, as shown in the illustration. Turn the dish over and write your name and the date on it.
5. Use clay to stand up the petri dish so that the arrow points upward. Put the petri dish in a dark place.
6. Once a day for a week, remove the petri dish and check it. Do not open the dish. Observe and sketch the seeds. Note the seeds' direction of growth. Then return the dish, making sure that the arrow points upward.

Analyze and Conclude

1. What new structures emerged as the seeds developed? How did the direction of growth compare from seed to seed?
2. Did your results confirm your hypothesis? If not, describe any differences between your hypothesis and your results.
3. Why was it necessary to grow these seeds in the dark?
4. **Think About It** What evidence or ideas did you consider when you wrote your hypothesis? Did any of your ideas change as a result of this experiment? Explain.

Design an Experiment

How will your seedlings respond if you now allow them to grow in the light? Design an experiment to find out. Obtain your teacher's approval before carrying out your experiment.

SECTION 1 Classifying Living Things

Key Ideas
◆ Biologists classify an organism by its structure, development, and DNA.
◆ The six kingdoms of organisms are archaebacteria, eubacteria, protists, fungi, plants, and animals.

Key Terms
classification   genus
taxonomy   species
binomial nomenclature

SECTION 2 Bacteria

Key Ideas
◆ Bacteria are prokaryotes. The genetic material in their cells is not contained in a nucleus.
◆ Although some bacteria cause disease, most bacteria are harmless or beneficial.

Key Terms
flagellum   endospore
binary fission   decomposer
conjugation

SECTION 3 Protists and Fungi

Key Ideas
◆ Animal-like protists are heterotrophs that have structures that enable them to move.
◆ Like plants, all algae are autotrophs.
◆ Fungus-like protists are heterotrophs, have cell walls, and use spores to reproduce.
◆ Fungi are eukaryotes, use spores to reproduce, and are heterotrophs that absorb their food.
◆ Most fungi reproduce both asexually and sexually.

Key Terms
protozoan   parasite   spore
pseudopod   host   hyphae
cilia   algae   budding

SECTION 4 The Plant Kingdom

Key Ideas
◆ Plants are multicellular eukaryotes that produce food through photosynthesis. Most plants have vascular tissue, leaves, roots, and stems.
◆ A seed has three main parts—an embryo, stored food, and a seed coat.
◆ Plants respond to external stimuli by growing either away from or toward the stimulus.

Key Terms
vascular tissue	seed	stamen
stomata	cotyledon	pistil
fertilization	pollen	fruit
zygote	ovule	tropism
embryo	flower	hormone

Organizing Information

Concept Map Copy the concept map about seed plants onto a separate piece of paper. Then complete the map. (For more on concept maps, see the Skills Handbook.)

Reviewing Content

Review key concepts online using iText at www.phschool.com

Multiple Choice
Choose the letter of the best answer.

1. The science of placing organisms into groups based on shared characteristics is called
   a. development.   b. biology.
   c. taxonomy.   d. DNA.

2. A genus is divided into
   a. species.   b. phyla.
   c. families.   d. classes.

3. Most bacteria are surrounded by a protective structure called the
   a. cell wall.   b. cilia.
   c. protein coat.   d. flagellum.

4. Fungus-like protists are
   a. autotrophs.
   b. heterotrophs.
   c. unable to move.
   d. prokaryotes.

5. Plants produce their food through
   a. chemical breakdown by structures called hyphae.
   b. photosynthesis.
   c. the production of gymnosperms.
   d. vascular tissue.

True or False
If the statement is true, write true. If it is false, change the underlined word or words to make the statement true.

6. <u>Linnaeus</u> devised a system of naming organisms that is called binomial nomenclature.

7. Most <u>archaebacteria</u> live in extreme conditions.

8. In a(n) <u>eukaryote,</u> genetic material is not contained in the nucleus.

9. Most fungi are made up of threadlike structures called <u>hyphae</u>.

10. Plants are <u>autotrophs</u>.

Checking Concepts

11. What does the scientific name of an organism tell you about that organism?

12. What are the parts of a bacterial cell? Explain the function of each.

13. Describe two ways in which bacteria reproduce.

14. Compare how animal-like, fungus-like, and plantlike protists obtain food.

15. What is the major difference between fungi and plants?

16. In what two ways is vascular tissue important to a plant? Give an example of a plant that has vascular tissue.

17. What is a plant hormone? Give three examples of the functions hormones have in the life of the plant.

18. **Writing to Learn** Imagine that you are a spore just released from a fungus growing on a decaying apple. The apple has been lying on the ground in a neglected orchard. Write a description about what happens to you next.

Thinking Critically

19. **Classifying** Which two of the following organisms are most closely related: *Entameba histolytica, Esherichia coli, Entameba coli?* Explain your answer.

20. **Problem Solving** Mildew is a fungus that grows on materials such as paper, leather, and wood. What are some actions that homeowners could take to discourage the growth of mildew in their basement? Explain why these actions might help solve the problem.

21. **Applying Concepts** Explain why people who grow houseplants on windowsills should turn the plants every week or so.

22. **Comparing and Contrasting** How are archaebacteria and eubacteria the same? How are they different?

Applying Skills

Some gardeners spread mulch—material such as wood chips, peat moss, or straw—on the soil around plants. The graph compares the moisture retained by soil with and without mulch. Use the graph to answer Questions 23–25.

Changes in Soil Moisture

- ● Soil with mulch
- ● Soil without mulch

23. **Comparing and Contrasting** How does the amount of moisture in soil covered with mulch differ from the amount of moisture in the uncovered soil?

24. **Inferring** The amount of moisture in both soils increased greatly between days 16 and 20. Explain why this might have happened.

25. **Drawing Conclusions** If you were a gardener, would you grow your plants in soil covered with mulch or in soil that was uncovered? Explain.

Performance ▾CHAPTER PROJECT Assessment

Present Your Project Design a poster that shows the results of your investigation. Do you think that the later generations of plants will go through a similar life cycle? Why or why not?

Reflect and Record What new information did you learn about seed plants by doing this project? If you could do another investigation using these plants, what would you do? Why?

Test Preparation

Use these questions to prepare for standardized tests.

Use the information to answer Questions 26–28.
When bracken ferns grow, their underground stems grow outward and produce new plants. As the map below shows, the new ferns spread into nearby open areas. The bands of color indicate the areas where bracken ferns grew over a four-year period.

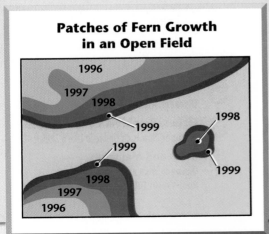

Patches of Fern Growth in an Open Field

26. During which year did the ferns grow most slowly?
    A 1996 B 1997
    C 1998 D 1999

27. In how many areas in the field were bracken ferns growing in 1997?
    F one   G two
    H three J four

28. The underground stems of bracken ferns do not grow far before producing new plants. What is the most likely explanation for how bracken ferns began to grow in the middle of the field in 1998?
    A It rained less than usual.
    B The temperatures were higher than normal.
    C The whole field was fertilized.
    D Spores blew into a moist part of the field.

This three-horned chameleon has just invited a cricket to lunch.

WEB ACTIVITY
www.phschool.com

Animal Adaptations

The chameleon sits still on a twig, as if frozen. Suddenly, the chameleon's long tongue shoots out and captures an unsuspecting cricket, pulling the insect into its mouth. Watch any animal for a few minutes and you will see many ways in which the animal's structure enables it to function in its environment. How does the animal capture food, escape from predators, or obtain oxygen? To help answer these questions, you will create models of two different animals—an invertebrate and a vertebrate—and show how each is adapted to the environment in which it lives.

Your Goal To construct three-dimensional models of an invertebrate and a vertebrate that show how the structure of each is adapted to carry out an essential life function in its environment.

To complete the project successfully, you must
- select one important structural characteristic to show
- build a three-dimensional model of each animal, showing how the structural characteristic carries out its function
- include a poster that explains how each animal's structure is suited to its environment
- follow the safety guidelines in Appendix A

Get Started Pair up with a classmate and share what you already know about animals. Discuss the following questions: Where do these organisms live? How do they move around? How do they protect themselves? Begin thinking about the characteristics that you would like to model.

Check Your Progress You'll be working on this project as you study this chapter. To keep your project on track, look for Check Your Progress boxes at the following points:

Section 1 Review, page 220: Select two animals to model.
Section 4 Review, page 236: Assemble materials and begin construction.
Section 5 Review, page 245: Finish the models. Begin your poster.

Present Your Project At the end of the chapter (page 259), you will display your models and poster.

TEKS

In addition to process TEKS, this chapter addresses these concept TEKS as they relate to the chapter's topic

(6.10) The student knows the relationship between structure and function in living systems. The student is expected to:
(A) differentiate between structure and function;
(B) determine that all orgnisms are composed of cells that carry on functions to sustain life; and
(C) identify how structure complements function at different levels of organization including organs, organ systems, organisms, and populations.

(6.12) The student knows that the responses of organisms are caused b external and internal stimuli. The student is expected to:
(A) identify responses in organisms to internal stimuli such as hunger or thirst;
(B) identify responses in organisms to external stimuli such as the presence or absence of heat or light.

① What Is an Animal?

Is It an Animal?

1. Carefully examine each of the organisms that your teacher gives you.

2. Decide which ones are animals. Think about the reasons for your decision. Wash your hands after handling each of the organisms.

Think It Over

Forming Operational Definitions What characteristics did you use to decide whether each organism was an animal?

GUIDE FOR READING

◆ What characteristics do all animals have in common?

◆ How are structure and function related in an animal's body?

Reading Tip Before you begin to read, write your own definition of *animal.* Add to it or change it as you read.

Key Terms adaptation
• herbivore • carnivore
• predator • prey • omnivore
• invertebrate • vertebrate

A hairy, brown tarantula lurks silently in its burrow under the ground. A beetle walks above the burrow, unaware of the danger. Suddenly the huge spider jumps out of its burrow, grabs the beetle, and injects venom into the beetle's body. Soon the beetle will be the tarantula's dinner.

Characteristics of Animals

Both the fast-moving tarantula and the unlucky beetle are animals. All species of animals are similar in some important ways. **Animals are many-celled organisms whose cells are specialized to carry on functions that sustain life. All animals are heterotrophs. In addition, most animals reproduce sexually and can move from place to place.**

Like all living things, animals must obtain everything they need, such as food, water, and oxygen, from their environment. To survive, animals also need to avoid danger. To reproduce, they must find mates. In accomplishing these tasks, animals respond to both external and internal stimuli. For example, when an animal senses danger in its environment, it responds by moving away. When the animal experiences the internal stimulus of thirst or hunger, it responds by drinking water or eating food.

◀ Tarantula

Figure 1 Animals have different methods of obtaining food. **(A)** A carpet snake uses its body to strangle a lizard for a meal. **(B)** A macaw uses its curved beak to feed on fruits and seeds.

How Animals Reproduce

Animals typically reproduce sexually. A male sperm cell and a female egg cell unite, producing a new individual. Some animals can also reproduce asexually. A tiny animal called a hydra, for example, reproduces asexually by forming buds that eventually break off to form new hydras.

Structure and Function in Animals

Animals' bodies and behaviors are adapted to their environments. An **adaptation** is a characteristic that helps an organism survive in its environment and reproduce. **Many animal body structures are adaptations that enable the animal to perform specific functions.** A box turtle, for example, has a strong, tough shell that helps the animal protect itself. The light-producing structures of fireflies function to attract mates.

Adaptations for Getting Food Every animal is a heterotroph—it must obtain food by eating other organisms. Some animals, **herbivores,** eat only plants. Grasshoppers, termites, cows, horses, and pandas are herbivores. Animals such as wolves and spiders that only eat other animals are **carnivores.** Many carnivores are **predators** that hunt and kill other animals, their **prey.** An animal that eats both plants and animals is an **omnivore.** Grizzly bears are omnivores. They eat berries and roots, as well as insects, fish, and other small animals.

Animals have adaptations for obtaining the kinds of food they eat. Wolves, for example, run down their prey. A wolf's adaptations include sharp claws, speed, and excellent hearing and eyesight. The mouths of insects are adapted for highly specific ways of getting food. For example, a bee has a bristly tongue that laps nectar from flowers, and a mosquito has sharp mouthparts for jabbing skin and sucking the blood that it feeds on.

✓ *Checkpoint* *What is the term for an animal that eats only plants?*

Figure 2 Animals move in different ways. A green sea turtle (left) swims, while a gannet (right) flies.
Applying Concepts How is the turtle's leg structure adapted for moving in water?

How Animals Move At some point in their lives, most animals can move freely. Many animal movements are related to obtaining food, reproducing, or escaping danger. Animals have various structures that function in movement. For example, earthworms have muscles for burrowing through the soil. Birds and insects have wings for flying. Long hind legs and powerful leg muscles enable frogs to leap.

Classification of Animals

Remember that biologists classify living things into six kingdoms, and that one of these is the animal kingdom. Within the animal kingdom there are about 35 phyla, or large groups.

One important characteristic used to classify animals is the presence or absence of a backbone. An animal that does not have a backbone is called an **invertebrate.** Jellyfishes, worms, snails, crabs, spiders, and insects are all invertebrates. Most animal species—about 95 percent—are invertebrates. In contrast, a **vertebrate** is an animal that has a backbone. Fishes, amphibians, reptiles, birds, and mammals are all vertebrates.

Section 1 Review

1. Describe two characteristics of all animals.
2. In what way is the structure of a box turtle's body adapted to function in protecting the turtle?
3. Define *invertebrate* and *vertebrate*. Give an example of each.
4. **Thinking Critically Applying Concepts** Why is it important for animals to be able to respond to stimuli in their external environment?

Check Your Progress
By now you should be narrowing your choices for the two animals to model. Remember that you need to choose one invertebrate and one vertebrate. (*Hint:* Skim Sections 3 through 6 in this chapter for ideas for animals that you might model.)

CHAPTER PROJECT

SECTION 2 Symmetry

DISCOVER

 ·······ACTIVITY·····

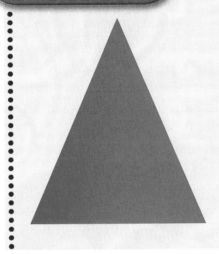

How Many Ways Can You Fold It?

1. Trace the triangle at left onto a sheet of paper and cut it out. Then draw a circle by tracing the rim of a glass or other round object. Cut out the circle.

2. Fold the triangle so that one half matches the other. Do the same with the circle.

3. See how many different ways you can fold each figure so that the two halves are identical.

Think It Over

Classifying Can you think of animals whose body shape could be folded in the same number of ways as the triangle? As the circle?

As they flit gracefully and delicately over a meadow, brightly colored butterflies are a beautiful sight on a sunny afternoon. As you can see in Figure 3, a large copper butterfly's body has two halves, and each half looks almost like a reflection of the other. A balanced arrangement, called symmetry, is characteristic of all complex animals. **Two kinds of symmetry—bilateral and radial—are found in animals.** The butterfly has bilateral symmetry. An object has **bilateral symmetry,** or line symmetry, if you could draw a line that would divide it into halves that are mirror images.

Unlike a butterfly, a sea anemone is circular if you look at it from the top. Any line drawn through its center will divide the sea anemone into two symmetrical halves. The sea anemone exhibits **radial symmetry**—it has many lines of symmetry that all go through a central point. You can see this in Figure 4 on the next page.

☑ *Checkpoint* How is radial symmetry different from bilateral symmetry?

GUIDE FOR READING

◆ What types of symmetry do complex animals exhibit?

Reading Tip Before you read, preview Figures 3 and 4. Write a few sentences comparing and contrasting the organisms in the illustrations.

Key Terms bilateral symmetry • radial symmetry

Figure 3 If you could draw a line through this butterfly's body, it would divide the animal into two mirror-image halves.
Applying Concepts What is this balanced arrangement called?

Animals With Radial Symmetry

Animals such as sea anemones, corals, and jellyfish have radial symmetry. The external body parts of these animals are equally spaced around a central point, like spokes on a bicycle wheel. Because of the circular arrangement of their parts, radially symmetrical animals do not have distinct front or back ends.

Animals with radial symmetry have several characteristics in common. All of them live in water. Most of them do not move very fast—either they stay in one spot, are moved along by water currents, or creep along the bottom. Few radially symmetrical animals are able to go out in search of prey. Instead, their watery environment carries food to them.

Animals With Bilateral Symmetry

Most animals you are familiar with, such as fishes, worms, and insects, have bilateral symmetry. For example, a fish has only one line of symmetry that divides it into mirror images. Each half of a fish has one eye, one nostril, half of a mouth, and one of each of the fish's pairs of fins. Your body also has bilateral symmetry.

In general, bilaterally symmetrical animals are larger and more complex than those with radial symmetry. Animals with bilateral symmetry have a front end that goes first as the animal moves along. Their bilaterally symmetrical structure enables them to move more quickly and efficiently than most animals with radial symmetry. This is partly because bilaterally symmetrical animals have sense organs in their front ends that function to pick up information about what is in front of them. Swift movement and sense organs help bilaterally symmetrical animals get food and avoid enemies.

Figure 4 Sea anemones have radial symmetry. A radially symmetrical object has many lines of symmetry that all go through a central point.

Section 2 Review

1. What two types of symmetry do complex animals exhibit? Describe each type.
2. What are the characteristics of radially symmetrical animals?
3. Draw a view of a bilaterally symmetrical animal that shows its symmetry. Draw the line of symmetry.
4. **Thinking Critically** **Relating Cause and Effect** How does a bilaterally symmetrical structure help a predator catch prey?

Science at Home

Front-End Advantages With a family member, observe as many different animals as possible in your yard or at a park. Look in lots of different places, such as in the grass, under rocks, and in the air. Explain to your family member the advantage to an animal of having a distinct front end. What is this type of body arrangement called?

SECTION 3 Sponges, Cnidarians, Worms, and Mollusks

DISCOVER

How Do Natural and Synthetic Sponges Compare?

1. Examine a natural sponge, and then use a hand lens or a microscope to take a closer look at its surface. Look carefully at the holes in the sponge. Draw what you see through the lens.

2. Cut out a small piece of sponge and examine it with a hand lens. Draw what you see.

3. Repeat Steps 1 and 2 with a synthetic kitchen sponge.

Think It Over

Observing What are three ways a natural and synthetic sponge are similar? What are three ways they are different?

Sponges don't look or act like most animals you know. In fact, they are so different that for a long time, people thought that sponges were plants. Like plants, adult sponges stay in one place. But unlike most plants, sponges take food into their bodies, which qualifies them for membership in the animal kingdom.

Characteristics of Sponges

You might use a brightly colored synthetic sponge to mop up a spill. That sponge is filled with holes, and so are the animals called sponges. **The body of a sponge is something like a bag that is pierced all over with openings called pores. The pores are important in functions such as reproducing and obtaining food and oxygen.** Most sponges have irregular shapes without symmetry. While some of their cells do specialized jobs, sponges lack the tissues and organs that most other animals have.

A sponge obtains everything it needs, including food and oxygen, from water that enters its body through its pores. Water flows from the pores into a central cavity. There, the sponge's cells take in oxygen from the water. Food particles in the water, including tiny organisms such as bacteria and protists, are trapped by cells that line the sponge's central cavity. Water then leaves the sponge through one large opening. Water that leaves the sponge carries waste materials away.

GUIDE FOR READING

◆ How are structure and function related in sponges and cnidarians?

◆ What are the three main groups of worms?

◆ What is the structure of a mollusk like?

Reading Tip As you read, create a compare/contrast table about sponges, cnidarians, worms, and mollusks. Indicate whether each kind of animal has specialized tissues and organs.

Key Terms cnidarian • anus • mollusk • gills • radula

Pink sponges on a Caribbean coral reef ▶

Chapter 7 **223**

A sponge the size of a teacup is able to remove food from about 5,000 liters of water per day. That's enough water to fill a truckload of two-liter soft-drink bottles!

Cnidarians

Jellyfishes, sea anemones, hydras, and corals are cnidarians. **Cnidarians** (nih DAIR ee uhnz) are soft-bodied, radially symmetrical invertebrates that have long, wavy tentacles arranged around an opening called a mouth. The tentacles are covered with stinging cells. **Cnidarians are carnivores that use stinging cells to capture their prey and to defend themselves.** Cnidarians reproduce both sexually and asexually.

Cnidarians have two different body plans. A polyp, such as the hydra in Figure 5, is shaped something like a vase and has its mouth opening at the top. A bowl-shaped medusa, such as a jellyfish, has its mouth opening at the bottom.

Structure and Function in Digestion A cnidarian captures its prey by using its stinging cells to inject venom, a poisonous substance that paralyzes fish and other prey. The tentacles then pull the prey into the cnidarian's mouth. From there the food passes into a body cavity where it is digested. Because cnidarians have a digestive system with only one opening, undigested food is expelled through the mouth.

Specialized Tissues Unlike sponges, cnidarians have specialized tissues. For example, muscle-like tissues enable cnidarians to move. Jellyfishes swim through the water, and hydras turn slow somersaults. These movements are directed by nerve cells that are spread out like a spider web, or net. This nerve net helps the cnidarian respond quickly to the external stimuli of danger or the presence of food.

✓ *Checkpoint* *How does a cnidarian obtain and digest food?*

Figure 5 All cnidarians live in watery environments. **(A)** Jellyfishes are cnidarians that live in the ocean. **(B)** Hydras live in freshwater ponds and lakes, where they reproduce by budding.

Figure 6 Planarians are flatworms that live in ponds, streams, and oceans. The eyespots on the planarian's head can distinguish between light and dark.
Inferring How is having a distinct front end an advantage to a planarian?

Worms

You might think that all worms are small, slimy, and wiggly. But many worms do not fit that description. Some worms are almost three meters long and are as thick as your arm. Others look like glowing, furry blobs.

Structure of Worms All worms are invertebrates with bilateral symmetry. They all have long, narrow bodies without legs. In addition, all worms have tissues, organs, and organ systems. Unlike sponges or cnidarians, worms have head and tail ends.

Function of a Brain Some kinds of worms have a brain, which is an organ made of nerve tissue located in the head end. A worm's brain and sense organs, such as organs sensitive to light and touch, are part of its nervous system. An animal's nervous system receives stimuli from outside and inside the body. It also directs the way in which the body responds to stimuli.

A worm's nervous system functions to detect and respond quickly to external stimuli such as food, predators, and light. Worms respond to the stimulus of food by moving toward it and eating it. Worms withdraw from predators, and many worms also avoid light.

Flatworms

Biologists classify worms into several phyla. **Three major worm phyla are flatworms, roundworms, and segmented worms. Flatworms have flat bodies, which distinguishes them from roundworms and segmented worms.** A planarian, which is one kind of flatworm, is shown in Figure 6. Planarians feed on smaller animals and decaying material. Planarians rely mainly on smell to locate food.

Roundworms

The next time you walk along a beach, consider that about a million tiny roundworms live in each square meter of damp sand. Roundworms have cylindrical bodies. **Unlike cnidarians or flatworms, roundworms have a digestive system that is like a tube, open at both ends.** Food enters at the animal's mouth.

Figure 7 If you were to look at roundworms such as these under a microscope, you would see their bodies thrashing from side to side.

Wastes exit through an opening, the **anus,** at the far end of the tube. Food travels in one direction through the roundworm's digestive system, as it does in most complex animals.

A one-way digestive system is something like an assembly line, with a different part of the digestive process happening at each place along the line. First food is broken down into small molecules. Then the small food molecules are absorbed into the animal's body. Finally wastes are eliminated.

☑ *Checkpoint* **What is a roundworm's digestive system like?**

Segmented Worms

When you look at an earthworm, you notice that its body seems to consist of a series of rings separated by grooves, something like a vacuum-cleaner hose. **Earthworms and other segmented worms have bodies made up of many linked sections called segments.** In Figure 8, you can see an earthworm's segments, as well as its internal organs. Like roundworms, earthworms have a one-way digestive system with two openings.

The circulatory system of an earthworm, like that of other animals, consists of the heart, blood vessels, and blood. An animal's circulatory system carries needed materials to cells and carries waste products away. Segmented worms have a closed circulatory system. In a closed circulatory system, like your own, blood moves only within a connected network of tubes called blood vessels. In contrast, some animals, such as insects, have an open circulatory system in which blood leaves the blood vessels and sloshes around inside the body. A closed circulatory system can move blood around an animal's body much more quickly than an open circulatory system can.

Figure 8 An earthworm's body is divided into over 100 segments. Some organs are repeated in most segments; others exist in only a few. *Interpreting Diagrams What is an earthworm's circulatory system like?*

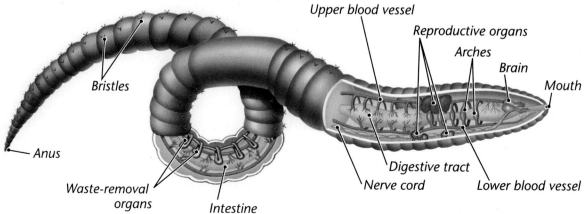

Upper blood vessel

Reproductive organs

Arches

Brain

Mouth

Bristles

Anus

Waste-removal organs

Intestine

Nerve cord

Digestive tract

Lower blood vessel

EXPLORING a Snail

Like other gastropods, a snail has a head with sense organs, and it has a wide, muscular foot. The snails shown here live in a pond.

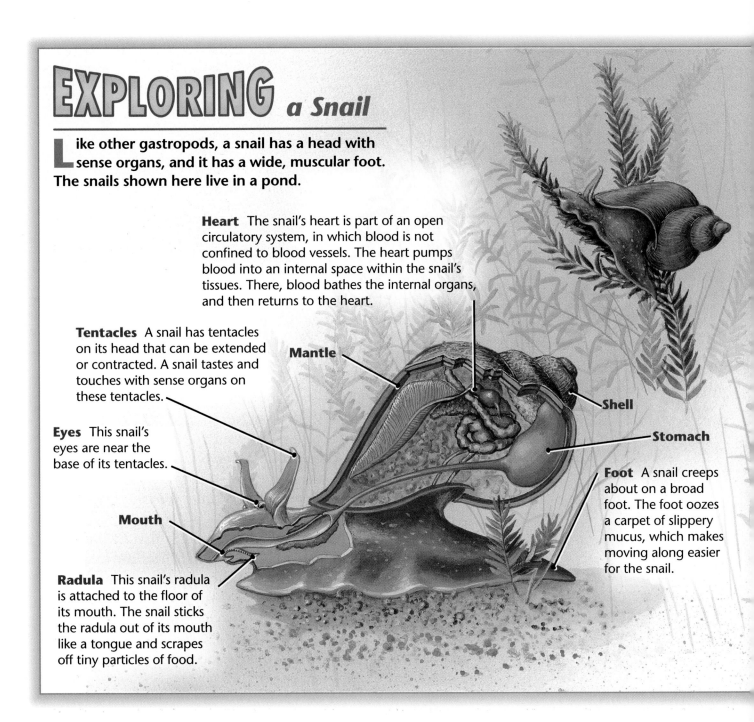

Heart The snail's heart is part of an open circulatory system, in which blood is not confined to blood vessels. The heart pumps blood into an internal space within the snail's tissues. There, blood bathes the internal organs, and then returns to the heart.

Tentacles A snail has tentacles on its head that can be extended or contracted. A snail tastes and touches with sense organs on these tentacles.

Eyes This snail's eyes are near the base of its tentacles.

Mouth

Radula This snail's radula is attached to the floor of its mouth. The snail sticks the radula out of its mouth like a tongue and scrapes off tiny particles of food.

Mantle

Shell

Stomach

Foot A snail creeps about on a broad foot. The foot oozes a carpet of slippery mucus, which makes moving along easier for the snail.

What Are Mollusks?

Snails, clams, and octopuses all belong to the **mollusk** phylum. **Mollusks are invertebrates with soft, unsegmented bodies that are often protected by hard outer shells. In addition, mollusks have a thin layer of tissue called a mantle, which covers their internal organs.** The mantle also produces the mollusk's shell. Most mollusks move with a muscular organ called a foot. You can see the foot of one kind of mollusk in *Exploring a Snail*. The feet of different kinds of mollusks have different structures for various functions, such as crawling, digging, or catching prey.

Figure 9 The octopus (below) and the nudibranch (right) belong to different groups of mollusks. *Applying Concepts What are the major structural characteristics of mollusks?*

Most water-dwelling mollusks have **gills,** organs that remove oxygen from water. The gills are attached to the mantle and have a rich supply of blood vessels. Within these thin-walled blood vessels, oxygen from the surrounding water moves into the blood, while carbon dioxide diffuses out. The gills of most mollusks are covered with tiny hairlike structures called cilia. The beating movement of these cilia makes water flow over the gills.

Many mollusks have a **radula** (RAJ oo luh), which is a flexible ribbon of tiny teeth. Acting like sandpaper, the tiny teeth scrape food from a surface such as a leaf. A radula may have as many as 250,000 teeth.

The shells of mollusks are strong shields that help protect the animals from predators. Some snails withdraw into their shells when conditions are dry and then come out when conditions are moist again. When they are sealed up in this way, snails can survive incredibly long times. In one museum the shells of two land snails, presumed to be dead, were glued to a piece of cardboard. Four years later, when someone put the cardboard in water, one of the snails crawled away!

Section 3 Review

1. Contrast the ways in which sponges and cnidarians obtain food.
2. List the three major phyla of worms and describe the shapes of the worms' bodies.
3. Describe the bodies of mollusks.
4. **Thinking Critically Applying Concepts** What is the function of gills? How does the structure of a mollusk's gills enable them to perform this function?

Science at Home

Edible Mollusks Visit a supermarket with a family member. Identify any mollusks that are being sold as food. Be sure to look in places other than the fish counter, such as the canned-foods section. Discuss the parts of the mollusks that are used for food and the parts that are not edible.

Earthworm Responses

I n this lab, you will make hypotheses about how earthworms respond to the stimuli of moisture and light.

Earthworms
Wet paper towel
Dry paper towel
Tray

Problem

Do earthworms prefer dry or moist conditions? Do they prefer light or dark conditions?

Materials

plastic dropper	water	cardboard
clock or watch	paper towels	flashlight
2 earthworms	storage container	tray

Procedure

1. Which environment do you think earthworms prefer—dry or moist? Record your hypothesis in your notebook.
2. Use the dropper to sprinkle water on the worms. Keep the worms moist at all times.
3. Fold a dry paper towel and place it on the bottom of one side of your tray. Fold a moistened paper towel and place it on the other side.
4. Moisten your hands. Then place the earthworms in the center of the tray. Make sure that half of each earthworm's body rests on the moist paper towel and half rests on the dry towel. Handle the worms gently.
5. Cover the tray with the piece of cardboard. After five minutes, remove the cardboard and observe whether the worms are on the moist or dry surface. Record your observations.
6. Repeat Steps 4 and 5.
7. Return the earthworms to their storage container. Moisten the earthworms with water.
8. Which do you think earthworms prefer—strong light or darkness? Record your hypothesis in your notebook.

9. Cover the whole surface of the tray with a moistened paper towel.
10. Place the earthworms in the center of the tray. Cover half of the tray with cardboard. Shine a flashlight onto the other half.
11. After five minutes, note the locations of the worms. Record your observations.
12. Repeat Steps 10 and 11.
13. Moisten the earthworms and put them in the location designated by your teacher. Wash your hands after handling the worms.

Analyze and Conclude

1. Which environment did the worms prefer—moist or dry? Bright or dark? Did the worms' behavior support your hypotheses?
2. Explain how the worms' responses to the external stimuli of moisture and light help them survive.
3. **Think About It** What knowledge or experiences helped you make your hypotheses at the start of the experiments?

Design an Experiment

Do earthworms prefer a smooth or rough surface? Write your hypothesis. Then design an experiment to answer the question. Check with your teacher before carrying out your experiment.

4 Arthropods and Echinoderms

DISCOVER ··········ACTIVITY····

Will It Bend and Move?

1. Have a partner roll a piece of cardboard around your arm to form a tube that covers your elbow. Your partner should put three pieces of tape around the tube to hold it closed—one at each end and one in the middle.

2. With the tube in place, try to write your name on a piece of paper. Then try to scratch your head.

3. Keep the tube on your arm for 10 minutes. Observe how the tube affects your ability to do things.

Think It Over
Inferring Insects and many other animals have rigid skeletons on the outside of their bodies. Why do their skeletons need joints?

GUIDE FOR READING

◆ What structures characterize arthropods?

◆ What combination of structures characterizes insects?

◆ What are typical echinoderm characteristics?

Reading Tip Before you read, rewrite the headings in this section as questions. Write answers to the questions as you read.

Key Terms arthropod
• exoskeleton • insect • thorax
• abdomen • metamorphosis
• larva • pupa • nymph
• crustacean • arachnid
• echinoderm • endoskeleton

Every September, thousands of visitors pass through central Texas. These visitors are monarch butterflies, flying southward toward their winter home in Mexico. Some fly thousands of kilometers before they reach their destination. The monarch butterflies that make this long journey have never been to Mexico before. But somehow they find their way to the same trees where their ancestors spent the previous winter.

The Arthropod Phylum

Monarch butterflies, which are insects, belong to the **arthropod** phylum. **An arthropod is a bilaterally symmetrical invertebrate with a structure that includes an external skeleton, a segmented body, and jointed attachments called appendages.** Wings, mouthparts, and legs are all appendages. In addition, arthropods have open circulatory systems—the blood leaves the blood vessels and bathes the internal organs.

A Skeleton on the Outside If you were an arthropod, you would be completely covered by a waterproof shell. This tough **exoskeleton,** or outer skeleton, functions to protect the animal and help prevent evaporation of water. As an arthropod grows larger, its skeleton cannot expand. Arthropods solve this problem by occasionally shedding their exoskeletons and growing new ones that are larger. The process of shedding an outgrown exoskeleton is called molting.

Figure 10 Some arthropods, like the Sally lightfoot crab at left, have a hard exoskeleton. Others, like the Promethea moth caterpillar below, have a leathery exoskeleton. *Making Generalizations* What role does an exoskeleton play?

Segmented Bodies Arthropods' bodies are segmented, something like an earthworm's. The segmented body plan is easiest to see in centipedes and millipedes, which have bodies made up of many identical-looking segments. You can also see segments on the tails of shrimp and lobsters.

In some groups of arthropods, several body segments are joined into distinct sections, with each section specialized to perform specific functions. Figure 11 shows the number of body sections and other physical characteristics that are typical of the three largest groups of arthropods.

Appendages Just as your fingers are jointed appendages attached to your palms, many arthropods have jointed appendages, such as legs, attached to their bodies. The jointed structure of appendages gives the animal flexibility and enables it to move. Some arthropod appendages are highly specialized. For example, many arthropods, including lobsters, crayfish, and insects, have antennae (singular *antenna*). An antenna is an appendage on the head that contains sense organs. A crayfish's antennae have organs for smelling, tasting, touching, and keeping balance. The balance-sensing structures enable a crayfish to respond to internal stimuli that indicate the position of the crayfish's body.

Figure 11 Arthropod groups differ in the numbers of body sections, legs, and antennae, and in where the animals are found.

Insect praying mantis

Crustacean fiddler crab

Arachnid tarantula

Comparisons of the Largest Arthropod Groups

Characteristic	Crustaceans	Arachnids	Insects
Number of body sections	2 or 3	2	3
Number of legs	5 or more pairs	4 pairs	3 pairs
Number of antennae	2 pairs	none	1 pair
Where found?	in water or damp places	mostly on land	mostly on land

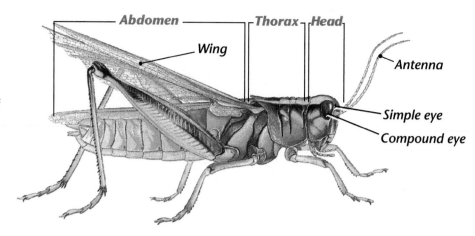

Abdomen — Thorax — Head

Wing

Antenna

Simple eye

Compound eye

Figure 12 A grasshopper's body, like that of every insect, consists of three sections. *Interpreting Diagrams To which section are a grasshopper's legs attached?*

Insects

Scientists have identified about 875,000 different species of arthropods, and there are probably many more that have not yet been discovered. The major groups of arthropods are insects, crustaceans, arachnids, centipedes, and millipedes. The largest arthropod group is the insects.

Characteristics of Insects A butterfly is an **insect,** as are dragonflies, cockroaches, and bees. **Insects are arthropods with three body sections, six legs, one pair of antennae, and usually one or two pairs of wings.** Sense organs, such as the eyes and antennae, are located on an insect's head. The three body regions are the head, thorax, and abdomen. An insect's **thorax,** or midsection, is the section to which wings and legs are attached. The **abdomen** contains many of the insect's internal organs. You can see all three body sections on the grasshopper in Figure 12.

From Egg to Adult Insects begin life as tiny, hard-shelled, fertilized eggs. After they hatch, insects develop into adults through **metamorphosis** (met uh MAWR fuh sis), a process in which an animal's body undergoes dramatic changes in form. As you can see in *Exploring Insect Metamorphosis*, each insect species undergoes one of two different types of metamorphosis. Complete metamorphosis has four dramatically different stages—egg, larva, pupa, and adult. A **larva** is an immature form of an animal that looks very different from an adult. Insect larvae usually look something like worms. After a time, a larva becomes a **pupa** (plural *pupae*). During the pupal stage, the insect is enclosed in a protective covering and gradually changes into the adult form.

In gradual metamorphosis, there is no distinctly different larval stage. An egg hatches into a stage called a **nymph,** which often resembles the adult insect. A nymph may molt several times before becoming an adult.

☑ *Checkpoint* List the stages of complete metamorphosis.

Figure 13 Most insects, like this black fly, have compound eyes with many lenses. Because compound eyes are very effective at seeing movement, insects can quickly escape from potential predators.

EXPLORING Insect Metamorphosis

Depending on the species, an insect develops into an adult through one of the two processes shown here. Fireflies undergo complete metamorphosis, while grasshoppers undergo gradual metamorphosis.

Adult male firefly

COMPLETE METAMORPHOSIS

1 Egg Female fireflies lay their eggs in moist places. The eggs of fireflies glow in the dark.

4 Adult When its development is complete, an adult firefly crawls out of its pupal case and unfurls its crumpled wings. After its exoskeleton hardens, the adult begins a life centered around feeding, flying into new areas, and mating. Adult fireflies flash their light to attract mates.

2 Larva The eggs hatch into larvae that feed on snails and slugs. Firefly larvae are called glowworms because they give off light.

3 Pupa After a time, the firefly larva becomes a pupa. Inside the protective pupal case, wings, legs, and antennae form.

GRADUAL METAMORPHOSIS

Adult male grasshopper

2 Nymph Eggs hatch into nymphs that look much like miniature adults, except that they have no wings, or only small ones.

1 Egg A female grasshopper uses the tip of her abdomen to jab holes in the soil where she lays her eggs.

3 Larger Nymph A nymph feeds until its exoskeleton becomes too tight, and then it molts. The nymph molts four or five times before becoming an adult.

4 Adult Most insects undergoing gradual metamorphosis emerge from the final molt equipped with full-sized wings. Once its wings have hardened, the adult flies off to mate and begin the cycle again.

Crustaceans

If you've ever eaten shrimp cocktail or crab cakes, you've dined on crustaceans. A **crustacean** is an arthropod that has two or three body sections and usually has three pairs of appendages that are structured for chewing. In addition, crustaceans always have five or more pairs of legs. Crabs, barnacles, shrimp, and lobsters are all crustaceans. Nearly every kind of watery environment, from the ocean depths to freshwater lakes to puddles, is home to crustaceans.

Arachnids

Spiders, mites, and ticks are the arachnids that people most often encounter. To qualify as an **arachnid** (uh RAK nid), an arthropod must have only two body sections. The first section is a combined head and chest. The hind section, the abdomen, contains the arachnid's reproductive organs and part of its digestive tract. Arachnids have eight legs, but no antennae. They breathe either with organs called book lungs or with a network of tiny tubes that lead to openings on the exoskeleton.

Spiders are the most familiar and most fascinating kind of arachnid. All spiders are predators, and most of them eat insects. Some spiders, such as tarantulas and wolf spiders, run after their prey, while others, such as golden garden spiders, spin webs and wait for their prey to become entangled in them. Spiders have hollow fangs, organs whose function is injecting venom into prey. Spider venom turns the tissues of the prey into mush. Later the spider uses its fangs like drinking straws to suck up the mush.

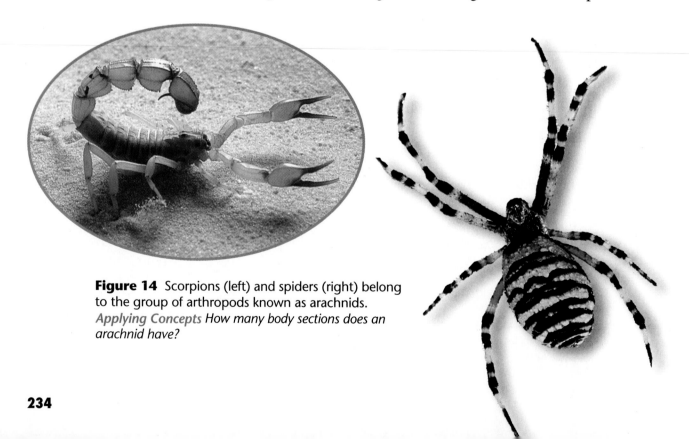

Figure 14 Scorpions (left) and spiders (right) belong to the group of arthropods known as arachnids. *Applying Concepts* How many body sections does an arachnid have?

Figure 15 Millipedes (left) and centipedes (right) are arthropods with many body segments.

Centipedes and Millipedes

Centipedes and millipedes have highly segmented bodies, as you can see in Figure 15. Centipedes have one pair of legs attached to each segment, and some centipedes have over 100 segments. In fact, the word *centipede* means "hundred feet." Centipedes are swift predators with sharp jaws. They inject venom into the smaller animals that they catch for food.

Millipedes, which may have more than 80 segments, have two pairs of legs on each segment—more legs than any other arthropod. Though *millipede* means "thousand feet," they don't have quite that many. Most millipedes are herbivores that graze on partly decayed leaves. When they are disturbed, millipedes can curl up into an armored ball and squirt an awful-smelling liquid at a potential predator.

✓ *Checkpoint* *How are millipedes different from centipedes?*

The Echinoderm Phylum

They look like stars, pincushions, coins, and cucumbers—are these creatures really animals? Sea stars, sea urchins, sand dollars, and sea cucumbers are echinoderms. An **echinoderm** (ee KY noh durm) is a radially symmetrical invertebrate that lives on the ocean floor. *Echinoderm* means "spiny skinned." This name is appropriate because the skin of most of these animals is supported by a spiny internal skeleton, or **endoskeleton,** made of plates.

Adult echinoderms have a unique kind of radial symmetry in which body parts, usually in multiples of five, are arranged like spokes on a wheel. If you count the legs on a sea star or the body sections of a sea urchin, you will almost always get five or a multiple of five.

Figure 16 The blue-and-red sea cucumber (**A**), sea star (**B**), and sand dollar (**C**) are all echinoderms. *Observing What type of symmetry do these organisms exhibit?*

In addition to five-part radial symmetry and an endoskeleton, echinoderms also have an internal fluid system called a water vascular system. The water vascular system functions in movement and food-gathering. The water vascular system consists of fluid-filled canals within the echinoderm's body. Portions of the canals can contract, squeezing water into organs called tube feet, which are external parts of the water vascular system.

If you turn a sea star upside down, you will see rows of moving tube feet. The ends of tube feet are sticky. When these organs are filled with water, they function like suction cups. The stickiness and suction enable the tube feet to grip the surface beneath the echinoderm. Because of this ability to grip surfaces, echinoderms can move across underwater rocks and the sea floor. They also use their tube feet to capture prey, such as clams, by sticking to them. The echinoderms then eat the soft parts of the prey.

Section 4 Review

1. Identify four structural characteristics that all arthropods share.
2. Describe the basic body structure of an insect.
3. What characteristics are shared by all echinoderms?
4. How does the structure of an echinoderm's water vascular system function in gripping objects?
5. **Thinking Critically** **Comparing and Contrasting** Describe the stages in complete metamorphosis and gradual metamorphosis. Explain how the two processes are both similar and different.

Check Your Progress

CHAPTER PROJECT

You should assemble the materials you need and begin to construct your models. Reference books, software, and magazine articles can give you information about the structures of the animals you have chosen. (*Hint:* Make a sketch of each model before you begin to put the parts together.)

SECTION 5 Fishes, Amphibians, and Reptiles

DISCOVER • ACTIVITY • • •

How Is an Umbrella Like a Skeleton?

1. Open an umbrella. Turn it upside down and examine how it is made.

2. Now fold the umbrella, and watch how the braces and ribs collapse against the central pole.

3. Think of what would happen if you removed the ribs from the umbrella and then tried to use it during a rainstorm.

Think It Over

Inferring What is the function of the ribs of an umbrella? How are the ribs of the umbrella similar to the bones in your skeleton? How are they different?

GUIDE FOR READING

◆ What is the function of a vertebrate's skeletal system?

◆ What are the main characteristics of fishes, amphibians, and reptiles?

Reading Tip As you read, write brief summaries of the information under each heading.

Key Terms vertebra
• ectotherm • endotherm
• cartilage • atrium • ventricle
• kidney

On a sunny day, a small yellow mud turtle crawls slowly but steadily out of a pond. The pond and its bank are the turtle's fast-food restaurant. The turtle finds a fat, juicy worm to eat. After feeding, the yellow mud turtle settles down on the pond bank to warm itself in the sun. As the turtle moves and feeds, and even as it lies still in the sun, its body is supported by its bony skeleton.

Vertebrates

Turtles are reptiles, and reptiles are vertebrates. Other vertebrates include fishes, amphibians, birds, and mammals. Vertebrates are animals with a backbone. The backbone is formed by many similar bones, called **vertebrae** (singular *vertebra*) that are lined up in a row like beads on a string. Joints between the vertebrae give the backbone flexibility. You are able to bend over and tie your sneakers partly because your backbone is flexible.

A vertebrate's backbone is part of an endoskeleton, or internal skeleton. The endoskeleton is made up of organs called bones. The endoskeleton supports and protects the body, helps give it shape, and gives muscles a place to attach. The muscles are part of the muscular system, which is the body system responsible for movement.

Yellow mud turtle ▼

Figure 17 An angelfish is supported by its bony skeleton. Also observe how the skeleton gives shape to the fish's body.
Comparing and Contrasting How is a vertebrate's endoskeleton different from an arthropod's exoskeleton?

In addition to the backbone, the vertebrate's skeletal system includes the skull and ribs. The hard skull protects the brain and sense organs. The ribs attach to the vertebrae and protect the heart, lungs, and other internal organs. Many vertebrates also have arm and leg bones adapted for a variety of movements, such as running and flying. When a vertebrate runs, flies, or even breathes, the muscular and skeletal systems work together. Because these two organ systems interact so closely, together they are sometimes called the musculoskeletal system.

☑ *Checkpoint* **What is a function of a skull?**

Regulating Body Temperature

When the yellow mud turtle basks in the sun, it has a higher body temperature than when it is swimming in the cool pond. Most fishes, amphibians, and reptiles are **ectotherms,** which are animals that have a body temperature that is close to the temperature of their environment. In contrast, birds and mammals are endotherms. **Endotherms** have a stable body temperature that is typically much warmer than their environment. Because endotherms can keep their body temperatures stable, they can live in a greater variety of environments than ectotherms can.

Characteristics of Fishes

Fishes make up the largest group of vertebrates—nearly half of all vertebrate species are fishes. **A fish is an ectothermic vertebrate that lives in the water and has fins, which are structures used for moving. Most fishes obtain oxygen through gills and have scales.** Scales are thin, overlapping plates that cover the skin.

Obtaining Oxygen A fish's gills are a good example of how structure relates to function. The gills, which look like tiny red feathers, contain many blood vessels that have a large combined surface area. This large surface area enables the gills to absorb a large

Sharpen your Skills

Communicating

Put on your goggles. **ACTIVITY** Observe a preserved fish. Note its size, shape, and the number and locations of its fins. Lift the gill cover and observe the gill with a hand lens. Make a diagram of your observations, and include a written description. Wash your hands.

Ask a classmate to check your work to make sure it clearly communicates what you observed. Then make any necessary improvements.

amount of oxygen. As water flows over the gills, oxygen moves from the water into the fish's blood, while carbon dioxide, a waste product, moves out of the blood and into the water.

The Circulatory System From the gills, blood travels throughout the fish's body, supplying the body cells with oxygen. In a fish's circulatory system, blood travels in one loop. The heart pumps blood to the gills. From the gills, blood travels to the rest of the body and then back to the heart. Trace this path in Figure 18.

Kinds of Fishes

Biologists classify fishes into three major groups: jawless fishes, cartilaginous fishes, and bony fishes. Mouth structure and type of skeleton distinguishes these types of fishes from one another.

Jawless Fishes Hagfish and lampreys are the only kinds of jawless fishes. Unlike other fishes, jawless fishes have no scales. Their skeletons are made of cartilage. Like bone, **cartilage** is a strong tissue that supports the body, but it is flexible and softer than bone. (The tip of your nose and your ears are supported by cartilage.) Most remarkably, jawless fishes cannot bite like other fishes because their mouths do not have jaws! Jawless fishes have mouth structures that scrape, suck, and stab their food.

Cartilaginous Fishes Sharks, rays, and skates are cartilaginous (cahrt uhl AJ uh nuhs) fishes. As the group's name suggests, the skeletons of these fishes are made of cartilage, just like the skeletons of jawless fishes. However, unlike lampreys and hagfishes, cartilaginous fishes have jaws and pairs of fins. Also, pointed, toothlike scales cover their bodies, giving them a texture that is rougher than sandpaper.

Figure 18 Trace the path of blood through a fish's one-loop circulatory system.

Figure 19 This sand tiger shark (left) has many sharp teeth. Lampreys (right) are jawless fish that also have sharp teeth. *Applying Concepts How are the structures of these fishes' teeth related to their functions?*

Bony Fishes Most familiar kinds of fishes, such as trout, tuna, and goldfish, have skeletons made of hard bone. Bony fishes make up about 95 percent of all fish species. Some live in the lightless depths of the ocean, while others thrive in light-filled waters, such as those in coral reefs or shallow ponds.

The body of a bony fish is covered with scales, and a pocket on each side of the head holds the fish's gills. Each gill pocket is covered by a flexible flap that opens to release water. Most bony fishes have an organ called a swim bladder, an internal gas-filled sac that helps the fish stabilize its body at different depths. To learn more about the functions of the major structures of bony fishes, look closely at the perch in *Exploring a Bony Fish*.

☑ *Checkpoint* **What is cartilage?**

EXPLORING *a Bony Fish*

In a quiet, shady area near the bank of a stream or pond, you might find some yellow perch swimming along. These freshwater fish, which like slow-moving water, travel in groups called schools.

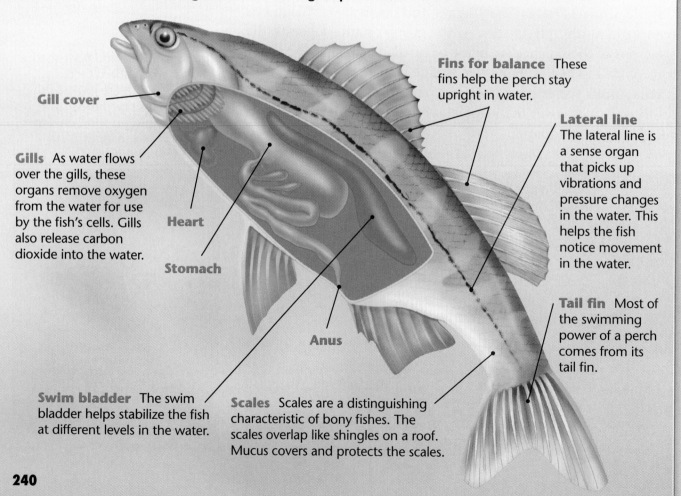

Gill cover

Gills As water flows over the gills, these organs remove oxygen from the water for use by the fish's cells. Gills also release carbon dioxide into the water.

Heart

Stomach

Anus

Swim bladder The swim bladder helps stabilize the fish at different levels in the water.

Scales Scales are a distinguishing characteristic of bony fishes. The scales overlap like shingles on a roof. Mucus covers and protects the scales.

Fins for balance These fins help the perch stay upright in water.

Lateral line The lateral line is a sense organ that picks up vibrations and pressure changes in the water. This helps the fish notice movement in the water.

Tail fin Most of the swimming power of a perch comes from its tail fin.

Figure 20 You can find barred tiger salamanders from Nebraska to Mexico. Salamanders are one kind of amphibian.

Amphibians

Frogs, toads, and salamanders are amphibians. **An amphibian is an ectothermic vertebrate that spends its early life in water and its adult life on land, returning to water to reproduce.**

Respiratory and Circulatory Systems The circulatory system of a tadpole—the larval form of a frog or toad—has a single loop structure, like that of a fish. In contrast, the circulatory system of many adult amphibians has a two-loop structure. As you read about the pattern of blood circulation, trace the path of blood through the amphibian's circulatory system shown in Figure 21. In the first loop, blood flows from the heart to the lungs and skin, where it picks up oxygen. Lungs and skin are organs in the respiratory system, the organ system that moves oxygen from the outside environment into the body. The respiratory system also removes waste carbon dioxide from the body.

From the lungs and skin, oxygen-rich blood returns to the heart. In the second loop, the blood flows to the rest of the body, delivering oxygen-rich blood to the cells. The respiratory and circulatory systems function together to deliver oxygen to the body's cells. Oxygen enters the body through the respiratory system, and blood carries the oxygen to the cells.

The hearts of most amphibians have three inner spaces, or chambers. The two upper chambers of the heart, called **atria** (singular *atrium*), receive blood. One atrium receives oxygen-rich blood from the lungs, and the other receives oxygen-poor blood from the rest of the body. From the atria, blood moves into the lower chamber, the **ventricle,** which pumps blood out to the lungs and body. In the ventricle, there is some mixing of oxygen-rich and oxygen-poor blood.

Metamorphosis Most amphibians lay their eggs in water. Amphibian eggs are coated with clear jelly that keeps moisture in and helps protect against infection. An embryo, or tiny living organism, develops inside each egg. Amphibian eggs hatch into larvae that swim and have gills for obtaining oxygen. Most amphibians undergo metamorphosis, and as they become adults, they lose their gills and acquire lungs.

Figure 21 An adult amphibian's circulatory system has two loops. One loop runs from the heart to the lungs and back, and the second runs from the heart to the body and back. *Interpreting Diagrams* *Where does the blood pick up oxygen?*

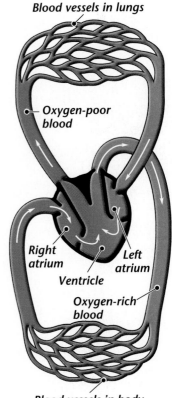

Blood vessels in lungs

Oxygen-poor blood

Right atrium

Left atrium

Ventricle

Oxygen-rich blood

Blood vessels in body

Figure 22 shows the process in which a frog tadpole undergoes metamorphosis. During metamorphosis, amphibians develop strong skeletons and muscular limbs. This body structure enables movement on land. Because it is not supported by water, a land animal needs a strong skeletal system to support its body against the pull of gravity.

☑ *Checkpoint* **Compare the functions of the atria and ventricle.**

Kinds of Amphibians

Frogs and toads are amphibians that are adapted for hopping and leaping. This movement requires powerful hind-leg muscles and a skeleton that can absorb the shock of landing. The feet of frogs and toads have other structural adaptations, too. The webbed feet and long toes of bullfrogs help the frogs dart through the water. Tree frogs have toe pads with adhesive suckers that function as secure holds when the frogs leap from twig to twig.

Salamanders are amphibians that keep their tails as adults. Their bodies are long and usually slender. The legs of salamanders are not adapted for jumping. Salamanders creep around and ambush the small invertebrates that they eat.

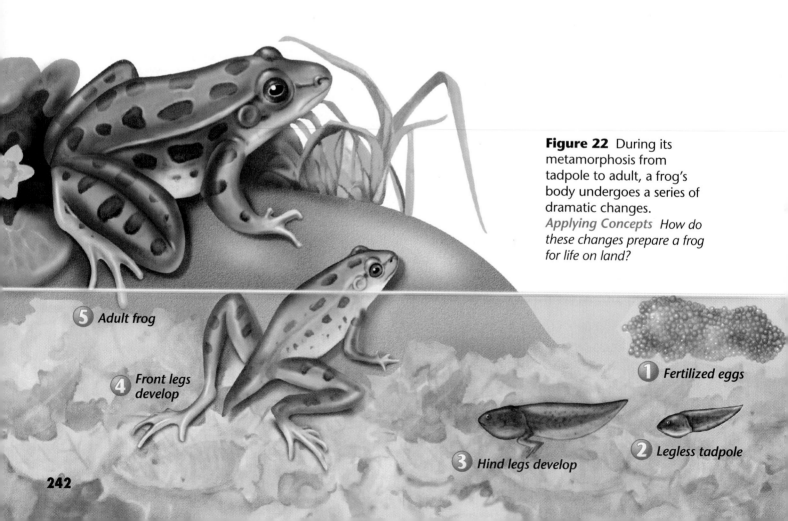

Figure 22 During its metamorphosis from tadpole to adult, a frog's body undergoes a series of dramatic changes.
Applying Concepts How do these changes prepare a frog for life on land?

5 *Adult frog*

4 *Front legs develop*

3 *Hind legs develop*

2 *Legless tadpole*

1 *Fertilized eggs*

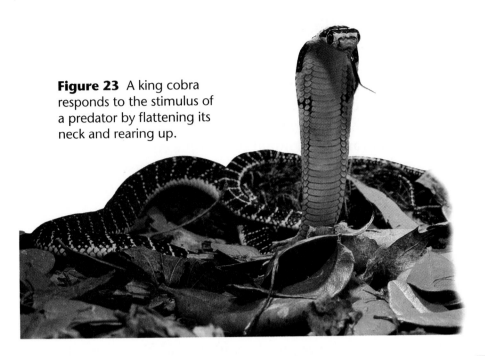

Figure 23 A king cobra responds to the stimulus of a predator by flattening its neck and rearing up.

Reptiles

The king cobra of Southeast Asia, which can grow to more than 4 meters, is the world's longest venomous snake. When it encounters a predator, a king cobra flattens its neck and rears up. Its ropelike body sways back and forth, and its tongue flicks in and out. The king cobra and other snakes are reptiles. Like other reptiles, king cobras lay their eggs on land rather than in water.

A reptile is an ectothermic vertebrate that has lungs and scaly skin. Unlike amphibians, reptiles can spend their entire lives on dry land. Reptiles usually get their oxygen only from the air. Most reptiles breathe entirely with lungs. Like adult amphibians, most reptiles have a two-loop circulatory system and a heart with three chambers.

Entire Life on Land You can think of a land animal as a pocket of water held within a bag of skin. To thrive on land, an animal must have adaptations that keep the water within the "bag" from evaporating in the dry air. Unlike amphibians, which have thin, moist skin, reptiles have dry, tough, scale-covered skin that functions both to protect the reptile and to keep water inside its body.

Another adaptation that helps keep water inside a reptile's body is its **kidneys**, which are organs of the excretory system. An animal's excretory system collects wastes that are produced by cells and removes them from the body. The kidneys filter wastes from the blood. The wastes are then excreted in a watery fluid called urine. As the kidneys of a reptile produce urine, they concentrate it, removing most of the water. Therefore, reptiles lose very little water in urine.

Sharpen your Skills

Drawing Conclusions

ACTIVITY

Scientists incubated, or raised, eggs of one alligator species at four different temperatures. When the alligators hatched, the scientists counted the numbers of males and females. The table below shows the results.

Incubation Temperature	Number of Females	Number of Males
29.4°C	80	0
30.6°C	19	13
31.7°C	13	38
32.8°C	0	106

Use the data to answer these questions.
1. What effect does incubation temperature have on the sex of the alligators?
2. Suppose a scientist incubated 50 eggs at 31°C. About how many of the alligators that hatched would be males? Explain.

An Egg With a Shell The reptile egg is one of the most important adaptations that enable reptiles to live their entire lives on land. Unlike an amphibian's egg, a reptile's egg has a shell and membranes, as you can see in Figure 24. One membrane holds the yolk, which provides food for the embryo. Another membrane holds the liquid that surrounds the embryo. Together, the shell, membranes, and liquid protect the embryo and help keep it from drying out. Because their eggs conserve water, reptiles—unlike amphibians—can lay their eggs on dry land.

☑ *Checkpoint* *List two functions of a reptile's skin.*

Kinds of Reptiles

About 7,000 kinds of reptiles are alive today. Most of these reptiles are either lizards or snakes. Other major groups of reptiles include turtles as well as alligators and crocodiles.

Lizards Lizards have four legs, usually with claws on the toes. Many lizards have long tails, slender bodies, movable eyelids, and external ears. A few lizards, such as the iguana, are herbivores that eat leaves. Most lizards, however, are carnivores. Chameleons, which are found in Africa and India, have a sticky tongue. When a chameleon sees an insect, its tongue shoots out rapidly in response to the stimulus. That tongue extends as long as the chameleon's head and body put together!

Snakes Unlike lizards, snakes have no legs. If you've ever seen a snake slither across the ground, you know that when it moves, its long, thin body bends into curves. Snakes, which are carnivores, have adaptations that help them eat large prey. For example, a snake's jawbones can spread widely apart. In addition, the bones of a snake's skull can move to let the snake swallow an animal much larger in diameter than itself.

Figure 24 The diagram shows the structure of the egg from which this turtle is hatching. One membrane holds the liquid that surrounds the embryo. The liquid keeps the embryo moist and keeps it from getting crushed. A second membrane holds the yolk, which provides the embryo with food.

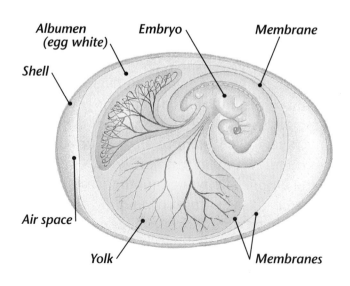

Albumen (egg white)   Embryo   Membrane

Shell

Air space

Yolk   Membranes

Figure 25 The chameleon (left) and the alligator (right) belong to different groups of reptiles.
Applying Concepts *To what group of reptiles does the chameleon belong?*

Turtles A turtle is a reptile whose body is covered by a protective shell, which is made from the turtle's ribs and backbone. The bony plates of the shell are covered by large scales. Some turtle shells can cover the whole body—a box turtle can draw its head, legs, and tail inside its shell for protection. Turtles like the snapping turtle have much smaller shells. Soft-shelled turtles, as their name suggests, have shells that are as soft as pancakes. Soft-shelled turtles lie in stream beds, concealed from predators, with only their nostrils and eyes above the sand.

Alligators and Crocodiles If you walk along a lake in Brazos Bend State Park, you just might see an alligator swimming silently in the water. Most of the alligator's body lies beneath the surface, but you can see its large, bulging eyes. Alligators and crocodiles are carnivores that hunt mostly at night. They have several structural adaptations that function to help them capture prey. For example, they use their strong, muscular tails to swim rapidly through the water after prey. Their jaws are also equipped with many large, sharp, pointed teeth. Their jaw muscles are extremely strong, helping the animals bite their prey.

Section 5 Review

1. What are three functions of a vertebrate's endoskeleton?
2. Describe the major characteristics of fishes, amphibians, and reptiles.
3. The Greek roots of the word *amphibian* mean "double life." Explain how "double life" applies to an amphibian's life cycle.
4. Describe three adaptations that enable reptiles to live on land.
5. **Thinking Critically** **Applying Concepts** Explain how the structure of a snake's jawbones and skull enable the snake to feed.

Check Your Progress

CHAPTER PROJECT

Complete the models and begin working on the poster. (*Hint:* Before you finish the models, ask a friend to help you check to make sure that your models demonstrate the structure-function relationships that you chose to model.)

Animals and Medical Research

In laboratories around the world, scientists search for cures for cancer, AIDS, and other diseases. Scientists use millions of animals each year in research—mostly to test drugs and surgical procedures. Finding treatments could save millions of human lives. However, these experiments can hurt and even kill animals.

The Issues

Why Is Animal Testing Done? If you have ever used an antibiotic or other medicine, animal testing has helped you. The United States Food and Drug Administration requires that new medicines be tested on research animals before they can be used by humans. Through testing, researchers can learn whether a drug works and what doses are safe. Because of animal research, many serious diseases can now be treated or prevented. New treatments for AIDS, cancer, and Alzheimer's disease are also likely to depend on animal testing.

Which Animals Are Used for Testing? Most often mice, rats, and other small mammals are used. These animals reproduce rapidly, so scientists can study many generations in a year. Since apes and monkeys are similar to humans in many ways, they are often used to test new treatments for serious diseases. In other cases, researchers use animals that naturally get diseases common to humans. Cocker spaniels, for example, often develop glaucoma, an eye disease that can cause blindness. Surgeons may test new surgical treatments for the disease on cocker spaniels.

What Happens to Research Animals? In a typical laboratory experiment, a group of animals will first be infected with a disease. Then they will be given a drug to see if it can fight off the disease. In many cases, the animals suffer, and some die. Some people are concerned that laboratory animals do not receive proper care.

What Are the Alternatives? Other testing methods do exist. For example, in some cases, scientists can use computer models to test drugs or surgical treatments. Another testing method is to mix drugs with animal cells grown in petri dishes. Unfortunately, neither computer models nor cell experiments are as useful as tests on living animals.

You Decide

1. Identify the Problem

In a sentence, describe the controversy over using animals in medical research.

2. Analyze the Options

Review the different positions. Is animal testing acceptable? Is it acceptable for some animals but not for others? Is animal research never acceptable? List the benefits and drawbacks of each option.

3. Find a Solution

Suppose you are a scientist who has found a possible cure for a type of cancer. The drug needs to be tested on research animals first, but you know that testing could harm the animals. What would you do? Support your opinion with sound reasons.

Birds and Mammals

What Are Feathers Like?

1. Examine a feather. Observe its overall shape and structure. Use a hand lens to examine the many hairlike barbs that project out from the feather's central shaft.

2. With your fingertip, gently stroke the feather from bottom to top. Observe whether the barbs stick together or separate.

3. Gently separate two barbs in the middle of the feather. Rub the separated edges with your fingertip.

4. Use a hand lens to examine the feather, including the edges of the two separated barbs. Draw a diagram of what you observe.

5. Now rejoin the two separated barbs by gently pulling outward from the shaft. Then wash your hands.

Think It Over

Observing Once barbs have been separated, is it easy to rejoin them? How might this be an advantage to the bird?

O n a clear spring morning, as the sun is beginning to rise, a male painted bunting flies from a low thicket to the high branch of a bush. He perches on the branch and sings his clear, musical song. With his brilliant red, blue, and green coloring, the male painted bunting is one of the most beautiful birds in North America. If you ever see one of these colorful birds, you won't soon forget it.

What Is a Bird?

Birds all share certain characteristics. **A bird is an endothermic vertebrate that has feathers and a four-chambered heart, and lays eggs.** Like reptiles, birds have scales on their feet. Most birds can fly.

Feathers are a major structural adaptation that enable birds to fly. Birds have different types of feathers. A contour feather is one of the large feathers that give shape to a bird's body. When a bird flies, these feathers help it balance and steer. In addition to contour feathers, birds have short, soft, fluffy down feathers next to the skin. Down feathers function to trap heat and keep the bird warm. In effect, down feathers cover a bird in lightweight long underwear.

GUIDE FOR READING

◆ What characteristics do birds have in common?

◆ What characteristics do all mammals share?

Reading Tip As you read this section, make a compare/contrast table in which you compare birds and mammals on their body coverings, pattern of blood circulation, and method of reproduction.

Key Terms diaphragm
• mammary glands
• monotreme • marsupial
• gestation period
• placental mammal
• placenta

◀ Painted bunting

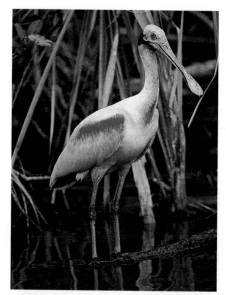

Figure 26 The roseate spoonbill catches small animals by sweeping its long, flattened bill back and forth under water. *Applying Concepts* How is the structure of this bird's bill related to its function?

Flight involves the muscular and skeletal systems. Large, powerful chest muscles attach to wing bones in the skeletal system. The chest muscles make the wing bones move. Many of a bird's bones are nearly hollow, making the bird's body extremely lightweight.

Eating Like a Bird

A bird's digestive system is also important in flight, because the digestive system delivers food to body cells. Like all animals, birds use the food they eat for energy. It takes an enormous amount of energy to power the muscles used in flight.

Birds respond to the internal stimulus of hunger by eating a huge amount of food. Each day an average bird eats food equal to about a quarter of its body weight. When people say, "You're eating like a bird," they usually mean that you're eating very little. But if you were actually eating as a bird does, you would be eating huge meals. You might eat 100 hamburger patties in one day!

Birds have no teeth. To capture, grip, and handle food, birds use their bills and claws. Each species of bird has a bill structured to help it feed. For example, the pointy, curved bill of a hawk acts like a meat hook. A hawk holds its prey with its claws and uses its sharp bill to pull off bits of flesh.

Each organ in a bird's digestive system is structured to process food. Many birds have a crop for storing food after swallowing it. Find the crop in *Exploring a Bird*. The crop is connected to the stomach, which begins to break food down. The gizzard squeezes and grinds the partially digested food.

Delivering Oxygen to Cells

Cells must receive plenty of oxygen to release the energy contained in food. The cells of flying birds need large amounts of energy to power flight. Therefore, birds need a highly efficient way to get oxygen into their lungs and to their cells. Birds have a system of air sacs that connect to their lungs. The air sacs enable birds to obtain much more oxygen from each breath of air than other animals can.

Recall from Section 5 that both the circulatory system and the respiratory system are involved in transporting oxygen to cells. Unlike amphibians and most reptiles, whose hearts have three chambers, birds have hearts with four chambers—two atria and two ventricles. Figure 27 shows the path of blood through a bird's two-loop circulatory system.

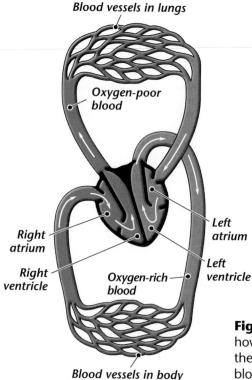

Blood vessels in lungs

Oxygen-poor blood

Right atrium

Right ventricle

Oxygen-rich blood

Left atrium

Left ventricle

Blood vessels in body

Figure 27 Birds have hearts with two chambers. Notice how the left side of the heart is completely separate from the right side. This separation prevents oxygen-rich blood from mixing with oxygen-poor blood.

The right side of a bird's heart pumps blood to the lungs, where the blood picks up oxygen. Oxygen-rich blood then returns to the left side of the heart, which pumps it to the rest of the body. The advantage of a four-chambered heart is that there is no mixing of oxygen-rich and oxygen-poor blood. Therefore, blood that arrives in the body's tissues has plenty of oxygen.

☑ *Checkpoint* *How does the structure of a bird's heart provide an efficient way of delivering oxygen to cells?*

EXPLORING *a Bird*

If you are strolling through a grassy field or meadow in spring, you might hear the beautiful song of a meadowlark. Notice how a meadowlark's body is adapted for flight and for a high level of activity.

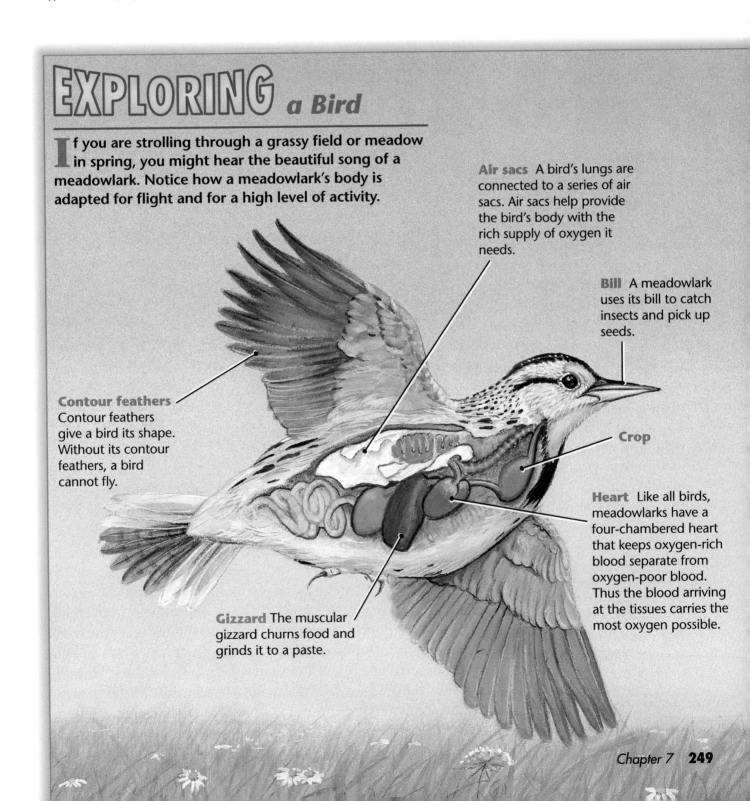

Air sacs A bird's lungs are connected to a series of air sacs. Air sacs help provide the bird's body with the rich supply of oxygen it needs.

Bill A meadowlark uses its bill to catch insects and pick up seeds.

Contour feathers Contour feathers give a bird its shape. Without its contour feathers, a bird cannot fly.

Crop

Heart Like all birds, meadowlarks have a four-chambered heart that keeps oxygen-rich blood separate from oxygen-poor blood. Thus the blood arriving at the tissues carries the most oxygen possible.

Gizzard The muscular gizzard churns food and grinds it to a paste.

Figure 28 Owls are predators that hunt mostly at night. Sharp vision and keen hearing help owls find prey in the darkness.
Relating Cause and Effect What organs enable birds to respond quickly to stimuli?

Eggs-amination

Like reptile eggs, bird eggs protect the developing embryo, provide food for it, and keep it from drying out.

1. Look at the surface of a chicken egg with a hand lens. Then gently crack the egg into a bowl. Do not break the yolk.

2. Note the membrane attached to the inside of the shell. Then look at the blunt end of the egg. What do you see?

3. Fill one part of the eggshell with water. What do you observe?

4. Find the egg yolk. What is its function?

5. Look for a small white spot on the yolk. This marks the spot where the embryo would have developed if the egg had been fertilized.

6. Wash your hands with soap.

Observing Draw a labeled diagram of the egg that names each structure and describes its function.

Quick Response to Stimuli

In order to fly, birds must be able to respond to stimuli very quickly. To appreciate why, imagine how quickly you would have to respond if you were a sparrow trying to land safely on a tree branch. You approach the tree headfirst, diving into a maze of tree branches. You have only an instant to find a place where you can land safely, without crashing into the other branches. A bird can respond quickly because of its well-developed brain and sense organs, including its eyes and ears. A flying vulture, for example, can spot food on the ground from a height of more than one and one-half kilometers.

Reproducing and Caring for Young

Bird eggs are similar to reptile eggs, except that the shells of bird eggs are harder. In most bird species, the female lays the eggs in a nest that has been prepared by one or both parents. Bird eggs will only develop at a temperature close to the body temperature of the parent bird. A parent bird usually incubates the eggs by sitting on them to keep them warm. When it is ready to hatch, a chick pecks its way out of the eggshell. Most parent birds feed and protect their young at least until they are able to fly.

☑ *Checkpoint* *How do bird eggs differ from reptile eggs?*

Why Birds Are Important

INTEGRATING ENVIRONMENTAL SCIENCE Birds play an important role in the environment. Nectar-eating birds, like hummingbirds, carry pollen from one flower to another, thus enabling some flowers to reproduce. Seed-eating birds, like painted buntings, and fruit-eating birds carry the seeds of plants to new places. This happens when the birds eat the fruits or seeds of a plant, fly to a new location, and then eliminate some of the seeds in digestive wastes. In addition, birds are some of the chief predators of pest animals. Hawks and owls eat many rats and mice, and many birds feed on insect pests.

What Is a Mammal?

Mammals are a diverse group of vertebrates that include dogs, cats, buffaloes, kangaroos, and spiny anteaters. Tiny mice are mammals, and so are huge elephants. Mammals share many characteristics. **All mammals are endothermic vertebrates with a four-chambered heart and skin covered with fur or hair. The young of most mammals are born alive, and every young mammal is fed with milk produced in its mother's body.** In addition, mammals have teeth of different shapes that are adapted to their diets. Like birds, mammals have a circulatory system with two loops. In one loop, blood picks up oxygen from the lungs. In the second loop, blood delivers oxygen to the body cells.

Fur and Hair

All mammals have fur or hair at some point in their lives. Like a bird's down feathers, thick fur provides lightweight insulation that prevents body heat from escaping. Fur and hair help mammals maintain a stable body temperature in cold weather. Mammals also have a layer of fat beneath their skins. Fat, like fur and feathers, is an insulating material that keeps heat in the body.

The amount of hair that covers the skin of a mammal varies a great deal from group to group. Some mammals, such as whales and manatees, have only a few bristles. Others, including dogs and weasels, have thick fur. In general, animals that live in cold regions have thicker coats of fur than animals that live in warm environments.

Figure 29 The amount of fur or hair covering a mammal's body varies greatly. Armadillos (left) live in hot regions and have little hair. Gray wolves (right) live in cooler regions and have thick fur coats during the cold winter months. *Applying Concepts What function does fur perform?*

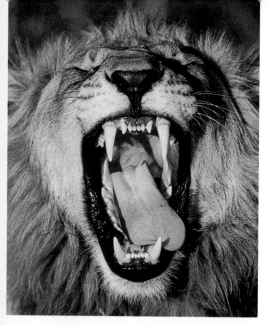

Figure 30 Lions have sharp, pointed teeth. Note the especially long canine teeth. *Inferring What kind of diet do lions eat?*

Structure and Function of Teeth

The structure of mammals' teeth enables mammals to chew their food, breaking it into small bits that make digestion easier. Unlike reptiles and fishes, whose teeth usually all have the same shape, most mammals have teeth with four different shapes. Incisors are flat-edged teeth used to bite off and cut parts of food. Canines are sharply pointed teeth that stab food and tear into it. Premolars and molars grind and shred food into tiny bits.

The size, shape, and hardness of a mammal's teeth reflect its diet. For example, the canines of carnivores are especially large and sharp. Large carnivores, such as lions and tigers, use their canines to hold prey while killing it. Herbivores, such as deer, have molars with broad, flat surfaces that can mash plants.

Breathing

Like reptiles and birds, all mammals breathe with lungs—even mammals such as whales that live in the ocean. Mammals breathe in and out because of the combined action of rib muscles and a large muscle called the **diaphragm**. The diaphragm is located at the bottom of the chest. The lungs are organs with a huge, moist surface area. Because of the large surface area, a lot of oxygen can move from the air into the bloodstream.

☑ *Checkpoint* *How do mammals take air into their bodies?*

Nervous System and Senses

The brains of mammals enable them to learn, remember, and respond to stimuli in complex ways. Squirrels, for example, feed on nuts. To do this, they must crack the nutshell to get to the nut meat inside. Squirrels learn to use different methods to crack different kinds of nuts, depending on where the weak points in each kind of shell are located.

The senses of mammals are highly developed and adapted for the ways that individual species live. Tarsiers, which are active at night, have huge eyes that enable them to see in the dark. Monkeys, gorillas, and chimpanzees are able to see objects in color. This ability is extremely useful because these mammals are most active during the day when colors are visible.

Figure 31 Young mammals usually require much parental care. On a rocky slope in Alaska, this Dall's sheep keeps a close watch on her lamb.

Reproduction

Although a few kinds of mammals lay shelled eggs, the young of most mammals develop within their mothers' bodies and are never enclosed in an eggshell. All mammals, even those that lay eggs, feed their young with milk produced in the mother's **mammary glands.**

Young mammals are usually quite helpless for a long time after being born. Many are born without a coat of insulating fur. Their eyes are often sealed and may not open for weeks. For example, black bear cubs are surprisingly tiny when they are born. The blind, nearly hairless cubs have a mass of only 240 to 330 grams—about as small as a grapefruit. The mass of an adult black bear, in contrast, ranges from about 120 to 150 kilograms—about 500 times as large as a newborn cub!

Young mammals generally stay with their mother or both parents for an extended time. For example, black bear cubs follow their mother for about a year after their birth. During that time, they learn how to be bears. They learn things that are important to their survival, such as which mushrooms and berries are good to eat and how to find the good-tasting grubs in a rotten log.

Figure 32 Mammals, like these springboks, have large brains. A springbok's brain processes complex stimuli from the external environment. This enables the springbok to respond quickly.

Sharpen your Skills

Inferring

Mammals move in a variety of ways—running, flying, swimming, climbing. Obtain photos of a variety of mammals, such as horses, bats, rabbits, whales, and seals. Observe the limbs of each animal. Infer how the structure of the animal's limbs functions to enable the mammal to move in a specific way.

Figure 33 The duck-billed platypus (left) is a monotreme. The opossums (right) are marsupials. *Comparing and Contrasting How are monotremes different from marsupials?*

Monotremes

Biologists classify mammals into three groups: monotremes, marsupials, and placental mammals. Mammals are classified into one of these groups on the basis of how their young develop. Mammals that lay eggs are called **monotremes.** Spiny anteaters and duck-billed platypuses, which are found only in Australia and New Guinea, are the only monotremes alive today. Like all mammals, monotremes feed their young with milk.

Spiny anteaters look like pincushions with long noses. As their name implies, spiny anteaters eat ants, which they dig up with their powerful claws. The duck-billed platypus has webbed feet and a bill, but it also has fur. Platypuses live in water. The female lays her eggs in an underground nest.

Marsupials

Koalas, kangaroos, wallabies, and opossums are some of the better-known marsupials. **Marsupials** are mammals whose young are born alive, but at an early stage of development. They usually continue to develop in a pouch on their mother's body. Marsupials are found mostly in South America, Australia, and New Guinea. Marsupials have a very short **gestation period,** the length of time between fertilization and birth. Opossums, which are the only marsupials found in North America, have a gestation period of only about 13 days.

Newborn marsupials are tiny—the newborns of one opossum species are only about 10 millimeters long! They crawl along the wet fur of their mother's belly until they reach her pouch. Once inside, they find one of her nipples and attach to it. They remain in the pouch at least until they have grown enough to peer out of the pouch opening.

☑ *Checkpoint What do the young of marsupials do immediately after they are born?*

Placental Mammals

Unlike a monotreme or a marsupial, a **placental mammal** develops inside its mother's body until its body systems can function independently. The name of this group comes from the **placenta,** an organ in pregnant female mammals through which materials pass between the mother and the developing embryo. Food and oxygen pass from the mother to her young through the placenta. Wastes pass from the young through the placenta to the mother, where they are eliminated by her body. The umbilical cord connects the young to the placenta. Most mammals are placental mammals.

Placental mammals are classified into groups on the basis of characteristics such as how they eat and how their bodies are adapted for moving. For example, whales, dolphins, and porpoises form one group of mammals that have adaptations for swimming. The mammals in the carnivore group, which includes cats, dogs, otters, and seals, are all predators that have enlarged canine teeth. Rabbits and hares are leaping mammals. They have long hind legs specialized for spectacular jumps.

Primates, which include monkeys, apes, and humans, all have large brains and eyes that face forward. In addition, the forelimbs of many primates have adaptations for grasping. Many primates have opposable thumbs—thumbs that can touch the other four fingers.

Placental mammals vary in the length of their gestation periods. Generally, the larger the placental mammal, the longer its gestation period. For example, African elephants are the largest land-dwelling placental mammals. The gestation period for an elephant averages about 21 months. A house mouse, on the other hand, gives birth after a gestation period of only about 21 days.

Figure 34 Jack rabbits have legs adapted for jumping. Streamlined bodies and flippers enable dolphins to move swiftly through water.

Section 6 Review

1. What are the characteristics of birds?
2. List five characteristics that all mammals share.
3. Describe the structure and function of down feathers and contour feathers.
4. Explain the difference in the development of the young of monotremes, marsupials, and placental mammals.
5. **Thinking Critically** Making Generalizations What characteristics enable birds and mammals to live in colder environments than reptiles can?

Science at Home

Mammals' Milk With a family member, examine the nutrition facts listed on a container of whole milk. What types of nutrients does whole milk contain? Discuss why milk is an ideal source of food for young, growing mammals.

KEEPING WARM

Any time you wear wool, you are using a mammalian adaptation to keep warm. Suppose a manufacturer were to claim that its wool socks keep your feet warm whether the socks are wet or dry. In this investigation, you will test that claim.

Problem

Do wool products provide insulation from the cold? How well does wool insulate when it is wet?

Skills Focus

controlling variables, interpreting data

Materials

tap water, hot
beaker, 1 L
clock or watch
a pair of wool socks
tap water, room temperature
3 containers, 250 mL, with lids

scissors
3 thermometers
graph paper
computer (optional)

Procedure

1. Put one container into a dry woolen sock. Soak a second sock with water at room temperature, wring it out so it's not dripping, and then slide the second container into the wet sock. Both containers should stand upright. Leave the third container uncovered.
2. Use your computer or a pencil and paper to create a data table. List the containers in the first column. Provide four more columns in which to record the water temperatures during the experiment.

3. Use scissors to carefully cut a small "X" in the center of each lid. Make the X just large enough for a thermometer to pass through.
4. Fill a beaker with about 800 mL of hot tap water. Then pour hot water nearly to the top of each of the three containers. **CAUTION:** *Avoid spilling hot water on yourself or others.*
5. Place a lid on each of the containers, and insert a thermometer into the water through the hole in each lid. Gather the socks around the thermometers above the first two containers so that the containers are completely covered.
6. Immediately measure the temperature of the water in each container, and record it in your data table. Take temperature readings every 5 minutes for at least 15 minutes.

Analyze and Conclude

1. Graph your results using a different color to represent each container. Graph time in minutes on the horizontal axis and temperature on the vertical axis.
2. Compare the temperature changes in the three containers. Relate your findings to the insulation characteristics of mammal skin coverings.
3. **Apply** Suppose an ad for wool gloves claims that the gloves keep you warm even if they get wet. Do your findings support this claim? Why or why not?

Design an Experiment

Design an experiment to compare how wool's insulating properties compare with those of other natural materials (such as cotton) or manufactured materials (such as acrylic). Obtain your teacher's approval before conducting your experiment.

SECTION 1 What Is an Animal?

Key Ideas
◆ Animals are many-celled heterotrophs that move, with structures for specific functions.

Key Terms

adaptation   predator   invertebrate
herbivore   prey   vertebrate
carnivore   omnivore

SECTION 2 Symmetry

INTEGRATING **MATHEMATICS**

Key Idea
◆ The bodies of most animals have symmetry.

Key Terms
bilateral symmetry   radial symmetry

SECTION 3 Sponges, Cnidarians, Worms and Mollusks

Key Ideas
◆ A sponge is pierced all over with pores.
◆ Cnidarians use stinging cells to capture prey.
◆ Three major phyla of worms are flatworms, roundworms, and segmented worms.
◆ Mollusks have soft bodies, mantles, and are often protected by shells.

Key Terms
cnidarian   anus   mollusk   gills   radula

SECTION 4 Arthropods and Echinoderms

Key Ideas
◆ An arthropod has an external skeleton, segmented body, and jointed appendages.
◆ Insects have three body sections and six legs.
◆ Echinoderms have five-part radial symmetry, an endoskeleton, and a water vascular system.

Key Terms

arthropod   metamorphosis   crustacean
exoskeleton   larva   arachnid
thorax   pupa   echinoderm
abdomen   nymph   endoskeleton

SECTION 5 Fishes, Amphibians, and Reptiles

Key Ideas
◆ A vertebrate's endoskeleton supports, protects, and gives shape to the body.
◆ A fish is an ectothermic vertebrate with fins. Most fishes have gills and scales.
◆ An amphibian spends its early life in water and its adult life on land.
◆ A reptile has lungs and scaly skin.

Key Terms

vertebra   cartilage   ventricle
ectotherm   atrium   kidney
endotherm

SECTION 6 Birds and Mammals

Key Ideas
◆ A bird is an egg-laying endothermic vertebrate that has feathers and a four-chambered heart.
◆ A mammal has a four-chambered heart and fur or hair. Young mammals are fed with milk.

Key Terms

diaphragm   gestation period
mammary glands   placental mammal
monotreme   placenta
marsupial

Organizing Information

Compare/Contrast Table Copy the table comparing fish groups onto a separate sheet of paper. Then complete the table and add a title.

Kind of Fish	Kind of Skeleton	Jaws?	Scales?	Example
Jawless Fishes	a. ?	no	b. ?	c. ?
d. ?	e. ?	f. ?	toothlike scales	shark
Bony Fishes	bone	g. ?	h. ?	i. ?

Reviewing Content

Review key concepts online using iText at www.phschool.com

Multiple Choice

Choose the letter of the best answer.

1. Organisms that eat both plants and animals are called
   a. autotrophs.   b. omnivores.
   c. herbivores.   d. carnivores.

2. An animal with many lines of symmetry
   a. is bilaterally symmetrical.
   b. is radially symmetrical.
   c. has no symmetry.
   d. has line symmetry.

3. Which of these is true of the legs of arthropods?
   a. They always number six.
   b. They are always attached to the abdomen.
   c. They are rigid.
   d. They are jointed.

4. Adult frogs must return to the water to
   a. catch flies.
   b. obtain their food.
   c. reproduce.
   d. moisten their gills.

5. Kangaroos, koalas, and opossums are all
   a. monotremes.
   b. cephalopods.
   c. marsupials.
   d. placental mammals.

True or False

If the statement is true, write true. If it is false, change the underlined word or words to make the statement true.

6. <u>All</u> animals are made up of many cells.
7. Fish have <u>radial</u> symmetry.
8. An earthworm has <u>an open</u> circulatory system.
9. Reptiles and amphibians are <u>ectotherms.</u>
10. Fur and <u>contour</u> feathers have similar functions.

Checking Concepts

11. Describe three structural adaptations that enable animals to move in specific ways.
12. How is an invertebrate different from a vertebrate? Identify two invertebrates and two vertebrates.
13. How does a sponge obtain oxygen?
14. Contrast a roundworm's digestive system to that of a planarian.
15. How do many worms respond to the stimulus of light?
16. Explain how a snail uses its radula.
17. How are salamanders different from frogs?
18. Describe the structure of a reptile's egg. Explain how the structure enables reptiles to lay eggs on land.
19. How is the structure of a bird's body adapted for flight?
20. What is the function of a placenta?
21. **Writing to Learn** Write a description of a cnidarian catching a fish. Explain the function of the cnidarian's nerve net and tentacles in this process. In your description, use the words *stimulus* and *response*.

Thinking Critically

22. **Applying Concepts** Which capital letters of the alphabet have bilateral symmetry? Radial symmetry?
23. **Inferring** Most echinoderms live in water that is churned by strong waves. How might the structure and function of an echinoderm's tube feet be an advantage in such an environment?
24. **Comparing and Contrasting** Contrast the circulatory systems of fishes, amphibians, and birds.
25. **Relating Cause and Effect** If a bird loses too many contour feathers, it cannot fly. Why do you think that this is the case?
26. **Comparing and Contrasting** Why do you think some scientists might consider monotremes to be a link between reptiles and mammals?

Applying Skills

The data table below shows the approximate gestation period of several mammals and the approximate length of time that those mammals care for their young after birth. Use the information in the table to answer Questions 27–29.

Mammal	Gestation Period	Time Spent Caring for Young After Birth
Deer mouse	0.75 month	1 month
Chimpanzee	8 months	24 months
Harp seal	11 months	0.75 month
Elephant	21 months	24 months
Bobcat	2 months	8 months

27. **Graphing** Decide which kind of graph would be best for showing the data in the table. Then construct two graphs—one for gestation period and the other for time.

28. **Interpreting Data** Which mammals in the table care for their young for the longest time? The shortest time?

29. **Drawing Conclusions** What seems to be the general relationship between the size of the mammal and the length of time for which it cares for its young? Which animal is the exception to this pattern?

Performance ▼ CHAPTER PROJECT Assessment

Present Your Project Display your models in a creative way—for example, show the models in action and show details of the animals' environments. Also display your poster.

Reflect and Record In your journal, list all the adaptations you learned from your classmates' presentations. How did constructing a three-dimensional model help you understand the characteristics of these animals? What were the limitations of the models you constructed?

Test Preparation

Use these questions to prepare for standardized tests.

Study the graph. Then answer Questions 30–33.

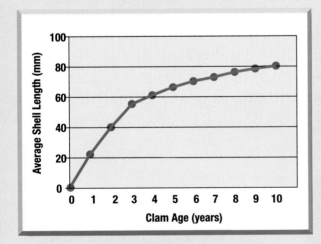

30. What is the best title for this graph?
    A Clamshell Growth over Time
    B The Ages of a Clam
    C The Maximum Size of Clams
    D The Life Span of Clams

31. In some states, the minimum harvesting size for clams is 40 millimeters. Approximately how long does it take new clams to reach this size?
    F 1 year   G 2 years
    H 3 years   J 4 years

32. Based on the graph, which generalization about clam growth is correct?
    A Clam growth is most rapid during years 5 through 10.
    B Clam growth is most rapid during years 0 through 5.
    C Clam growth is equally rapid each year.
    D Clam growth is very slow.

33. How many millimeters larger was the average clam at age 2 compared to age 1?
    F 8 millimeters
    G 15 millimeters
    H 18 millimeters
    J 25 millimeters

UNLOCKING THE
Secrets of Cells

It takes courage and dedication to follow your dreams. Lydia Villa-Komaroff learned that early in her career. She comes from a family of courageous Mexican American women. Her mother and both grandmothers were strong role models for her. Their support, as well as her father's, encouraged her to pursue a career in science. As a molecular biologist, Dr. Villa-Komaroff studies the role of proteins in the growth and development of living things.

In 1976, Lydia was part of a team conducting genetic engineering, a technique by which scientists transfer genes from one organism into another. Today, scientists use this technique to produce medicines, to treat diseases, and to improve crops. In the 1970s, genetic engineering was a new idea. It was feared by many people who thought it might have harmful results. In fact, the city where Lydia worked banned genetic engineering.

To continue her research, Lydia was forced to move her lab to another state. She spent a year away from many of her colleagues and friends. "It was a frustrating and lonely time," she recalls.

Lydia Villa-Komaroff is Vice President for Research at Northwestern University in Chicago, Illinois. She earned her Ph.D. in cell biology at the Massachusetts Institute of Technology. An avid skier and photographer, Lydia also loves to read, particularly mysteries and biographies.

But her hard work paid off. The ban was lifted, and soon after, Lydia helped discover a method for making insulin. Insulin is used to treat people who suffer from diabetes. Discovering a way to make insulin launched a new industry—biotechnology. It marked a personal triumph for Lydia. "Scientifically, that was the most exciting time of my life," she says. "There were any number of reasons to think we couldn't make insulin. But we planned it, we tried it, and no experiment before or since has worked so smoothly."

Many secrets of the human cell remain to be unlocked. Lydia hopes to provide some of the keys.

Talking With Dr. Lydia Villa-Komaroff

Q *How did you become interested in science?*

A My Mexican grandmother was very interested in natural history—plants in particular. She had books we used to look at with beautiful color pictures of plants. What really sparked my interest was just following her around, learning about the plants in our garden, and going out collecting wild spinach with her.

Q *What made you choose a career in biology?*

A I had an incredibly exciting developmental biology course in college. One time we camped out in the lab for 36 hours so we could watch frogs develop. Normally you study that in pictures in textbooks. But we were seeing it happen in real life. It was very exciting.

Q *What does a molecular biologist do?*

A We study development at the most basic level: what goes on within a cell. Think of the cell as a house, with many different parts—the foundation, the walls, the roof, and lots of bricks and wood and wiring. I'm interested in finding out how that structure gets built.

Dr. Villa-Komaroff explains her work to a group of students.

1 *The gene for human insulin is isolated from its chromosome*

3 *The insulin gene is inserted into the bacterial plasmid.*

2 *Plasmids, small circular rings of DNA, are removed from bacterial cells.*

Bacterial chromosome

Plasmid

Dr. Villa-Komaroff pioneered the use of genetic engineering to produce human proteins, such as insulin.

Q *Is there a plan or blueprint for building a cell?*

A All the instructions are in the DNA. That is the material in the nucleus of a cell that carries the hereditary information that determines traits, such as your skin and hair color. The machinery, which is made up of proteins, comes in and reads bits of that information, which are called genes. Then DNA is copied into RNA, a message that travels out to the part of the cell where all the building activity goes on. Other proteins read it and start to produce the materials that the cell needs to work.

Q *Are proteins the tools or the structure of a cell?*

A Actually, they're both. Proteins are the building blocks of cells, like the bricks and mortar in a house. But they're also the machinery that builds cells, like hammers and drills. Proteins make up the cell, and build the cell.

Q *What other information does DNA contain?*

A It contains coding instructions to make sure the right information gets used at the right time. If you were building a house, you couldn't put up the roof before you had walls. In building a human, a certain amount of the head needs to be in place, for example, before you can make eyes. So it's very important for a cell to know what information to use, and when to use it.

Q *How do cells know when to start and stop building?*

A It's still not clear how that process is coordinated. There are certain genes that we understand very well. We know what signals they send the cell to say it's time to become a heart or a liver. But how does the cell know when to use that information, and when to stop? Those are some of the big questions that we're trying to answer.

4 *Plasmids with the insulin gene are taken up by the bacterial cells. The gene directs the cell to produce insulin.*

5 *The insulin is collected and used to treat people with diabetes.*

Q *What was the significance of the technique you developed to produce insulin?*

A People with diabetes used to be treated with pig insulin. But pig insulin is in short supply and therefore expensive. The work we did showed how to make a lot of insulin very cheaply, by growing it in bacteria. And it's human insulin.

Q *How did you trick the cell into making insulin?*

A We were able to isolate the gene with instructions for making insulin. We then inserted it into bacteria. Basically, we tricked the bacteria into thinking the gene was one of its own pieces of DNA. The bacteria then made insulin.

Q *Why didn't you give up when your research was banned?*

A We were doing very important work. To quit would have been to admit that the ban was right. We knew that others were doing the same research. You can't win a race if you quit.

Q *Were you ever discouraged?*

A There were times when I was discouraged, but I think that is true of anyone doing something where there is no guarantee of success. I think I've always approached a project with the idea that I have to give it my best shot.

Q *What advice would you give a person planning a science career?*

A You can't be entirely sure what you'll be able to do. The world is changing too fast. The important thing is to find something you like, and learn it very well. If you follow what you like, it may be different in 10 years, but it will be a logical extension of your own interests.

In Your Journal

As a young scientist, Lydia continued her research in genetic engineering in spite of obstacles that blocked her work. What does her action tell you about her as a person? Describe some character traits that you think would help a scientist to be successful. Why would those traits be important?

CHAPTER

8 Ecosystems

www.phschool.com

What's a Crowd?

How many sunflowers are there in this photograph? Certainly too many to count! But there is a limit to how many more sunflowers can grow in this fertile field. The limit is determined by what the sunflowers need to survive.

In this chapter, you will explore how living things obtain the things they need from their surroundings. You will also learn how organisms interact with and respond to the living and nonliving things around them. As you study this chapter, you will observe plants as sample organisms.

Your Goal To design and conduct an experiment to determine the effect of crowding on plant growth.

To complete your project successfully, you must

◆ develop a plan for planting different numbers of seeds in identical containers

◆ observe and collect data on the growing plants

◆ present your results in a written report and a graph

◆ follow the safety guidelines in Appendix A

Get Started With your group, brainstorm ideas for your plan. What conditions do plants need to grow? How will you arrange your seeds in their containers? What types of measurements will you make when the plants begin to grow? Submit your draft plan to your teacher for review.

Check Your Progress You'll be working on this project as you study this chapter. To keep your project on track, look for Check Your Progress boxes at the following points.

Section 1 Review, page 271: Plant the seeds. Measure the plants' growth and record your observations.

Section 3 Review, page 286: Analyze your data and prepare your report.

Present Your Project At the end of the chapter (page 289), your group will present your results and conclusions to the class.

Row after row of bright sunflowers blanket a field in Provence, France.

TEKS

In addition to process TEKS, this chapter addresses these concept TEKS as they relate to the chapter's topics.

(6.8) The student knows that complex interactions occur between matter and energy. The student is expected to:
(B) explain and illustrate the interactions between matter and energy in the water cycle and in the decay of biomass such as in a compost bin; and
(C) describe energy flow in living systems including food chains and food webs.

(6.10) The student knows the relationship between structure and function in living systems. The student is expected to:
(C) identify how structure complements function at different levels of organization including organs, organ systems, organisms, and populations.

(6.12) The student knows that the responses of organisms are caused by internal or external stimuli. The student is expected to:
(C) identify components of an ecosystem to which organisms may respond.

1 Components of an Ecosystem

DISCOVER

What's in the Scene?

1. Choose a magazine picture of a nature scene. Paste the picture onto a sheet of paper, leaving space all around the picture.

2. Identify all the things in the picture that are alive. Use a colored pencil to draw a line from each living thing. Label the organism if you know its name.

3. Use a different colored pencil to draw a line from each nonliving thing and label it.

Think It Over

Inferring How do the organisms in the picture depend on the nonliving things? Using a third color, draw lines connecting organisms to the nonliving things they need.

GUIDE FOR READING

◆ What components of an ecosystem do organisms respond to?

◆ What are the levels of organization within an ecosystem?

Reading Tip Write the section headings in your notebook. As you read, make a list of main ideas and supporting details under each heading.

Key Terms ecosystem • habitat • biotic factor • abiotic factor • population • society • community • ecology

A s the sun rises on a warm summer morning, the Texas town is already bustling with activity. Some residents are building homes underground, where it is dark and cool. Other inhabitants are collecting seeds for breakfast. Some younger residents are at play, chasing each other through the grass.

Suddenly, an adult spots a threatening shadow approaching— an enemy has appeared in the sky! The adult cries out, warning the others. Within moments, the town's residents disappear quickly into their underground homes. The town is silent and still, except for a single hawk circling overhead.

Have you guessed what kind of town this is? It is a prairie dog town on the Texas plains. As these prairie dogs dug their burrows, searched for food, and hid from the hawk, they interacted with and responded to their environment, or surroundings. The prairie dogs interacted with living things, such as the grass and the hawk, and with nonliving things, such as the soil. All the living and nonliving things that interact in a particular area make up an **ecosystem.**

◄ **Black-tailed prairie dogs**

A prairie is just one of the many different ecosystems found on Earth. Other ecosystems in which living things make their homes include mountain streams, deep oceans, swamps, and dense forests.

Habitats

A prairie dog is one type of organism, or living thing. Organisms live in a specific place within an ecosystem. An organism obtains food, water, shelter, and other things it needs to live, grow, and reproduce from its surroundings. The place where an organism lives and that provides the things the organism needs is called its **habitat.**

A single ecosystem may contain many habitats. For example, in a forest ecosystem, mushrooms grow in the damp soil, bears live on the forest floor, termites live in fallen tree trunks, and woodpeckers build nests in the trunks.

Organisms live in different habitats because they have different requirements for survival. A prairie dog obtains the food and shelter it needs from its habitat. It could not survive in a tropical rain forest or on the rocky ocean shore. Likewise, the prairie would not meet the needs of a gorilla, a penguin, or a hermit crab.

Biotic Factors

An organism interacts with and responds to both the living and nonliving things in its environment. The living parts of an ecosystem are called **biotic factors** (by AHT ik). Biotic factors in the prairie dogs' ecosystem include the grass and plants that provide seeds and berries. The hawks, ferrets, badgers, and eagles that hunt the prairie dogs are also biotic factors. In addition, worms, fungi, and bacteria are biotic factors that live in the soil underneath the prairie grass. These organisms keep the soil rich in nutrients as they break down the remains of other living things.

☑ *Checkpoint* *Name a biotic factor in your environment.*

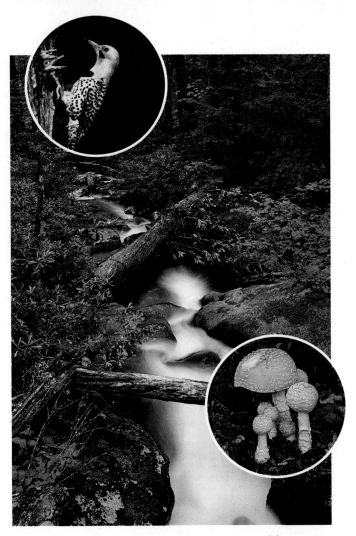

Figure 1 A stream tumbles over mossy rocks in a lush Tennessee forest. This ecosystem contains many different habitats.
Comparing and Contrasting How is the mushrooms' habitat in the forest different from the woodpecker's habitat?

Figure 2 This eastern banjo frog is burrowing in the sand to stay cool in the hot Australian desert. *Interpreting Photographs With which abiotic factors is the frog interacting in this scene?*

With or Without Salt?

In this activity you will explore salt as an abiotic factor.

1. Label four 600-mL beakers A, B, C, and D. Fill each with 500 mL of room-temperature spring water.

2. Set beaker A aside. It will contain fresh water. To beaker B, add 2.5 grams of noniodized salt. Add 7.5 grams of salt to beaker C and 15 grams of salt to beaker D. Stir beakers B, C, and D.

3. Add about $\frac{1}{4}$ of a spoonful of brine shrimp eggs to each beaker.

4. Cover each beaker with a square of paper. Keep them away from direct light or heat. Wash your hands.

5. Observe the beakers daily for three days.

Drawing Conclusions In which beakers did the eggs hatch? What can you conclude about the amount of salt in the shrimps' natural habitat?

Abiotic Factors

The nonliving parts of an ecosystem are called **abiotic factors** (ay by AHT ik). The abiotic factors to which organisms respond include water, sunlight, oxygen, temperature, and soil.

Water All living things need water to carry out their life processes. Water is particularly important to plants and algae. These organisms use water, along with sunlight and carbon dioxide, to make food in the process called photosynthesis. Other living things eat the plants and algae to obtain energy.

Sunlight Because sunlight is necessary for photosynthesis, it is an important abiotic factor for plants, algae, and other living things. In places that do not receive sunlight, such as dark caves, plants cannot grow. Without plants or algae to provide a source of food, few other organisms can live.

Oxygen Most living things require oxygen to carry out their life processes. Organisms that live on land obtain oxygen from the air, which is about 20 percent oxygen. Fish and other water organisms obtain dissolved oxygen from the water around them.

Temperature The temperatures that are typical of an area determine the types of organisms that can live there. For example, if you took a trip to a warm tropical island, you would see palm trees, bright hibiscus flowers, and tiny lizards. These organisms could not survive on the frozen plains of Siberia.

Some animals respond to very hot or very cold temperatures by altering their environment. For example, prairie dogs line their dens with grass. The grass keeps the prairie dogs warm during the cold and windy winters.

Soil Soil is a mixture of rock fragments, nutrients, air, water, and the decaying remains of living things. Soil in different areas consists of varying amounts of these materials. The type of soil in an area influences the kinds of plants that can grow there.

Many animals, such as prairie dogs, use the soil itself as a home. Billions of microscopic organisms such as bacteria also live in the soil. These tiny organisms play an important role in the ecosystem by breaking down the remains of other living things.

☑ *Checkpoint* **How do biotic factors differ from abiotic factors?**

Structure and Function in Populations

In 1900, travelers saw a prairie dog town in Texas covering an area twice the size of the city of Dallas. The sprawling town contained more than 400 million prairie dogs! These prairie dogs were all members of one species. All the members of one species in a particular area are referred to as a **population.** The 400 million prairie dogs in the Texas town are one example of a population. All the daisies in a field make up a population. In contrast, all the trees in a forest do not make up a population, because they do not all belong to the same species. The area in which a population lives can be as small as a single blade of grass or as large as the whole planet.

In the populations of many species, such as daisies in a field or frogs in a pond, individual members do not interact much except for reproducing and competing with one another for resources. In contrast, the populations of other species are structured: that is, members of the population relate to one another in specific ways. Prairie dogs, for example, live together in colonies. Members of the colony cooperate with one another in functions such as warning about danger. If a prairie dog senses danger, it gives a warning call, and the members of the colony quickly scramble into their burrows. A different call tells the prairie dogs when it is safe to come out. Cooperation helps the members of the population survive.

Figure 3 This milkweed plant is home to a small population of ladybug beetles.

Some animal populations form highly structured groups called societies. A **society** is a closely related population of animals that work together for the benefit of the whole group. Every member of a honeybee hive, for example, has a specific function. The queen bee lays eggs from which new bees hatch. All the other females, called worker bees, perform such tasks as making honey and defending the hive. Male bees, called drones, function in reproduction by mating with the queen bee.

Organism

Population

Language Arts
CONNECTION

The word *ecology* comes from two Greek root words: *oikos*, which means "house or place to live," and *logos*, which means "study." Put together, these root words create a term for studying organisms in the place where they live. Many science terms are derived from Greek and Latin root words.

In Your Journal

Use a dictionary to find root words for the following terms from this section: *habitat*, *biotic*, *community*, and *population*. For each root word, list its meaning, original language, and other English words containing the root.

Communities

Of course, most ecosystems contain more than one type of organism. The prairie, for instance, includes prairie dogs, hawks, grasses, badgers, and snakes, along with many other organisms. All the different populations that live together in an area make up a **community.**

Figure 4 shows the levels of organization in the prairie ecosystem. **The smallest unit of organization is a single organism, which belongs to a population of other members of its species. The population belongs to a community of different species. The community and abiotic factors together form an ecosystem.**

To be considered a community, the different populations must live close enough together to interact. One way the populations in a community may interact is by using the same resources, such as food and shelter. For example, the tunnels dug by the prairie dogs also serve as homes for burrowing owls and black-footed ferrets. The prairie dogs share the grass with other animals. Meanwhile, prairie dogs themselves serve as food for many species.

What Is Ecology?

Because the populations in the prairie ecosystem interact with one another, any changes in a community affect all the different populations that live there. The study of how living things interact with one another and with their environment is called **ecology.** Ecologists, scientists who study ecology, look at how all the biotic and abiotic factors in an ecosystem are related.

Community

Ecosystem

Figure 4 The smallest level of ecological organization is an individual organism. The largest is the entire ecosystem.

As part of their work, ecologists study how organisms respond to changes in their environment. Living things constantly interact with their surroundings, responding to changes in the conditions around them. Some responses are very quick. For example, when a hawk sees a prairie dog, the hawk responds immediately by swooping down and trying to catch the prairie dog. The prairie dog responds to the hawk by giving a warning bark—and running for cover. Other responses to change in the environment occur more slowly. For example, after a fire on the prairie, it takes some time for the grass to reach its former height and for all the animals to return to the area.

Section 1 Review

1. What are biotic factors? What are abiotic factors?
2. List the following levels of organization in order from the smallest level to the largest: population, organism, ecosystem, community.
3. Why do ecologists study both biotic and abiotic factors in an ecosystem?
4. What is the structure of a honeybee society? What functions do the different members perform?
5. **Thinking Critically Applying Concepts** Would all the insects in a forest be considered a population? Why or why not?

CHAPTER PROJECT

Check Your Progress
After your teacher has reviewed your plan, prepare the containers and plant the seeds. Design a data table to record the information you will use to compare the growth in the different containers. When the plants begin to grow, examine them daily and record your observations. Be sure to continue caring for your plants according to your plan. (Hint: Use a metric ruler to measure your growing plants. Besides size, look for differences in leaf color and the number of buds among the plants.)

A World in a Bottle

I n this lab, you will study the interactions between biotic and abiotic factors in a model ecosystem.

Problem

How do organisms survive in a closed ecosystem?

Materials

pre-cut, clear plastic
   bottle
gravel
soil
moss plants
plastic spoon   rubber band
charcoal   2 vascular plants
spray bottle   plastic wrap

Procedure

1. In this lab, you will place plants in moist soil in a bottle that is then sealed. This setup is called a terrarium. Predict whether the plants can survive in this habitat.
2. Spread about 2.5 cm of gravel on the bottom of a pre-cut bottle. Then sprinkle a spoonful or two of charcoal over the gravel.
3. Use the spoon to layer about 8 cm of soil over the gravel and charcoal. As you add the soil, tap it down gently.
4. Scoop out two holes in the soil. Remove the vascular plants from their pots. Gently place their roots in the holes. Then pack the loose soil firmly around the plants' stems.

5. Fill the spray bottle with water. Spray the soil until you see water collecting in the gravel.
6. Cover the soil with the moss plants, including the areas around the stems of the vascular plants. Lightly spray the mosses with water.
7. Tightly cover your terrarium with plastic wrap. Secure the cover with a rubber band. Place the terrarium in bright, indirect light.
8. Observe the terrarium daily for two weeks. Record your observations in your notebook. If its sides fog, move the terrarium to an area with a different amount of light. You may have to move it a few times before the fog disappears. Write down any changes you make in your terrarium's location.

Analyze and Conclude

1. What are the components of the ecosystem in the bottle?
2. Were any biotic or abiotic factors able to enter the terrarium? If so, which ones?
3. Draw a diagram of the interactions between the terrarium's biotic and abiotic factors.
4. Suppose a plant-eating insect were added to the terrarium. Predict whether it would be able to survive. Explain your prediction.
5. **Think About It** Explain how your terrarium models an ecosystem. How does your model differ from an actual ecosystem on Earth?

More to Explore

Make a plan to model a freshwater ecosystem. How would this model be different from the land ecosystem? Obtain your teacher's approval before carrying out your plan.

SECTION 2 Studying Populations

DISCOVER ·ACTIVITY· · · ·

What's the Bean Population?

1. Fill a plastic jar with dried beans. This is your model population.

2. Your goal is to determine the number of beans in the jar, but you will not have time to count every bean. You may use any of the following to help you determine the size of the bean population: a ruler, a small beaker, another large jar. Set a timer for two minutes when you are ready to begin.

3. After two minutes, record your answer. Then count the actual number of beans. How close was your answer?

Think It Over
Forming Operational Definitions
In this activity, you came up with an estimate of the size of the bean population. Write a definition of the term *estimate* based on what you did.

How would you like to change jobs for the day? Instead of being a student, today you are an ecologist. You are working on a project to study the bald eagle population in your area. One question you might ask is how the population size has changed over time. Is the number of bald eagles higher, lower, or the same as it was 50 years ago? To answer this question, you must first determine the present size of the bald eagle population.

Population Density

Ecologists may describe the size of a population as **population density**—the number of individuals in a specific area. Population density can be written as an equation:

$$Population\ density = \frac{Number\ of\ individuals}{Unit\ area}$$

For instance, suppose you counted 50 monarch butterflies in a garden measuring 10 square meters. The population density would be 50 butterflies per 10 square meters, or 5 butterflies per square meter.

GUIDE FOR READING

◆ How do ecologists determine the size of a population?

◆ What causes populations to change in size?

◆ What factors limit population growth?

Reading Tip Before you read, predict some factors that might cause a population to increase or decrease.

Key Terms population density
• estimate • birth rate
• death rate • immigration
• emigration • limiting factor
• carrying capacity

Bald eagles in Alaska ▶

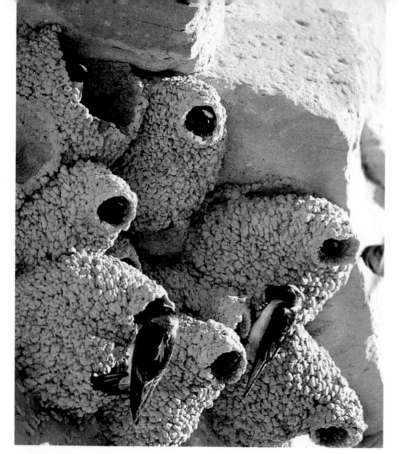

Figure 5 These cone-shaped structures are nests built by cliff swallows in Dinosaur National Monument, Utah. Counting the nests is one way to estimate the cliff swallow population.

Determining Population Size

In your work as an ecologist, how can you determine the size of the population you are studying? **Some methods of determining the size of a population are direct and indirect observations, sampling, and mark-and-recapture studies.**

Direct Observation The most obvious way to determine the size of a population is to count, one by one, all of its members. You could count all the bald eagles that live along a river, all the red maple trees in a forest, or all the elephants in a valley in Kenya.

Indirect Observation The members of a population may be small or hard to find. It may then be easier to observe their tracks or other signs rather than the organisms themselves. Look at the mud nests built by cliff swallows in Figure 5. Each nest has one entrance hole. By counting the entrance holes, you can determine the number of swallow families nesting in this area. Suppose that the average number of swallows per nest is four: two parents and two offspring. If there are 120 nests in an area, you can find the number of swallows by multiplying 120 by 4, or 480 swallows.

Sampling In most cases, it is not possible to count every member of a population. The population may be very large, or it may be spread over a wide area. It may be hard to find every individual or to remember which ones have already been counted. Instead, ecologists usually make an estimate. An **estimate** is an approximation of a number, based on reasonable assumptions.

One type of estimating involves counting the number of organisms in a small area (a sample), and then multiplying to find the number in a larger area. To get an accurate estimate, the sample should have the same population density as the larger area. For example, suppose you count 8 red maples in a 10 meter-by-10 meter area of the forest. If the entire forest were 100 times that size, you would multiply your count by 100 to estimate the total population, or 800 red maples.

Mark-and-Recapture Studies Another estimating method is a technique called "mark and recapture." This technique gets its name because some animals are captured and marked, and then released into the environment. Then another group of animals is captured.

The number of marked animals in this second group indicates the population size. For example, if half the animals in the second group are marked, the first sample represented about half the total population.

Here's an example showing how mark and recapture works. First, deer mice in a field are caught in a trap that does not harm the mice. Ecologists count the mice and mark each mouse with a dot of hair dye before releasing it again. Two weeks later, the researchers return and capture mice again. They count how many mice have marks, showing that they were captured the first time, and how many are unmarked. Using a mathematical formula, the scientists can estimate the total population of mice in the field. You can try this technique for yourself in the Real-World Lab at the end of this section.

Figure 6 This young hawk is part of a mark-and-recapture study in a Virginia marsh. *Inferring What is the purpose of the silver band on the hawk's leg?*

✓ *Checkpoint* When is sampling used to estimate a population?

Changes in Population Size

By returning to a location often and using one of the methods described here, ecologists can monitor the size of a population over time. **Populations can change in size when new members enter the population or when members leave the population.**

Births and Deaths The major way in which new individuals are added to a population is through the birth of offspring. The **birth rate** of a population is the number of births in a population in a certain amount of time. For example, suppose a population of 1,000 snow geese produces 1,400 goslings in a year. The birth rate in this population would be 1,400 goslings per year.

Similarly, the major way that individuals leave a population is by dying. The **death rate** is the number of deaths in a population in a certain amount of time. Suppose that in the same population, 500 geese die in a year. The death rate would be 500 geese per year.

Figure 7 The birth of new individuals can increase the size of a population. This cheetah mother added five offspring to the population in her area.

Math TOOLBOX

Inequalities

The population statement is an example of an inequality. An inequality is a mathematical statement that compares two expressions. Two signs that represent inequalities are:

< (is less than)
> (is greater than)

For example, an inequality comparing the fraction $\frac{1}{2}$ to the decimal 0.75 would be written:

$$\frac{1}{2} < 0.75$$

Write an inequality comparing each pair of expressions below.

1. 5 ? −6
2. 0.4 ? $\frac{3}{5}$
3. −2 − (−8) ? 7 − 1.5

The Population Statement When the birth rate in a population is greater than the death rate, the population will generally increase in size. This statement can be written as a mathematical statement using the "is greater than" sign:

If birth rate > death rate, population size increases.

For example, in the snow goose population, the birth rate of 1,400 goslings per year was greater than the death rate of 500 geese per year, and the population would increase in size.

However, if the death rate in a population is greater than the birth rate, the population size will generally decrease. This can also be written as a mathematical statement:

If death rate > birth rate, population size decreases.

Immigration and Emigration The size of a population also can change when individuals move into or out of the population, just as the population of your town changes when families move into town or move away. **Immigration** (im ih GRAY shun) means moving into a population. **Emigration** (em ih GRAY shun) means leaving a population. Emigration can occur when part of a population gets cut off from the rest of the population. For instance, if food is scarce, some members of an antelope herd may wander off in search of better grassland. If they become permanently separated from the original herd, they will no longer be part of that population.

Graphing Population Changes You can see an example of changes in a population of rabbits in Figure 8. The vertical axis shows the numbers of rabbits in the population, while the horizontal axis shows time. The graph shows the size of the population over a 10-year period.

☑ *Checkpoint Name two ways individuals can join a population.*

Figure 8 From Year 0 to Year 4, more rabbits were added to the population than were lost, so the population increased. From Year 4 to Year 8, more rabbits left the population than joined it, so the population decreased. From Year 8 to Year 10, the rates of rabbits leaving and joining the population were about equal, so the population remained steady.
Interpreting Graphs In what year did the rabbit population reach its highest point? What was the size of the population in that year?

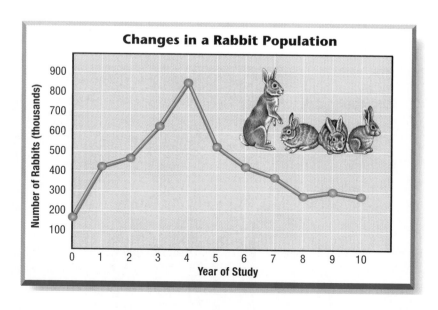

Changes in a Rabbit Population

Number of Rabbits (thousands)

Year of Study

Figure 9 These gannets seem to have heard the saying "Birds of a feather flock together." When there are more birds than the space can support, the population will have exceeded the carrying capacity of the shore.

Limiting Factors

When conditions are good, a population will generally increase. But a population does not keep growing forever. Eventually, some factor in its environment causes the population to stop growing. A **limiting factor** is an environmental factor that prevents a population from increasing. **Some limiting factors for populations are food, space, and weather conditions.**

Food Organisms require food to survive. In an area where food is scarce, this becomes a limiting factor. Suppose a giraffe needs to eat 10 kilograms of leaves each day to survive. The trees in an area can provide 100 kilograms of leaves a day while remaining healthy. Five giraffes could live easily in this area, since they would only require a total of 50 kilograms of food. But 15 giraffes could not all survive—there would not be enough food for all of them. No matter how much shelter, water, and other resources there might be, the population will not grow much higher than 10 giraffes. The largest population that an environment can support is called its **carrying capacity.** The carrying capacity of this environment is 10 giraffes.

Space The birds in Figure 9 are rarely seen on land. These birds, called gannets, spend most of their lives flying over the ocean. They only land on this rocky shore to nest. But as you can see, the shore is very crowded. If a pair of gannets does not have room to build a nest, that pair will not be able to produce any offspring.

Elbow Room

ACTIVITY

Using masking tape, mark off several one-meter squares on the floor of your classroom. Your teacher will form groups of 2, 4, and 6 students. Each group's task is to put together a small jigsaw puzzle in one of the squares. All the group members must keep their feet within the square. Time how long it takes your group to finish the puzzle.

Making Models How long did it take each group to complete the task? How does this activity show that space can be a limiting factor? What is the carrying capacity of puzzle-solvers in a square meter?

Figure 10 A snowstorm can limit the size of the orange crop.

Those gannets will not contribute to an increase in the gannet population. This means that space for nesting is a limiting factor for these gannets. If the shore were bigger, more gannets would be able to nest there, and the population would increase.

Space is often a limiting factor for plants. The amount of space in which a plant grows can determine how much sunlight, water, and other necessities the plant can obtain. For example, many pine seedlings sprout each year in a forest. But as the trees get bigger, those young trees that are too close together do not have room to spread their roots underground. Other tree branches block out the sunlight that the pine seedlings need to carry on photosynthesis. Some of the seedlings die, limiting the size of the pine population.

Weather Weather conditions such as temperature and amount of rainfall can also limit population growth. Many insect species breed in the warm spring weather. As winter begins, the first frost kills many of the insects. This sudden rise in the death rate causes the insect population to decrease.

A single severe weather event can dramatically change the size of a population by killing many organisms. For instance, a flood or hurricane can wash away nests and burrows just as it damages the homes of humans. An ice storm can limit the populations of crops planted in the early spring.

Section 2 Review

1. List four ways of determining population size.
2. How is birth rate related to population size?
3. List three limiting factors for populations. Choose one and explain how this factor can limit population growth.
4. Explain why it is often necessary for ecologists to estimate the size of a population.
5. **Thinking Critically Problem Solving** A field measures 50 meters by 90 meters. In one square meter, you count 3 grasshoppers. Estimate the total population of grasshoppers in the field. What method did you use to make your estimate?

Science at Home

Word Estimates Choose a page of a dictionary or other book that has a lot of type on it. Challenge your family members to estimate the number of words on the page. Have each person explain the method he or she used. Now count the actual number of words on the page. Whose estimate was closest?

Counting Turtles

For three years, the mark-and-recapture method has been used to monitor the turtle population in a pond. In this lab, you will model this method to complete the study.

Problem

How can the mark-and-recapture method help ecologists monitor the size of a population?

Skills Focus

calculating, graphing, predicting

Materials

model paper turtle population
computer and spreadsheet program (optional)
calculator   graph paper

Procedure

1. The data table shows the results from the first three years of the study. Copy it into your notebook or spreadsheet, leaving spaces for your data as shown.
2. Your teacher will give you a box representing the pond. Fifteen of the turtles have been marked, as shown in the data table for Year 4.
3. Capture a member of the population by randomly selecting one turtle. Set it aside.
4. Repeat Step 3 nine times. Record the total number of turtles you captured.

5. Examine each turtle to see whether it has a mark. Count the number of recaptured (marked) turtles. Record this number in your data table.

Analyze and Conclude

1. Use the equation below to estimate the turtle population for each year. The first year is done for you as a sample. If your answer is a decimal, round it to the nearest whole number so that your estimate is in "whole turtles." Record the population for each year in the last column of the data table.

$$\text{Total population} = \frac{\text{Number marked} \times \text{Total number captured}}{\text{Number recaptured (with marks)}}$$

Sample (Year 1):

$$\frac{32 \times 28}{15} = 59.7 \text{ or } 60 \text{ turtles}$$

2. Graph the estimated total populations for the four years. Mark years on the horizontal axis. Mark population size on the vertical axis.
3. Describe how the turtle population has changed over the four years of the study. Suggest three possible causes for the changes.
4. **Apply** Use your graph to predict the turtle population in Year 5. Explain your prediction.

Getting Involved

Find out whether any wildlife populations in your area are being monitored by national, state, or local agencies. Make a poster or write an article for the school paper about the population and the method being used to study it.

DATA TABLE

Year	Number Marked	Total Number Captured	Number Recaptured (with Marks)	Estimated Total Population
1	32	28	15	
2	25	21	11	
3	23	19	11	
4	15			

3 Energy in an Ecosystem

DISCOVER ································· ACTIVITY····

What's Eating What?

1. With a teacher, visit an ecosystem, such as a park. Bring field equipment such as field guides, binoculars, and a hand lens.

2. Observe your surroundings. Your teacher will tell you how to use the field equipment.

3. Identify as many different organisms as possible, and list them on a sheet of paper.

4. Divide the organisms on the list into two categories: those that make their own food and those that depend on other organisms for food.

Think It Over

Inferring Choose three organisms that do not make their own food. Think of two possible food sources for each organism.

GUIDE FOR READING

◆ How does energy flow in living systems?

◆ What are some cycles in nature in which matter and energy interact?

◆ What happens when biomass decays?

Reading Tip Before you read, rewrite each section heading as a "what" or "how" question. Then write answers to each question as you read.

Key Terms producers
• consumer • decomposer
• food chain • food web
• nitrogen fixation • biomass

It's a warm spring afternoon, a perfect day for a barbecue. Your family and friends are gathered to have a good time. People are talking, playing baseball, and laughing. You're slicing tomatoes for a salad while your cousin pours lemonade. The smell of the chicken sizzling on the grill makes your mouth water. The sun shines brightly on the whole scene.

This barbecue is all about energy. It takes energy to play frisbee and slice tomatoes, and even to talk and laugh. You get the energy to do these things from the food you eat. But where does the energy in the salad and barbecued chicken come from? As you will see, it all starts with that bright sunlight.

An Ecosystem's Energy Source

Since the people at the barbecue must eat food to obtain energy, all of them are heterotrophs. Remember from Chapter 4 that a heterotroph is an organism that cannot make its own food. Animals and fungi are two kinds of heterotrophs. Other organisms, such as plants, can make their own food. As you know, such organisms are called autotrophs.

Depending on Autotrophs
Heterotrophs are dependent on autotrophs for food, either directly or indirectly. At the barbecue, for example, when you eat potato salad, you are obtaining energy from an autotroph, because the potatoes were produced by potato plants. But even when you eat a hamburger, you are obtaining energy originally produced by autotrophs. Beef cattle—the source of hamburgers—are heterotrophs. But the main source of cattle's food is grass. All plants including grasses are autotrophs.

Figure 11 Plants, which are autotrophs, use the energy in sunlight to make molecules in which energy is stored.
Applying Concepts How do animals use the energy stored in plants?

Sunlight and Food Energy Energy enters most ecosystems from sunlight. That is because most autotrophs make their food through photosynthesis. As you read in Chapter 6, photosynthesis is the process by which plants, algae, and certain microorganisms convert the energy in sunlight to energy stored in plants. In the presence of sunlight, the plant produces molecules in which energy is stored.

By breaking down energy-containing molecules, the plant can use this stored energy to grow and carry out other life processes. When animals and other heterotrophs eat plants, they too can use the energy stored in plants during photosynthesis.

☑ *Checkpoint* *What is the ultimate source of energy for most ecosystems?*

Energy Roles in Ecosystems

Ecologists classify organisms by their role in the flow of energy through ecosystems. The terms ecologists use to describe energy roles are *producer, consumer,* and *decomposer.* Because autotrophs produce food and store energy, they are called **producers.** Flowers, grass, seaweed, and cacti are familiar producers.

Heterotrophs that obtain food and energy by eating other organisms are called **consumers.** Consumers include herbivores, carnivores, and omnivores. Herbivores, as you learned in Chapter 7, eat only plants. Cattle, which eat grass, are herbivores. Consumers that eat only animals are called carnivores. Coyotes, which eat other animals such as chickens and rabbits, are carnivores. Omnivores, such as bears and most humans, eat both plants and animals.

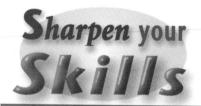

Figure 12 Plants such as the yucca (**A**) are producers that make their own food. Consumers such as these javelina (**B**) obtain energy by eating other organisms. Mold (**C**) is a decomposer that breaks down wastes and dead organisms.

Some heterotrophs, called **decomposers,** obtain energy by breaking down wastes and the remains of dead organisms. The decomposers break down large molecules in dead organisms into small chemicals, such as minerals, water, and other simple molecules. The decomposers use some of these molecules in their own bodies. The other small molecules are returned to the environment. Mold and some bacteria are decomposers.

✓ *Checkpoint* *What are the three major energy roles organisms play in an ecosystem?*

Energy Flow in Food Chains and Food Webs

Energy enters an ecosystem when producers convert the sun's energy into stored food energy. When a consumer eats a producer, some of this stored food energy is transferred to the consumer. This consumer may be eaten by another consumer, and so on. Each time an organism eats another, some energy is transferred to the feeding organism. Finally, a decomposer breaks down the remains of organisms. Some energy is transferred to the decomposer, and the rest is released, often as heat.

Ecologists use a diagram called a **food chain** to show the flow of energy from organism to organism. **In general, energy flows from producers to consumers to decomposers in an ecosystem.** Follow the energy through the ecosystem shown in *Exploring a Food Chain*.

EXPLORING a Food Chain

This food chain is an example of the feeding relationships that might occur in one part of a Texas brush country ecosystem. A food chain always begins with a producer.

④ Bobcat
Third-level consumer
The bobcat is also a carnivore. When a bobcat eats a second-level consumer such as the weasel, the bobcat is called a third-level consumer.

① Prickly pear cactus
Producer
The cactus converts the sun's energy into the matter that makes up its thick leaves and flowers.

② Woodrat
First-level consumer
This small rodent obtains energy by eating other organisms, such as the prickly pear cactus. Consumers that eat producers are called first-level consumers.

③ Weasel
Second-level consumer
The weasel is a carnivore and feeds on other consumers. When the weasel eats a first-level consumer such as the woodrat, the weasel is considered a second-level consumer.

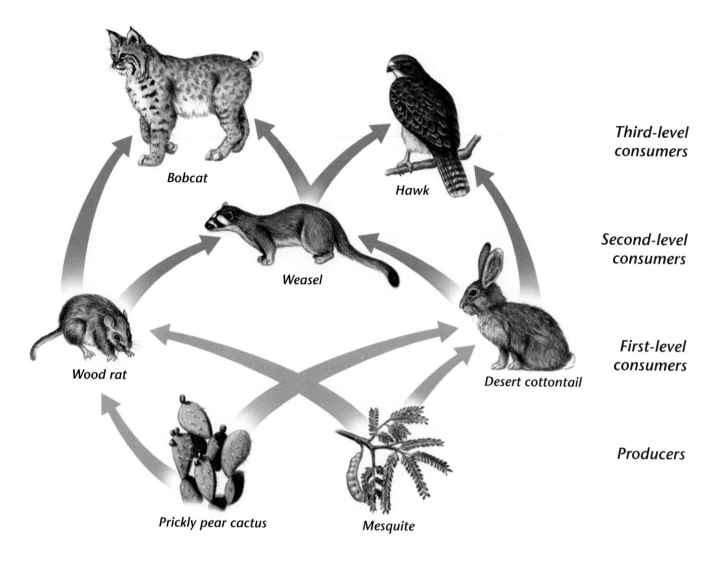

Third-level consumers

Second-level consumers

First-level consumers

Producers

Bobcat

Hawk

Weasel

Wood rat

Desert cottontail

Prickly pear cactus

Mesquite

Figure 13 In an ecosystem, many food chains overlap to form a food web, such as the one shown here.

Many food chains exist in each ecosystem. Some of these food chains overlap. For example, a producer such as a prickly pear is food for other consumers besides a wood rat. A wood rat feeds on other producers besides a prickly pear. And a hawk feeds on many different animals. A diagram called a **food web** shows how many food chains are connected. Figure 13 shows one food web.

☑ *Checkpoint* *What is a food chain?*

Cycles in Ecosystems

As you have read, organisms use energy as it moves through an ecosystem from producer to consumer to decomposer. Certain matter that organisms need, such as water, carbon, and nitrogen, cycles through the ecosystem as well. When a consumer eats a producer, for example, more than just a transfer of energy occurs. A transfer of matter, such as carbon molecules, also occurs. **Some cycles in which matter and energy interact in an ecosystem are the water cycle, the carbon and oxygen cycles, and the nitrogen cycle.** You will read about the water cycle in Chapter 12.

The Carbon and Oxygen Cycles The recycling of carbon and oxygen is linked to the flow of energy in an ecosystem. As you read about the carbon and oxygen cycles, follow the diagram in Figure 14. Carbon dioxide in the air contains the element carbon. Producers take in carbon dioxide gas during photosynthesis. They use the carbon from the carbon dioxide to produce other carbon-containing molecules such as the sugars and starches that are stored in their bodies. A consumer such as a horse then eats plants. It obtains energy from these molecules by breaking them down into simpler molecules. Recall that this process is called respiration. Carbon dioxide gas is released as a waste product of respiration.

Meanwhile, oxygen is also cycling through the ecosystem. Producers release oxygen as a result of photosynthesis. Most organisms take in oxygen and use it during respiration.

The Nitrogen Cycle Although air is about 78 percent nitrogen gas, most organisms cannot use nitrogen. Nitrogen gas, which is called "free" nitrogen, is not combined with other elements. Most organisms can only use nitrogen that is combined with other elements.

The process of combining free nitrogen with other elements is called **nitrogen fixation.** Bacteria that live in swellings called nodules on the roots of some plants perform much nitrogen fixation. These bacteria combine nitrogen with other elements, forming fixed nitrogen, or nitrogen-containing compounds. Consumers use this fixed nitrogen to build proteins and other substances. Nitrogen is also fixed in other ways, such as through the action of lightning on free nitrogen.

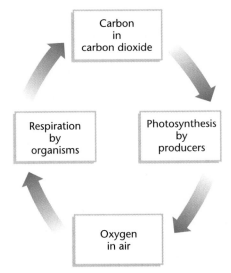

Figure 14 Carbon dioxide is used during photosynthesis. Photo-synthesis, in turn, produces oxygen, which is used in respiration. Respiration produces carbon dioxide, and the cycle begins again.

Figure 15 In the nitrogen cycle, nitrogen moves from the air to the soil, into living things, and back into the air.
Interpreting Diagrams How do consumers obtain nitrogen?

Free nitrogen in air

Consumers eat nitrogen compounds in plants

Bacteria release some free nitrogen back to air

Decomposers break down wastes and the remains of organisms and return nitrogen compounds to soil

Bacteria in root nodules fix free nitrogen into compounds

The Decay of Biomass

If you walk in a forest, you can see many living things. And whether or not you are aware of it, the forest also contains the remains of organisms that have died. The total amount of living matter, and the remains of dead organisms, in an area is the area's **biomass.**

Biomass is matter that contains energy stored in its chemical compounds. When living things die, bacteria and other decomposers break down the material in the biomass. In this decay process, the decomposers break large molecules into smaller ones. **The decay of biomass produces matter in the form of small molecules. This chemical breakdown also releases the energy stored in the chemical compounds in the biomass.** The energy is released in the form of heat.

Gardeners who keep compost piles take advantage of the decay of biomass. You may have seen gardeners add things such as corn husks, rotten vegetables, and grass clippings to a compost pile. The biomass in a compost pile is broken down by decomposers in the pile. Compost makes good fertilizer because producers, such as garden plants, can absorb and use the small molecules produced by the decay of biomass. The chemical breakdown of compost also releases energy. This is why you can often feel heat rising from a compost pile.

Figure 16 As the matter in a compost pile decays, both small molecules and energy are produced.
Relating Cause and Effect Why is compost beneficial to plants?

Section 3 Review

1. Describe how energy flows through most ecosystems.
2. Name three cycles in which matter and energy interact in ecosystems.
3. Explain what happens to matter and energy as compost decays.
4. What is the role of plants in the carbon and oxygen cycles?
5. **Thinking Critically Comparing and Contrasting** Compare and contrast consumers and decomposers.

Check Your Progress ···· CHAPTER PROJECT
By now you should be making your final observations of your plants and planning your report. How can you present your data in a graph? Think about what you should put on each axis of your graph. (*Hint:* Draft the written portion of your report early enough to look it over and make any necessary changes.)

SECTION 1 — Components of Ecosystems

Key Ideas

- All the living and nonliving things that interact in an area make up an ecosystem.
- An organism's habitat provides food, water, shelter, and other things the organism needs to live, grow, and reproduce.
- Organisms in an ecosystem respond to both biotic and abiotic factors. Abiotic factors found in many environments include water, sunlight, oxygen, temperature, and soil.
- A population consists of a single species. The different populations living together in one area make up a community. The community plus abiotic factors form an ecosystem.
- Ecologists study how biotic and abiotic factors interact within an ecosystem.

Key Terms

ecosystem	population
habitat	society
biotic factor	community
abiotic factor	ecology

SECTION 2 — Studying Populations

INTEGRATING **MATHEMATICS**

Key Ideas

- Ecologists can estimate population size by direct and indirect observations, sampling, and mark-and-recapture studies.
- A population changes in size as a result of changes in the birth rate or death rate, or when organisms move into or out of the population.
- Population size is controlled by limiting factors such as food, space, and weather conditions.

Key Terms

population density	immigration
estimate	emigration
birth rate	limiting factor
death rate	carrying capacity

SECTION 3 — Energy in an Ecosystem

Key Ideas

- Energy enters most ecosystems from sunlight.
- The terms *producer*, *consumer* and *decomposer* describe the energy roles of organisms in an ecosystem.
- In general, energy flows from producers to consumers to decomposers in an ecosystem.
- Some cycles in which matter and energy interact are the water cycle, the carbon and oxygen cycles, and the nitrogen cycle.

Key Terms

producer	food web
consumer	nitrogen fixation
decomposer	biomass
food chain	

Organizing Information

Concept Map Copy the flow chart about energy in ecosystems onto a sheet of paper. Complete it and add a title. (For more on flow charts, see the Skills Handbook.)

Reviewing Content

Review key concepts online using
iText at www.phschool.com

Multiple Choice
Choose the letter of the best answer.

1. Which of the following is *not* an example of a population?
   a. the pets in your neighborhood
   b. the people in a city
   c. the rainbow trout in a stream
   d. the ants in an anthill

2. A prairie dog, a hawk, and a badger all are members of the same
   a. habitat.
   b. community.
   c. species.
   d. population.

3. All of the following are examples of limiting factors for populations *except*
   a. space
   b. food
   c. time
   d. weather

4. Energy enters an ecosystem from
   a. decomposers.
   b. sunlight.
   c. consumers.
   d. producers.

5. An omnivore is a kind of
   a. herbivore.
   b. carnivore.
   c. consumer.
   d. producer.

True or False
If the statement is true, write true. If it is false, change the underlined word or words to make the statement true.

6. Grass is an example of a(n) <u>abiotic</u> factor in a habitat.

7. A rise in birth rate while the death rate remains steady will cause a population to <u>increase</u> in size.

8. A population in an ecosystem belongs to a <u>community</u> consisting of different species.

9. The <u>consumers</u> in an ecosystem produce food and stored energy.

10. A <u>food chain</u> shows how energy flows from organism to organism in an ecosystem.

Checking Concepts

11. Name two biotic and two abiotic factors you might find in a forest ecosystem.

12. Explain how sunlight is used by plants and algae. How is this process important to other living things in an ecosystem?

13. Describe how ecologists use the technique of sampling to estimate population size.

14. Give an example showing how space can be a limiting factor for a population.

15. Explain why nitrogen fixation is important to organisms. How does it occur?

16. Explain why decomposers are important in an ecosystem.

17. Organisms produce carbon dioxide in the process of respiration. Explain how this carbon dioxide is recycled in an ecosystem.

18. **Writing to Learn** Write a brochure for home gardeners that explains how a compost pile can improve their garden.

Thinking Critically

19. **Making Generalizations** Explain why ecologists usually study a specific population of organisms rather than studying the entire species.

20. **Applying Concepts** Name a biotic factor that you might find in a prairie ecosystem. Describe how a prairie dog might respond to that biotic factor.

21. **Problem Solving** In a summer job working for an ecologist, you have been assigned to estimate the population of grasshoppers in a field. Propose a method to get an estimate and explain how you would carry it out.

22. **Comparing and Contrasting** Explain how a food chain and a food web are similar and how they are different.

23. **Relating Cause and Effect** Nitrogen-fixing bacteria grow in nodules on the roots of clover plants. Farmers sometimes plant clover instead of a crop for one growing season. Explain why this makes the soil more fertile.

Applying Skills

Ecologists monitoring a deer population collected data during a 30-year study. Use the data to answer Questions 24–27.

Year	0	5	10	15	20	25	30
Population (thousands)	15	30	65	100	40	25	10

24. **Graphing** Make a line graph using the data in the table. Plot years on the horizontal axis and population on the vertical axis.
25. **Interpreting Data** In which year did the deer population reach its highest point? Its lowest point?
26. **Communicating** Write a few sentences describing how the deer population changed during the study.

27. **Developing Hypotheses** In Year 16 of the study, this region experienced a very severe winter. How might this have affected the deer population?

Performance CHAPTER PROJECT Assessment

Present Your Project Review your report and graph to be sure that they clearly state your conclusion about the effects of crowding on plant growth. With your group, decide how you will present your results. Do a practice run-through to make sure all group members feel comfortable with their part.

Reflect and Record Compare your group's results with those of your classmates. Suggest possible explanations for any differences. How could you have improved your plan for your experiment?

Test Preparation
Use these questions to prepare for standardized tests.

Study the graph. Then answer Questions 28–31.

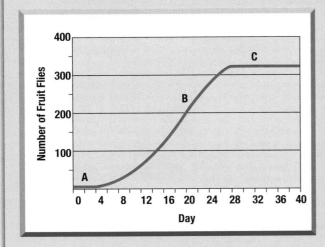

28. What is the best title for this graph?
    A Fruit Fly Population Density
    B Abiotic Factors and Fruit Flies
    C Fruit Fly Population Growth
    D Fruit Fly Death Rate

29. At what point on the graph is the population of fruit flies increasing?
    F Point A   G Point B
    H Point C   J none of the above

30. Which of the following statements may be true of the fruit fly population at Point C?
    A The death rate is approximately equal to the birth rate.
    B A limiting factor in the environment is preventing the population from increasing.
    C There may not be enough food or space to support a larger population.
    D All of the above statements may be true.

31. Based on the graph, what is the carrying capacity of the environment in which the fruit flies live?
    F approximately 320 fruit flies
    G approximately 220 fruit flies
    H approximately 410 fruit flies
    J approximately 160 fruit flies

Energy Resources

Electricity makes
downtown Los Angeles
sparkle at dusk.

WEB ACTIVITY
www.phschool.com

Energy Audit

The Los Angeles skyline comes alive with electric lights as the sun goes down. It takes a lot of energy to keep a city running. Energy keeps the people of Los Angeles cool, provides them with electricity, and helps them move from place to place. Energy is also needed to make the products that clothe, feed, inform, and entertain them.

How much energy does it take to keep your school running? Throughout the chapter, you will work in a group to study energy use in your school.

Your Goal To write a report on a type of energy use in your school including your suggestions for saving energy.

To complete the project, you must
◆ Survey the types and amount of energy used in the area
◆ Identify ways to conserve energy in that area
◆ Prepare a written report summarizing your observations and proposing your suggestions

Get Started With your group, select an area of the school to study, such as a classroom, the cafeteria, or the school grounds. You could also consider the school's heating or cooling system or transportation to and from school. Brainstorm a list of the ways in which you think energy is used in and around your school.

Check Your Progress You'll be working on this project as you study this chapter. To keep your project on track, look for Check Your Progress boxes at the following points.

Section 1 Review, page 298: Observe the area and record the types of energy used.

Section 2 Review, page 304: Collect data on the amount of energy used and look for ways to reduce it.

Section 3 Review, page 311: Write a draft of your report.

Present Your Project At the end of the chapter (page 319), you will present your group's proposal to make your school more energy-efficient.

TEKS

In addition to process TEKS, this chapter addresses these concept TEKS as they relate to the chapter's topics.

(6.9) The student knows that obtaining, transforming, and distributing energy affects the environment. The student is expected to:
(A) identify energy transformations occurring during the production of energy for human use such as electrical energy to heat energy or heat energy to electrical energy;

(B) compare methods used for transforming energy in devices such as water heaters, cooling systems, or hydroelectric and wind power plants; and
(C) research and describe energy types from their source to their use and determine if the type is renewable, nonrenewable, or inexhaustible.

Energy and Fossil Fuels

DISCOVER •• ACTIVITY ••••

What's in a Piece of Coal?

1. Observe a chunk of coal. Record your observations in as much detail as possible, including color, texture, and shape.

2. Now use a hand lens to observe the coal more closely.

3. Examine your coal for fossils, imprints of plant or animal remains.

Think It Over
Observing What did you notice when you used the hand lens compared to your first observations? What do you think coal is made of?

GUIDE FOR READING

◆ How do fuels provide energy?

◆ Why are fossil fuels considered nonrenewable resources?

Reading Tip As you read, make a table comparing coal, oil, and natural gas. Describe each fuel and note how it is obtained and used.

Key Terms
• energy transformation • fuel
• combustion • fossil fuel
• hydrocarbon
• nonrenewable resource
• petroleum • refinery
• petrochemical
• reserves

◀ Electric power lines stretch against the evening sky.

Try to imagine what would happen if the electricity suddenly went off. The lights would go out, plunging your school into darkness. Traffic signals would stop working, causing traffic jams. Computers, microwave ovens, clocks, and radios—nothing would work! Such an event would remind you of the importance of one form of energy—electrical energy, or electricity.

Recall from Chapter 1 that energy is the ability to do work or cause change. Energy exists in several different forms: mechanical, thermal, chemical, electrical, electromagnetic, and nuclear. All the different forms of energy help to meet people's energy needs.

Energy Transformation

Energy can be changed from one form to another. To see how, rub your hands together quickly for several seconds. Did you feel them become warmer? When you moved your hands, they had mechanical energy, the energy of motion. The friction of your hands rubbing together changed some of the mechanical energy to thermal energy, which you felt as heat.

A change from one form of energy to another is called an **energy transformation**, or an energy conversion. Any form of energy can be transformed into any other form.

You encounter energy transformations frequently. A toaster, for example, transforms electrical energy to thermal energy. In an electric motor, electrical energy is transformed to mechanical energy that can be used to run a machine.

Furnace

Steam

Transformer **Power lines**

Turbine

Water

Generator

Fuel **Condenser**

Intake pipe

Fuels and Energy

INTEGRATING PHYSICS How did you travel to school today? Whether you traveled in a car or a bus, walked, or rode your bike, your trip involved transformations of energy. A substance called a **fuel** was the source of that energy. **A fuel is a substance that provides a form of energy—such as heat, light, electricity, or motion—as the result of a chemical change.**

Combustion Fuels contain stored chemical energy, which can be released by burning. The process of burning a fuel is called **combustion.** For example, the fuel used by most cars is gasoline. When gasoline is burned in a car engine, it undergoes a chemical change. The gasoline combines with oxygen, producing carbon dioxide and water. The combustion of gasoline also converts some of the stored chemical energy into thermal energy. This thermal energy is converted to mechanical energy that moves the car.

Production of Electricity The energy stored in fuels can be used to generate electricty. In most power plants, the thermal energy produced by burning fuel is used to boil water, making steam. The mechanical energy of the steam turns the blades of a turbine. The shaft of the turbine is connected to a generator. The generator consists of powerful magnets surrounded by coils of copper wire. As the shaft rotates, the magnets turn inside the wire coil, producing an electric current. The electric current flows through power lines to homes and industries.

Checkpoint *What are three energy transformations that might occur in a power plant?*

Figure 1 Electric power plants generate electricity by converting energy from one form to another. In the furnace, fuel is burned, releasing thermal energy. This energy is used to boil water and make steam. The mechanical energy of the moving steam turns the blades of a turbine. The turbine turns the shaft of the generator, producing an electric current.

Energy Transformations in the Home

Energy transformations continue even after electrical energy has been produced at a power plant. Household appliances and other devices powered by electricity all transform energy in various ways to perform useful work.

Water Heaters One example of energy transformation in the home is a water heater. Electric water heaters contain a heating element that transforms electrical energy into thermal energy, causing the water to become hotter. In some water heaters, natural gas provides the energy source. Burning this fuel changes stored chemical energy into thermal energy and heats the water.

Cooling Systems Energy transformation can also be used to keep food and buildings cool inside. Does that surprise you? After all, heat naturally flows from a warm object to a cold object—not the other way around. So how are food and buildings kept cool?

Figure 2 This diagram shows the basic parts of a refrigerator.
Interpreting Diagrams How are energy transformations used to cool food?

Heat

MILK

Heat into room   Compressor   Refrigerant

A refrigerator is a device that keeps food cold. It uses an outside energy source to transfer thermal energy from a cool area to a warm area. In your refrigerator, that energy is provided by an electric motor. Perhaps you have felt this energy in the warm air blowing out at the bottom of a refrigerator.

The electric motor in a refrigerator runs a compressor that contains a refrigerant substance. The compressor squeezes together the refrigerant particles in the gas state. This causes the refrigerant's pressure and temperature to rise. When this happens, the gas loses thermal energy. This thermal energy is transferred to the outside air as heat. As the gas loses thermal energy, it becomes a liquid. The liquid is then allowed to evaporate. As it evaporates, it cools. The cold gas is then pumped through tubes inside the walls of the refrigerator. There the gas absorbs thermal energy from inside the refrigerator. The gas then returns to the compressor, and the whole cycle begins again.

An air conditioner operates in the same way. But it cools the air inside a building and transfers thermal energy to the air outdoors.

Figure 3 Coal, a fossil fuel, provides the energy for this historic steam engine.

What Are Fossil Fuels?

Most of the energy used today comes from organisms that lived hundreds of millions of years ago. As these plants, animals, and other organisms died, their remains piled up. Layers of sand, rock, and mud buried the dead organisms. Over time, heat and pressure changed the material into other substances. **Fossil fuels** are the energy-rich substances formed from the remains of once-living organisms. The three fossil fuels are oil, natural gas, and coal.

Fossil fuels are made of hydrocarbons. **Hydrocarbons** are energy-rich chemical compounds that contain carbon and hydrogen atoms. During combustion, the carbon and hydrogen combine with oxygen in the air to form carbon dioxide and water. This process releases energy in the forms of heat and light.

Fossil fuels have more hydrocarbons per kilogram than most other fuels. For this reason, they are excellent sources of energy. Combustion of one kilogram of coal, for example, provides twice as much heat as burning one kilogram of wood. Oil and natural gas provide three times the energy of wood.

Because fossil fuels take hundreds of millions of years to form, they are considered nonrenewable resources. Earth's **nonrenewable resources** are natural resources that are not replaced as they are used. For example, Earth's known oil reserves took 500 million years to form. One fourth of this oil has already been used. The rate at which fossil fuels are used continues to speed up. If fossil fuels continue to be used more rapidly than they are formed, they will eventually run out.

Sharpen your Skills

Graphing ACTIVITY

Use the data in the table below to make a circle graph showing the uses of energy in the United States. (To review circle graphs, see the Skills Handbook.) You can use the computer to make your graph.

End Use of Energy	Percent of Total Energy
Transportation	26.5
Industry	38.1
Homes and businesses	35.4

Figure 4 These workers are preparing to drill an oil well.

Oil

Oil is a thick, black, liquid fossil fuel. It formed from the remains of small animals, algae, and protists that lived in oceans and shallow inland seas hundreds of millions of years ago. **Petroleum** is another name for oil, from the Latin words *petra* (rock) and *oleum* (oil). Most oil deposits are located underground in tiny holes in sandstone or limestone. The oil fills the holes somewhat like water trapped in the holes of a sponge.

Petroleum accounts for more than one third of the energy produced in the world. Fuel for most cars, airplanes, trains, and ships comes from petroleum. Many homes are heated by oil.

The United States consumes about one third of all the oil produced in the world. But only three percent of the world's supply is located in this country. The difference must be purchased from countries with large oil supplies.

Petroleum is a relatively cheap and plentiful energy source. But producing and using petroleum does affect the environment. For example, oil may be spilled into the ocean when an oil tanker runs aground. The spilled oil harms organisms such as fish and birds. Gasoline spilled on land may seep into groundwater, polluting the water supply. Another environmental effect of oil is that burning it contributes to air pollution.

Locating Oil Deposits Because it is usually located deep below the surface, finding oil is difficult. *INTEGRATING TECHNOLOGY* Scientists can use sound waves to test an area for oil without drilling. This technique relies on the fact that sound waves bounce off objects and return as echoes. Scientists send pulses of sound down into the rocks below ground. Then they measure how long it takes the echoes to return. The amount of time depends on whether the sound waves must travel through solid rock or liquid oils. This information can indicate the most likely places to find oil. However, only about one out of every six wells drilled produces a usable amount of oil.

Refining Oil When oil is first pumped out of the ground, it is called crude oil. Crude oil can be a runny or a thick liquid. In order to be made into useful products, crude oil must undergo a process called refining. A factory where crude oil is separated into fuels and other products by heating is called a **refinery.**

In addition to gasoline and heating oil, many products you use every day are made from refined crude oil. **Petrochemicals** are compounds that are made from oil. Petrochemicals are used in plastics, paints, medicines, and cosmetics.

Oil refineries can affect the environment. Chemicals produced in the refining process may escape into the air or water, causing pollution.

☑ *Checkpoint* How is petroleum used?

Natural Gas

Another fossil fuel is natural gas, a mixture of methane and other gases. Natural gas forms from the same organisms as petroleum. Because it is less dense than oil, natural gas often rises above an oil deposit, forming a pocket of gas in the rock.

Pipelines transport the gas from its source to the places where it is used. Natural gas can also be compressed into a liquid and stored in tanks.

Natural gas has several advantages. It produces large amounts of energy, but lower levels of many air pollutants than coal or oil. It is also easy to transport once the network of pipelines is built. One disadvantage of natural gas is that a gas leak can cause a violent explosion and fire.

Gas companies help to prevent dangerous explosions from leaks. If you use natural gas in your home, you probably are familiar with the "gas" smell that alerts you whenever there is unburned gas in the air. You may be surprised to learn that natural gas actually has no odor at all. What causes the strong smell? The gas companies add a chemical with a distinct smell to the gas before it is piped to homes and businesses so that any leaks will be noticed.

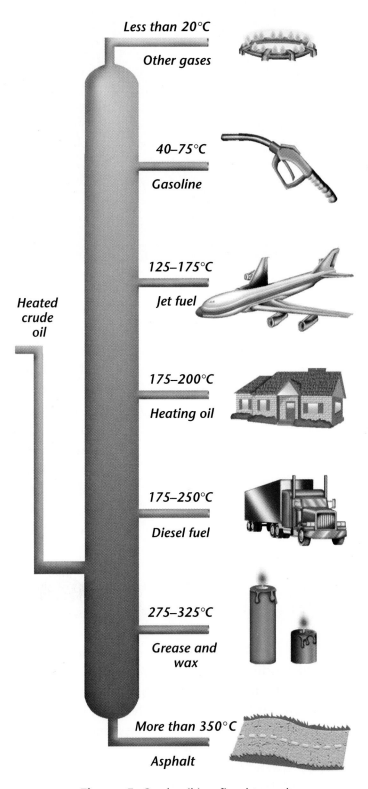

Less than 20°C
Other gases

40–75°C
Gasoline

125–175°C
Jet fuel

Heated crude oil

175–200°C
Heating oil

175–250°C
Diesel fuel

275–325°C
Grease and wax

More than 350°C
Asphalt

Figure 5 Crude oil is refined to make many different products. In the refining process, heat causes the different molecules in crude oil to separate. Different substances vaporize at specific temperatures.

Figure 6 A miner obtains hard coal from a shaft deep underground.

Coal

Coal is a solid fossil fuel formed from plant remains. People have burned coal to produce heat for thousands of years. Today, coal provides 23 percent of the energy used in the United States. The major use of coal is to fuel electric power plants.

Coal Mining Before it can be used to produce energy, coal has to be removed from the ground, or mined. Some coal is located very deep underground or is mixed with other materials, making it too difficult to obtain. **Reserves** are known deposits of coal (and other fossil fuels) that can be obtained using current technology.

INTEGRATING TECHNOLOGY

Coal as an Energy Source Coal is the most plentiful fossil fuel in the United States. It is fairly easy to transport, and provides a lot of energy when burned. But coal also has some disadvantages. Coal mining can increase erosion. Runoff from mines can cause water pollution. Finally, burning most types of coal results in more air pollution than burning other fossil fuels.

In addition, coal mining can be a dangerous job. Thousands of miners have been killed or injured in accidents in the mines. Many more suffer from "black lung," a disease caused by years of breathing coal dust. Fortunately, the mining industry has been working hard to improve conditions. New safety procedures and better equipment, including robots and drills that produce less coal dust, have made coal mining safer.

Section 1 Review

1. Describe the role of energy transformation in the production of electricity.
2. Explain how fuels provide energy.
3. Name and briefly describe the three fossil fuels.
4. Explain why fossil fuels are classified as nonrenewable resources.
5. List two advantages and one disadvantage of natural gas as an energy source.
6. **Thinking Critically Comparing and Contrasting** Compare and contrast the advantages of coal, oil, and natural gas as fuel sources for an electrical power plant. Which would make the best fuel for the power plant?

CHAPTER PROJECT

Check Your Progress
With your team, observe your selected area of the school. Determine which types of energy use take place in this area: heating, cooling, lighting, mechanical devices, electronic equipment, or moving vehicles. Record the specific types and amounts of energy use in a data table. To find the amounts, you will need to collect data from electric meters or fuel gauges. (*Hint:* Observe your area at several different times of the day, since the pattern of energy use may vary.)

2 Renewable Sources of Energy

Can You Capture Solar Energy?

1. Pour 250 milliliters of water into each of two sealable, clear plastic bags.

2. Measure and record the water temperature in each bag. Seal the bags.

3. Put one bag in a dark or shady place. Put the other bag in a place where it will receive direct sunlight.

4. Predict what the temperature of the water in each bag will be after 30 minutes.

5. Measure and record the ending temperatures.

Think It Over

Developing Hypotheses How did the water temperature in each bag change? What could account for these results?

A s the sun rises over the rim of the canyon where your family is camping, you feel its warmth on your face. A breeze stirs, carrying with it the smell of the campfire. Maybe you'll take a morning dip in the warm water of a nearby hot spring.

Even in this remote canyon, there are energy resources all around you. The sun warms the air, the wind blows, and heat from inside Earth warms the waters of the spring. These sources of energy are all **renewable resources**—that is, they are constantly being supplied. Renewable resources, such as sunlight, wind, and trees, are naturally replaced in a short period of time. These resources help meet people's energy needs.

Energy From the Sun

The warmth you feel on a sunny day is **solar energy,** energy from the sun. **The sun constantly gives off energy in the form of light and heat.** In one day, Earth receives enough solar energy to meet the energy needs of the entire world for 40 years. **Solar energy is the source, directly or indirectly, of most renewable energy resources.** Solar energy does not cause pollution. Because solar energy will not run out for several billion years, you could also think of it as an inexhaustible resource. An **inexhaustible resource** is a resource that exists in such large supply that it can be considered almost limitless.

So why hasn't solar energy replaced fossil fuels? One reason is that solar energy is available only when the sun is shining. A backup energy source must be available on cloudy days and at night.

GUIDE FOR READING

◆ How does the sun provide energy?

◆ What are some renewable sources of energy?

Reading Tip Before you read, preview the headings in this section. Predict some sources of energy that are renewable.

Key Terms
• renewable resource
• solar energy
• inexhaustible resource
• hydroelectric power
• biomass fuel
• geothermal energy

Figure 7 Aimed at the sun, these mirrors provide power to an electric plant in New South Wales, Australia. *Inferring How does the shape of these mirrors make them more effective?*

Another problem is that although Earth receives a lot of energy from the sun, this energy is spread out. To obtain enough power, the energy must be collected from a huge area.

Solar Technologies

INTEGRATING TECHNOLOGY Improving technologies to capture and use solar energy will help meet future energy needs. Some current solar technologies are described below.

Solar Plants One way to capture the sun's energy involves using giant mirrors. In a solar plant, rows of mirrors focus the sun's rays to heat a tank of water. The water boils, making steam that can be used to generate electricity.

Solar Cells Solar energy can be converted directly into electricity in a solar cell. A solar cell consists of a "sandwich" of very thin layers of the element silicon and other materials. The upper and lower parts of the sandwich have a negative and a positive terminal, like a battery. When light hits the cell, electrons move across the layers, producing an electric current.

The amount of electricity produced by solar cells depends on the area of the cell and the amount of light available. Solar cells are used to power calculators, lights, telephones, and other small devices. However, it would take more than 5,000 solar cells the size of your palm to produce enough electricity for a typical American home. Building solar cells on a large scale is very expensive. As a result, solar cells are used mostly in areas where fossil fuels are difficult to transport.

Checkpoint What are solar cells made of, and how do they work?

Solar Heating Systems Solar energy can be used to heat buildings. As shown in *Exploring a Solar House,* there are two types of solar heating systems: passive and active.

A passive solar system converts sunlight into thermal energy without using pumps or fans. If you have ever stepped into a car on a sunny day, you have experienced passive solar heating. Solar energy passes through the car's windows as light. The sun's rays heat the seats and other parts of the car, which then transfer heat to the air. The heated air is trapped inside, so the car gets warmer. The same principle can be used to heat a home.

An active solar system captures the sun's energy, then uses fans and pumps to distribute the heat. Light strikes the black metal surface of a solar collector. There, it is converted to thermal energy. Water is pumped through pipes in the solar collector to absorb the thermal energy. The heated water flows to a storage tank. Pumps and fans distribute the heat throughout the building.

EXPLORING a Solar House

This solar house uses passive and active heating systems and solar cells to convert solar energy into heat and electricity.

Passive interior heating
Sunlight that passes through the windows is absorbed by the walls and floors and converted to heat. At night shades covering the windows prevent the heat from flowing back outside.

Solar cells
Active solar cells on the roof generate an electric current. A battery stores energy for night use.

Window design
Large windows on the south and west sides act as passive solar collectors. They let sunlight enter during the winter. Overhangs shade the windows during the summer.

Solar water heater
Cool water is pumped from a storage tank to an active solar collector on the roof. Sunlight heats the water in the collector panels. Then the water is returned to the tank. From there it is piped to the different rooms. Air moves over the pipes and is heated.

Backup heat source
The house has a wood stove to provide backup heat, especially on cloudy days.

EXPLORING *a Hydroelectric Power Plant*

4 Electrical energy is sent to homes through cables.

Hydroelectric power is generated by changing energy from one form to another.

Reservoir

Dam

Transformer

Generator

Electromagnet

Spillway

Turbine

Discharge pipe

1 Water stored behind a dam is under pressure from gravity. This water has potential energy.

2 When the floodgates open, the water is released through tunnels to the bottom of the dam. The kinetic energy of the moving water turns the blades of a turbine, producing mechanical energy.

3 The shaft of the turbine is connected to a generator that contains a large magnet surrounded by coils of wire. The shaft turns the magnet inside the wire coils and produces electricity.

Figure 8 This photograph shows the Theodore Roosevelt Dam in Arizona. *Interpreting Photographs What natural feature of the river made this a good location to build a dam?*

Other Sources of Renewable Energy

The sun is one source of renewable energy. **Other renewable energy sources include water, biomass materials, wind, Earth's interior, and hydrogen.**

Flowing Water As water flows over the land into lakes and oceans, it provides another source of energy. Flowing water can turn a turbine and generate electricity in the same way as steam or wind can. A dam across a river blocks the flow of water, creating an artificial lake called a reservoir. Water flows through tunnels at the bottom of the dam. As the water moves through the tunnels, it turns turbines connected to a generator.

Hydroelectric power is electricity produced by flowing water. This type of power is the most widely used source of renewable energy in the world today. Hydroelectric power is inexpensive and does not create air pollution. But hydroelectric power does have drawbacks. In the United States, for example, most suitable rivers have already been dammed. And dams can have negative effects on the environment.

Biomass Fuels Wood is one of a group of renewable fuels, called **biomass fuels,** which are fuels made from things that were once alive. Other biomass fuels include crop wastes such as stalks and leaves, food wastes, and even manure. Burning breaks down complex molecules in these fuels, releasing energy.

Biomass materials also can be converted into other fuels. For example, corn, sugar cane, and other crops can be used to make alcohol. Adding the alcohol to gasoline forms a mixture called gasohol. Gasohol can be used as fuel for cars and trucks. The methane produced in some landfills is used for heating buildings. When bacteria decompose waste materials, they convert the waste into methane gas.

Biomass fuels are not widely used. Producing alcohol and methane in large quantities can be expensive. And although wood is renewable, it takes time for new trees to grow. But in the future, biomass fuels may play a larger role in meeting energy needs.

✓ *Checkpoint* *What are the advantages and disadvantages of biomass fuels?*

Geothermal Energy In certain regions, such as Iceland and New Zealand, magma heats underground water to the boiling point. The hot water and steam are valuable sources of **geothermal energy.** In Reykjavik, Iceland, 90 percent of homes are heated by water warmed underground in this way. Geothermal energy can also be used to generate electricity.

Geothermal energy is an unlimited source of cheap energy. Unfortunately, there are only a few places where magma comes close to Earth's surface. Elsewhere, very expensive, deep wells must be drilled to tap this energy. Although it can be costly, geothermal energy is likely to play a part in meeting energy needs in the future.

Wind Wind can be used to turn a turbine and generate electricity. Wind power plants or "wind farms" consist of many windmills. Together, the windmills generate large amounts of electric power.

Although wind now provides less than 1 percent of the world's electricity, it is the fastest-growing energy source. Wind energy is free and does not cause pollution.

Wind energy is not ideal for all locations. Few places have winds that blow steadily enough to be a worthwhile energy source. But as fossil fuels become more scarce and expensive, wind generators will become more important.

Figure 9 A geothermal power plant uses heat from Earth's interior as an energy source. Cold water is piped deep into the ground, where it is heated by magma. The resulting steam can be used for heat or to generate electricity.

Cooling tower

Power plant

Pump

Steam rises to plant

Cold water pumped down

Bedrock

Magma

Figure 10 The object fascinating these three astronauts is a bubble of water—the harmless byproduct of the hydrogen fuel cells used on the space shuttle.

Hydrogen Power

This fuel burns cleanly, forming only water as a byproduct. It creates no smoke, smog, or acid rain. It can be handled and transported through pipelines, much like natural gas. This fuel exists on Earth in such large supply that it could be considered an inexhaustible resource.

This ideal-sounding fuel is real—it's hydrogen. However, there is an obstacle. Almost all the hydrogen on Earth is combined with oxygen in the form of water. Pure hydrogen can be obtained by passing an electric current through water. But it takes more energy to obtain the hydrogen than is produced by burning it again.

Scientists aren't ruling out hydrogen as a good fuel for the future. At present, hydroelectric plants decrease their activity when the demand for electricity is low. Instead, they could run at full power all the time, using the excess electricity to produce hydrogen. Similarly, solar power plants often generate more electricity than is needed during the day. This extra electricity could be used to produce hydrogen. If a way can be found to produce hydrogen cheaply, it could someday be an important source of energy.

Section 2 Review

1. What is solar energy?
2. What are some advantages and disadvantages of solar energy?
3. How are active and passive solar heating systems different?
4. List three examples of biomass fuels.
5. What limits the use of geothermal energy?
6. **Thinking Critically** **Predicting** Which of the renewable sources of energy do you think is most likely to be used in your community in 100 years? Give reasons to support your answer.

Check Your Progress **CHAPTER PROJECT**
Continue to collect data on how much energy is used in your group's area of the school. Begin to brainstorm ideas for reducing energy usage in this area. For example, is there a way to use some electrical devices for shorter periods of time? (*Hint:* Interviewing some adults who are responsible for the operation of the school building may give you some good ideas. Be sure to check with your teacher before interviewing anyone.)

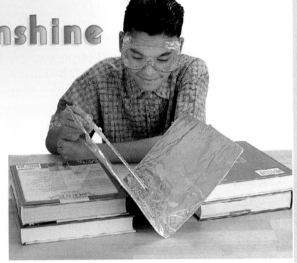
Cooking With Sunshine

In the future, will you cook your meals with sunshine instead of electricity? That's certainly a possibility. In this lab, you'll investigate how solar energy can be used to cook food.

Problem

What is the best shape for a solar cooker?

Skills Focus

predicting, designing experiments, forming operational definitions

Suggested Materials

scissors	glue	3 thermometers
3 dowels	tape	marshmallows
3 sheets of aluminum foil		clock or watch
3 sheets of oaktag paper		

Procedure

Part 1 Capturing Solar Energy

1. Read over the entire lab. Then predict which shape will produce the largest temperature increase when placed in the sun.
2. Glue a sheet of aluminum foil, shiny side up, to each sheet of oaktag paper. Before the glue dries, gently smooth out any wrinkles in the foil.
3. Bend one sheet into a V shape. Bend another sheet into a U shape. Leave the last sheet flat.
4. Place the aluminum sheets in direct sunlight, using wood blocks or books to hold the U- and V-shapes in position.
5. Tape a dowel to each thermometer. Record the starting temperature on each thermometer.
6. Use the dowels to hold the thermometer bulbs in the center of the aluminum shapes. After 15 minutes, record the final temperature on each thermometer.

Part 2 Designing a Solar Cooker

7. Use the results from Step 6 to design a solar cooker that can toast a marshmallow. Prepare a written description of your plan for your teacher's approval. Include an operational definition of a "well-toasted" marshmallow.
8. After your teacher has approved your plan, test your design by placing a marshmallow on a wooden dowel. Record the time it takes to toast the marshmallow.

Analyze and Conclude

1. What was the role of the aluminum foil in this investigation? What other materials could you have used instead? Explain.
2. Which of the three shapes—V, U, or flat— produced the largest increase in temperature? Propose an explanation for this result.
3. What other variables might have affected your results? Explain.
4. **Apply** What are some possible advantages of a solar cooker based on this design? What are some possible disadvantages?

More to Explore

Try adapting your design to heat water. Show your new design to your teacher before trying it.

Hydroelectric Dams: Are They All Here to Stay?

There are hundreds of hydroelectric dams on United States rivers. These dams provide electricity for millions of people. Hydroelectric dams provide clean, inexpensive, and renewable energy. They are a good source of power.

Recently, however, people have learned that dams can have negative effects on river ecosystems. Some people have even suggested removing certain dams. But is this wise? When do the benefits of dams outweigh the problems?

The Issues

How Do Dams Affect the Environment?

Because dams change water depth and flow, they can alter the temperature of a river. The water may become too cold or too warm for fish that normally live there. A change in temperature can also reduce the number of algae in a river. This affects other organisms in the river food web.

Some species of fish, such as salmon, herring, and menhaden, hatch in rivers but then travel to the ocean. To breed, they must return to the river. Dams can block the movement of these fish populations. For example, the Columbia River Basin, which has more than 50 dams, once contained more than 10 million salmon. Today it is home to only 2 million salmon.

What Are the Effects of Removing Dams?

Some people say that the only way to restore ecosystems is to remove dams. However, these dams supply a small but important part of the nation's electricity. Removing them could force the United States to use more nonrenewable fossil fuels. Fossil fuels also produce more pollution than hydroelectric plants.

The reservoirs behind hydroelectric dams supply water for irrigation and drinking. These supplies would be difficult to replace. In addition, a series of dams on a river can reduce flooding downstream during heavy rains.

What Can People Do?

Removing dams might restore some river ecosystems. For example, Edwards Dam on the Kennebec River in Maine was removed in 1999 to allow several threatened fish species to spawn. Edwards Dam provided only a small percent of Maine's electric power. This small amount was easier to replace than the power provided by a much larger dam.

There are other ways to protect migrating fish. Fish ladders, for example, are step-like waterways that help fish pass over dams. Fish can even be carried around dams in trucks. Still, these methods are costly and not always successful.

The government issues licenses for hydroelectric dams. In considering license renewals, officials examine environmental impact as well as energy production.

You Decide

1. Identify the Problem
In your own words, explain some of the major issues surrounding hydroelectric dams.

2. Analyze the Options
Examine the pros and cons of removing dams. What are the benefits? What are the costs? Who will be affected by the change?

3. Find a Solution
The license of a nearby dam is up for review. The dam provides electricity, but also blocks the migration of fish. What do you recommend? Explain.

SECTION 3 Nuclear Energy

Why Do They Fall?

1. Line up 15 dominoes to form a triangle, as shown.

2. Knock over the first domino so that it falls against the second row of dominoes. Observe the results.

3. Set up the dominoes again, but then remove the dominoes in the third row from the lineup.

4. Knock over the first domino again. Observe what happens.

Think It Over

Inferring Suppose each domino produced a large amount of energy when it fell over. Why might it be helpful to remove the dominoes as you did in Step 3?

W ouldn't it be great if people could use the same method as the sun to produce energy? In a way, they can! The kind of reactions that power the sun involve the central cores of atoms. The central core of an atom that contains the protons and neutrons is called the **nucleus** (plural *nuclei*). The reactions that involve nuclei, called nuclear reactions, involve tremendous amounts of energy. Two types of nuclear reactions are fission and fusion.

Fission Reactions and Energy

Nuclear reactions convert matter into energy. In 1905, Albert Einstein developed a formula that described the relationship between energy and matter. You have probably seen this famous equation, $E = mc^2$. In the equation, the E represents energy and the m represents mass. The c, which represents the speed of light, is a very large number. This equation states that when matter is changed into energy, an enormous amount of energy is released.

Nuclear fission is the splitting of an atom's nucleus into two smaller nuclei. The fuel for the reaction is a large atom that has an unstable nucleus, such as uranium-235 (U-235). A neutron is shot at the U-235 atom at high speed. **When the neutron hits the U-235 nucleus, the nucleus splits apart into two smaller nuclei and two or more neutrons.** The total mass of all these particles is a bit less than the mass of the original nucleus. The small amount of mass that makes up the difference has been converted into energy—a lot of energy, as described by Einstein's equation.

GUIDE FOR READING

◆ What happens during fission and fusion reactions?

◆ How does a nuclear power plant produce electricity?

Reading Tip As you read, create a Venn diagram to compare and contrast nuclear fission and nuclear fusion.

Key Terms nucleus
• nuclear fission
• reactor vessel • fuel rod
• control rod • meltdown
• nuclear fusion

Albert Einstein ▶ in 1930

Figure 11 In a nuclear fission reaction, a neutron "bullet" strikes a U-235 nucleus. As a result, the nucleus splits into two smaller nuclei. More neutrons are released, along with a great deal of energy.

Krypton-92 nucleus

Neutron

Neutron

Neutron

Neutron

Uranium-235 nucleus

Barium-141 nucleus

Meanwhile, the fission reaction has produced three more neutrons. If any of these neutrons strikes another nucleus, the fission reaction is repeated. More neutrons and more energy are released. If there are enough nuclei nearby, the process continues over and over in a chain reaction, just like a row of dominoes falling. In a nuclear chain reaction, the amount of energy released increases rapidly with each step in the chain.

What happens to all the energy released by these fission reactions? If a nuclear chain reaction is not controlled, the released energy causes a huge explosion. The explosion of an atomic bomb is an uncontrolled nuclear reaction. A few kilograms of matter explode with more force than several thousand tons of a nonnuclear explosive such as dynamite. However, if the chain reaction is controlled, the energy is released as heat, which can be used to generate electricity.

Nuclear Power Plants

Controlled nuclear fission reactions take place inside nuclear power plants. **In a nuclear power plant, the heat released from the reactions is used to change water into steam. As in other types of power plants, the steam then turns the blades of a turbine to generate electricity.** Look at the diagram of a nuclear power plant in Figure 12. In addition to the generator, it has two main parts: the reactor vessel and the heat exchanger.

Reactor Vessel The **reactor vessel** is the section of a nuclear reactor where nuclear fission occurs. The reactor contains rods of U-235, called **fuel rods.** When several fuel rods are placed close together, a series of fission reactions occurs. The reactions are controlled by placing **control rods** made of the metal cadmium between the fuel rods. The cadmium absorbs the neutrons

Shoot the Nucleus

In an open area of your classroom, make a model of a nuclear fission reaction. Place a handful of marbles on the floor in a tight cluster, so that they touch one another. Step back about a half-meter from the marbles. Shoot another marble at the cluster.

Making Models What does the marble you shot at the cluster represent? What effect did the marble have on the cluster? How is this similar to a nuclear fission reaction?

released during the fission reactions. As the cadmium control rods are removed, the fission reactions speed up. If the reactor vessel starts to get too hot, the control rods are moved back in place to slow the chain reaction.

Heat Exchanger Heat is removed from the reactor vessel by water or another fluid that is pumped through the reactor. This fluid passes through a heat exchanger. There, the fluid boils water to produce steam, which runs the electrical generator. The steam is condensed again and pumped back to the heat exchanger.

☑ *Checkpoint* *How are fission reactions controlled?*

The Risks of Nuclear Fission

When it was first demonstrated, people thought that nuclear fission would provide an almost unlimited source of clean, safe energy. Today nuclear power plants generate much of the world's electricity—about 20 percent in the United States and more than 70 percent in France. But these plants have some problems.

In 1986, in Chernobyl, Ukraine, the reactor vessel in a nuclear power plant overheated. The fuel rods generated so much heat that they started to melt, a condition called a **meltdown.** The excess heat increased the steam pressure in the generator. A series of explosions blew parts of the roof off and injured or killed dozens of plant workers and firefighters. Radioactive materials escaped into the environment. Today, the soil in an area the size of Florida remains contaminated with radioactive waste.

Figure 12 In a nuclear plant, uranium fuel undergoes fission, producing heat. The heat boils water, and the resulting steam drives the turbines that generate electricity. *Interpreting Diagrams From which part of the power plant is heat released to the environment?*

Figure 13 One problem with nuclear power is disposal of the used radioactive fuel rods. In this plant in France, the fuel rods are stored in a deep pool of water.

Chernobyl and less serious accidents at other nuclear power plants have led to public concerns about nuclear plant safety.

The danger of a meltdown is a serious concern. However, a meltdown can be avoided by careful planning. A more difficult problem is the disposal of radioactive wastes produced by power plants. Radioactive wastes remain dangerous for many thousands of years. Scientists must find a way to safely store these wastes for a long period of time. Finally, nuclear power has turned out to be a much more costly source of power than was originally expected. The safety features required for nuclear plants make the plants very expensive.

☑ *Checkpoint* What are three problems with using nuclear fission as an energy source?

The Quest to Control Fusion

A second type of nuclear reaction is fusion. **Nuclear fusion** is the combining of two atomic nuclei to produce a single larger nucleus. **As shown in Figure 14, two kinds of hydrogen nuclei are forced together in a fusion reaction.** One kind (hydrogen-2) has one proton and one neutron, and the other kind (hydrogen-3) has one proton and two neutrons. The tremendous heat and pressure

Figure 14 In a nuclear fusion reaction, two nuclei combine to form a single larger nucleus. *Interpreting Diagrams What is released during a fusion reaction?*

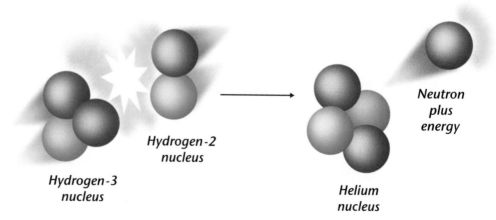

Hydrogen-3 nucleus

Hydrogen-2 nucleus

Helium nucleus

Neutron plus energy

cause them to combine and create a helium nucleus with two protons and two neutrons. This helium nucleus has slightly less mass than the total mass of the two hydrogen nuclei. The difference is converted to energy.

Nuclear fusion would have many advantages as an energy source. Fusion can produce much more energy per atom than nuclear fission. The fuel for a nuclear fusion reactor is also readily available. Water, which is plentiful in Earth's oceans, contains one of the kinds of hydrogen needed for fusion. Fusion should be safer and less polluting than nuclear fission. You can see why scientists are eager to find a way to build a nuclear fusion reactor!

Although some fusion bombs have been exploded, scientists have not yet been able to control a large-scale fusion reaction. The biggest problem is temperature. In the sun, nuclear fusion occurs at 15 million degrees Celsius. Such conditions are almost impossible to control on Earth. No material has been found that can serve as a reactor vessel under the high temperature and pressure of a nuclear fusion reaction. Extremely powerful magnetic fields can contain a fusion reaction. However, it takes more energy to generate these fields than the fusion reaction produces.

Although many more years of research are expected, some scientists believe that they will eventually be able to control fusion reactions. If they succeed, the quest for a clean, cheap energy source may be over at last.

Figure 15 Researchers at Los Alamos National Laboratory in New Mexico are studying fusion as an energy source. This machine creates strong magnetic fields that allow fusion to occur for short periods of time.

Section 3 Review

1. Draw and label a simple diagram of a nuclear fission reaction. Include the following labels: U-235 nucleus, neutrons, smaller nuclei, and energy.
2. How can the energy released in a fission reaction be used to produce electricity?
3. Explain the purpose of control rods.
4. Give two reasons that people have not been able to use nuclear fusion as an energy source.
5. **Thinking Critically Classifying** Is nuclear fission a renewable or nonrenewable energy source? Is nuclear fusion renewable or nonrenewable? Explain.

Check Your Progress CHAPTER PROJECT
By now you should begin preparing the written report of your findings about energy use in your group's area of the school. Your report should include the major ways energy is used in your chosen area. You should also include recommendations on how energy use might be reduced.

Keeping Comfortable

Two ways to use less energy are to keep heat *out* of your home during hot weather, and to keep it *in* during cold weather. In this lab, you will investigate how to do both things.

Problem

How well do different materials stop heat transfer?

Suggested Materials

watch or clock   beakers
ice water   hot water
thermometers or temperature probes
containers and lids made of paper, plastic foam,
    plastic, glass, and metal

Design a Plan

Part 1 Measuring Temperature Changes

1. Use a pencil to poke a hole in the lid of a paper cup. Fill the cup about halfway with cold water.
2. Put the lid on the cup. Insert a thermometer or temperature probe into the water through the hole. When the temperature stops dropping, place the cup in a beaker. Add hot water to the beaker until the water level is about 1 cm below the lid.
3. Record the water temperature once every minute until it has increased by 5 degrees. Use the time it takes for the temperature to increase 1 degree to measure how well the paper cup prevents heat transfer.

Part 2 Comparing Materials

4. Use the ideas from Part 1 to design a controlled experiment to rank the effectiveness of different materials in preventing heat transfer.

5. Use these questions to help you plan your experiment:
   ◆ What hypothesis will you test?
   ◆ Which materials do you predict will be the best and worst at preventing heat transfer? How will you define these terms?
   ◆ What will your manipulated variable be? What will your responding variable be?
   ◆ What variables do you need to control? How will you control them?
   ◆ What step-by-step procedures will you use?
   ◆ What kind of data table will you use?
6. After your teacher has reviewed your plans, make any necessary changes in your design. Then perform your experiment.

Analyze and Conclude

1. In Part 1, what was the starting temperature of the hot water? What was the starting temperature of the cold water? In which direction did the heat flow? How do you know?
2. If the materials in Part 1 are used to represent your home in very hot weather, which material would represent the rooms in your home? Which would represent the outdoor weather? Which would represent the walls of the building?
3. Which material was most effective at preventing the transfer of heat? Which was the least effective? Explain.
4. **Think About It** Would experiments similar to this one provide you with enough information to choose materials to build a home? Explain.

Design an Experiment

Design an experiment to compare how well the materials would work if the hot water were inside the cup and the cold water were outside. With your teacher's permission, carry out your experiment.

SECTION
4 Energy Conservation

Which Bulb Is More Efficient?

1. Record the light output (listed in lumens) from the packages of a 60-watt incandescent light bulb and a 15-watt compact fluorescent bulb.

2. Place the fluorescent bulb in a lamp socket. **CAUTION:** *Make sure the lamp is unplugged.*

3. Plug in the lamp and turn it on. Hold the end of a thermometer about 8 centimeters from the bulb.

4. Record the temperature after 5 minutes.

5. Turn off and unplug the lamp. When the bulb is cool, remove it. Repeat Steps 2, 3, and 4 with the incandescent light bulb.

Think It Over

Inferring The 60-watt bulb uses about 4 times more energy than the 15-watt bulb. How does the light output of each bulb compare with the energy it uses? How can the difference in efficiency be explained?

Imagine what would happen if the world ran out of fossil fuels today. Much of the electric power that people depend on would disappear. Most buildings would lose their heating and cooling. Forests would disappear as people began to burn wood for heat and cooking. Almost all transportation would stop. Cars, buses, trains, airplanes, and ships would be stranded wherever they ran out of fuel. Since radios, televisions, computers, and telephones depend on electricity, communication would be greatly reduced.

Although fossil fuels won't run out immediately, they also won't last forever. Most people think that it makes sense to start planning now to avoid a fuel shortage in the future. **One approach to the problem is to find new sources of energy. The second approach is to make the fuels that are available now last as long as possible while other solutions are being developed.**

Conservation and Efficiency

Reducing energy use is called **energy conservation.** For example, if you walk to the store instead of getting a ride, you are conserving the gasoline needed to drive to the store. Reducing energy use is a solution to energy problems that will help no matter what form of energy is used in the future.

GUIDE FOR READING

◆ What are two ways to make sure there will be enough energy for the future?

◆ How does insulation help conserve energy?

Reading Tip Before you read, list ways to conserve energy. As you read, add to the list.

Key Terms energy conservation • efficiency • insulation

Electricity Production by Energy Source

Other 0.2%
Petroleum 2.2%
Natural gas 8.5%
Hydroelectric 10.7%
Coal 56.4%
Nuclear 21.9%

Figure 16 Nonrenewable fossil fuels generate over two thirds of the nation's electricity.

A way to get as much work as possible out of fuels is to use them efficiently. **Efficiency** is the percentage of energy that is actually used to perform work. The rest of the energy is "lost" to the surroundings, usually as heat. People have developed many ways to increase energy efficiency.

Lighting Lights can use as much as 10 percent of the electricity in your home, but much of that electricity is wasted. An incandescent light bulb converts less than 10 percent of the electricity it uses into light. The rest is given off as heat. You can prove this to yourself by holding your hand close to an incandescent light bulb. But don't touch it! Compact fluorescent bulbs, on the other hand, use only about one fourth as much energy to provide the same amount of light.

☑ *Checkpoint* *Which type of light bulb is more energy-efficient?*

SCIENCE & History

Energy-Efficient Devices

Scientists and engineers have developed many technologies that improve energy efficiency and reduce energy use.

1932
Fiberglass Insulation

Long strands of glass fibers trap air and keep buildings from losing heat. Less fuel is used for heating.

1958
Solar Cells

More than 150 years ago, scientists discovered that silicon can convert light into electricity. The first useful application of solar cells was to power the radio on a satellite. Now solar cells are even used on experimental cars like the one below.

1930   **1940**   **1950**

1936
Fluorescent Lighting

Fluorescent bulbs were introduced to the public at the 100th anniversary celebration of the United States Patent Office. Because these bulbs use less energy than incandescent bulbs, most offices and schools use fluorescent lights.

Heating and Cooling One method of increasing the efficiency of heating and cooling systems is insulation. **Insulation** is a layer of material that helps block the transfer of heat between the air inside and outside a building. You have probably seen insulation made of fiberglass, which looks like fluffy pink cotton candy. The mat of thin glass fibers trap air. **This layer of trapped air helps keep the building from losing or gaining heat from the outside.** A layer of fiberglass 15 centimeters thick insulates a room as well as a brick wall 2 meters thick or a stone wall almost 6 meters thick!

Buildings lose a lot of heat around the windows. Look at the windows in your school or home. Was the building built after 1980? Have the windows been replaced recently? If so, you will most likely see two panes of glass with space between them. The air between the panes of glass acts as insulation.

In Your Journal

Design an advertisement for one of the energy-saving inventions described in this time line. The advertisement may be a print, radio, or television ad. Be sure that your advertisement clearly explains the benefits of the invention.

1967

Microwave Ovens

The first countertop microwave oven for the home was introduced. Microwaves cook food by heating the water the food contains. The microwave oven heats only the food, not the air, racks, and oven walls as in a conventional oven. Preheating is also not required, saving even more energy.

1997
Smart Roads

The Department of Transportation demonstrated that cars can be controlled by computers. Sensors built into the road control all the cars, making traffic flow more smoothly. This uses less energy.

1970	1980	1990	2000

1981
High-Efficiency Window Coatings

Materials that reflect sunlight were first used to coat windows in the early 1980s. This coating reduces the air conditioning needed to keep the inside of the building cool.

Figure 17 A single city bus can transport dozens of people, reducing the number of cars on the roads and saving energy. *Applying Concepts How does riding a bus conserve energy?*

Transportation Engineers have improved the energy efficiency of cars by designing better engines and tires. Another way to save energy is to reduce the number of cars on the road. In many communities, public transit systems provide an alternative to driving. Other cities encourage car-pooling. If four people travel together in one car, they use much less energy than they would by driving separately. Many cities now set aside lanes for cars containing two or more people.

In the future, cars that run on electricity may provide the most energy savings of all. Electric power plants can convert fuel into electricity more efficiently than a car engine converts gasoline into motion. Therefore, a car that runs on electricity is more energy-efficient than one that runs directly on fuel.

What You Can Do

You can reduce your personal energy use by changing your behavior in some simple ways.

- ◆ Keep your home cooler in winter and warmer in summer. Instead of turning up the heat, put on a sweater. Use fans instead of air conditioners.
- ◆ Use natural light instead of electric lights when possible.
- ◆ Turn off the lights or television when you leave a room.
- ◆ Walk or ride a bike for short trips. Ride buses and trains.
- ◆ Recycle, especially metal products. Recycling an aluminum can uses only 5 percent of the energy making a new can uses!

The items in this list are small things, but multiplied by millions of people they add up to a lot of energy saved for the future.

Section 4 Review

1. What are two ways to make energy resources last longer?
2. Explain how putting insulation in a building conserves energy.
3. How does carpooling conserve energy?
4. **Thinking Critically Predicting** An office building contains only incandescent lights. The building next door contains fluorescent lights. Predict which building has higher energy bills. Explain your answer.

Science at Home

Saving Energy With an adult family member, conduct an energy audit of your home. Look for places where energy is being lost, such as cracks around windows and doors. Also look for ways to reduce energy use, such as running the dishwasher only when it is full. Together, create a list of energy-saving suggestions for your family. Post the list where everyone can see it.

SECTION
1 Energy and Fossil Fuels

Key Ideas

◆ A fuel is a substance that provides a form of energy as a result of a chemical change.

◆ Energy can be converted from one form to another.

◆ The three major fossil fuels are coal, oil, and natural gas. These fuels release more energy when they are burned than most other substances do.

◆ Because fossil fuels take hundreds of millions of years to form, they are considered nonrenewable resources.

Key Terms

fuel	nonrenewable resource
energy transformation	petroleum
combustion	refinery
fossil fuel	petrochemical
hydrocarbon	reserves

SECTION 2 Renewable Sources of Energy

Key Ideas

◆ The sun constantly gives off energy in the form of heat and light. Solar energy can serve directly or indirectly as a renewable energy source.

◆ Because the sun causes winds and drives the water cycle, wind power and water power are considered indirect forms of solar energy.

◆ Biomass fuels, geothermal energy, and hydrogen power are other renewable energy sources that are currently in limited use.

Key Terms

renewable resource	hydroelectric power
solar energy	biomass fuel
inexhaustible resource	geothermal energy

SECTION 3 Nuclear Energy

INTEGRATING **CHEMISTRY**

Key Ideas

◆ Nuclear reactions include fission reactions and fusion reactions.

◆ In a fission reaction, the impact of a neutron splits an atom's nucleus into two smaller nuclei and two or more neutrons. In a fusion reaction, two kinds of hydrogen nuclei are forced together. A large amount of energy is released in both processes.

◆ In a nuclear power plant, the thermal energy released from controlled fission reactions is used to generate electricity.

◆ Disadvantages of nuclear power include the risk of a meltdown and radioactive waste.

Key Terms

nucleus	fuel rod	meltdown
nuclear fission	control rod	nuclear fusion
reactor vessel		

SECTION 4 Energy Conservation

Key Ideas

◆ To avoid an energy shortage in the future, people must find new sources of energy and conserve the fuels that are available now.

◆ Insulation keeps a building from losing heat to, or gaining heat from, the outside.

◆ Ways to conserve energy use in transportation include making more efficient vehicles, carpooling, and using public transit.

Key Terms

energy conservation	efficiency	insulation

Organizing Information

Compare/Contrast Table Make a table listing an advantage and a disadvantage for each of the following types of energy: coal, petroleum, solar, wind, water, geothermal, nuclear. For example, one advantage of coal is that it produces a large amount of energy. (For tips on making compare/contrast tables see the Skills Handbook.)

Reviewing Content

 Review key concepts online using iText at www.phschool.com

Multiple Choice
Choose the letter of the best answer.

1. Which of the following is *not* a fossil fuel?
   a. coal
   b. wood
   c. oil
   d. natural gas
2. An appliance that transfers thermal energy from a cold space inside to a warm space outside is a
   a. refrigerator.
   b. solar oven.
   c. water heater.
   d. microwave.
3. Which of the following is *not* a biomass fuel?
   a. methane
   b. gasohol
   c. hydrogen
   d. sugar-cane wastes
4. The particle used to start a nuclear fission reaction is a(n)
   a. neutron.
   b. nucleus.
   c. proton.
   d. atom.
5. A part of a nuclear power plant that undergoes a fission reaction is called a
   a. turbine.
   b. control rod.
   c. heat exchanger.
   d. fuel rod.

True or False
If the statement is true, write true. If it is false, change the underlined word or words to make the statement true.

6. A change of energy from one form to another is called <u>energy transformation</u>.
7. The process of burning a fuel for energy is <u>combustion</u>.
8. Geothermal energy is an example of a <u>nonrenewable</u> energy source.
9. Solar energy is harnessed to run calculators using <u>nuclear fusion</u>.
10. Most of the energy used in the United States today comes from <u>fossil fuels</u>.

Checking Concepts

11. What are some negative impacts of petroleum on the environment?
12. Describe how coal forms.
13. Why is solar energy an inexhaustible resource?
14. Describe three features of a solar home. (Your answer may include passive or active solar systems.)
15. Explain how wind can be used to generate electricity.
16. What factors limit the use of biomass fuels as an energy source?
17. Describe the advantages and disadvantages that hydrogen power would have as a source of energy.
18. How is a nuclear fission reaction controlled in a nuclear power plant?
19. Define *energy efficiency*. Give three examples of inventions that increase energy efficiency.
20. **Writing to Learn** Suppose you had no electricity. Write a journal entry describing a typical weekday, including your meals, classes, and after-school activities. Explain how you might get things done without electricity.

Critical Thinking

21. **Comparing and Contrasting** Discuss how the three fossil fuels are alike and how they are different.
22. **Classifying** State whether each of the following energy sources is renewable or nonrenewable: coal, solar power, methane, hydrogen. Give a reason for each answer.
23. **Making Judgments** Write a short paragraph explaining why you agree or disagree with the following statement: "The United States should build more nuclear power plants to prepare for the future shortage of fossil fuels."
24. **Relating Cause and Effect** Explain the steps by which an electric power plant generates electricity by burning a fossil fuel.

Applying Skills

The table below shows how the world's energy production changed between 1973 and 1995. Use the information in the table to answer Questions 25–28.

Source of Energy	Energy Units Produced 1973	Energy Units Produced 1995
Coal	1,498	2,179
Gas	964	1,775
Hydroelectric	107	242
Nuclear	54	646
Oil	2,730	3,228
TOTAL Energy Units	5,353	8,070

25. Interpreting Data How did total energy production change from 1973 to 1995?

26. Calculating What percentage of total world energy production did nuclear power provide in 1973? In 1995?

27. Classifying Classify the different types of energy as renewable or nonrenewable. How important was renewable energy in 1995?

28. Drawing Conclusions Which energy source was the most important in 1995?

Performance ▼ CHAPTER PROJECT Assessment

Present Your Project Have another group review your report for clarity, organization, and detail. Make revisions based on feedback from the other group. As a class, discuss each group's findings. Make a list of suggestions for conserving energy in your school.

Reflect and Record In your project notebook, explain what types of energy use were the hardest to measure. What other information would you have liked to have when making your recommendations? Record your overall opinion of energy efficiency in your school.

Test Preparation

Use these questions to prepare for standardized tests.

Read the passage. Then answer Questions 29–33.

Tides are a source of renewable energy. Along some coasts, great amounts of water move into bays at high tide and flow out to sea again as the tide falls.

A few tidal power plants have been built to take advantage of this regular motion. A low dam across the entrance to a shallow bay holds water in the bay at high tide. As the tide goes out, water flowing past turbines in the dam generates electricity, as in a hydroelectric power plant.

Tidal power will probably never become a major source of energy because only a few coastal areas in the world are suitable for building tidal power plants. Also, a dam across a bay blocks boats and fish from traveling up the river.

29. How many tidal power plants are now in use?
   A only a few   **B** several dozen
   C zero   **D** several hundred

30. Tides are an energy source that is
   F widely used throughout the world.
   G renewable.
   H nonrenewable.
   J impossible to use in generating power.

31. Tidal power plants most resemble
   A geothermal power plants.
   B windmills.
   C hydroelectric power plants.
   D water-cooled nuclear power plants.

32. The selection concludes that tidal power
   F will replace other types of power.
   G already produces too much energy.
   H can be developed wherever the tide rises.
   J won't become a major source of energy.

33. A good title for this reading selection would be
   A The Limitless Power of Tides.
   B Tidal Power Blocks Boats.
   C A Minor Source of Renewable Energy.
   D A Major Source of Energy.

PROTECTING DESERT WILDLIFE

Elroy Masters likes working outdoors. One day he hikes a mountain trail, looking for desert tortoises. The next morning he may be in a boat on the Colorado River, counting birds along the riverbank. Another day he may be in the Arizona hills, building a water container for thirsty bighorn sheep. Elroy is a biologist working for the federal government's Bureau of Land Management (BLM). His job is to protect wildlife habitat in the desert along the Colorado River between California and Arizona.

"People may come in wanting to run a pipeline across public land or needing to build a road," he explains. "Part of my job is to check out the biological effect of that action on different species of animals and plants. If people are going to build a road where there are a lot of tortoises, we might try to have them work from November to March. Since tortoises hibernate during those months, we reduce the chance of a tortoise getting run over."

Growing up in Arizona, Elroy lived in a farming community. "I was always outdoors. I was able to have animals that a lot of people don't have—chickens, pigeons, ducks, and a horse. I always loved animals. I always hoped for some type of career with them."

Elroy Masters studied biology at Phoenix College and Northern Arizona University. He started working for the Bureau of Land Management when he was still a college student. He now works as a Wildlife Management Biologist. In this photograph, Elroy is about to release a razorback sucker, an endangered species of fish, into the Colorado River.

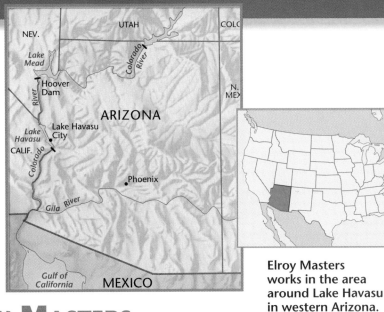

Today, Elroy and his co-workers make surveys of desert animals. They count the animals in different areas and make maps of their habitats. They locate where the animals live, what they eat, and where they build their nests and raise their young. Elroy uses that information to protect the animals when natural events or human activities threaten them.

Elroy Masters works in the area around Lake Havasu in western Arizona.

TALKING WITH ELROY MASTERS

Q *What wildlife do you protect?*

A One of the neatest animals we deal with is the desert bighorn sheep. In an average summer, it can get as hot as 120 degrees here. Sometimes the heat lasts for weeks. But with the number of people living around the river, the animals are no longer able to travel to water. So we go up into the mountains to construct catchments (containers) to collect water and store it. That way the sheep can stay in the mountains without trying to cross freeways to get to water.

We fly in big storage tanks that hold about 10,000 gallons of water. We bury them in the ground or put them on a platform. We use paint to mask them into the color of the scenery. We sometimes build a dam or put out a metal sheet to catch drizzle rain.

A catchment can hold 10,000 gallons of water (right). It is buried in the ground. The drinking container provides water for desert bighorn sheep (below), mule deer, and other wildlife.

Q *What else are you doing to protect the bighorn sheep?*

A We're going to work with the Fish and Wildlife Department to capture and transplant bighorn sheep to a mountain range in my area. There are already sheep and some mountain lions here. But the sheep aren't doing as well as we expected. We want to bring in some bighorn sheep that are used to lions. We hope these lion-savvy sheep will teach the sheep in our area how to avoid lions. To catch the sheep, we'll use a helicopter. We'll shoot a net over the sheep and a couple of guys will jump out to secure the animals and then bring them to our herd.

The Colorado River valley is home to the Southwestern willow flycatcher and the desert tortoise.

Q *What other animals are you responsible for protecting?*

A I work a lot with desert tortoises. I'm responsible for two different populations, one on either side of the river. The tortoises live in the drier, hilly areas away from the river. Any time we go out into the field, we try to collect data. We keep track of where they've been and where they feed.

Q *How do you find the tortoises?*

A We have maps that indicate their habitat. Based on the habitat, we'll go out, walk around, and look under rocks and boulders to see if we can find a burrow. The tortoises are good diggers. They find a good boulder and go underground 10 or 12 feet. That's where they'll spend the winter.

Southwestern willow flycatcher

Desert tortoise

Q *Do you also work with birds?*

A Right now we're working with the Southwestern willow flycatcher. It's a small bird that depends on thick riparian (riverbank) vegetation to build nests and breed. The flycatcher is a migratory bird. Each spring, the birds fly to Arizona from Central America and Mexico. In the early summer months, we go out to find how many are breeding. We're trying to learn what's needed to prevent flycatchers from becoming extinct. We need to survey and protect the remaining stands of habitat. The flycatchers like to nest in thick stands of willow. But they will also build nests in another tree, salt cedar. The birds don't prefer it, but sometimes salt cedar is the only vegetation remaining, so they use it.

Q *What's threatening the riverbank plants?*

A The low water level in the river—due to human use—is a big threat. So is fire. During summer months, there are large numbers of recreational boats. Careless boaters can cause fires. Some fires get pretty big along the river and destroy a lot of the habitat where the birds nest and raise their young.

Q *Can you see the benefits of your work?*

A Yes, I see it especially in riverbank zones where areas are protected so that vegetation and trees can grow back. This year we did a new bird count in one area. Species that hadn't been seen in a while, like tanagers, showed up. Some of the migratory birds are already stopping in young cottonwood trees. That's the best gauge I've had—seeing birds returning to these new trees.

There are also quick results with the water catchments in the hills. We put the water in a year ago. They're aimed at bighorn sheep and mule deer. But now we've also got a lot of different birds—doves and quails—that come into the area.

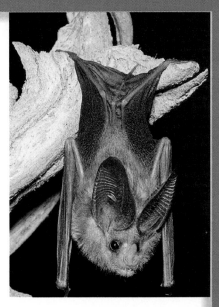

Elroy Masters also works with populations of the California leaf-nosed bat. This bat has large ears and a leaf-shaped, turned-up nose. The bats are threatened by the loss of their habitat.

In Your Journal

Elroy Masters and his co-workers "survey" the wildlife in their area in order to learn how to protect them. Think of a wild animal that lives in a park or open area near you—squirrels, frogs, birds, even insects. Work out a step-by-step plan to draw a simple map marking the places where the animal is found.

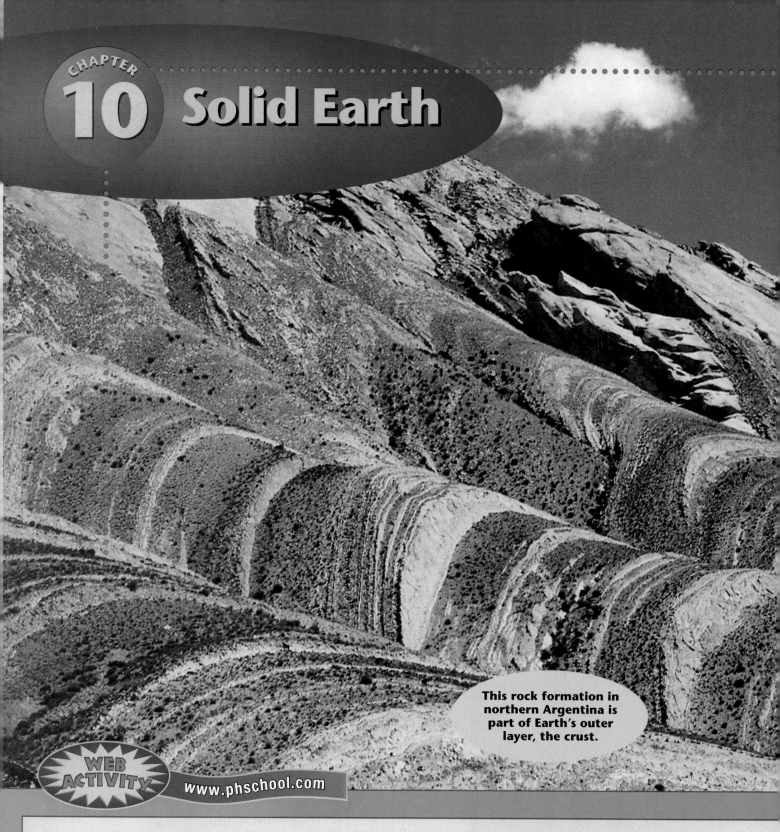

This rock formation in northern Argentina is part of Earth's outer layer, the crust.

www.phschool.com

Cutaway Earth

From dazzling crystals to a huge sphere of molten metal—Earth's interior holds many surprises. What is the planet's structure? What is Earth made of? In this chapter you will learn how layers deep within Earth differ from the materials that make up the planet's outer covering. You will also build a model that shows the structure of Earth's interior.

Your Goal To build a three-dimensional model that represents a cutaway view of Earth's interior.

To complete this project, you must
◆ build a scale model of the layers of Earth's interior
◆ show the composition of each layer
◆ show changes in temperature and pressure from the surface to the center of Earth
◆ label all physical features clearly
◆ follow the safety guidelines in Appendix A

Get Started Begin now by previewing the chapter to learn about Earth's structure. Brainstorm a list of the kinds of materials that could be used to make a three-dimensional model. Start a project folder in which you will keep your sketches, ideas, and any information needed to design and build your model.

Check Your Progress You will be designing and building your model as you study this chapter. To keep your project on track, look for Check Your Progress boxes at the following points.
Section 1 Review, page 329: Begin sketching and designing your model.
Section 3 Review, page 347: Revise your design and build your model.

Present Your Project At the end of the chapter (page 351), you will present your completed model to the class and discuss the features you included.

TEKS

In addition to process TEKS, this chapter addresses these concept TEKS as they relate to the chapter's topics.

(6.14) The student knows the structures and functions of Earth systems.
The student is expected to:
(A) summarize the rock cycle.

How Can Scientists Find Out What's Inside Earth?

1. Your teacher will give you a spherical object, such as a sports ball. You can think of the sphere as a model of planet Earth.

2. Carefully observe your sphere. What characteristics of the sphere can you observe and measure directly?

3. What characteristics of the sphere cannot be directly observed and measured?

Think It Over

Posing Questions In your notebook, list several questions that you have about Earth. Which of these questions could you answer based on direct observation? Which questions would need to be answered based on indirect evidence?

GUIDE FOR READING

◆ What conditions and forces do geologists study?

◆ What are the major layers of Earth's interior?

Reading Tip As you read, make a list of Earth's layers. Write a sentence about each layer.

Key Terms rock • crust
• geology • geologist
• seismic wave • inner core
• outer core • mantle
• lithosphere

You probably already know something about Earth's surface. Beneath the buildings, grass, and roads around your home and school there is a layer of soil and rock. **Rock** is the material that makes up Earth's hard outer surface. A layer of solid rock called the **crust** surrounds Earth's surface like the tough shell of a walnut.

But what's inside Earth? Scientists have drilled deep holes into the crust to study the rocks below the surface. The scientists use a drill with diamond teeth that cuts a thin cylinder of rock called a core. The core is then brought to the surface. For example, equipment carried by the drillship *JOIDES Resolution* drilled about two kilometers into the crust beneath the ocean floor. On land, scientists have drilled the "superdeep" borehole in Kola, Russia, which reached a depth of approximately 12 kilometers.

Drilling helps scientists obtain samples of the rock that makes up the crust, which ranges from about 5 to 40 kilometers in thickness. But to sample material from Earth's center, you would need to drill down nearly 6,400 kilometers! Fortunately, scientists also have other ways of learning about Earth's interior.

◄ **Earth from space**

The Science of Geology

Learning about Earth's interior is one goal of the science of geology. **Geology** is the study of planet Earth, including Earth's surface and interior. Scientists who study Earth and the processes that have shaped Earth over time are called **geologists.** Geologists also study the physical and chemical characteristics of minerals and rocks.

Why do geologists study Earth's interior? They want to know what materials make up Earth. They try to determine how those materials are arranged beneath the surface. **Geologists study physical conditions, such as temperature and pressure, inside Earth. Geologists also study the forces inside Earth that affect the surface.** You will learn about some of these forces in this chapter and in Chapter 11.

You know that drilling has provided geologists with some data on Earth's crust. But most of what geologists know about the interior below the crust is based on indirect evidence. Suppose a friend or relative gave you a birthday gift in a wrapped box. You might try tapping and shaking it to obtain indirect evidence of its content. Based on this evidence, you might be able to infer what was in the box.

In a similar way, geologists use indirect evidence from seismic waves to learn about Earth's interior. **Seismic waves** are vibrations that travel through Earth every time an earthquake shakes the ground. As seismic waves travel through Earth, they may be slowed down, bent, or reflected by different structures inside Earth. Geologists have recorded these different paths taken by seismic waves. From this evidence, they have inferred Earth's composition and structure.

Figure 1 Geologists' work often takes them into the field. **(A)** This geologist is using a rock hammer to obtain a sample of rock. **(B)** These geologists are observing red-hot, molten lava near Mt. Kilauea volcano in Hawaii. *Posing Questions If you were a geologist, what questions would you ask about the rocks in each photo?*

 Checkpoint *What is a geologist?*

Figure 2 The Canadian Shield covers a large part of northern North America. It is a region where the rock that makes up much of Earth's crust can often be seen at the surface.

Earth's Interior

If you could slice Earth in half, you would see that the planet is made up of layers like an onion. Each layer completely surrounds the layer beneath it. **The major layers that make up Earth are the inner core, outer core, mantle, and lithosphere. The lithosphere includes the crust and the uppermost part of the mantle.** These layers differ in composition or physical conditions. For example, temperature and pressure increase with depth beneath Earth's surface. You may be surprised to learn that the center of Earth is as hot as the surface of the sun!

Core As you can see in Figure 3, the dense core forms the center of Earth. The core is divided into two layers. The **inner core** is a sphere of hot, solid metal. Surrounding the inner core is the liquid **outer core.** The core is extremely hot—hot enough to melt the metal in the outer core. But pressure in the inner core is so great that it remains solid.

Most scientists accept the hypothesis that both parts of the core are made of iron and nickel. But some scientists also have found data suggesting that the density of Earth's core is a bit less than it would be if the core were made only of iron and nickel. Therefore, they hypothesize that the core also contains less-dense elements such as oxygen, sulfur, and silicon. Scientists must seek additional data before they decide whether to accept either hypothesis—or develop a new hypothesis about the composition of Earth's core.

Scientists hypothesize that circulation of molten metal within Earth's core helps to create a magnetic field. As a result, Earth has an immense magnetic field surrounding it, just as there is a magnetic field around a bar magnet. Earth's magnetic field is still not completely understood. But the fact that Earth has a magnetic field explains why a compass works as it does. The poles of the magnetized needle on the compass align themselves with Earth's magnetic field.

✓ *Checkpoint* *What type of material makes up Earth's core?*

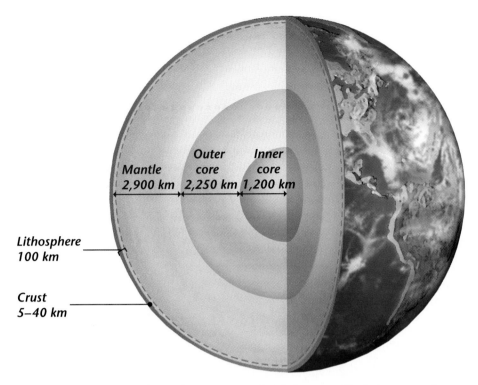

Figure 3 Parts of Earth's crust are covered with ice. But scientists estimate that the temperature of the core could be as hot as 5000° C. Pressure also increases greatly between the crust and Earth's center. *Interpreting Diagrams* *Which layer of Earth's interior is the thickest?*

Labels in figure:
Mantle 2,900 km
Outer core 2,250 km
Inner core 1,200 km
Lithosphere 100 km
Crust 5–40 km

Mantle Surrounding the core is a thick layer called the **mantle.** The mantle is made of hot but mostly solid material. Mantle material is less dense than the material that makes up the core. In a few places, volcanoes have brought up material from a depth of about 150 kilometers in the mantle.

Toward the upper part of the mantle is a layer of soft but solid material a few hundred kilometers thick. Over time, this material can flow very slowly, like road tar softened by the heat of the sun.

Lithosphere and Crust Like a giant golf ball, Earth has a rigid outer covering—the **lithosphere.** The crust is the thin, rock layer of the lithosphere that forms Earth's surface. The lithosphere also includes the uppermost part of the mantle down to a depth of about 100 kilometers.

Section 1 Review

1. What do geologists study about Earth's interior?
2. Describe the characteristics and structure of the different layers of Earth.
3. **Thinking Critically** Inferring The outer core is liquid, and the lithosphere is solid. What can be inferred about the temperature of the mantle, which contains a layer that can flow slowly?
4. **Thinking Critically** Posing Questions What questions would you want to answer before developing a new hypothesis about the composition of the core?

Check Your Progress
CHAPTER PROJECT

Begin by drawing a sketch of your three-dimensional model of Earth. Think about how you will show the thicknesses of Earth's different layers at the correct scale. What materials can you use for building your model? Experiment with materials that might work well for showing the physical composition of Earth's layers.

DISCOVER •••ACTIVITY••••

How Do Minerals Break Apart?

1. Mold some clay into a cube about 3 cm on a side.

2. Roll an equal amount of clay into a sheet about 0.5 cm thick. Cut the sheet of clay into six squares about 3 cm on a side.

3. Assemble the squares to form a second cube made up of layers of clay. Gently press the layers so that they hold together.

4. Holding the first cube between your fingers, pull it apart into two pieces.

5. Hold the second cube so that the layers are vertical and perpendicular to your body. Then pull the second cube apart.

6. Compare the surfaces along which the two cubes came apart. How are they similar? How are they different?

Think It Over

Observing The two cubes are models of two groups of minerals that break apart in different ways. Based on your observations, what might be two ways that minerals can break apart?

GUIDE FOR READING

◆ What is a mineral?

◆ What are some properties of minerals?

◆ How do minerals form?

Reading Tip Before you read, use the section headings to make an outline. Leave space in your outline to take notes.

Key Terms mineral • crystal • streak • luster • cleavage • fracture • density • magma • lava • vein • gemstone

Y ou have probably seen a sieve in your kitchen at home. A sieve is made of wire mesh. Particles can pass through the sieve only if they are smaller than the openings in the mesh. Now imagine a sieve that can separate different molecules. This sieve allows some molecules to pass, but traps or absorbs others. If you're wondering whether there really are any materials that can do this—meet the zeolites!

Zeolites are a group of materials that can act like a sieve to separate molecules of different sizes. Zeolites are useful for many purposes. In your home, you might find zeolites in water purifiers, water softeners, and deodorizers. Some cities add zeolites to their landfills to absorb polluting liquids. Oil refineries and other industries use zeolites to speed up chemical changes.

Figure 4 The light-colored crystals are natrolite, which is one of the zeolite minerals.

What Is a Mineral?

You can find zeolites on Earth's surface. Zeolites sometimes occur in areas where geologists think there was once a lake. Millions of years ago, material from a volcano filled in the lake bed. Then chemicals in the lake water changed some of the volcanic material into hard, glassy particles—zeolites. But what are these particles? Zeolites are minerals.

Minerals come in many colors and shapes. Minerals can be as rare as a precious diamond. Or they can be as common as halite, which you know as table salt. Geologists have identified more than 3,000 different minerals. But all of these minerals share certain characteristics. **A mineral is a solid, inorganic material that forms naturally on or beneath Earth's surface. Almost all minerals have a crystal structure. Each mineral also has a definite chemical composition.** The example of halite may help you to understand these characteristics of minerals.

Solid If you pour some halite into the palm of your hand, you can see that it is made up of small, solid particles. Recall that a solid is a material with a definite volume and a definite shape. Minerals generally remain solid under ordinary conditions on Earth's surface. But high temperatures inside Earth can cause minerals deep beneath the surface to melt.

Inorganic Halite is inorganic. A material that is inorganic did not arise from a living thing. Unlike halite, coal is not a mineral, because coal is formed from the remains of plants that lived millions of years ago.

Naturally Occurring A substance that is naturally occurring is the result of processes that take place in the natural world. For example, halite often occurs naturally in areas once occupied by seas. Deposits of halite were left behind when the sea water evaporated. Materials made by people, such as cement, plastic, glass, and steel, are not minerals.

Wulfenite

Coal

Figure 5 A substance must be naturally occurring to be a mineral. The yellow crystals of the mineral wulfenite (left) form thin, rectangular plates. Coal (right) is not considered a mineral because it is formed from once-living things. *Comparing and Contrasting How are the samples of wulfenite and coal similar? How are they different?*

Figure 6 Each of these minerals has its own combination of crystal structure and chemical composition. The red crystals of sphalerite (left) contain zinc and sulfur. Microcline feldspar (middle) is made up of potassium, aluminum, silicon, and oxgen. Quartz (right) is a compound made of silicon dioxide.

Sphalerite

Quartz

Microcline feldspar

Figure 7 Halite has a cubic crystal structure. A mineral's crystal structure remains the same even when the mineral is broken into pieces.

Crystal Structure If you look at Figure 7, you can see that the atoms in halite line up in a regular way. The atoms that make up a mineral line up in a pattern that repeats over and over again. The repeating pattern of a mineral's atoms forms a solid called a **crystal.** Halite crystals are cubic, that is, shaped like a cube. You can break a large piece of halite into smaller pieces. But the smaller halite pieces still have a cubic crystal structure.

Other minerals have crystal structures that differ from halite's structure. Geologists classify crystals according to the number of faces, or sides, on the crystal. They also measure the angle at which the faces meet. But all the crystals of a particular mineral have the same crystal structure.

Definite Chemical Composition What does it mean to say that a mineral has a definite chemical composition? Every mineral is made up of certain elements in definite proportions. For example, the mineral halite is made up of one atom of sodium for every atom of chlorine. Other minerals can be compounds of several elements. A few minerals are made up of only one element. Copper, silver, gold, and sulfur sometimes occur naturally in a pure form. These pure elements are also considered minerals.

☑ *Checkpoint* *What characteristics do all minerals share?*

Identifying Minerals

Suppose that you are a geologist exploring a cave. In the cave, you find crystals of a mineral you have never seen before. To learn about this new mineral you test to determine its properties. A mineral's properties are the characteristics of the mineral that make it different from other minerals. **Some properties of minerals include hardness, color, streak, luster, how a mineral breaks apart, and density.** Geologists use a variety of tests to determine a mineral's properties.

Hardness Talc is a mineral that is so soft, you can scratch it with a fingernail. But nothing can scratch the hardest mineral, diamond. To classify minerals according to their hardness, geologists use the Mohs hardness scale. The scale was invented nearly 200 years ago by a German geologist named Friedrich Mohs.

There are ten minerals on the Mohs scale. Talc, the first and softest mineral on the scale, has a hardness of 1. As you can see in Figure 8, the scale continues up to diamond, with a hardness of 10.

Geologists use a scratch test to determine the hardness of minerals on the Mohs scale. The scratch test compares the hardness of a mineral sample with the minerals on the scale. If you tested the hardness of a piece of halite, you would find that halite can scratch gypsum. Halite, however, cannot scratch calcite. Therefore, halite's hardness is between the hardness of gypsum and calcite, or between 2 and 3 on the Mohs scale.

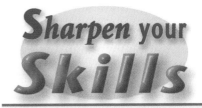

Mohs Hardness Scale		
Mineral	**Rating**	**Testing Method**
Talc	1	Softest known mineral. It flakes easily when scratched by a fingernail.
Gypsum	2	A fingernail can easily scratch it.
Calcite	3	A fingernail cannot scratch it, but a copper penny can.
Fluorite	4	A steel knife can easily scratch it.
Apatite	5	A steel knife can scratch it.
Feldspar	6	Cannot be scratched by a steel knife, but it can scratch window glass.
Quartz	7	Can scratch steel and hard glass easily.
Topaz	8	Can scratch quartz.
Corundum	9	Can scratch topaz.
Diamond	10	Hardest known mineral. Diamond can scratch all other substances.

Figure 8 The Mohs hardness scale rates the hardness of minerals on a scale of 1 to 10. Minerals on the scale can only scratch minerals that are rated lower on the scale. *Drawing Conclusions* You find a mineral that can be scratched by a steel knife, but not by a copper penny. What is this mineral's hardness on the Mohs scale?

Figure 9 Quartz (left) occurs in a variety of colors. Azurite (right) is a mineral that is easily identifed by its blue color.

Quartz

Azurite

Color, Streak, and Luster You may have heard the expression, "You can't judge a book by its cover." Well, you usually can't always judge a mineral by its color alone. Different forms of the same mineral may have different colors. Quartz, for example comes in a variety of colors. There are some minerals, however, that can be easily identified by color. One example is azurite, which is always bright blue.

Geologists test a mineral's streak to tell it apart from minerals with the same color. **Streak** is the color of a mineral's powder. Geologists determine a mineral's streak by rubbing the mineral on an unglazed piece of tile called a streak plate. A mineral's streak often differs from the color of a sample of that mineral. For example, gold and pyrite are both yellow minerals. Yet gold has a yellow streak, while pyrite's streak is greenish brown to black. The streak test can help you find out whether you have real gold or pyrite—also known as "fool's gold."

Geologists also use a property called luster to tell minerals apart by their appearance. **Luster** is the way a mineral reflects light from its surface. Some of the many terms used to describe luster include glassy, pearly, silky, metallic, and earthy.

Figure 10 A mineral's luster is the way its surface reflects light. Pyrite (left) has a metallic luster. One type of gypsum, called satin spar (middle), has a satiny luster. *Applying Concepts What word could you use to describe the luster of limonite (right)?*

Pyrite

Satin spar

Limonite

Figure 11 Minerals that split apart evenly along flat surfaces have cleavage; minerals that break in an irregular way have fracture. Mica (left), which has cleavage, splits into thin sheets. However, quartz (right), which has fracture, breaks into irregular pieces that look like chipped glass.

Cleavage and Fracture Observing how a mineral breaks apart can also help a geologist identify the mineral. Some minerals split apart easily along flat surfaces. These minerals have a property called **cleavage.** Muscovite, a common type of mica, has cleavage. You can easily split apart muscovite into paper-thin, translucent layers using a pocketknife.

Many minerals lack cleavage. Instead, these minerals form irregular surfaces when they break apart. These minerals have the property called **fracture.** Minerals that have fracture can break apart in several ways. When quartz fractures, it looks like the surface of a thick piece of glass that has been chipped. Other minerals with fracture may produce rough, jagged surfaces.

Density Another property that geologists use to identify a mineral is density. You may recall from Chapter 2 that **density** is a measurement of how much mass is contained in a given volume. The density of a cubic centimeter of quartz, for example, is about 2.6 times the density of the same volume of water. But the density of a cubic centimeter of gold is 19.3 times the density of the same volume of water.

Other Properties of Minerals Minerals have a variety of other properties that geologists can use to identify them. For example, a mineral that contains iron may be magnetic. Minerals that contain carbon react with certain acids. A drop of vinegar reacts with the carbon in calcite, forming carbon dioxide gas. The gas bubbles up from the surface of the calcite. Some minerals glow with bright colors when placed under ultraviolet light. Such minerals are said to be fluorescent.

Quartz and a few other minerals have electrical properties. Their crystals vibrate if they come in contact with an electric current. Because of these properties, quartz crystals are used in microphones, radio transmitters and watches.

✓ *Checkpoint* *What are cleavage and fracture?*

Calculating Density

To calculate the density of a mineral, divide the mass of a sample by its volume.

$$Density = \frac{Mass}{Volume}$$

Suppose you have a sample of quartz, a common rock-forming mineral. The sample you have has a mass of 13 grams and a volume of 5 cubic centimenters. What is the density of that sample?

Figure 12 One way minerals can form is by evaporation of solutions that contain mineral-forming material. These gypsum crystals, which formed by evaporation, look like the petals of a rose.

How Minerals Form

Have you ever made a tray of ice cubes in your home freezer? If you have, you already know something about how minerals can form. Some minerals form when a substance "freezes"—that is, changes from the liquid state to the solid state.

In general, there are two ways that minerals can form. **Many minerals form when molten material cools and hardens inside Earth or on the surface. Other minerals form when materials dissolved in water come out of solution.** Molten material inside Earth is called **magma.** Formed in the mantle, hot, liquid magma rises through the crust toward the surface. Molten material that reaches the surface is called **lava.**

When magma and lava cool and harden, crystals form. Large crystals form if cooling takes place slowly. Small crystals form if the cooling is rapid. For example, feldspar minerals form by slow cooling of magma deep beneath Earth's surface. Crystals of feldspar are large—they can range from several centimeters to a meter across. But lava that cools and hardens on the surface often forms such small crystals that you need a microscope to see them.

Sometimes, mineral-forming material dissolves in hot water beneath the surface. The water is heated by the heat of Earth's interior. As these solutions cool, the mineral-forming material comes out of solution, forming crystals of different minerals. Minerals that form from solutions often occur underground in narrow bands called **veins.** Sometimes, veins contain pure elements such as copper, silver, and gold.

Minerals can also form when a solution evaporates on Earth's surface. Halite and gypsum are two common minerals that are formed by this process.

How People Use Minerals

A **gemstone** is a mineral that is valued for its beautiful color, hardness, and glassy luster. Gemstones may be cut into gems for use in jewelry. Some gemstones are used to make fine machine parts. But minerals have many other uses.

Minerals are probably most important as the source of metals. Everything that's made of metal—from car engines to eyeglass frames—began as minerals inside Earth.

Minerals that do not contain metals are also very important in everyday life. Some medicines, building materials, electronic parts, and chemicals used in agriculture and industry contain minerals. Many useful minerals are mined in Texas. Look at *Exploring Texas Minerals* to learn what some of these minerals are and how they are used.

Figure 13 Some gemstones have become popular as birthstones—one for each month. However, one of the birthstones shown below—the pearl—is not a mineral because it is formed inside a living thing.

EXPLORING Texas Minerals

A mineral does not have to be a precious metal or gemstone to be of economic value. These Texas minerals have many uses.

▲ **Salt** Texas has large underground deposits of halite (sodium chloride) along the Gulf Coast.

▲ **Sulfur** Sulfur often occurs in Texas in areas where salt and oil are also found. Sulfur is used in fertilizers, medicines, petroleum refining, and many chemical processes.

▲ **Clay minerals** Clay minerals, which are found in Texas, are used in many kinds of ceramics and in building materials such as bricks. A clay called fuller's earth is used in refining oils and fats used in foods.

▼ **Gypsum** Widely mined in Texas, gypsum goes into building materials such as the "sheetrock" used to surface inside walls.

Section 2 Review

1. Define *mineral* in your own words.
2. How could you use the Mohs hardness scale to identify a mineral?
3. What is a mineral's streak? How can streak be helpful in identifying a mineral?
4. Describe two ways in which minerals can form.
5. **Thinking Critically Applying Concepts** Petroleum (oil) is a naturally occurring substance from inside Earth. Can petroleum be considered a mineral? Explain.

Science at Home

Pick the Mineral Gather at least three of the following materials: an ice cube, a piece of charcoal, a teaspoon of salt, a penny, and a glass marble. Then give family members your definition of a mineral. Ask family members to decide, based on your definition, which materials are, or contain, minerals. Discuss their choices based on what you have learned about minerals.

Observing

Mineral I.D.

In this lab, you will use a variety of tests to determine the properties of several minerals.

Problem

How can the properties of minerals be used to classify them?

Materials

samples of quartz, pyrite, hematite, calcite, talc, magnetite, or halite
hand lens   hardness point kit (optional)
copper penny   streak plate
iron nail   plastic dropper
scissors   vinegar
magnet

Procedure

1. Make a data chart like the one below to organize your observations.
2. Your teacher will give you 6 mineral samples labeled A through F.

3. Observe the color of each mineral and record the mineral's color in your chart.
4. Using the hand lens, carefully observe the size of the crystals in each mineral. Minerals with large crystals have a coarse texture. Minerals with small or hard-to-see crystals have a fine texture. Record what you observe.
5. Now observe the luster of your mineral. Is it metallic or nonmetallic? Would you describe your nonmetallic minerals as having a glassy, pearly, silky, or earthy luster? Record your observations in your data chart.
6. Try to scratch Mineral A with your fingernail. If a scratch appears, record this in your table. If your fingernail does not scratch Mineral A, try the penny, then the iron nail, and then the scissors. Record the softest material that can first scratch each mineral. (You may also use hardness points to determine the hardness of each mineral.)

DATA CHART

Sample	Color (dark, light, or mixed colors)	Crystal Size (fine or coarse-grained)	Luster	Hardness	Streak	Magnetic	Reaction to Vinegar
A							
B							
C							
D							
E							
F							

7. To test the streak of a mineral, push down on the mineral as you rub it across the streak plate. Observe the color of the streak and record it in your data chart.

8. Hold a magnet next to each mineral. Record the results.

9. Calcite will fizz as it reacts with the acid in the vinegar to produce tiny bubbles of carbon dioxide gas. To test for the mineral calcite, place 3 drops of vinegar on each of your minerals. Record the results.

10. Wash your hands when you are finished.

Analyze and Conclude

1. Use your chart to examine and evaluate your data. Did any of your minerals have the same color? How useful is color in determining a mineral's identity?

2. Classify your minerals in two groups according to crystal size. How do you think each group of minerals formed?

3. Did any of your minerals have a glassy or sparkly luster? Why do you think that minerals with a glassy or sparkly luster are important to people?

4. How would knowing the hardness of a mineral help you decide how the mineral could be used?

5. Was streak color ever different from the color of the mineral? How could streak be useful in identifying minerals that are the same color?

6. **Think About It** What physical property was most useful in classifying minerals? Why?

More to Explore

The different properties of your mineral samples can help you identify them. Use a field guide to rocks and minerals to identify the specific name of each mineral sample.

Rocks and the Rock Cycle

DISCOVER ••••••••••••••••••••••••••••••••••••••• ACTIVITY••••

What Is Earth's Crust Made Of?

1. Your teacher will give you three different rocks.

2. Observe each rock under a hand lens. In your notebook, describe the color or colors that you see in the rocks. Also describe any shapes or patterns in the rocks.

3. Make a sketch of each of your rocks.

Think It Over

Forming Operational Definitions Are your rocks made up of one material or several materials? How can you tell? How are the rocks similar? How are they different? Based on your observations, how would you define "rock"?

GUIDE FOR READING

◆ What are the three major groups of rocks?

◆ How do different kinds of rocks form?

◆ What is the rock cycle?

Reading Tip Before you read, rewrite the section headings as questions. As you read, write answers to the questions.

Key Terms rock • texture
• grain • igneous rock
• intrusive rock • extrusive rock
• sedimentary rock • sediment
• erosion • deposition
• metamorphic rock
• rock cycle

There is a huge dragon climbing out of the Black Canyon of the Gunnison River in Colorado. The dragon has jaws like an alligator, a twisting body, and a tail. But this dragon is not a fire-breathing monster. It is a bright pattern on a cliff that forms one side of the Black Canyon. Because of colorful patterns in the rock, this cliff is called the Painted Wall. The pattern shaped like a dragon is actually a thick vein of rock called pegmatite. Veins of bright pink and white pegmatite stand out against the dark purple-gray rocks that make up most of the canyon.

Building Blocks of the Crust

Like many kinds of rock, pegmatite is a mixture of several minerals. Recall from Section 1 that rock forms Earth's crust. **Rock** is a solid material made up of one or more minerals or other substances, including the remains of once-living things. Some rocks contain material that comes from plants or animals. For example, clam shells can be found in some rocks. Other rocks are made up of only one mineral. One such rock is "rock salt," which is made up only of the mineral halite.

You may be surprised to learn that most of Earth's rocks are made up of about 20 common minerals. These minerals are called rock-forming minerals.

Figure 14 The Painted Wall in the Black Canyon of the Gunnison in Colorado is a sheer rock cliff more than 750 meters high.

Slate *Fine-grained*

Diorite *Coarse-grained*

Flint *No visible grain*

Figure 15 The size, shape, and pattern of a rock's grains determine its texture.

Conglomerate *Rounded grain*

Breccia *Jagged grain*

Classifying Rocks

Geologists classify rocks based on the rocks' color, texture, composition, and how the rocks formed.

Color The color of a rock depends on the colors of the minerals that make up the rock. The color of the minerals, in turn, reflects their chemical composition. For example, certain rocks made up of minerals that are rich in silicon and aluminum are often light in color. But other rocks made up of minerals rich in iron and magnesium tend to be dark in color. As with minerals, classifying a rock just by color is not always helpful. For one thing, weather can change the color of a rock's outer surface over time.

Texture Usually, the word "texture" means how a surface feels to the touch. But to a geologist, **texture** refers to the size, shape, and arrangement of a rock's grains. A **grain** is one of the particles that make up a rock. A grain can be made up of crystals of a mineral. Or a grain can be a piece of another rock.

Geologists use several terms to describe a rock's texture. A rock with a coarse-grained texture has large grains. A rock with a fine-grained texture has small grains. You can see examples of different rock textures in Figure 15.

Composition How do geologists determine a rock's composition? First, they try to identify the minerals the rock contains. Identifying the minerals can be quite easy if the rock is made up of large crystals. But it can be much harder to identify small crystals. One method is to make a slice of rock called a "thin section." A geologist can prepare a thin section by cutting and grinding a rock. Finally, the rock becomes so thin that light shines through. By viewing the thin section under a microscope, a geologist can identify the minerals in the thin section.

▲ *Basalt*

▼ *Granite*

Figure 16 Two common igneous rocks are basalt and granite. Basalt (above) is a dark, extrusive rock that makes up much of the oceanic crust. Granite (right) is a light-colored intrusive rock that is common in continental crust.

To See or Not to See

Learn about the difference in texture between intrusive and extrusive rocks.

ACTIVITY

1. Obtain samples of igneous rocks from your teacher.

2. Observe the rocks carefully with a hand lens.

3. Can you see separate crystals of rock-forming minerals, or are the crystals too small to see?

4. Separate your rocks into two piles: those with a coarse-grained texture and those with a fine-grained texture.

Classifying Which samples are intrusive rocks? Which are extrusive rocks? How do you know?

How Rock Forms Geologists also classify rocks based on how the rocks form. **Geologists classify rocks into three major groups: igneous, sedimentary, and metamorphic.** As you will see, the rocks in each of these groups are formed in a different way.

Igneous Rock

The pegmatite in the Black Canyon is an igneous rock. **Igneous rock forms when magma or lava cools and hardens.** Pegmatite is formed when hot, liquid magma rises through cracks in rock deep beneath the surface. The magma cools very slowly underground, producing the large crystals often found in pegmatite.

Geologists further classify igneous rocks according to whether the rocks formed above or beneath Earth's surface. Igneous rock formed from magma beneath the surface is called **intrusive rock.**

One common intrusive rock is granite, often made up of the minerals quartz, feldspar, mica, and hornblende. If you look at the picture of granite in Figure 16, you can see the crystals of these minerals. Granite forms much of the continental crust—the part of the crust that makes up Earth's continents.

When igneous rock forms from lava on the surface, it is called **extrusive rock.** A type of rock called basalt is probably the most common extrusive rock on Earth. Basalt is a dark, dense rock made up of several minerals. Basalt forms much of the oceanic crust—the part of the crust that makes up the ocean floor. Basalt forms as a result of volcanic activity. You will learn more about igneous rocks and volcanic activity in Chapter 11.

☑ *Checkpoint* *What are two ways in which igneous rocks can form?*

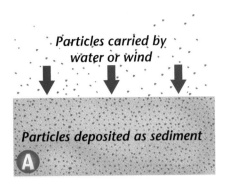

Particles carried by water or wind

Particles deposited as sediment

A

Loosely packed sediment

B Densely packed sediment

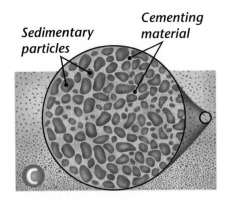

Sedimentary particles

Cementing material

C

Figure 17 Sedimentary rocks form through the erosion, deposition, compaction, and cementation of sediments. **(A)** Water or wind deposits sediment. **(B)** The heavy sediments press down on the layers beneath. **(C)** Dissolved minerals flow between the particles and cement them together.
Relating Cause and Effect What conditions are necessary for sedimentary rock to form?

Sedimentary Rock

Another group of rocks arises from bits and pieces of rock and other substances. **Sedimentary rock forms when particles of rock and other materials are pressed and stuck together.** Geologists use the term **sediment** for particles of rock or material from living things. The sand and gravel on a beach and the mud on a riverbank are sediment. Seashells, leaves, twigs, and other remains of animals or plants are also sediment. All these different kinds of sediment can become sedimentary rock.

Have you ever watched rushing water from a heavy rain wash soil and gravel down a slope? If so, you have seen the beginning of the process that forms sedimentary rock. First, **erosion** moves sediment from place to place on Earth's surface. Flowing water, waves, wind, and ice can all cause erosion. Second, sediment is laid down in a process called **deposition.** For example, deposition occurs when water slows down or stops moving. The sediment sinks out of the water and comes to rest.

Slowly, thick layers of sediment build up. The weight of the layers above presses down on the layers below. This process, called compaction, squeezes the layers of sediment together. Another process, called cementation, glues the sediment together. Cementation can occur in several ways. Sometimes, cementation occurs when water dissolves some of the sediment. The solution then forms mineral crystals that cement the sediment particles together. Compaction and cementation may continue for millions of years. Eventually, the sediment changes to sedimentary rock.

There are three major kinds of sedimentary rock: clastic rock, organic rock, and chemical rock. Each type of sedimentary rock forms in a different way.

Figure 18 The sedimentary rock conglomerate is made up of sediment particles of different sizes that have been pressed and cemented together.

Figure 19 These colorful layers of sandstone in Utah are examples of clastic sedimentary rocks.

Clastic Rock Can a sedimentary rock be like a gelatin dessert with pieces of fruit mixed in? The answer is yes, if the rock is a clastic rock. Pieces of rock that have been pressed and stuck together are called clastic rock. One common clastic rock is conglomerate. Conglomerate is made up of rounded pieces of rock. It may contain sand and pebbles, or even large rocks and boulders. Another clastic rock, sandstone, is made up of grains of sand cemented together by dissolved quartz.

Organic Rock Sedimentary rock formed from the remains of plants and animals is called organic rock. One of the most common rocks is limestone. Limestone is formed from the shells and skeletons of animals that lived in ancient seas. The shells and skeletons are made up of the mineral calcite. Some of the calcite dissolves in water as a result of a chemical change. The dissolved calcite cements the shells and skeletons together to form limestone.

Figure 20 Some sedimentary rocks, such as the gypsum that covers this dry lake bed, form when dissolved minerals come out of solution.

Coal is an organic rock formed from the remains of plants that lived in swamps millions of years ago. Over time, thick layers of plant remains were changed to coal.

Chemical Rock A chemical rock is formed when dissolved minerals come out of solution and form crystals. Deposits of chemical rock are often found in areas that were once covered by water. The chemical rock was formed as water containing dissolved minerals evaporated. Halite, or rock salt, is an example of a common chemical rock.

Granite → **Gneiss**

Figure 21 Heat and pressure can change any rock into metamorphic rock. For example, granite becomes gneiss, and sandstone changes to quartzite.
Observing What evidence of heat or pressure can you see in the gneiss and quartzite?

Sandstone → **Quartzite**

Metamorphic Rock

Sometimes, sediment buries rock deep beneath the surface. The weight of thick layers of sediment pushes the rock down toward the heat of Earth's mantle. **Heat and great pressure deep beneath Earth's surface can change rock to metamorphic rock.** Sometimes, heat from a volcano causes nearby rock to become metamorphic rock.

A metamorphic rock is different from the rock that formed it. For example, a rock's texture changes as it becomes metamorphic rock. Chemical reactions may also occur that change the minerals in the rock.

Any kind of rock can become a metamorphic rock. For example, the igneous rock granite can become the metamorphic rock, gneiss. You know that granite is made up of large crystals. When granite changes to gneiss, the crystals are flattened into parallel rows called bands. Therefore, gneiss is a metamorphic rock with a banded texture.

Other metamorphic rocks do not have bands. Their texture is nonbanded. For example, the sedimentary rock sandstone can become quartzite, a nonbanded metamorphic rock. Look at Figure 21 to see how gneiss and quartzite differ from the rocks from which they formed.

☑ *Checkpoint* **What are metamorphic rocks and how are they formed?**

The Rock Cycle

Earth's rocks are not as unchanging as they seem. **Forces inside Earth and at the surface produce a rock cycle that builds, destroys, and changes the rocks in the crust.** The **rock cycle** is a series of processes on and beneath Earth's surface that slowly change rocks from one kind to another.

Figure 23 shows that the rock cycle can follow many different pathways. Here is one possible pathway: the igneous rock granite formed beneath the surface millions of years ago. Then, the forces of mountain building slowly pushed the granite upward, forming a mountain. Slowly, water and weather wore away the granite through the process of erosion. These granite particles became sand, carried by streams to the ocean.

Over millions of years, layers of sandy sediment piled up on the ocean floor. Slowly, the sediments were pressed together and cemented to form sandstone, a sedimentary rock.

Over time, more and more sediment piled up on the sandstone. As the sandstone became deeply buried, pressure on the rock increased. The rock became hot. Heat and pressure changed the rock's texture from gritty to smooth. After millions of years, the sandstone changed into the metamorphic rock quartzite.

Metamorphic rock does not end the rock cycle. Sometimes, forces inside Earth push all three types of rock many kilometers beneath the surface. There the heat of Earth's interior melts the rock. This molten material can form new igneous rock.

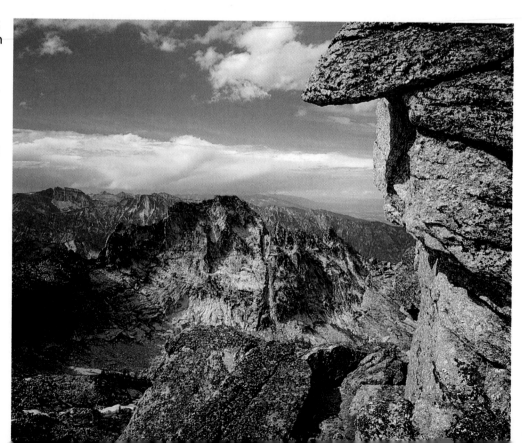

Figure 22 The Bitterroot Mountains in Idaho began as a great mass of intrusive igneous rock deep beneath the surface. Over time, some of the rock changed to metamorphic rock. As forces inside Earth pushed the rock above the surface, erosion began to sculpt the rock into mountains.
Predicting What type of rock might begin to form next in the Bitterroot Mountains?

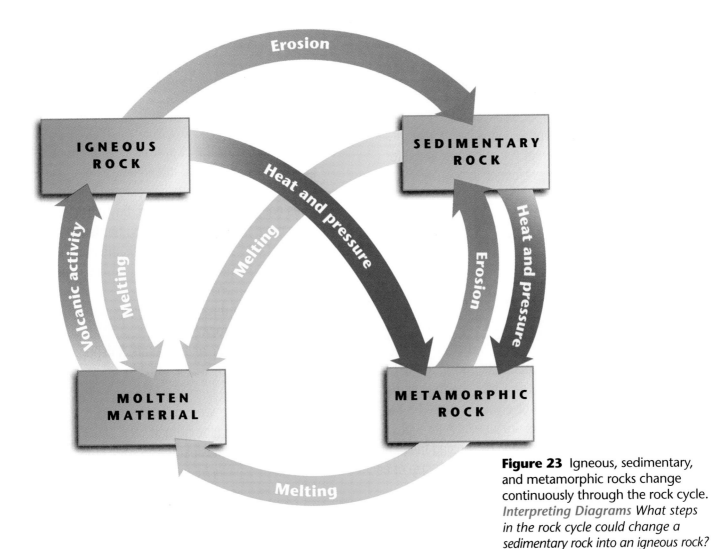

Figure 23 Igneous, sedimentary, and metamorphic rocks change continuously through the rock cycle. *Interpreting Diagrams* What steps in the rock cycle could change a sedimentary rock into an igneous rock?

 ## Section 3 Review

1. Briefly describe how rocks in the three major groups are formed.
2. How are the ways that intrusive and extrusive rocks form similar? How are they different?
3. What are four ways in which geologists classify rocks?
4. **Thinking Critically Inferring** A geologist finds a coarse-grained rock with crystals arranged in rows. What can the geologist infer about how this rock formed and what group it belongs to?
5. **Thinking Critically Applying Concepts** What rock comes before quartzite in the rock cycle? What rock or rocks could come just after quartzite in the rock cycle? Explain your answer.

Check Your Progress

CHAPTER PROJECT

Draw a revised sketch of your model. How will you show Earth's crust? How will your three-dimensional model show the composition, temperature, and pressure of layers beneath the crust? Revise your list of materials. Construct your model, including all the required features. Be sure to label the features on your model.

How It Works

Rock Recycling

In this lab, you will identify the rock group to which different rocks belong and infer how they could have formed through the rock cycle.

Problem

How can rocks be classified by how they formed?

Materials

10 rocks   hand lens   computer (optional)

Procedure

1. ▣ Copy the data table into your notebook or create a data table on the computer.
2. Your teacher will give you 10 rocks for this activity. The rocks are labeled A through J.
3. Carefully observe each rock using the hand lens. Record the color and crystal size of each rock in your data table.
4. Carefully observe the rocks again. Look for clues that a rock formed from molten material. Is one glassy? Does one have bubbles? Does one have large crystals distributed randomly? Record your observations.
5. Look for clues that show that a rock was formed from particles of other rocks. Is one layered as if made from fine silt? Can it be scratched with your fingernail? Is one made of sand particles? Is one made of many kinds and sizes of pebbles and minerals cemented together? Does one contain fossil shells? Record your observations.

6. Look for clues that show whether the rock formed under heat and pressure. Do the rock's grains look melted and interlocked? Does one have flat layers of crystals in colored bands? Does one look as if the original tiny particles have been pressed together and hardened in layers? Does one look as if tiny sand particles have been heated so that larger crystals could grow? Record your observations.
7. Complete your data table by filling in the rock group for each rock.
8. Wash your hands when you are finished.

Analyze and Conclude

1. Which properties were most useful in classifying each type of rock?
2. Which rock was easiest to classify? Which was hardest to classify? Explain.
3. **Think About It** Choose one rock from each group and arrange them according to one possible pathway in the rock cycle. (*Hint:* Think about the ways rocks are formed.) Be prepared to explain your choices to another person. What inferences did you make to arrange your rocks according to the steps in the rock cycle?

More to Explore

Using a field guide to rocks and minerals, find several rocks that are formed from another kind of rock. Create a display showing several of these rock cycle pathways to share with your class.

DATA TABLE

Sample	Color (dark, medium, light, or mixed colors)	Crystal Size (fine, medium, or coarse-grained)	Other Observations (Record clues of how the rock formed)	Rock Group (igneous, metamorphic, sedimentary)
A				
B				
C				
D				

SECTION 1 Inside Earth

Key Ideas
◆ Geologists study Earth and the processes that have shaped Earth over time. They study the minerals and rocks that make up Earth, physical conditions inside Earth, and the forces inside Earth that affect the surface.
◆ Earth's interior is divided into the crust, the mantle, the outer core, and the inner core. The crust and the rigid uppermost part of the mantle are called the lithosphere.

Key Terms
rock	inner core
crust	outer core
geology	mantle
geologist	lithosphere
seismic wave	

SECTION 2 Minerals

Key Ideas
◆ A mineral is a solid, inorganic material that forms naturally on or beneath Earth's surface. A mineral generally has a definite chemical composition and a crystal structure.
◆ Some of the properties of minerals include hardness, color, luster, density, and how the mineral breaks apart.
◆ Many minerals form when molten material cools and hardens. Other minerals form when materials dissolved in water come out of solution.

Key Terms
mineral	fracture
crystal	magma
streak	lava
luster	vein
density	gemstone
cleavage	

SECTION 3 Rocks and the Rock Cycle

Key Ideas
◆ The three major groups of rocks are igneous, sedimentary, and metamorphic.
◆ Rocks can be formed when magma or lava hardens, when sediments are cemented and compacted together, or when heat and pressure change rock deep beneath Earth's surface.
◆ The series of processes on and beneath Earth's surface that change rocks from one type to another is called the rock cycle.

Key Terms
rock	sedimentary rock
texture	sediment
grain	erosion
igneous rock	deposition
intrusive rock	metamorphic rock
extrusive rock	rock cycle

Organizing Information

Cycle Diagram Copy the cycle diagram onto a sheet of paper. This diagram shows one possible pathway through the rock cycle. Place these descriptions on the diagram in the correct order: Sedimentary rock, Metamorphic rock, Melting, and Igneous rock. Then add a title. (For help in making cycle diagrams, see the Skills Handbook.)

Reviewing Content

Review key concepts online using iText at www.phschool.com

Multiple Choice

Chose the letter of the answer that best completes each statement.

1. Earth's rigid outer layers make up the
   a. inner core.
   b. outer core.
   c. mantle.
   d. lithosphere.
2. To learn the structure of Earth's interior, geologists study
   a. the magnetic compass.
   b. the luster of minerals.
   c. sedimentary rocks.
   d. seismic waves.
3. The hardest mineral in the Mohs hardness scale is
   a. talc.
   b. diamond.
   c. quartz.
   d. calcite.
4. How is halite formed?
   a. cooling of magma
   b. cooling of lava
   c. sea-floor spreading
   d. evaporation
5. An example of an igneous rock is
   a. gneiss.
   b. basalt.
   c. marble.
   d. limestone.

True or False

If the statement is true, write true. If it is false, change the underlined word or words to make the statement true.

6. Earth's <u>inner core</u> is largely made of basalt and granite.
7. Pearly is an example of the <u>luster</u> of a mineral.
8. <u>Rocks</u> have specific crystal structures.
9. <u>Erosion</u> moves particles of sediment from place to place on Earth's surface.
10. <u>Sedimentary rocks</u> are formed by heat and pressure deep beneath Earth's surface.

Checking Concepts

11. What are two aspects of Earth that geologists study?
12. How is the outer core different from the inner core?
13. Describe one way in which geologists have gained indirect evidence about Earth's interior.
14. Describe how temperature changes between the crust and the center of Earth.
15. What is one explanation of Earth's magnetic field?
16. Name four properties of minerals that are used to tell them apart.
17. **Writing to Learn** Use five index cards and write the names of five rocks, one on each card. On the other side write the rock group each belongs to, a description of how each rock was made, and from what types of particles it was made. Have a classmate read each description and see if he or she can guess the name of the rock.

Thinking Critically

18. **Classifying** Classify these layers of Earth's crust as liquid or solid: crust, lithosphere, mantle, outer core, inner core.
19. **Inferring** What does the size of a mineral's crystals tell you about how it was formed?
20. **Relating Cause and Effect** Describe the processes that occur to form a clastic sedimentary rock such as sandstone.
21. **Comparing and Contrasting** How are sandstone and quartzite similar? How are they different?
22. **Predicting** What will form if a sedimentary rock melts?
23. **Applying Concepts** Is there an end to the rock cycle? Explain your answer.

Applying Skills

You are given a number of minerals to identify. All of them can be found on the Mohs hardness scale. Using the information below, answer Questions 24–27.

Mineral	Rating	Testing Method
Talc	1	Flakes easily when scratched by a fingernail.
Calcite	3	A copper penny scratches it, but not a fingernail.
Feldspar	6	Cannot be scratched by a steel knife. Scratches window glass.
Quartz	7	Can scratch steel and hard glass easily.

24. Predicting Which mineral could be most easily turned into a powder?

25. Inferring This mineral cannot be scratched by a fingernail, a copper penny, or a steel knife. It can scratch hard glass and a piece of steel. What is it?

26. Inferring This mineral can be scratched by a steel knife and a copper penny, but not a fingernail. Identify the mineral.

27. Drawing Conclusions This mineral can scratch calcite, but it can be scratched by quartz. What is the mineral and how did you determine the answer?

Performance ▼ CHAPTER PROJECT Assessment

Present Your Project Now you are ready to explain your model of Earth's interior to your class. Label your model to indicate the physical features you have included.

Reflect and Record In your journal, write about the easiest and hardest parts of this project. What other materials could you have used? How many times did you revise your design?

Test Preparation

Use these questions to prepare for standardized tests.

A rock's texture gives clues to how the rock was formed. Use the information below to answer Questions 28–31.

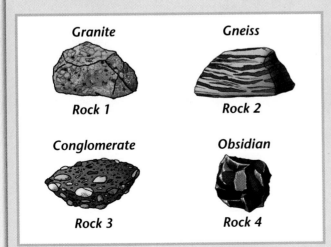

Granite — Rock 1

Gneiss — Rock 2

Conglomerate — Rock 3

Obsidian — Rock 4

28. Which of the rocks is a sedimentary rock made up of other rocks that have been cemented together?

   A Rock 1   **B** Rock 2
   C Rock 3   **D** Rock 4

29. Which rock appears to be a banded metamorphic rock?

   F Rock 1   **G** Rock 2
   H Rock 3   **J** Rock 4

30. Which rock formed from molten material that cooled quickly, giving the rock a glassy texture?

   A Rock 1   **B** Rock 2
   C Rock 3   **D** Rock 4

31. Which rock is an igneous rock made up of large crystals of several different minerals?

   F Rock 1   **G** Rock 2
   H Rock 3   **J** Rock 4

Earthquakes and Volcanoes

Kilauea volcano is on Hawaii, the largest of the Hawaiian Islands.

www.phschool.com

Volcanoes and People

The frequent eruptions of Mount Kilauea can be spectacular. And they can be dangerous. Yet volcanoes and people have been closely connected throughout history, not only in Hawaii, but around the world. People often live near volcanoes because of the benefits they offer, from rich soil to minerals to hot springs. In your chapter project, you will research how volcanoes have affected the people living in a volcanic region.

Your Goal To make a documentary about life in a volcanic region.

Your project must

◆ describe the type of volcano you chose and give its history
◆ focus on one topic, such as how people have benefited from living near the volcano or how people show the volcano in their art and stories
◆ use a variety of media in your documentary presentation

Get Started Brainstorm with a group of other students which geographic area you would like to learn about. Your teacher may suggest some volcanic regions for you to check out. What research resources will your group need? Start planning what media you want to use to present your documentary. You might consider video, computer art, overhead transparencies, a rap song, a skit, or a mural. Be creative!

Check Your Progress You'll be working on this project as you study this chapter. To keep your project on track, look for Check Your Progress boxes at the following points.

Section 2 Review, page 365: Select the topic and region you will investigate and begin collecting information.

Section 4 Review, page 383: Use storyboards to organize your materials.

Section 5 Review, page 390: Prepare your visuals and narration.

Present Your Project At the end of the chapter (page 393), practice your presentation, and then present your documentary to your class.

TEKS

In addition to process TEKS, this chapter addresses these concept TEKS as they relate to the chapter's topics.

(6.6) The student knows that there is a relationship between force and motion. The student is expected to:
(C) identify forces that shape features of the Earth including uplifting, movement of water, and volcanic activity.

Plate Tectonics

•• **ACTIVITY**••••

How Slow Can It Flow?

1. Put a spoonful of honey on a plate.

2. Using a ruler, place a piece of tape 2 cm away from the edge of the honey.

3. Lift one side of the plate just high enough that the honey is visibly flowing.

4. Reduce the angle of the plate a small amount so that the honey appears to be barely moving. Prop up the plate at this angle.

5. Time how long it takes the honey to flow to the tape. Use this information to calculate the speed of the honey.

Think It Over

Forming Operational Definitions
How can you tell that an object is moving if it doesn't appear to be moving at first glance? Can you think of some other examples of motion that are too slow to see?

GUIDE FOR READING

◆ What is the theory of plate tectonics?

Reading Tip As you read, make a list of main ideas and supporting details about plate tectonics

Key Terms plates • Pangaea
• plate tectonics
• plate boundaries

You may be surprised to learn that Earth's lithosphere can move. After all, you know that the lithosphere is made up of solid rock! In fact, the lithosphere is broken into a number of large pieces called **plates.** The plates completely cover Earth's surface and even extend under the oceans.

The plates are made up of oceanic crust and continental crust. A few plates are made only of oceanic crust. Each plate also includes the part of the lithosphere that lies beneath it. Most of the United States is located on the North American plate.

Earth's Moving Plates

The plates move very slowly—at rates of several centimeters per year. That's about as fast as your fingernails grow! As the plates move, the continents also move, or "drift," over Earth's surface.

Looking at a world map, you may have observed that the coastlines of the continents on both sides of the Atlantic Ocean seem to match. People have noticed this remarkable fact for centuries. In the early 1900s, a German scientist named Alfred Wegener also saw that some continents seemed to fit together like pieces of a jigsaw puzzle. Wegener developed a hypothesis to explain this observation.

Figure 1 This jagged valley in Iceland marks the line where two of Earth's plates meet.

260 million years ago

Present

According to Wegener's hypothesis, the fit of the continents was not the result of chance. Wegener found evidence that the continents that existed millions of years ago moved together. As these continents collided, they formed a great landmass, or "supercontinent," called **Pangaea** (pan JEE uh). Millions of years after Pangaea formed, it slowly broke apart. The continents then moved to their present positions. You can compare a map of Pangaea with a modern world map in Figure 2.

Figure 2 The supercontinent Pangaea began to break apart about 225 million years ago. *Observing How have North America and South America moved in relation to Africa and Europe?*

The Theory of Plate Tectonics

During much of the twentieth century, geologists did not accept the idea of continental drift. Wegener had not been able to explain how continental drift occurred. But during the 1960s, several geologists proposed a new theory—the theory of **plate tectonics** (tek TAHN iks). They based the theory on new information about Earth's lithosphere and the interior of the planet.

Figure 3 The black outlines show the boundaries of some of Earth's plates.

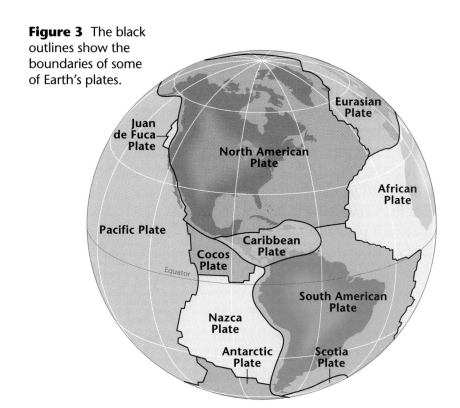

Sharpen your **Skills**

Predicting

ACTIVITY

Los Angeles, on the Pacific Plate, is slowly moving northwest. San Francisco, on the North American plate, is slowly moving southeast. These two cities are moving toward each other at a rate of about 5 cm/yr. If the two cities are now 554,000 m apart, how long will it take for the two cities to be next to each other?

EXPLORING *Plate Tectonics*

The movement of Earth's plates produces features on Earth's continents and on the ocean floor.

When two plates of oceanic crust collide, one plate sinks beneath the other. One of the plates is pushed beneath the deep-sea trench down toward the mantle.

Sea-floor spreading occurs as oceanic plates pull apart along the mid-ocean ridge, a mountain range that winds through Earth's oceans. Lava erupts through narrow cracks along the ridge, adding new rock to the ocean floor.

Trench

Trench

Mid-ocean ridge

Oceanic crust

Oceanic crust

Subduction zone

Beneath the trench, the plate melts and becomes magma. The magma erupts to the surface forming a row of volcanic islands.

A deep-ocean trench may form where oceanic crust sinks toward the mantle beneath continental crust. Some of the oceanic crust melts to form magma.

Lithosphere

Magma

The theory of plate tectonics states that Earth's plates are in constant, slow motion. The theory explains how Earth's plates form and move. It also explains how plates interact, producing volcanoes, mountain ranges, earthquakes, and features of the ocean floor.

What causes the plates to move? Scientists think that plate motion is the result of the movement of material in the upper mantle. Recall from Chapter 10 that beneath the lithosphere is a layer of material in the mantle that can flow slowly. According to the theory of plate tectonics, the plates of the lithosphere float on this layer. As the material in the upper mantle moves, it drags the overlying plates across Earth's surface.

Effects of Plate Movement

Like the covering of a baseball, the lithosphere has seams, or cracks, between the different pieces. The cracks between the plates of the lithosphere are called **plate boundaries.** Along plate boundaries, the plates slide past each other, pull apart, or move together.

In some places on Earth's surface, two plates slide past each other, moving slowly in opposite directions. One effect of this movement is frequent earthquakes.

A rift valley froms when two pieces of continental crust pull apart. Over millions of years, the rift valley could widen and sink below sea level, forming a new ocean.

If two plates carrying continental crust collide, neither plate sinks beneath the other. Instead, the plates slowly fold and pile on top of each other, forming a mountain range.

Rift valley

Continental crust

Magma

Lithosphere

These movements produce spectacular changes in Earth's surface. For example, the Andes mountains formed where the Nazca plate slides beneath the South American plate. In *Exploring Plate Tectonics*, you can see how plate movements change Earth's surface.

 ## Section 1 Review

1. What does the theory of plate tectonics explain?
2. What are Earth's plates and what are they made of?
3. What was Alfred Wegener's hypothesis about Pangaea?
4. What do scientists think is the cause of plate motion?
5. **Thinking Critically Relating Cause and Effect** Describe how new features of Earth's surface result from the movement of Earth's plates.

Science at Home

Measuring Slow Motion Have each member of your family measure the length of the white part at the end of one fingernail. Write down the results (and which finger you used) and mark your calendar for a date in exactly three weeks. On that day, measure the new length of the white part of the same fingernail. Then calculate the speed, in millimeters per day, at which your fingernail grew. Discuss with your family how your results compare with the typical speed with which continents move.

SECTION 2 Earth's Crust in Motion

 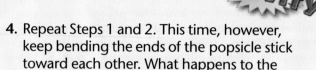
GUIDE FOR READING

◆ How do stress forces affect rock?

◆ Why do faults form and where do they occur?

◆ How do uplift and fault movements affect Earth's surface?

Reading Tip Before you read, use the headings to make an outline about stress in the crust, faults, and mountain building.

Key Terms earthquake
• stress • shearing • tension
• compression • fault
• strike-slip fault
• normal fault • hanging wall
• footwall • reverse fault
• fold • plateau

You are sitting at the kitchen table eating breakfast. Suddenly you notice a slight vibration, as if a heavy truck were rumbling by. At the same time, your glass of orange juice jiggles. Dishes rattle in the cupboards. After a few seconds, the rattling stops. Later, when you listen to the news on the radio, you learn that your region experienced a small earthquake. Earthquakes are a reminder that Earth's crust can move.

Stress in the Crust

An **earthquake** is the shaking and trembling that results from the movement of rock beneath Earth's surface. The movement of Earth's plates creates powerful forces that squeeze or pull the rock in the crust. These forces are examples of **stress,** a force that acts on rock to change its shape or volume. (Volume is the amount of space an object takes up.) Because stress is a force, it adds energy to the rock. The energy is stored in the rock until the rock either breaks or changes shape.

Figure 4 Stress in the crust folded this rock like a sheet of ribbon candy.

Types of Stress

Three different kinds of stress occur in the crust—shearing, tension, and compression. **Shearing, tension, and compression work over millions of years to change the shape and volume of rock.** These forces cause some rocks to become brittle and snap. Other rocks tend to bend slowly like road tar softened by the heat of the sun.

Stress that pushes a mass of rock in two opposite directions is called **shearing.** Shearing can cause rock to break and slip apart or to change its shape.

The stress force called **tension** pulls on the crust, stretching rock so that it becomes thinner in the middle. The effect of tension on rock is somewhat like pulling apart a piece of warm bubble gum. Tension occurs where two plates are moving apart.

The stress force called **compression** squeezes rock until it folds or breaks. One plate pushing against another can compress rock like a giant trash compactor.

Any change in the volume or shape of Earth's crust is called deformation. Most changes in the crust occur so slowly that they cannot be observed directly. But if you could speed up time so a billion years passed by in minutes, you could see the deformation of the crust. The crust would bend, stretch, break, tilt, fold, and slide. The slow shift of Earth's plates causes this deformation.

☑ *Checkpoint* *How does deformation change Earth's surface?*

Figure 5 Deformation pushes, pulls, or twists the rocks in Earth's crust. *Relating Cause and Effect Which type of deformation tends to shorten part of the crust?*

Ⓐ
Before stress

Ⓒ
Tension
Tension stretches rock.

Ⓑ
Shearing
Shearing can cause masses of rock to slip.

Ⓓ
Compression
Compression pushes rock together.

Strike-slip fault

Figure 6 A strike-slip fault that is clearly visible at the surface is the San Andreas Fault in California.

Kinds of Faults

If you try to break a caramel candy bar in two, it may only bend and stretch at first. Like a candy bar, many types of rock can bend or fold. But beyond a certain limit, even these rocks will break. And it takes less stress to snap a brittle rock than it does to snap one that can bend.

When enough stress builds up in rock, the rock breaks, creating a fault. A **fault** is a break in the crust where slabs of crust slip past each other. The rocks on both sides of a fault can move up or down or sideways. **Faults usually occur along plate boundaries, where the forces of plate motion compress, pull, or shear the crust so much that the crust breaks.** There are three main types of faults: strike-slip faults, normal faults, and reverse faults.

Strike-Slip Faults Shearing creates strike-slip faults. In a **strike-slip fault,** the rocks on either side of the fault slip past each other sideways with little up-or-down motion. Figure 6 shows the type of movement that occurs along a strike-slip fault. A strike-slip fault that forms the boundary between two plates is called a transform boundary. The San Andreas fault in California is an example of a strike-slip fault that is a transform boundary.

Normal Faults Tension forces in Earth's crust cause normal faults. In a **normal fault,** the fault is at an angle, so one block of rock lies above the fault, while the other block lies below the fault. The half of the fault that lies above is called the **hanging wall.** The half of the fault that lies below is called the **footwall.** Look at Figure 7 to see how the hanging wall lies above the footwall.

Figure 7 A normal fault created the Sandia Mountains in New Mexico.

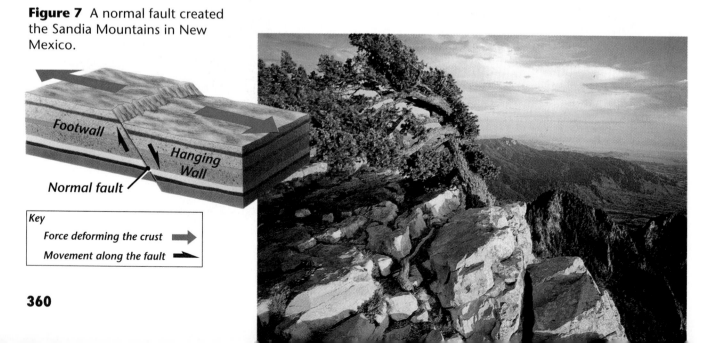

Footwall

Hanging Wall

Normal fault

Key

Force deforming the crust ➡

Movement along the fault ▶

When movement occurs along a normal fault, the hanging wall slips downward. Tension forces create normal faults where plates diverge, or pull apart. For example, normal faults occur along the Rio Grande rift valley in New Mexico, where two pieces of Earth's crust are diverging.

Reverse Faults Compression forces produce reverse faults. A **reverse fault** has the same structure as a normal fault, but the blocks move in the opposite direction. Look at Figure 8 to see how the rocks along a reverse fault move. As in a normal fault, one side of a reverse fault lies at an angle above the other side. The rock forming the hanging wall of a reverse fault slides up and over the footwall. Reverse faults produced part of the Appalachian Mountains in the eastern United States.

A type of reverse fault formed the majestic peaks in Glacier National Park in Montana shown in Figure 8. Over millions of years, a huge block of rock slid along the fault, moving up and over the surface rock. Parts of the overlying block then wore away, leaving the mountain peaks.

☑ *Checkpoint* *What are the three types of fault? What force of deformation produces each?*

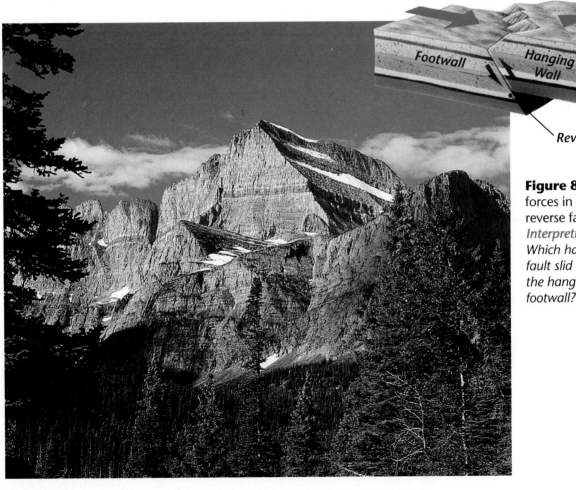

Key

Force deforming the crust ➡️

Movement along the fault ➡️

Reverse fault

Figure 8 Compression forces in the crust cause reverse faults to form. *Interpreting Diagrams Which half of the reverse fault slid up and across the hanging wall or the footwall? Explain.*

Friction Along Faults

INTEGRATING PHYSICS How rocks move along a fault depends on how much friction there is between the opposite sides of the fault. Friction is the force that opposes the motion of one surface as it moves across another surface. Friction exists because surfaces are not perfectly smooth.

Where friction along a fault is low, the rocks on both sides of the fault slide by each other without much sticking. Where friction is moderate, the sides of the fault jam together. Then from time to time they jerk free, producing small earthquakes. Where friction is high, the rocks lock together and do not move. In this case, stress increases until it is strong enough to overcome the friction force. A powerful quake results.

The San Andreas fault forms a transform boundary between the Pacific plate and the North American plate. In many places along the San Andreas fault, friction is high and the plates lock. Stress builds up until an earthquake releases the stress and the plates slide past each other.

Figure 9 The San Andreas fault extends from the Salton Sea in southern California to the point in northern California where the plate boundary continues into the Pacific Ocean.

Mountain Building and Uplift

The forces of plate movement can build up Earth's surface. **Over millions of years, fault movement can cause uplift, changing a flat plain into a towering mountain range or plateau.**

Mountains Formed by Faulting When normal faults uplift a block of rock, a fault-block mountain forms. You can see a diagram of this process in Figure 10. How does this process begin?

Figure 10 Two normal faults can form fault-block mountains, such as the Teton Range near the border of Wyoming and Idaho.

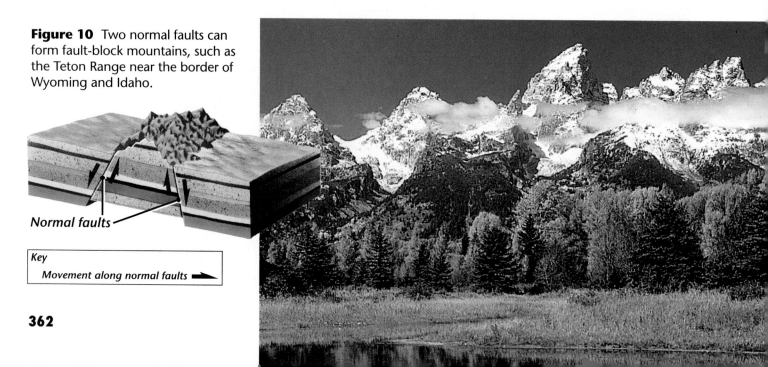

362

Where two plates move away from each other, tension forces create many normal faults. When two of these normal faults form parallel to each other, a block of rock is left lying between them. As the hanging wall of each normal fault slips downward, the block in between moves upward. When a block of rock lying between two normal faults slides downward, a valley forms.

If you traveled by car from Salt Lake City to Los Angeles you would cross the Great Basin, a region with many ranges of fault-block mountains separated by broad valleys, or basins. This "basin and range" region covers much of Nevada and western Utah.

Mountains Formed by Folding Under certain conditions, plate movement causes the crust to fold. Have you ever skidded on a rug that wrinkled up as your feet pushed it across the floor? Much as the rug wrinkles, rock stressed by compression may bend slowly without breaking. **Folds** are bends in rock that form when compression shortens and thickens part of Earth's crust.

The collisions of two plates can cause compression and folding of the crust. Some of the world's largest mountain ranges, including the Himalayas in Asia and the Alps in Europe, formed when pieces of the crust folded during the collision of two plates. Such plate collisions also lead to earthquakes, because folding rock can fracture and produce faults.

Individual folds can be only a few centimeters across or hundreds of kilometers wide. You can often see small folds in the rock exposed where a highway has been cut through a hillside.

Sharpen your Skills

Measuring

You can measure the force of friction.

1. Place a small weight on a smooth, flat tabletop. Use a spring scale to pull the weight across the surface. How much force is shown on the spring scale? (*Hint*: The unit of force is newtons.)

2. Tape a piece of sandpaper to the tabletop. Repeat Step 1, pulling the weight across the sandpaper.

Is the force of friction greater for a smooth surface or for a rough surface?

Figure 11 Compression forces cause folds in Earth's crust. **(A)** Some mountains are made up of folded rock. **(B)** The satellite image shows folded mountains west of Harrisburg, Pennsylvania.

Anticlines and Synclines Geologists use the terms anticline and syncline to describe upward and downward folds in rock. You can compare anticlines and synclines in the diagram in Figure 12. A fold in rock that bends upward into an arch is an anticline. A fold in rock that bends downward in the middle to form a bowl is a syncline. Anticlines and synclines are found on many parts of Earth's surface where compression forces have folded the crust.

One example of an anticline is the Black Hills of South Dakota. The Black Hills began to form about 65 million years ago. At that time, forces in Earth's crust produced a large dome-shaped anticline. Over millions of years, a variety of processes wore down and shaped the rock of this anticline into the Black Hills.

You may see a syncline where a valley dips between two parallel ranges of hills. But a syncline may also be a very large feature, as large as the state of Illinois. The Illinois Basin is a syncline that stretches from the western side of Indiana about 250 kilometers across the state of Illinois. The basin is filled with soil and rock that have accumulated over millions of years.

Figure 12 (A) Over millions of years, compression and folding of the crust produce anticlines, which arch upward, and synclines, which dip downward. (B) The folded rock layers of an anticline can be seen on this cliff on the coast of England.

Anticline   Syncline

A

B

Plateaus Uplift, the force that raises mountains, can also raise plateaus. A **plateau** is a large area of flat land elevated high above sea level. Some plateaus form when vertical faults push up a large, flat block of rock. Like a fancy sandwich, a plateau consists of many different flat layers, and is wider than it is tall.

Forces deforming the crust uplifted the Colorado Plateau in the "Four Corners" region of Arizona, Utah, Colorado, and New Mexico. The Colorado Plateau is a roughly circular area of uplifted rock more than 500 kilometers across. This vast slab of rock once formed part of a sea floor. Today, much of the plateau lies more than 1,500 meters above sea level.

Figure 13 The flat land on the horizon is the Kaibab Plateau, which forms the North Rim of the Grand Canyon in Arizona. The Kaibab Plateau is part of the Colorado Plateau.

 Section 2 Review

1. What are the three main types of stress in rock?
2. Describe the movements that occur along each of the three types of faults.
3. How does Earth's surface change as a result of movement along faults?
4. **Thinking Critically Predicting** If plate motion compresses part of the crust, what landforms will form there in millions of years? Explain.

Check Your Progress   CHAPTER PROJECT
Start by selecting the volcanic region you will study. Possible topics to investigate are myths and legends about volcanoes, the importance of volcanic soils, mineral resources from volcanoes, tourism, and geothermal power. Choose the topic that interests you the most. Begin your research and take notes on the information you collect.

Skills Lab

MODELING MOVEMENT ALONG FAULTS

Faults are cracks in Earth's crust where masses of rock move over, under, or past each other. In this lab, you will make a model of the movements along faults.

Problem

How does the movement of rock along the sides of a fault vary for different types of faults?

Materials

Modeling compound in two or more colors
Marking pen
Plastic butter knife

Procedure

1. Roll some modeling compound into a sheet about 0.5 centimeter thick and about 6 centimeters square. Then make another sheet of the same size and thickness, using a different color.

2. Cut each square in half and stack the sheets on top of each other, alternating colors. **CAUTION:** *To avoid breaking the plastic knife, do not press too hard as you cut.* The sheets of modeling compound stand for different layers of rock. The different colors will help you see where similar layers of rock end up after movement occurs along the model fault.

3. Press the layers of modeling compound together to form a rectangular block that fits in the palm of your hand.

4. Use the butter knife to slice carefully through the block at an angle, as shown in the photograph.

5. Place the two blocks formed by the slice together, but don't let them stick together.

6. Review the descriptions and diagrams of faults in Section 1. Decide which piece of your block is the hanging wall and which is the footwall. Using the marking pen, label the side of each block. What part of your model stands for the fault itself?

7. What part of the model stands for the land surface? Along the top surface of the two blocks, draw a river flowing across the fault. Also draw an arrow on each block to show the direction of the river's flow. The arrow should point from the footwall toward the hanging wall.

8. Make a table that includes the headings Type of Fault, How the Sides of the Fault Move, and Changes in the Land Surface.

Type of Fault	How the Sides of the Fault Move	Changes in the Land Surface

9. Using your blocks, model the movement along a strike-slip fault. Record your motion and the results on the data table.
10. Repeat Step 9 for a normal fault.
11. Repeat Step 9 for a reverse fault.

Analyze and Conclude

Refer to your data table to draw a chart that will help you answer Questions 1 through 4.

1. On your chart, show the direction in which the sides of the fault move for each type of fault.
2. On your chart, show how movement along a strike-slip fault is different from movement along the other two types of fault.
3. Add to your chart a column that shows how the river on the surface might change for each type of fault.
4. Assuming that the river is flowing from the footwall toward the hanging wall, which type of fault could produce small waterfalls in the surface river? (*Hint:* Recall how you tell which block is the hanging wall and which block is the footwall.)
5. If you could observe only the land surface around a fault, how could you tell if the fault is a strike-slip fault? A normal fault?
6. If you slide the hanging wall of your fault model upward in relation to the footwall, what type of fault forms? If this movement continues, where will the slab of rock with the hanging wall end up?

7. From an airplane, you see a chain of several long, narrow lakes along a fault. What type of fault would cause these lakes to form?
8. **Think About It** In what ways does the model help you picture what is happening along a fault? In what ways does the model not accurately reflect what happens along a fault? How is the model still useful in spite of its inaccuracies?

More to Explore

On Earth's surface, individual faults do not exist all by themselves. With one or more of your classmates, combine your models to show how a fault-block mountain range or a rift valley could form. (*Hint:* Both involve normal faults.) How could you combine your models to show how reverse faults produce a mountain range?

How Do Seismic Waves Travel Through Earth?

1. Stretch a spring toy across the floor while a classmate holds the other end. Do not overstretch the toy.

2. Gather together about 4 coils of the spring toy and release them. In what direction do the coils move?

3. Once the spring toy has stopped moving, jerk one end of the toy from side to side once. In what direction do the coils move? Be certain your classmate has a secure grip on the other end.

Think It Over

Observing Describe the two types of wave motion that you observed in the spring toy.

GUIDE FOR READING

◆ **How does the energy of an earthquake travel through Earth?**

◆ **What are the different kinds of seismic waves?**

◆ **What are the scales used to measure the strength of an earthquake?**

Reading Tip Before you read, rewrite the headings in the section as *what, how,* or *why* questions. As you read, look for answers to these questions.

Key Terms focus • epicenter
• P waves • S waves
• surface waves • seismograph
• magnitude • Mercalli scale
• Richter scale
• moment magnitude scale

Earth is never still. Every day, worldwide, there are about 8,000 earthquakes. Most of them are too small to notice. But when an earthquake is strong enough to rattle dishes in kitchen cabinets, people sit up and take notice. "How big was the quake?" and "Where was it centered?" are two questions just about everyone asks after an earthquake.

To know where an earthquake was centered, you need to know where it began. Earthquakes always begin in rock below the surface. Most earthquakes begin in the lithosphere within 100 kilometers of Earth's surface. An earthquake starts at one particular point. The **focus** (FOH kus) is the point beneath Earth's surface where rock that is under stress breaks, triggering an earthquake. The point on the surface directly above the focus is called the **epicenter** (EHP uh sen tur).

Seismic Waves

If you have ever played a drum, you know that the sound it makes depends on how hard you strike it. Like a drumbeat, an earthquake produces vibrations called waves. These waves carry energy as they travel outward through solid material. During an earthquake, seismic waves race out from the focus in all directions. Seismic waves are vibrations that travel through Earth carrying the energy released during an earthquake. The seismic waves move like ripples in a pond. Look at Figure 14 to see how seismic waves travel outward in all directions from the focus.

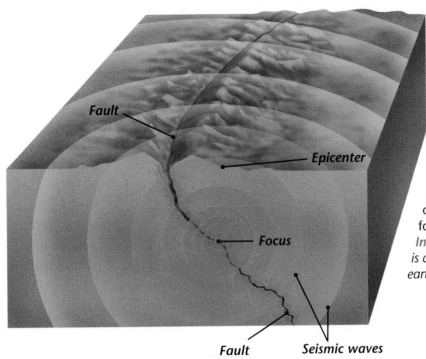

Figure 14 An earthquake occurs when rocks fracture at the focus, deep in Earth's crust.
Interpreting Diagrams *What point is directly above the focus of the earthquake?*

Seismic waves carry the energy of an earthquake away from the focus, through Earth's interior, and across the surface. The energy of the seismic waves that reach the surface is greatest at the epicenter. The most violent shaking during an earthquake, however, may occur kilometers away from the epicenter. The types of rock and soil around the epicenter can affect where and how much the ground shakes. For example, seismic waves in solid rock transmit their energy to the soil. The loose soil shakes more violently than the surrounding rock.

There are three categories of seismic waves: P waves, S waves, and surface waves. An earthquake sends out two types of waves from its focus: P waves and S waves. When these waves reach Earth's surface at the epicenter, surface waves develop.

Primary Waves The first waves to arrive are primary waves, or P waves. **P waves** are earthquake waves that can compress and expand the ground like an accordion. P waves cause buildings to contract and expand. Look at Figure 15 to compare P waves and S waves.

Secondary Waves After P waves come secondary waves, or S waves. **S waves** are earthquake waves that vibrate from side to side as well as up and down. They shake the ground back and forth. When S waves reach the surface, they shake structures violently. Unlike P waves, which travel through both solids and liquids, S waves cannot move through liquids.

Figure 15 **(A)** In P waves, the particles of the crust vibrate forward and back along the path of the wave. **(B)** In S waves, the particles of the crust vibrate from side to side and up and down.

Surface Waves When P waves and S waves reach the surface, some of them are transformed into surface waves. **Surface waves** move more slowly than P waves and S waves, but they can produce severe ground movements. Some surface waves make the ground roll like ocean waves. Other surface waves shake buildings from side to side.

☑ *Checkpoint* *What are the three types of seismic waves?*

Detecting Seismic Waves

To record and measure the vibrations of seismic waves, geologists use instruments called seismographs. A **seismograph** (SYZ muh graf) records the ground movements caused by seismic waves as they move through the Earth.

Until recently, scientists used mechanical seismographs. As shown in Figure 16, a mechanical seismograph consists of a heavy weight attached to a frame by a spring or wire. A pen connected to the weight rests its point on a rotating drum. When the drum is still, the pen draws a straight line on paper wrapped around the drum. During an earthquake, seismic waves cause the drum to vibrate. Meanwhile, the pen stays in place and records the drum's vibrations. The height of the jagged lines drawn on the seismograph's drum is greater for a more severe earthquake.

Today, scientists use electronic seismographs that work according to the same principle as the mechanical seismograph. The electronic seismograph converts ground movements into a signal that can be recorded and printed.

Figure 16 The mechanical seismograph records seismic waves. The record made by a seismograph shows the arrival times of different types of seismic waves.

The Mercalli Scale	
Earthquake Intensity	**Earthquake Effects**
I–II	Almost unnoticeable
III–IV	People notice vibrations like those from a passing truck. Unstable objects disturbed.
V–VI	Dishes and windows rattle. Books knocked off shelves. Slight damage.
VII–VIII	People run outdoors. Moderate to heavy damage.
IX–X	Buildings jolted off foundations or destroyed. Cracks appear in ground and landslides occur.
XI–XII	Severe damage. Wide cracks appear in ground. Waves seen on ground surface.

Figure 17 An earthquake in 1997 damaged the tower of this city hall in Foligno, Italy (left). The Mercalli scale (right) uses Roman numerals to rank earthquakes by how much damage they cause.
Applying Concepts How would you rate the damage to the Foligno city hall on the Mercalli scale?

Measuring Earthquakes

When geologists want to know the size of an earthquake, they must consider many factors. As a result, there are at least 20 different measures for rating earthquakes, each with its strengths and shortcomings. Three ways of measuring earthquakes, the Mercalli scale, the Richter scale, and the moment magnitude scale, are described here. **Magnitude** is a measurement of earthquake strength based on seismic waves and movement along faults.

The Mercalli Scale Early in the twentieth century, geologists developed the **Mercalli scale** to rate earthquakes according to their intensity. An earthquake's intensity is the strength of ground motion in a given place. The Mercalli scale is not a precise measurement. But the 12 steps of the Mercalli scale describe how earthquakes affect people, buildings, and the land surface. The same earthquake can have different Mercalli ratings because it causes different amounts of damage at different locations.

The Richter Scale The **Richter scale** is a rating of the size of seismic waves as measured by a particular type of mechanical seismograph. The Richter scale was developed in the 1930s. Geologists all over the world used this scale for about 50 years. Eventually, electronic seismographs replaced the mechanical seismographs used for the Richter scale. The Richter scale provides accurate measurements for small, nearby earthquakes. But the scale does not work well for large or distant earthquakes.

Earthquake Magnitudes	
Earthquake	Moment Magnitude
San Francisco, California, 1906	7.7
Southern Chile, 1960	9.5
Anchorage, Alaska, 1964	9.2
Loma Prieta, California, 1989	7.2
Northridge/ Los Angeles, California, 1994	6.7
Izmit, Turkey, 1999	7.4

Figure 18 The table lists the moment magnitudes for some of the twentieth century's biggest earthquakes.

The Moment Magnitude Scale Today, geologists use the **moment magnitude scale,** a rating system that estimates the total energy released by an earthquake. **The moment magnitude scale can be used to rate earthquakes of all sizes, near or far.** You may hear news reports that mention the Richter scale. But the magnitude number they quote is almost always the moment magnitude for that earthquake.

To rate an earthquake on the moment magnitude scale, geologists first study data from modern electronic seismographs. The data show what kinds of seismic waves the earthquake produced and how strong they were. The data also help geologists infer how much movement occurred along the fault and the strength of the rocks that broke when the fault slipped. Geologists combine all this information to rate the earthquake on the moment magnitude scale.

Earthquakes with a magnitude below 5.0 on the moment magnitude scale are small and cause little damage. Those with a magnitude above 5.0 can produce great destruction. A magnitude 6.0 quake releases 32 times as much energy as a magnitude 5.0 quake, and nearly 1,000 times as much as a magnitude 4.0 quake.

✓ *Checkpoint* *What are three scales for measuring earthquakes?*

Locating the Epicenter

Geologists use seismic waves to locate an earthquake's epicenter. Seismic waves travel at different speeds. P waves arrive first at a seismograph, with S waves following close behind. To tell how far the epicenter is from the seismograph, scientists measure the difference between the arrival times of the P waves and S waves.

Figure 19 In terms of magnitude, the 1906 San Francisco earthquake was not the strongest of the century. But it toppled buildings and caused fires that devastated the city.

KEY
■ Seismographic station
✳ Earthquake epicenter

Chicago ■

Savannah ■

Houston ■

0   200   400 mi
0   200   400 km

N
W — E
S

The farther away an earthquake is, the greater the time between the arrival of the P waves and the S waves.

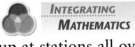 **INTEGRATING MATHEMATICS** Geologists then draw at least three circles using data from different seismographs set up at stations all over the world. The center of each circle is a particular seismograph's location. The radius of each circle is the distance from the seismograph to the epicenter. The point where the three circles intersect is the location of the epicenter. If you look at Figure 20, you can see why two circles would not give enough information to pinpoint the epicenter.

Figure 20 The map shows how to find the epicenter of an earthquake using data from three seismographic stations. *Measuring Use the map scale to determine the distances from Savannah and Houston to the epicenter. Which is closer?*

Section 3 Review

1. How does the energy from an earthquake reach Earth's surface?
2. Describe the three types of seismic waves.
3. What system do geologists use today for rating the magnitude of an earthquake?
4. **Thinking Critically Relating Cause and Effect** Describe how energy released at an earthquake's focus, deep inside Earth, can cause damage on the surface many kilometers from the epicenter.

Science at Home

Toppling Towers Show your family how an earthquake can affect two structures—one with more weight on top, the other with more weight on the bottom. Make a model of a fault by placing two small, folded towels side by side on a flat surface. Pile a stack of books on the fault by placing the light books on the bottom and the heaviest ones on top. Then, gently pull the towels in opposite directions until the pile topples. Repeat the process, but this time with the heavier books on the bottom. Discuss with your family which makes a more stable structure.

SECTION 4 Volcanic Activity

DISCOVER

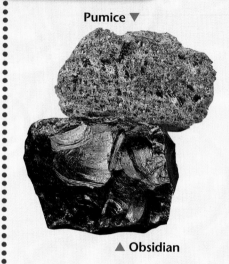

Pumice ▼

▲ Obsidian

What Are Volcanic Rocks Like?

Volcanoes produce lava, which hardens into rock. Two of these rocks are pumice and obsidian.

1. Observe samples of pumice and obsidian with a hand lens.

2. How would you describe the texture of the pumice? What could have caused this texture?

3. Observe the surface of the obsidian. How does the surface of the obsidian differ from pumice?

Think It Over

Developing Hypotheses What could have produced the difference in texture between the two rocks? Explain your answer.

GUIDE FOR READING

◆ **What happens when a volcano erupts?**

◆ **How do the two types of volcanic eruptions differ?**

◆ **What are some hazards of volcanoes?**

Reading Tip Before you read, preview *Exploring a Volcano* on page 376. Write a list of any questions you have about how a volcano erupts.

Key Terms magma chamber • pipe • vent • lava flow • crater • silica • pahoehoe • aa • pyroclastic flow • active • dormant • extinct • geyser • geothermal energy

In Hawaii, there are many myths about Pele (PAY lay), the fire goddess of volcanoes. In these myths, Pele is the creator and the destroyer of the Hawaiian islands. She lives in the fiery depths of erupting volcanoes. According to legend, when Pele is angry, she releases the fires of Earth through openings on the mountainside. Evidence of her presence is "Pele's hair," a fine, threadlike rock formed by lava. Pele's hair forms when lava sprays out of the ground like water from a fountain. As it cools, the lava stretches and hardens into thin strands.

How Magma Reaches Earth's Surface

Where does this hot, molten lava come from? Lava begins as magma in the mantle. There, magma forms in the asthenosphere, which lies beneath the lithosphere. The materials of the asthenosphere are under great pressure.

Magma Rises Because liquid magma is less dense than the surrounding solid material, magma flows upward into any cracks in the rock above. Magma rises until it reaches the surface, or until it becomes trapped beneath layers of rock.

Figure 21 Pele's hair is a type of rock formed from lava. Each strand is as fine as spun glass.

Figure 22 Molten lava from Kilauea volcano in Hawaii.

A Volcano Erupts Just like the carbon dioxide trapped in a bottle of soda pop, the dissolved gases trapped in magma are under tremendous pressure. You cannot see the carbon dioxide gas in a bottle of soda pop because it is dissolved in the liquid. But when you open the bottle, the pressure is released. The carbon dioxide forms bubbles, which rush to the surface.

As magma rises toward the surface, the pressure decreases. The dissolved gases begin to separate out, forming bubbles. A volcano erupts when an opening develops in weak rock on the surface. **During a volcanic eruption, the gases dissolved in magma rush out, carrying the magma with them.** Once magma reaches the surface and becomes lava, the gases bubble out.

Inside a Volcano

All volcanoes have a pocket of magma beneath the surface and one or more cracks through which the magma forces its way. You can see these features in *Exploring a Volcano*. Beneath a volcano, magma collects in a pocket called a **magma chamber.** The magma moves through a **pipe,** a long tube in the ground that connects the magma chamber to Earth's surface. Molten rock and gas leave the volcano through an opening called a **vent.** Often, there is one central vent at the top of a volcano. However, many volcanoes also have other vents that open on the volcano's sides. A **lava flow** is the area covered by lava as it pours out of a vent. A **crater** is a bowl-shaped area that may form at the top of a volcano around the volcano's central vent.

✓ *Checkpoint* How does magma rise through the lithosphere?

Gases in Magma

This activity models the gas bubbles in a volcanic eruption.

1. In a 1- or 2-liter plastic bottle, mix 10 g of baking soda into 65 mL of water.
2. Put about six raisins in the water.
3. While swirling the water and raisins, add 65 mL of vinegar and stir vigorously.
4. Once the liquid has stopped moving, observe the raisins.

Making Models What happens after you add the vinegar? What do the raisins and bubbles represent? How is this model similar to the way magma behaves in a volcano?

EXPLORING *a Volcano*

A volcano forms where magma breaks through Earth's crust and lava flows over the surface.

Crater
Lava collects in the crater, the bowl-shaped area that forms around the volcano's vent.

Vent
The point on the surface where magma leaves the volcano's pipe is called the vent.

Side vent
Sometimes magma forces its way out of a volcano through a side vent.

Lava
Magma that reaches the surface is called lava.

Lava flow
The river of lava that pours down a volcano and over the land is called a lava flow.

Pipe
A pipe is a narrow, almost vertical crack in the crust through which magma rises to the surface.

Magma
Magma is extremely hot, molten material that also contains dissolved gases including water vapor.

Magma chamber
As magma rises toward the surface, it forms a large underground pocket called a magma chamber.

Characteristics of Magma

The force of a volcanic eruption depends partly on the amount of gas dissolved in the magma. But gas content is not the only thing that affects an eruption. How thick or thin the magma is, its temperature, and its silica content are also important factors.

Some types of magma are thick and flow very slowly. Other types of magma are fluid and flow almost as easily as water. Magma's temperature partly determines whether it is thick or fluid. The hotter the magma, the more fluid it is.

The amount of silica in magma also helps to determine how easily the magma flows. **Silica,** which is a material that is formed from the elements oxygen and silicon, is one of the most abundant materials in Earth's crust and mantle. The more silica magma contains, the thicker it is.

Magma that is high in silica produces light-colored lava that is too sticky to flow very far. When this type of lava cools, it forms the rock rhyolite, which has the same composition as granite. Pumice and obsidian, which you observed if you did the Discover activity, also form from high-silica lava. Obsidian forms when lava cools very quickly, giving it a smooth, glossy surface. Pumice forms when gas bubbles are trapped in cooling lava, leaving spaces in the rock.

Magma that is low in silica flows readily and produces dark-colored lava. When this kind of lava cools, rocks such as basalt are formed.

Figure 23 Rhyolite (top) forms from high-silica lava. Basalt (bottom) forms from low-silica lava. When this type of lava cools, it sometimes forms six-sided columns like the ones in the picture.

Types of Volcanic Eruptions

A volcano's magma influences how the volcano erupts. **The silica content of magma helps to determine whether the volcanic eruption is quiet or explosive.**

Quiet Eruptions A volcano erupts quietly if its magma flows easily. In this case, the gas dissolved in the magma bubbles out gently. Thin, runny lava oozes quietly from the vent. The islands of Hawaii and Iceland were formed from quiet eruptions. On the Big Island of Hawaii, lava pours out of the crater near the top of Mount Kilauea (kee loo AY uh). Lava also flows out of long cracks on the volcano's sides. Quiet eruptions like the ones that regularly take place on Mount Kilauea have built up the Big Island over hundreds of thousands of years. In Iceland, lava usually emerges from gigantic fissures many kilometers long. The fluid lava from a quiet eruption can flow many kilometers from the volcano's vent.

Quiet eruptions produce two different types of lava: pahoehoe and aa. **Pahoehoe** (pah HOH ee hoh ee) is fast-moving, hot lava. The surface of a lava flow formed from pahoehoe looks like a solid mass of wrinkles, billows, and ropelike coils. Lava that is cooler and slower-moving is called **aa** (AH ah). When aa hardens, it forms a rough surface consisting of jagged lava chunks. Figure 24 shows how different these types of lava can be.

☑ *Checkpoint* **What types of lava are produced by quiet eruptions?**

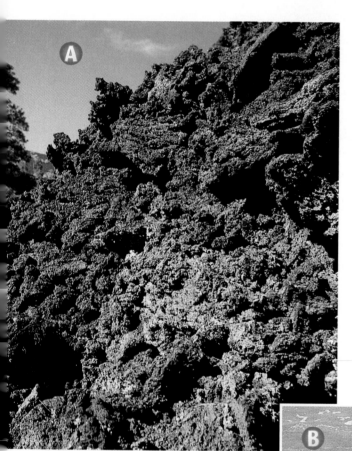

Figure 24 Both pahoehoe and aa can come from the same volcano. **(A)** Aa hardens into rough chunks. **(B)** Pahoehoe flows easily and hardens into a rippled surface. *Inferring What accounts for the differences between these two types of lava?*

Figure 25 Mount St. Helens erupted at 8:30 A.M. on May 18, 1980. **(A)** A large bulge that had formed on the north side of the mountain crashed downward.

(B) As the mountainside collapsed, bottled-up gas and magma inside began to escape.

(C) Shattered rock and pyroclastic flows blasted out sideways from the volcano.

(D) The blast traveled outward, leveling the surrounding forest and causing mudflows that affected a wide area around the volcano.

Explosive Eruptions If its magma is thick and sticky, a volcano erupts explosively. The thick magma does not flow out of the crater and down the mountain. Instead, it slowly builds up in the volcano's pipe, plugging it like a cork in a bottle. Dissolved gases cannot escape from the thick magma. The trapped gases build up pressure until they explode. The erupting gases push the magma out of the volcano with incredible force.

The explosion breaks the lava into fragments that quickly cool and harden into pieces of different sizes. The smallest pieces are volcanic ash—fine, rocky particles as small as a grain of sand. Cinders are pebble-sized particles. Larger pieces, called bombs, may range from the size of a baseball to the size of a car. A **pyroclastic flow** (py roh KLAS tik) occurs when an explosive eruption hurls out ash, cinders, and bombs as well as gases.

Look at Figure 25 to see the 1980 eruption of Mount St. Helens in the state of Washington. It was one of the most violent explosive eruptions that has ever occurred in the United States.

✓ *Checkpoint* **What causes an explosive eruption?**

Social Studies CONNECTION

In A.D. 79, Mount Vesuvius in Italy erupted. A thick layer of ash from Vesuvius buried the Roman city of Pompeii. Beginning in the 1700s, about half of the buried city was dug out, and scientists now know a great deal about daily life in Pompeii, a bustling city that was home to 20,000 people.

In Your Journal

Research Pompeii to find out what scientists have learned about daily life in the city. Write a paragraph summarizing your findings.

Stages of a Volcano

The activity of a volcano may last from less than a decade to more than 10 million years. Most long-lived volcanoes, however, do not erupt continuously. Geologists often describe volcanoes with terms usually reserved for living things, such as sleeping, awakening, alive, and dead. An **active,** or live, volcano is one that is erupting or has shown signs that it may erupt in the near future. A **dormant,** or sleeping, volcano is like a sleeping bear. Scientists expect a dormant volcano to awaken in the future and become active. However, there may be thousands of years between eruptions. An **extinct,** or dead, volcano is unlikely to erupt again.

SCIENCE & History

The Power of Volcanoes

Within the last 150 years, major volcanic eruptions have greatly affected the land and people around them.

1883 Indonesia

The violent eruption of Krakatau volcano threw 18 cubic kilometers of ash skyward. The blast was heard 5,000 kilometers away.

1912 Alaska, U.S.A.

Today, a river in Alaska cuts through the thick layer of volcanic ash from the eruption of Mount Katmai. Mount Katmai blasted out almost as much ash as Krakatau.

1850

1900

1902 Martinique

Mount Pelée, a Caribbean volcano, erupted a burning cloud of hot gas and pyroclastic flows. Within two minutes of the eruption, the cloud had killed the 29,000 residents of St. Pierre, a city on the volcano's flank. Only two people survived.

Monitoring Volcanoes

To tell if a volcano is becoming active, geologists use a variety of instruments to detect slight surface changes caused by magma moving underground. Changes in and around a volcano usually give warning a short time before the volcano erupts. Geologists monitor the local magnetic field, water level in a volcano's crater lake, and any gases escaping from a volcano. They take the temperature of underground water to see if it is getting hotter—a sign that magma may be nearing the surface.

Geologists also monitor the many small earthquakes that occur in the area around a volcano before an eruption. The movement of magma into the magma chamber and through the volcano's pipe triggers these quakes.

In Your Journal

People have written eyewitness accounts of famous volcanic eruptions. Research one of the eruptions in the time line. Then write a letter describing what someone observing the eruption might have seen.

1991 Philippines

Mount Pinatubo was dormant for hundreds of years before erupting in June 1991. Pinatubo spewed out huge quantities of ash that rose high into the atmosphere and also buried the surrounding countryside.

1950

2000

1980 Washington, U.S.A.

When Mount St. Helens exploded, it blasted one cubic kilometer of rock fragments and volcanic material skyward. The eruption was not unexpected. For months, geologists had monitored releases of ash, small earthquakes, and a bulge on the mountain caused by the buildup of magma inside.

1995 Montserrat

For more than two years, eruptions of volcanic ash from the Soufrière Hills volcano poured down on this small Caribbean island. Geologists anxiously waited for the eruption to run its course, not knowing whether it would end in a huge explosion.

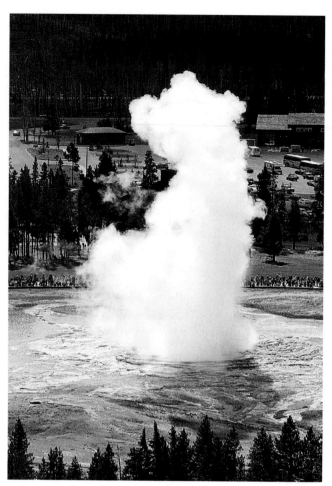

Figure 26 Old Faithful, a geyser in Yellowstone National Park, erupts about every 33 to 93 minutes. That's how long it takes for the pressure to build up again after each eruption.

Other Types of Volcanic Activity

Hot springs and geysers are two examples of volcanic activity that do not involve the eruption of lava. These features may occur in any volcanic area—even around an extinct volcano.

A hot spring forms when groundwater heated by a nearby body of magma rises to the surface and collects in a natural pool. (Groundwater is water that has seeped into the spaces among rocks deep beneath Earth's surface.) Water from hot springs may contain dissolved gases and other substances from deep within Earth.

Sometimes, rising hot water and steam become trapped underground in a narrow crack. Pressure builds until the mixture suddenly sprays above the surface as a geyser. A **geyser** (GY zur) is a fountain of water and steam that erupts from the ground.

INTEGRATING TECHNOLOGY In volcanic areas, water heated by magma can provide a clean, reliable energy source called **geothermal energy.** The people of Reykjavik, Iceland, pipe this hot water directly into their homes for warmth. Geothermal energy is also a source of electricity in Iceland as well as northern California and New Zealand. Steam from deep underground is piped into turbines. Inside a turbine, the steam spins a wheel in the same way that blowing on a pinwheel makes the pinwheel turn. The moving wheel in the turbine turns a generator that changes the energy of motion into electrical energy.

Volcano Hazards

The time between volcanic eruptions may span hundreds of years. So people living near a dormant volcano may be unaware of the danger. Before 1980, the people who lived, worked, and vacationed in the region around Mount St. Helens viewed it as a peaceful mountain. Few imagined the destruction the volcano would bring when it awakened from its 123-year slumber.

Although quiet eruptions and explosive eruptions involve different volcano hazards, both types of eruption can cause damage far from the crater's rim. **During a quiet eruption, lava flows pour from vents, setting fire to and then burying everything in their path. During an explosive eruption, a volcano can belch out hot, burning clouds of volcanic gas, ash, cinders, and bombs.**

Figure 27 (A) Mudflows were one of the hazards of Mt. Pinatubo's 1991 eruption. (B) People around Mt. Pinatubo wore masks to protect themselves from breathing volcanic ash.

Volcanic ash can bury entire towns, damage crops, and clog car engines. If it becomes wet, the heavy ash can cause roofs to collapse. If a jet plane sucks ash into its engine, the engine may stall. Eruptions can also cause landslides and avalanches of mud, melted snow, and rock. Figure 27 shows some effects of mud and ash from Mount Pinatubo's eruption. When Mount St. Helens erupted, gigantic mudflows carried ash, trees, and rock fragments 29 kilometers down the nearby Toutle River.

Section 4 Review

1. What are the stages that lead up to a volcanic eruption?
2. Compare and contrast quiet and explosive eruptions.
3. Describe some of the hazards posed by volcanoes.
4. **Thinking Critically** **Drawing Conclusions** A geologist times a passing lava flow at 15 kilometers per hour. The geologist also sees that lava near the edge of the flow is forming smooth-looking ripples as it hardens. What type of lava is this? What type of magma produced it? Explain your conclusions.

Check Your Progress CHAPTER PROJECT
By now you should have collected information about what it's like to live in a volcanic region. Do you need to do more research? Now begin to plan your presentation. One way to plan a presentation is to prepare storyboards. In a storyboard, you sketch each major step in the presentation on a separate sheet of paper. Decide who in your group is presenting each portion.

Real-World Lab

Gelatin Volcanoes

Does the magma inside a volcano move along fractures, or through tubes or pipes? How does the eruption of magma create features such as dikes and sills? You can use a gelatin volcano model and red-colored liquid "magma" to find answers to these questions.

Problem

How does magma move inside a volcano?

Skills Focus

developing hypotheses, making models, observing

Materials

plastic cup   tray or shallow pan
plastic knife
aluminum pizza pan with holes punched
   at 2.5-cm intervals
unflavored gelatin mold in bowl
red food coloring and water
plastic syringe, 10 cc
3 small cardboard oatmeal boxes
rubber gloves
unlined paper

Procedure

1. Before magma erupts as lava, how does it travel up from underground magma chambers? Record your hypothesis.
2. Remove the gelatin from the refrigerator. Loosen the gelatin from its container by briefly placing the container of gelatin in a larger bowl of hot water.
3. Place the pizza pan over the gelatin so the mold is near the center of the pizza pan. While holding the pizza pan against the top of the mold, carefully turn the mold and the pizza pan upside down.
4. Carefully lift the bowl off the gelatin mold to create a gelatin volcano.
5. Place the pizza pan with the gelatin mold on top of the oatmeal boxes as shown in the photograph.
6. Fill the syringe with the red water ("magma"). Remove air bubbles from the syringe by holding it upright and squirting out a small amount of water.
7. Insert the tip of the syringe through a hole in the pizza pan near the center of the gelatin volcano. Inject the magma into the gelatin very slowly. Observe what happens to the magma.
8. Repeat Steps 6 and 7 as many times as possible. Observe the movement of the magma each time. Note any differences in the direction the magma takes when the syringe is inserted into different parts of the gelatin volcano. Record your observations.
9. Look down on your gelatin volcano from above. Make a sketch of the positions and shapes of the magma bodies. Label your drawing "Top View."
10. Carefully use a knife to cut your volcano in half. Separate the pieces and examine the cut surfaces for traces of the magma bodies.
11. Sketch the positions and shapes of the magma bodies on one of the cut faces. Label your drawing "Cross Section."

Analyze and Conclude

1. Describe how the magma moved through your model. Did the magma move straight up through the center of your model volcano or did it branch off in places? Explain why you think the magma moved in this way.

2. What knowledge or experience did you use to develop your hypothesis? How did the actual movement compare with your hypothesis?

3. Were there differences in the direction the magma flowed when the syringe was inserted in different parts of the gelatin volcano?

4. **Apply** How does what you observed in your model compare to the way magma moves through real volcanoes?

Design an Experiment

Plan to repeat the experiment using a mold made of two layers of gelatin. Before injecting the magma, predict what effect the layering will have on magma movement. Record your observations to determine if your hypothesis was correct. What volcanic feature is produced by this version of the model? Can you think of other volcanic features that you could model using gelatin layers?

Volcanic Landforms

How Can Volcanic Activity Change Earth's Surface?

1. Use tape to secure the neck of a balloon over one end of a straw.

2. Place the balloon in the center of a box with the straw protruding.

3. Partially inflate the balloon.

4. Put damp sand on top of the balloon until it is covered.

5. Slowly inflate the balloon more. Observe what happens to the surface of the sand.

Think It Over

Making Models This activity models one of the ways in which volcanic activity can cause a mountain to form. What do you think the sand represents? What does the balloon represent?

GUIDE FOR READING

◆ What landforms are formed from magma that hardened beneath the surface?

◆ What landforms does lava create on Earth's surface?

Reading Tip As you read, make a table comparing volcanic landforms. Include what formed each landform— lava, ash, or magma—as well as its characteristics.

Key Terms volcanic neck
• dike • sill • batholith
• shield volcano • cinder cone
• composite volcano • caldera

Volcanoes have created some of Earth's most spectacular landforms. For example, the perfect volcanic cone of Mt. Fuji in Japan and the mysterious profile of Ship Rock rising above the grasslands of New Mexico are famous around the world.

Some volcanic landforms, like Mt. Fuji, arise when lava flows build up mountains and plateaus on Earth's surface. Other volcanic landforms, like Ship Rock, are the result of the buildup of magma beneath the surface.

Landforms From Magma

Sometimes magma forces its way through cracks in the upper crust, but fails to reach the surface. There the magma cools and hardens into rock. Eventually, the forces that wear away Earth's surface—such as flowing water, ice, or wind—may strip away the layers of rock above the magma and expose it. **Features formed by magma include volcanic necks, dikes, and sills, as well as batholiths and dome mountains.**

◀ Ship Rock, New Mexico

Figure 28 Magma that hardens beneath the surface may form volcanic necks, dikes, and sills. *Compare and Contrast What is the difference between a dike and a sill?*

Volcanic Necks, Dikes, and Sills A volcanic neck looks like a giant tooth stuck in the ground. A **volcanic neck** forms when magma hardens in a volcano's pipe. The softer rock around the pipe wears away, exposing the hard rock of the volcanic neck. Ship Rock in northwestern New Mexico is an example of a volcanic neck. Magma that forces itself across rock layers hardens into a **dike.** On the other hand, when magma squeezes between layers of rock, it forms a **sill.**

Batholiths Large rock masses called batholiths form the core of many mountain ranges. A **batholith** (BATH uh lith) is a mass of rock formed when a large body of magma cools inside the crust. The diagram in Figure 29 shows how a batholith looks when it forms. Over millions of years, uplift may slowly push the batholith toward the surface. Gradually, the layers of rock above the batholith wear away. As uplift continues, erosion shapes the batholith itself into a mountain range.

Figure 29 A batholith forms when magma cools inside the crust.

1. In a plastic pan with a flat bottom, mold a volcano out of clay that is lower than the top of the container.
2. Fill the pan to a depth of 1 cm using water colored with a few drops of food coloring.
3. Place a clear plastic sheet over the container and trace the outline of the pan with a marking pencil.
4. Looking straight down into the pan, trace the outline the water makes around the edges of the clay model.
5. Add another 1 cm of water, then replace the plastic sheet exactly as before and trace the water level again.
6. Repeat Step 5 several times to complete your topographic map.

Making Models How does your topographic map of the volcano compare with the clay model?

Dome Mountains Other, smaller bodies of magma can create dome mountains. A dome mountain forms when rising magma is blocked by horizontal layers of rock. The magma forces the layers of rock to bend upward into a dome shape. Eventually, the rock above the dome mountain wears away, leaving it exposed. This process formed the Black Hills in South Dakota.

☑ *Checkpoint* How can magma cause a dome mountain to form?

Landforms From Lava and Ash

Rock and other materials formed from lava create a variety of landforms including shield volcanoes, composite volcanoes, cinder cone volcanoes, and lava plateaus. Look at *Exploring Volcanic Mountains* on page 389 to see the similarities and differences among these features.

Shield Volcanoes At some places on Earth's surface, thin layers of lava pour out of a vent and harden on top of previous layers. Such lava flows gradually build a wide, gently sloping mountain called a **shield volcano.** Shield volcanoes rising from a hot spot on the ocean floor created the Hawaiian Islands.

Cinder Cone Volcanoes A volcano can also be a **cinder cone,** a steep, cone-shaped hill or mountain. If a volcano's lava is thick and stiff, it may produce ash, cinders, and bombs. These materials pile up around the vent in a steep, cone-shaped pile. For example, Paricutín in Mexico erupted in 1943 in a farmer's cornfield. The volcano built up a cinder cone about 400 meters high.

Composite Volcanoes Sometimes, lava flows alternate with explosive eruptions of ash, cinder, and bombs. The result is a composite volcano. **Composite volcanoes** are tall, cone-shaped mountains in which layers of lava alternate with layers of ash. Examples of composite volcanoes include Mount Fuji in Japan and Mount St. Helens in Washington state.

Lava Plateaus Instead of forming mountains, some eruptions of lava form high, level areas called lava plateaus. First, lava flows out of several long cracks in an area. The thin, runny lava travels far before cooling and solidifying. Again and again, floods of lava flow on top of earlier floods. After millions of years, these layers of lava can form high plateaus. One example is the Columbia Plateau, which covers parts of Washington, Oregon, and Idaho.

Figure 30 Thick layers of lava formed the Columbia Plateau.

EXPLORING Volcanic Mountains

Volcanic activity is responsible for building up much of Earth's surface. Lava from volcanoes cools and hardens into three types of mountains.

Crater

Side vent

Central vent

Magma chamber

Shield Volcano
Repeated lava flows during quiet eruptions gradually build up a broad, gently sloping volcanic mountain known as a shield volcano.

▲ Mauna Loa is one of the shield volcanoes that built the island Hawaii.

Cinder Cone Volcano
When cinders erupt explosively from a volcanic vent, they pile up around the vent, forming a cone-shaped hill called a cinder cone.

▲ Sunset Crater is an extinct cinder cone in Arizona.

Layers of cinders

Crater

Central vent

Composite Volcano
Layers of lava alternate with layers of ash, cinders, and bombs in a composite volcano, which has both quiet and explosive eruptions.

Central vent

Crater

Lava layers

Ash layers

▲ Mt. Hood is a composite volcano in Oregon.

Figure 31 Crater Lake in Oregon fills the caldera formed after an eruption that destroyed the top 2,000 meters of Mount Mazama nearly 7,000 years ago.
Developing Hypotheses Develop a hypothesis to explain the formation of Wizard Island, the small island in Crater Lake.

Calderas Enormous eruptions may empty the main vent and the magma chamber beneath a volcano. The mountain becomes a hollow shell. With nothing to support it, the top of the mountain collapses inward. The huge hole left by the collapse of a volcanic mountain is called a **caldera** (kal DAIR uh). The hole is filled with the pieces of the volcano that have fallen inward, as well as some lava and ash. In Figure 31 you can see one of the world's largest calderas.

Soils From Lava and Ash

 INTEGRATING ENVIRONMENTAL SCIENCE The lava, ash, and cinders that erupt from a volcano are initially barren. Over time, however, the hard surface of the lava flow breaks down to form soil. As soil develops, plants are able to grow. Some volcanic soils are among the richest soils in the world. Saying that soil is rich means that it's fertile, or able to support plant growth. Volcanic ash also breaks down and releases potassium, phosphorus, and other materials that plants need. Why would anyone live near an active volcano? People settle close to volcanoes to take advantage of the fertile volcanic soil.

Section 5 Review

1. What features form as a result of magma hardening beneath Earth's surface?
2. Describe how a dome mountain can eventually form out of magma that hardened beneath Earth's surface.
3. Describe five landforms formed from lava and ash.
4. Describe the process that creates a lava plateau.
5. **Thinking Critically Relating Cause and Effect** Explain the formation of a volcanic landform that can result when a volcano uses up the magma in its magma chamber.

Check Your Progress

CHAPTER PROJECT

By this time, your group should have planned your documentary and know what materials you will need. Put the finishing touches on your presentation. Make sure any posters, overhead transparencies, or computer art will be easy for your audience to read. If you are using video or audio, make your recordings now. Revise and polish any narrative, rap, or skit. *(Hint: Check the length of your presentation.)*

Plate Tectonics

Key Ideas

◆ According to the theory of plate tectonics, the movement of Earth's plates produces volcanoes, mountain ranges, earthquakes, and features of the ocean floor.

Key Terms

plates
Pangaea

plate tectonics
plate boundaries

Earth's Crust in Motion

Key Ideas

◆ Stresses on Earth's crust produce compression, tension, and shearing in rock.
◆ Faults are cracks in Earth's crust that result from stress.
◆ Faulting, folding, and uplift cause mountains to form on Earth's surface.

Key Terms

earthquake
stress
shearing
tension

compression
fault
strike-slip fault
normal fault

hanging wall
footwall
reverse fault
fold
plateau

Measuring Earthquakes

Key Ideas

◆ Seismic waves carry the energy of an earthquake from the focus to the surface.
◆ Earthquakes produce P waves, S waves, and surface waves.
◆ The scales used to measure earthquakes include the moment magnitude scale, the Mercalli scale, and the Richter scale.

Key Terms

focus
epicenter
P waves
S waves
surface waves

seismograph
magnitude
Mercalli scale
Richter scale
moment magnitude scale

Volcanic Activity

Key Ideas

◆ An eruption occurs when gases trapped in magma rush through an opening at the Earth's surface, carrying magma with them.
◆ Volcanoes can erupt quietly or explosively, depending on the silica content of the magma.
◆ Volcano hazards include pyroclastic flows, avalanches of mud, damage from ash, lava flows, flooding, and deadly gases.

Key Terms

magma chamber
pipe
vent
lava flow
crater
silica
pahoehoe

aa
pyroclastic flow
active
dormant
extinct
geyser
geothermal energy

Volcanic Landforms

Key Ideas

◆ Magma that hardens beneath the surface forms batholiths, dome mountains, dikes, and sills, which are eventually exposed by erosion.
◆ Lava and other volcanic materials on the surface create shield volcanoes, cinder cones, composite volcanoes, and plateaus.

Key Terms

volcanic neck
dike
sill

batholith
shield volcano
cinder cone

composite volcano
caldera

Organizing Information

Compare/Contrast Table On a separate piece of paper, make a table comparing shield volcanoes, cinder cones, composite volcanoes, and lava plateaus. Your table should compare these volcanic landforms in terms of volcanic material, shape, and structure. Then complete your table and add a title. For more on compare/contrast tables, see the Skills Handbook.

Reviewing Content

 Review key concepts online using iText at www.phschool.com

Multiple Choice

Choose the letter of the answer that best completes each statement.

1. Earth's lithosphere is broken into large pieces called
   a. plateaus.   b. continents.
   c. plates.   d. faults and folds.
2. Shearing is the force in Earth's crust that
   a. squeezes the crust together.
   b. pushes the crust in opposite directions.
   c. forces the crust to bend and fold.
   d. stretches the crust apart.
3. When the hanging wall of a fault slips down with respect to the footwall, the result is a
   a. reverse fault.   b. syncline.
   c. normal fault.   d. strike-slip fault.
4. Geologists use the difference in the arrival times of P waves and S waves at a seismograph to determine
   a. the magnitude of the earthquake.
   b. the depth of the earthquake's focus.
   c. the strength of the surface waves.
   d. the distance to the epicenter.
5. A quiet volcanic eruption would most likely produce
   a. pahoehoe lava flows. b. a cinder cone.
   c. a caldera.   d. pyroclastic flows.

True or False

If the statement is true, write true. If it is false, change the underlined word or words to make the statement true.

6. Plates pull apart, come together, or slide past each other along plate boundaries.
7. Rock uplifted by strike-slip faults creates fault-block mountains.
8. An earthquake's epicenter is located deep underground.
9. As S waves move through the ground, they cause it to compress and then expand.
10. A volcano formed by explosive eruptions of lava and ash is called a shield volcano.

Checking Concepts

11. What was Pangaea?
12. Explain the process that forms a fault-block mountain.
13. What type of stress in the crust results in the formation of folded mountains? Explain your answer.
14. Describe what happens along a fault beneath Earth's surface when an earthquake occurs.
15. Explain how the moment magnitude and Richter scales of earthquake measurement are similar and how they are different.
16. While observing a lava flow from a recently active volcano, you notice an area of lava with a rough, chunky surface. What type of lava is this and how does it form?
17. What are two different ways in which plateaus can form?
18. **Writing to Learn** Suppose you are a newspaper reporter in 1980. You have been assigned to report on the eruption of Mount St. Helens. Write a news story describing your observations.

Thinking Critically

19. **Predicting** If two plates made of continental crust crash together, what changes in Earth's surface might result?
20. **Classifying** How would you classify a fault in which the hanging wall has slid up and over the footwall?
21. **Comparing and Contrasting** Compare and contrast P waves and S waves.
22. **Comparing and Contrasting** Compare and contrast faulting and folding. What types of stress in the crust are involved? How do faulting and folding change Earth's surface?
23. **Applying Concepts** Describe the "life cycle" of a volcano from the time the volcano forms until it becomes extinct.
24. **Making Generalizations** How might a volcanic eruption affect the area around a volcano, including its plant and animal life?
25. **Relating Cause and Effect** What is a caldera and how does a caldera form?

Applying Skills

The graph shows the seismograph record for an earthquake. The y-axis of the graph shows the up-and-down shaking in millimeters at the seismograph station. The x-axis shows time in minutes.

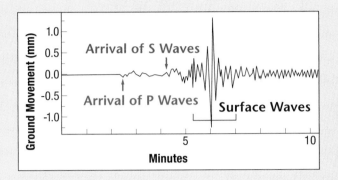

26. Interpreting Diagrams In what order do the seismic waves arrive at the seismograph station? Which type of seismic wave produces the largest ground movement?

27. Interpreting Diagrams What is the difference in arrival times for the P waves and S waves?

28. Predicting What would the seismograph record look like several hours after this earthquake? How would it change if an aftershock occurred?

29. Drawing Conclusions If the difference in arrival times for P waves and S waves is 5 minutes longer at a second seismograph station than at the first station, what can you conclude about the location of the second station?

Performance ▽ Assessment

CHAPTER PROJECT

Present Your Project Rehearse your documentary with your group before presenting it to the class. All group members should be able to answer questions about the visuals.

Reflect and Record In your journal evaluate how well your documentary presented the information you collected. How could you have improved your presentation? As you watched the other documentaries, did you see any similarities between how people in different regions live with volcanoes?

Test Preparation
Use these questions to prepare for standardized tests.

Use the diagram of a fault to answer Questions 30–34.

30. The rock on the side of the fault labeled B is the
  A footwall.   B shearing wall.
  C hanging wall.   D seismic wall.

31. The rock on the side of the fault labeled A is the
  F hanging wall.   G strike-slip wall.
  H reverse wall.   J footwall.

32. The thick arrows in the diagram stand for forces in Earth's crust pulling apart the two slabs of rock. This force is called
  A shearing.   B compression.
  C elevation.   D tension.

33. In the fault shown, the footwall
  F does not move.
  G moves down relative to the hanging wall.
  H moves up relative to the hanging wall.
  J slides sideways along the hanging wall.

34. The fault in the diagram is a(n)
  A normal fault.   B strike-slip fault.
  C reverse fault.   D inactive fault.

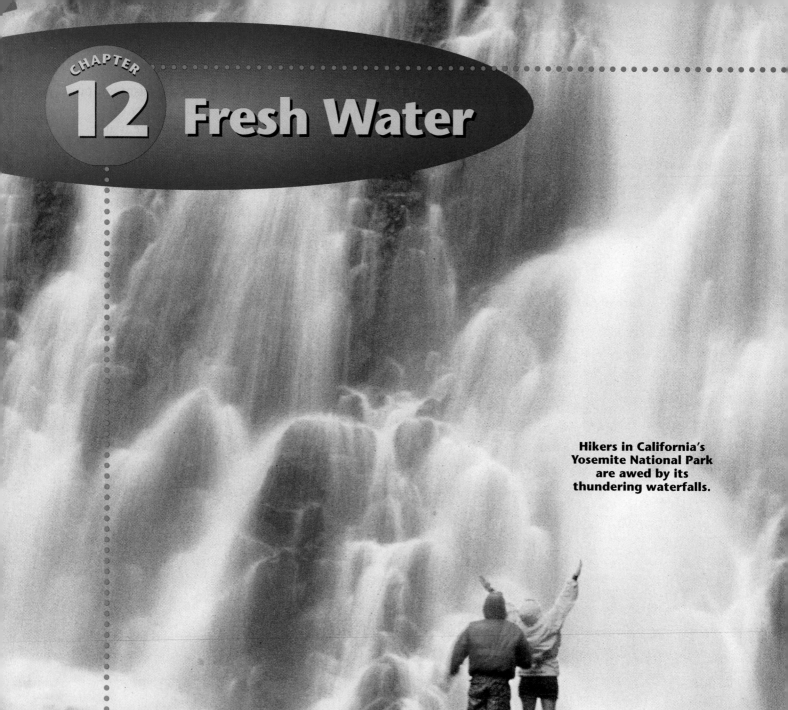

CHAPTER
12 Fresh Water

Hikers in California's
Yosemite National Park
are awed by its
thundering waterfalls.

WEB
ACTIVITY
www.phschool.com

Every Drop Counts

With an almost deafening roar, water rushes over this waterfall and plunges into the rocky pool below. Every day, hundreds of thousands of liters of water flow over the falls. How do you think this amount compares with the amount of water that flows out of your faucets at home each day?

In this chapter, you will explore the many ways that living things depend on Earth's water. To learn how water is used in your own home and community, you will design a method for tracking water use over a one-week period.

Your Goal To monitor water use in your home and in another building in your community for one week.

To complete the project you will
- track your personal water use at home
- determine the total amount of water used in your home
- find out how much water is used by a business, school, hospital, or other building in your community

Get Started Begin now by brainstorming the ways you use water at home. Use this list to create a data table in which you will record each time you perform these activities during the week.

Check Your Progress You'll be working on this project as you study this chapter. To keep your project on track, look for Check Your Progress boxes at the following points.

Section 1 Review, page 402: Calculate your total water use.
Section 3 Review, page 415: Investigate water use at another building in your community.
Section 4 Review, page 422: Make graphs of the water-use data for your household and your community.

Present Your Project At the end of the chapter (page 431), you will share your water-use data with your class and discuss the information with your classmates.

TEKS

In addition to process TEKS, this chapter addresses these concept TEKS as they relate to the chapter's topics.

(6.5) The student knows that systems may combine with other systems to form a larger system. The student is expected to:
(B) describe how the properties of a system are different from the properties of its parts.

(6.8) The student knows that complex interactions occur between matter and energy. The student is expected to:
(B) explain and illustrate the interactions between matter and energy in the water cycle and in the decay of biomass such as in a compost bin.

(6.14) The student knows the structures and functions of Earth systems. The student is expected to:
(B) identify relationships between groundwater and surface water in a watershed.

Where Does the Water Come From?

1. Fill a glass with ice cubes and water, being careful not to spill any water. Set the glass aside for 5 minutes.

2. Observe the outside of the glass and the surface it was sitting on.

Think It Over

Inferring Where did the water on the outside of the glass come from? How do you think it got there?

Why do you think Earth is often called the "water planet"? Perhaps an astronaut suggested this name. From space, an astronaut can see that there is much more water than land on planet Earth. Oceans cover nearly 71 percent of Earth's surface.

Water on Earth

Figure 1 shows how Earth's water is distributed. **Most of Earth's water — roughly 97 percent — is salt water that is found in the oceans. Only 3 percent is fresh water.** Of that 3 percent, about three quarters is found in the huge masses of ice near the North and South Poles. A fraction more is found in the atmosphere. Most water in the atmosphere is invisible **water vapor,** the gaseous form of water. Less than 1 percent of the water on Earth is fresh water that is available for humans to use.

Oceans To explore where Earth's water is found, you can take an imaginary boat trip around the world. Your journey starts in Miami, Florida. From here, you can sail completely around the world without ever going ashore. Although people have given names to regions of the ocean, these regions are all connected, forming a single world ocean.

First you sail southeast across the Atlantic Ocean toward Africa. Swinging around the continent's southern tip, you enter the smaller but deeper Indian Ocean. Next, you head east across the Pacific Ocean, the longest part of your trip. This vast ocean, dotted with islands, covers an area greater than all the land on Earth put together.

Ice How can you get back to Miami? You could sail all the way around South America. But watch out for icebergs! These floating chunks of ice are made of fresh water. Icebergs in the southern Pacific and Atlantic oceans have broken off the massive sheets of ice that cover most of Antarctica. You would also find icebergs in the Arctic Ocean around the North Pole.

Rivers and Lakes To see examples of fresh water in rivers and lakes, you'll have to make a side trip inland. Sail north past Nova Scotia, Canada, to the beginning of the St. Lawrence Seaway. Navigate through the series of locks along the St. Lawrence River. Suddenly the river widens and you enter Lake Ontario, one of North America's five Great Lakes. Together, the Great Lakes contain nearly 20 percent of all the water in the world's freshwater lakes.

Below Earth's Surface When rain or snow falls, some of the water soaks into the ground. This water trickles down through spaces between the particles of soil and rock. Eventually the water reaches a layer that it cannot move through. Water that fills the cracks and spaces in underground soil and rock layers is called **groundwater.** Far more fresh water is located underground than in all Earth's rivers and lakes. You will learn more about groundwater in Section 3.

Calculating

This activity shows how Earth's water is distributed.

1. Fill a one-liter plastic bottle with water. This represents the total water on Earth.

2. First, measure 97 percent, or 970 milliliters (mL), of the water and pour it into a large bowl. This represents the salt water in Earth's oceans and salt lakes.

3. Next, you will demonstrate how the remaining fresh water is divided. Label five cups to match the freshwater sources in Figure 1. Calculate how much of the remaining 30 mL of water you should pour into each cup to represent the percentage of Earth's fresh water found there.

4. Use a plastic graduated cylinder to measure out the amount of water for each cup. Use a plastic dropper to approximate amounts that are too small to measure accurately.

Which cups contain water that is available for humans to use? How does the amount of water in these cups compare to the original one liter?

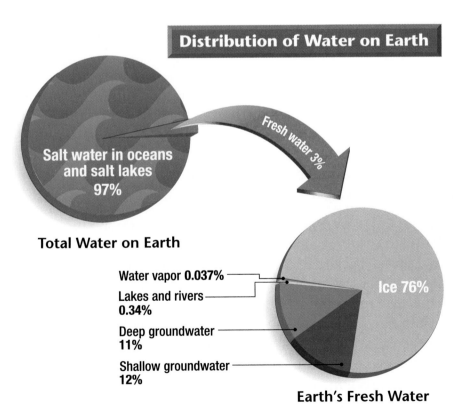

Distribution of Water on Earth

Salt water in oceans and salt lakes 97%

Fresh water 3%

Total Water on Earth

Water vapor 0.037%
Lakes and rivers 0.34%
Deep groundwater 11%
Shallow groundwater 12%
Ice 76%

Earth's Fresh Water

Figure 1 Most of Earth's water is salt water. Of the freshwater sources shown in the bottom circle graph, only the water in lakes, rivers, and shallow groundwater is available for human use.

Tabletop Water Cycle

In this activity you will build a model of the water cycle.

1. Put on your goggles. Pour enough water into a flat-bottomed bowl to cover the bottom. Fill a small jar with sand and place it in the bowl.
2. Loosely cover the top of the bowl with plastic wrap. Secure with a rubber band.
3. Place a rock on top of the plastic, directly over the jar.
4. Place the bowl in direct sunlight or under a lamp. After one hour, observe the bowl and plastic wrap.

Making Models What features of the water cycle are represented in your model?

The Water Cycle

Water is recycled through the water cycle. The **water cycle** is the continuous process by which water moves through the living and nonliving parts of the environment. **In the water cycle, water moves from bodies of water, land, and living things on Earth's surface to the atmosphere and back to Earth's surface.** The sun is the source of energy that drives the water cycle.

Water Evaporates Water moves continuously through the water cycle. The cycle has no real beginning or end. You can follow a water molecule through one complete cycle in *Exploring the Water Cycle* on the facing page.

Think about a molecule of water floating near the surface of an ocean. The sun is shining and the air is warm. Soon, the molecule has absorbed enough heat energy to change state. It evaporates and becomes water vapor. **Evaporation** is the process by which molecules at the surface of a liquid absorb enough energy to change to the gaseous state. Although the water comes from the salty ocean, it becomes fresh through the process of evaporation. The salt remains in the ocean.

Large amounts of water evaporate constantly from the surfaces of oceans and large lakes. In addition, small amounts evaporate from the soil, puddles, and even from your skin. A significant amount of water is given off by plants. Plants draw in water from the soil through their roots. Eventually the water is given off through the leaves as water vapor in a process called **transpiration.**

Clouds Form Once a water molecule has found its way into the atmosphere, warm air carries it upward. Higher up, the air tends to become much colder. Cold air holds less water vapor than warm air. Some of the water vapor cools and condenses into liquid water. Condensed droplets of water clump together around tiny dust particles in the air, forming clouds.

Water Falls as Precipitation As more water vapor condenses, the water droplets in a cloud eventually become so heavy that they fall back to Earth. Water that falls to Earth as rain, snow, hail, or sleet is called **precipitation.** Most water molecules probably spend only about 10 days in the atmosphere before falling back to Earth. Most precipitation falls directly into the oceans. Water in the ocean may stay there for many years before evaporating, thus continuing the cycle.

When precipitation falls on land, some of the water evaporates again immediately. Some runs off the surface of the land into rivers and lakes. From there, it may eventually evaporate or flow back into the ocean. Some water trickles down into the ground and forms groundwater. Groundwater may move underground until it reaches a river, lake, or ocean. Once groundwater reaches the surface, it can continue through the cycle by evaporating again.

Precipitation is the source of all fresh water on and below Earth's surface. The water cycle renews the usable supply of fresh water on Earth. For millions of years, the total amount of water on Earth has remained fairly constant. In the world as a whole, the rates of evaporation and precipitation are balanced.

☑ *Checkpoint* List three places from which water evaporates.

EXPLORING the Water Cycle

The water cycle is the continuous process by which water moves through the environment. The sun is the source of energy that drives the water cycle.

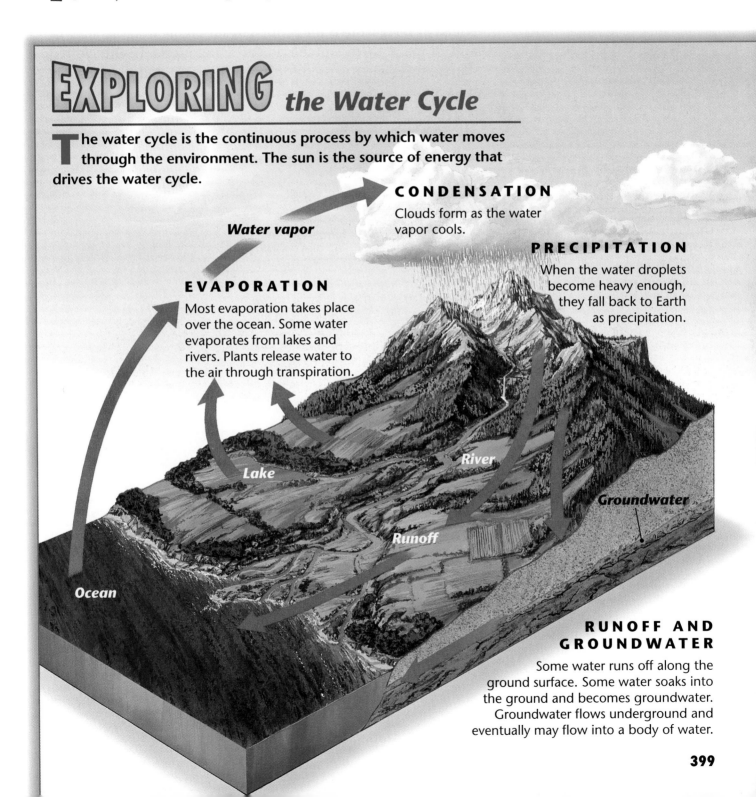

CONDENSATION
Clouds form as the water vapor cools.

Water vapor

PRECIPITATION
When the water droplets become heavy enough, they fall back to Earth as precipitation.

EVAPORATION
Most evaporation takes place over the ocean. Some water evaporates from lakes and rivers. Plants release water to the air through transpiration.

Lake

River

Groundwater

Runoff

Ocean

RUNOFF AND GROUNDWATER
Some water runs off along the ground surface. Some water soaks into the ground and becomes groundwater. Groundwater flows underground and eventually may flow into a body of water.

How Do People Use Water?

The water people use at home is just a small percentage of all the water used in the United States. **In addition to household purposes, people use water for agriculture, industry, transportation, and recreation.**

Agriculture Has your family ever had a garden? If so, you know that growing fruits and vegetables requires water. On a large farm, a constant supply of fresh water is essential.

However, some parts of the United States don't receive enough regular rainfall for agriculture. In such areas, farmland must be irrigated. **Irrigation** is the process of supplying water to areas of land to make them suitable for growing crops. In the United States, more water is used for irrigating farmland than for any other single purpose.

Water and Agriculture

Plants require a steady supply of water to grow. How have farmers throughout history provided their crops with water? This time line shows some methods developed in different parts of the world.

2000 B.C. Egypt

Egyptian farmers invented a way to raise water from the Nile River. The device, called a *shaduf*, acted as a lever to make lifting a bucket of water easier. The farmers then emptied the water into a network of canals to irrigate their fields. The *shaduf* is still in use in Egypt, India, and other countries.

3000 B.C.	2000 B.C.	1000 B.C.

3000 B.C. China

One of the oldest known methods of irrigation was developed for growing rice. Farmers built paddies, or artificial ponds with raised edges. The farmers flooded the paddies with water from a nearby stream. This ancient technique is still widely used throughout Southeast Asia.

700 B.C. Assyria

Sennacherib, king of the ancient nation Assyria, surrounded the capital city of Nineveh with fruit trees, cotton, and exotic plants. To help irrigate the plantations, he built a 10-kilometer canal and a stone aqueduct to transport water from the nearby hills.

Industry   Think about the objects in a typical school locker. Did you know that water is needed to produce all these objects? Even though water is not part of the final products, it plays a role in the industrial processes that created them.

Industries use water in many other ways. For example, power plants and steel mills both need huge volumes of water to cool down hot machinery. Water that is used for cooling can often be recycled, or used again for another purpose.

Transportation   Oceans and rivers have been used for transporting people and goods since ancient times. If you look at a map of the United States, you will notice that many large cities are located on the coasts. Ocean travel led to the growth of such port cities. In early America, rivers also served as natural highways.

In Your Journal

Find out more about one of these agricultural techniques. Imagine that you are a farmer seeing the method in action for the first time. Write a letter to a friend describing the new technique. What problem will it solve? How will it improve your farming?

A.D. 1870 United States

When homesteaders arrived on the dry Great Plains of the central United States, they had to rely on water stored underground. Windmills provided the energy to pump the groundwater to the surface. The farmers dug ditches to carry the water to irrigate their fields.

A.D. 1   A.D. 1000   A.D. 2000

A.D. 500 Mexico

To grow crops in areas covered by swampy lakes, the Aztecs built raised plots of farmland called *chinampas.* They grew maize on fertile soil scooped from the lake bottom. A grid of canals kept the crops wet and allowed the farmers to navigate boats between the *chinampas.*

Present Israel

Irrigation is the key to survival in desert regions. Today, methods such as drip irrigation ensure that very little water is wasted when crops are watered. Holes in the pipe allow water to drip directly onto the soil around the roots of each plant.

Water Used in the Home	
Task	Water Used (liters)
Showering for 5 minutes	95
Brushing teeth	10
Washing hands	7.5
Flushing standard toilet	23
Flushing "low-flow" toilet	6
Washing one load of laundry	151
Running dishwasher	19
Washing dishes by hand	114

Figure 2 Many common household activities involve water.

Recreation Do you like to swim in a neighborhood pool? Catch fish from a rowboat in the middle of a lake? Walk along a beach collecting seashells? Or maybe just sit on the edge of a dock and dangle your feet in the water? Then you know some ways that water is used for recreation. And if you brave the winter cold to ski, snowboard, or skate, you are enjoying water in its frozen form.

Water and Living Things

INTEGRATING LIFE SCIENCE Here's a riddle for you: What do you and an apple have in common? You both consist mostly of water! In fact, water is a large part of every living thing. Water makes up nearly two thirds of your body. That water is necessary to keep your body functioning. You know that if you exercise vigorously outdoors on a hot day, your body can rapidly lose water through perspiration. That's why athletes such as bicycle racers and marathon runners must make sure to drink plenty of water before, during, and after their events.

Water is essential for living things to grow, reproduce, and carry out other important processes. For example, plants use water, plus carbon dioxide and energy from the sun, to make food in a process called photosynthesis. Animals and many other living things depend on the food made by plants. They may eat the plants directly or eat other organisms that eat plants.

Another way that living things use water is as a home. An organism's habitat is the place where it lives and that provides the things it needs to survive. Both fresh water and salt water provide habitats for many different types of living things.

Section 1 Review

1. Where is most of the fresh water on Earth found?
2. Describe the general path of water as it moves through the water cycle.
3. How does the water cycle renew Earth's supply of fresh water?
4. What are five major ways that people in the United States use water?
5. **Thinking Critically** Relating Cause and Effect How might cutting down trees affect the amount of evaporation in an area?

Check Your Progress CHAPTER PROJECT

Use Figure 2 to estimate the water used for some common activities. Then determine how much water your family used during the week. You can do this by reading your water meter, estimating based on your personal water use, or having your family members record their usage. *(Hint: Convert all amounts to liters.)* Complete your water-use data table by calculating the total amount of water you used during the week.

Water from Trees

Trees play many important roles in the environment—they keep the soil from washing away, remove carbon dioxide from the air, and produce oxygen. Trees are also a vital part of the water cycle. In this lab you will discover how trees help to keep water moving through the cycle.

Problem

How much water do the leaves on a tree give off in a 24-hour period?

Skills Focus

observing, calculating, inferring

Materials

3 plastic sandwich bags   balance
3 small pebbles   3 twist ties
computer (optional)

Procedure

1. Copy the data table into your notebook or create a spreadsheet on the computer.
2. Place the sandwich bags, twist ties, and pebbles on a balance. Determine their total mass to the nearest tenth of a gram.
3. Select an outdoor tree or shrub with leaves that are within your reach.
4. Put one pebble into a sandwich bag and place the bag over one of the tree's leaves as shown. Fasten the twist tie around the bag, forming a tight seal around the stem of the leaf.
5. Repeat Step 4 with the other plastic bags on two more leaves. Leave the bags in place for 24 hours.
6. The following day, examine the bags and record your observations in your data table.

DATA TABLE	
Starting mass of bags, ties, and pebbles	
Mass of bags, ties, and pebbles after 24 hours	
Difference in mass	

7. Carefully remove the bags from the leaves and refasten each twist tie around its bag so that the bag is closed tightly.
8. Place the three bags, including pebbles and twist ties, on the balance. Determine their total mass to the nearest tenth of a gram.
9. Subtract the original mass of the bags, ties, and pebbles that you found in Step 2 from the mass you found in Step 8.

Analyze and Conclude

1. Based on your observations, how can you account for the difference in mass?
2. What is the name of the process that caused the results you observed? Explain the role of that process in the water cycle.
3. A single birch tree may transpire as much as 260 liters of water in a day. How much water would a grove of 1,000 birch trees return to the atmosphere in a year?
4. **Apply** Based on what you learned from this investigation, what is one reason that people may be concerned about the destruction of forests around the world?

More to Explore

Find another type of tree and repeat this experiment. What might account for any differences in the amount of water the two trees transpire?

What's in Pond Water?

1. Using a hand lens, observe a sample of pond water.

2. Make a list of everything you see in the water. If you don't know the name of something, write a short description or draw a picture.

3. Your teacher has set up a microscope with a slide of pond water. Observe the slide and add any new items to your list. Wash your hands with soap when you are done.

Think It Over

Classifying Use one of these systems to divide the items on your list into two groups: moving/still, living/nonliving, or microscopic/visible without a microscope. What does your classification system tell you about pond water?

GUIDE FOR READING

◆ What is a river system?

◆ What conditions can cause a flood?

◆ How do ponds and lakes form?

Reading Tip Before you read, use the section headings to make an outline. Leave space to take notes as you read.

Key Terms tributary • watershed • divide • levee • reservoir

Standing on a bridge in Albuquerque, New Mexico, you look through your binoculars at the waters of the Rio Grande—the "Big River." The name fits this broad, deep stretch of water. But 700 kilometers upstream, the Rio Grande looks very different. The river begins as trickles of melting snow high in the San Juan Mountains in Colorado. As more water joins the river, it carves deep, narrow canyons out of the rock.

By the time it reaches Albuquerque the river has grown wider. It continues into Texas, winding back and forth across the dusty desert valley. In places, the river is so shallow that it may even dry up during the summer. When the Rio Grande finally empties into the Gulf of Mexico, it is sluggish and heavy with mud.

River Systems, Watersheds, and Divides

If you were hiking in the San Juan Mountains, you could observe the path of the runoff from melting snow. As you followed one small stream downhill, you would notice that the stream reached a larger stream and joined it. You could then continue along this stream until it flowed into a small river. Eventually this path would lead you to the Rio Grande itself.

Tributaries are the smaller streams and rivers that feed into a main river. **A river and all its tributaries together make up a river system.** The tributaries flow toward the main river following a downhill path due to the pull of gravity.

Watersheds Just as all the water in a bathtub flows toward the drain, all the water in a river system drains into the main river. The land area that supplies water to a river system is called a **watershed.** Watersheds are also called drainage basins.

A river can flow into another, larger river. When rivers join another river system, the areas they drain become part of the largest river's watershed. You can identify a river's watershed on a map by drawing an imaginary line around the region drained by all its tributaries. Some watersheds are very small. By contrast, the watershed of the Mississippi River covers more than 3 million square kilometers!

Divides One watershed is separated from another by a ridge of land called a **divide.** Streams on each side of the divide flow in different directions. The Continental Divide, the longest divide in North America, follows the line of the Rocky Mountains. West of the Continental Divide, water either flows toward the Pacific Ocean or into the dry Great Basin. Between the Rocky Mountains and the Appalachian Mountains, water flows toward the Mississippi River or directly into the Gulf of Mexico.

☑ *Checkpoint* *Into what ocean do rivers east of the Appalachian Mountains flow?*

The Knuckle Divide

ACTIVITY

Make your hand into a fist and put it on a paper towel, knuckles facing up. With your other hand, dribble water from a spoon so that it falls onto your knuckles. Observe how the water flows over your hand.

Making Models How are your knuckles similar to a mountain range on land? What parts of your hand represent a watershed?

Major Watersheds of the United States

Figure 3 This map shows the watersheds of several large rivers in the United States.
Interpreting Maps Name four tributaries of the Mississippi River. Which tributary has the largest watershed?

Rivers and Floods

Spring floods occur frequently on rivers in the Midwest, but the floods of 1997 were far worse than usual. The residents of Fargo, North Dakota, had already used a million sandbags, and the Red River of the North was still rising! As the flood waters rose, people piled the sandbags higher around their houses, hoping no water would break through. People moved their belongings to their attics, then watched as water flowed through their homes.

The Red River floods went on for weeks, fed by rain and melting snow. A spring blizzard added more snow. Other nearby rivers also flooded. Parts of North Dakota, South Dakota, and Minnesota were declared a disaster area. Weary residents just waited for the waters to recede so they could start to repair the damage.

What caused the Red River to flood so badly? **A flood occurs when the volume of water in a river increases so much that the river overflows its channel.** As rain and melting snow added more and more water, the river gained in speed and strength. Recall that as the speed of a river increases, so does the amount of energy it has. A flooding river can uproot trees and pluck boulders from the ground. As it overflows onto its floodplain, the powerful water can even wash away bridges and houses.

Throughout history, people have both feared and welcomed floods. Ancient Egyptians, for instance, called their fertile cropland "the gift of the Nile." Deposition from regular floods left a layer of rich soil on each side of the river, creating a green strip of good land in the middle of the desert. But floods can also destroy farms, towns, and crops. In the United States, 20 million people live in places where flooding is likely. Even in the last century, floods have killed millions of people around the world, many of them in the heavily populated flood plains of China, Bangladesh, and India.

Figure 4 These people are working together to protect their community during a flood.

Can Floods Be Controlled?

INTEGRATING TECHNOLOGY For as long as people have lived on flood plains, they have tried to control floods. Building dams is one method of flood control. A dam is a barrier across a river that may redirect the flow of a river to other channels or store the water in an artificial lake. Engineers can open the dam's floodgates to release water in dry seasons. Dams work fairly well to control small floods. During severe floods, however, powerful flood waters can wash over the top of a dam or break through it.

Sediment deposits actually build a natural defense against floods. As a river overflows onto its flood plain, it slows down, depositing the heavier sediments alongside the channel. Over time, these deposits build up into long ridges called **levees.** These natural levees help keep the river inside its banks. People sometimes build up the natural levees with sandbags or stone and concrete to provide further protection against floods.

But building up levees can sometimes backfire. These walls prevent the natural channel-widening process that rivers normally undergo as their volume increases. As a result, during a flood, the water has nowhere to go except downstream. Although built-up levees can work well to prevent small floods, they often make heavy flooding worse for areas farther downstream. The full power of the surge of flood water is passed on to flood the downstream areas.

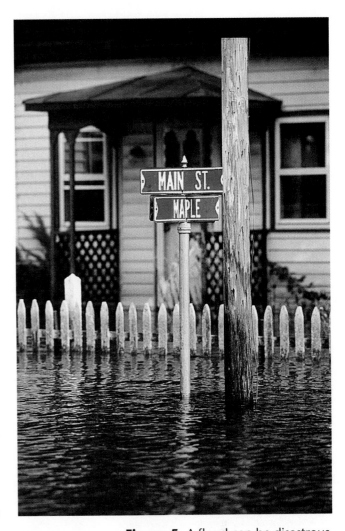

Figure 5 A flood can be disastrous for residents of a flooded area. *Making Generalizations Explain how floods can be both harmful and helpful to people.*

Bodies of Fresh Water

While water in streams and rivers is always on the move, the water in lakes and ponds is still, or standing, water. Although there is no definite rule to determine whether a body of water is called a pond or a lake, ponds are generally smaller and shallower than lakes. Sunlight usually reaches to the bottom of all parts of a pond. Most lakes have parts where the water is too deep for sunlight to reach all the way to the bottom.

Ponds and lakes form when water collects in hollows and low-lying areas of land. Rainfall, melting snow and ice, and runoff supply water to ponds and lakes. Others are fed by rivers or groundwater. Eventually, water may flow out of a pond or lake into a river, or evaporate from its surface.

EXPLORING a Pond

Many organisms live in the different habitats within a pond. From the shallow edges to the muddy bottom, conditions in each habitat vary in important ways.

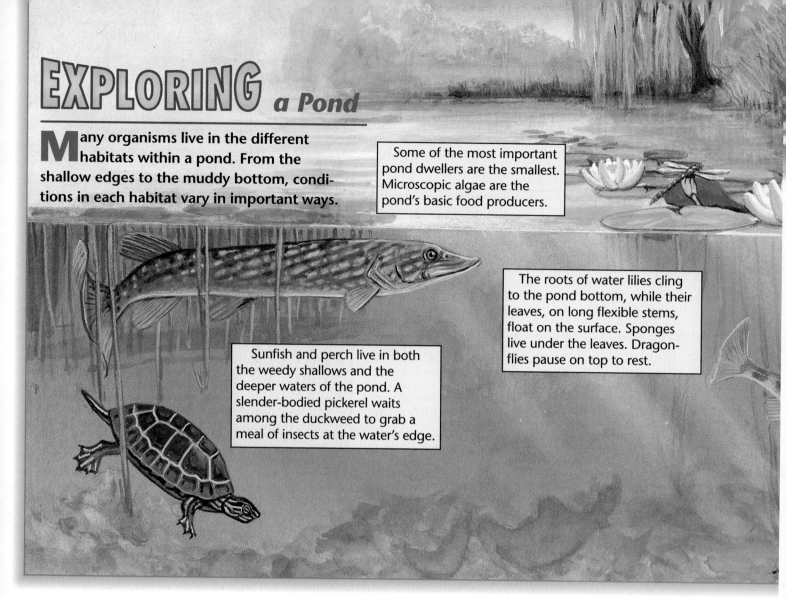

Some of the most important pond dwellers are the smallest. Microscopic algae are the pond's basic food producers.

The roots of water lilies cling to the pond bottom, while their leaves, on long flexible stems, float on the surface. Sponges live under the leaves. Dragonflies pause on top to rest.

Sunfish and perch live in both the weedy shallows and the deeper waters of the pond. A slender-bodied pickerel waits among the duckweed to grab a meal of insects at the water's edge.

Ponds

INTEGRATING LIFE SCIENCE Compared to a tumbling mountain stream, a pond seems still and peaceful at first glance. Silvery minnows glide smoothly below the surface. A dragonfly touches the water, then whirs away. Lily pads with broad, green leaves and waxy, white blossoms float on the surface. This quiet pond is actually a thriving habitat, supporting a wide diversity of living things.

If you have ever waded in a pond, you know that the muddy bottom is often covered with weeds. Because the water is shallow enough for sunlight to reach the bottom, plants grow throughout a pond. Plantlike organisms called algae also live in the pond. As the plants and algae use sunlight to make food through photosynthesis, they also produce oxygen. Animals in the pond use the oxygen and food provided by plants and algae. You can see some common pond organisms in *Exploring a Pond*.

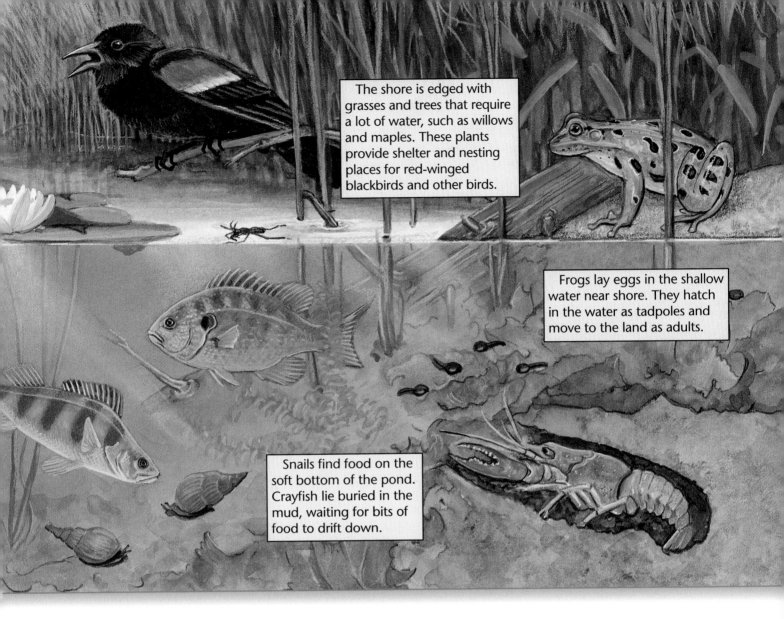

The shore is edged with grasses and trees that require a lot of water, such as willows and maples. These plants provide shelter and nesting places for red-winged blackbirds and other birds.

Frogs lay eggs in the shallow water near shore. They hatch in the water as tadpoles and move to the land as adults.

Snails find food on the soft bottom of the pond. Crayfish lie buried in the mud, waiting for bits of food to drift down.

Not all ponds exist year-round. For example, some ponds in the northern and western United States appear only in the spring, when runoff from spring rains and melting snow collects in low areas. The ponds dry up by midsummer as the shallow water quickly evaporates in the heat.

Ponds in colder climates often freeze over during the winter. Recall that ice floats because it is less dense than liquid water. As a result, ice forms on the surface of the pond, while the living things survive in the liquid water below.

☑ *Checkpoint* *Why can plants grow throughout a pond?*

Lakes

Suppose you suddenly found yourself on a sandy beach. Waves break on the shore. The water stretches as far as your eye can see. Gulls screech overhead. Where are you? Although you might think you're at the ocean, this immense body of water could

Figure 6 Standing water is found in lakes and ponds. **(A)** The cold waters of Crater Lake in Oregon fill the hollow of an ancient volcano. **(B)** Water lilies float in a Colorado pond. *Interpreting Photographs In which of these bodies of water does sunlight reach the bottom? Give evidence to support your answer.*

actually be a lake! You could be on a beach in Indiana, on the shore of Lake Michigan.

Although most lakes are not as large as Lake Michigan, they are generally bigger and deeper than ponds. Most lakes are deep enough that sunlight does not reach all the way to the bottom. A lake bottom may consist of sand, pebbles, or rock. The bottom of a pond is usually covered with mud and algae.

Lake Formation Lakes form in many ways. For example, a cut-off river meander may become an oxbow lake. Ice sheets that melted at the end of the Ice Age created depressions that became lakes. Some lakes were created by movements of Earth's crust. Such movements created the deep valleys in central Africa that lie below Lake Tanganyika and Lake Victoria. Other lakes are the result of volcanoes. An erupting volcano can cause a flow of lava or mud that blocks a river and forms a lake. Some lakes, like the one in Figure 6, form in the empty craters of volcanoes.

People can also create a lake by building a dam across a river. The lake may be used for supplying drinking water, for irrigating fields, and for boating and fishing. A lake that stores water for human use is called a **reservoir.** One of the largest reservoirs in the United States is Lake Mead in Nevada, behind Hoover Dam on the Colorado River.

Lake Habitats Like a pond, a lake provides habitats for many

INTEGRATING
LIFE SCIENCE

different kinds of organisms. In the shallow water near shore, the wildlife is similar to that in a pond. Water beetles scurry over the slippery, moss-covered rocks. Loons and kingfishers pluck fish from the open water.

But unlike a pond, sunlight does not reach the bottom at the center of a lake. Without sunlight, plants cannot live in the deep water. As a result, fewer other organisms live in the chilly, dark depths of the lake. A few worms and mollusks do live on the bottom. They feed on food particles that drift down from the surface. The deep waters of lakes are also the home of large, bony fish such as pike and sturgeon. These fish eat the tiny bottom dwellers. They also swim to the surface to feed on fish and even small birds.

Icebergs

You may be surprised to learn that 76 percent of Earth's fresh water exists as ice frozen in glaciers. A glacier is a mass of ice and snow that moves slowly over land. When a glacier reaches the seacoast, icebergs form. With a loud roar, large chunks break off, or calve, and float away. Although icebergs are found in the salty ocean, remember that they consist of fresh water.

In the North Atlantic and Arctic oceans, about 10,000 new icebergs form every year. Many of these icebergs calve from Greenland's continental glacier. As they drift south, the icebergs break into chunks as big as houses. They begin to melt in the warmer water.

The ocean around Antarctica is filled with even larger icebergs. Flat-topped pieces calve from the edges of the glaciers along the coast. In 1995, a giant iceberg broke off Antarctica's Larsen Ice Shelf. Scientists flying over the new iceberg reported that it was about 70 kilometers long and 25 kilometers wide—more than half the size of the state of Rhode Island!

Figure 7 If you could see an entire iceberg at once, how would it look? An artist created this composite photograph to reveal the hidden part of the iceberg.

Section 2 Review

1. What bodies of water make up a river system?
2. Why do floods occur?
3. Explain how ponds and lakes form.
4. Give three examples of typical pond organisms. Describe where in a pond each is found.
5. Where do icebergs form?
6. **Thinking Critically Relating Cause and Effect** How is the depth of the water in the middle of a lake related to the variety of living things there?

Science at Home

Homemade Iceberg With a family member, make a model iceberg. Fill the cut-off bottom of a milk or juice carton with water and freeze. When the water has frozen, peel the carton away from the iceberg. Add salt to a large bowl of water to create an "ocean." Float the iceberg in the bowl. Help your family member use a ruler to measure how much of the iceberg's thickness is above the surface of the water and how much is below. Use these measurements to explain why icebergs can be dangerous to ships.

Where Does the Water Go?

1. Add pebbles to a jar to form a layer about 5 centimeters deep. Cover the pebbles with a layer of dry sand about 3 centimeters thick. Pour the sand in slowly to avoid moving the pebbles. These materials represent underground soil layers.

2. Sprinkle water onto the sand to simulate rainfall.

3. Looking through the side of the jar, observe the path of the water as it soaks through the layers. Wash your hands when you are finished with this activity.

Think It Over

Observing Describe what happens when the water reaches the bottom of the jar.

◆ How does water move through underground layers of soil and rock?

◆ How do people obtain water from an aquifer?

Reading Tip As you read, create a flowchart that shows one possible path of water from a cloud to a well.

Key Terms pore • permeable
• impermeable
• saturated zone • water table
• unsaturated zone
• aquifer • spring • recharge
• artesian well

When you were younger, did you ever dig a hole in the ground hoping to find a buried treasure? Though you probably never found a trunk full of gold, you could have found a different kind of treasure without even realizing it. If you continued to dig deeper, past tangled grass roots and small stones, you would have noticed the soil begin to feel heavier and wetter. If you dug deep enough, the bottom of your hole would have started to fill up with water. You would have "struck groundwater!" In the days before pipes and public water systems, such a discovery was like finding a treasure. A usable source of fresh water enabled people to build a house or farm and settle on that land. Today, many people still rely on the water underground to meet their water needs.

Underground Layers

Where does this underground water come from? Like the water in rivers, lakes, and glaciers, it comes from precipitation. Recall what can happen to precipitation when it falls. It can evaporate right away, run off the surface, or soak into the ground. The water that soaks in trickles downward, following the pull of gravity.

If you pour water into a glass full of pebbles, the water trickles down around the pebbles until it reaches the bottom of the glass. Then the water begins to fill up the spaces between the pebbles. **In the same way, water underground trickles down between particles of soil and through cracks and spaces in layers of rock.**

Unsaturated zone

Water table

Saturated zone

Solid rock

Unconnected pores

Air

Water

Permeable layers

Impermeable layer

Figure 8 Differences in the materials that form layers underground determine where groundwater forms. Water can move through the pores of permeable layers, but not through impermeable layers.
Interpreting Diagrams What is the difference between the saturated and unsaturated zone?

Different types of rock and soil have different-sized spaces, or **pores,** between their particles. How easily water moves through the material depends not only on the size of the pores, but also on whether the pores are connected to each other. Materials that allow water to easily pass through, or permeate, are called **permeable.** Sand and gravel are permeable materials.

As water soaks down through permeable rock, it eventually reaches layers of material that it cannot pass through. These materials have few or no pores or cracks for the water to flow through. Materials that water cannot pass through easily are called **impermeable.** Clay and granite are impermeable materials.

Once water reaches an impermeable layer, it is trapped. It can't soak any deeper. Instead, the water begins to fill up the spaces above the impermeable material. The area of permeable rock or soil that is totally filled, or saturated, with water is called the **saturated zone.** The top of the saturated zone is the **water table.** Knowing the depth of the water table in an area tells you how deep you must dig to reach groundwater.

Soil and rock layers above the water table contain some moisture, too. But here the pores contain air as well as water. They are not saturated with water. Therefore, the layer of rocks and soil above the water table is called the **unsaturated zone.**

☑ *Checkpoint* *Give an example of a permeable material other than sand or gravel.*

Sharpen your Skills

Drawing Conclusions

ACTIVITY

You have just bought some land and need to dig a well. By drilling a number of holes on your property, you learn that there is a layer of impermeable granite rock located approximately 12 meters underground. If the saturated zone is 3 meters thick, how deep should you dig your well? (*Hint:* Drawing a diagram may be helpful.)

An Artesian Well

In this activity you will build a model of an artesian well. Before you start, cover your desk or table with newspaper.

1. Cover the bottom of a loaf pan with clay. Pile the clay higher at one end.

2. Cover the clay with about 4 cm of moist sand.

3. Cover the sand with a thin sheet of clay. Seal the edges of the clay tightly against the sides of the pan.

4. Push a funnel into the high end so that the bottom of the funnel is in the sand.

5. Insert a short piece of plastic straw through the clay and into the sand layer at the low end. Remove the straw, discard it, and then insert a new piece of straw in the same hole.

6. Slowly pour water into the funnel. Do not let the water overflow the funnel.

7. Observe the level of water in the straw. Wash your hands after this activity.

Making Models What real-world feature does each part of your model represent? How is your model like a real artesian well? How is it different?

Aquifers

Any underground layer of rock or sediment that holds water is called an **aquifer.** Aquifers can range in size from a small underground patch of permeable material to an area the size of several states. The huge Ogallala aquifer lies beneath the plains of the midwest, stretching from South Dakota to Texas. Millions of people obtain their drinking water from this underground storehouse. The Ogallala aquifer also provides water for crops and livestock.

Maybe you picture groundwater as a large, still pool beneath Earth's surface. In fact, the water is actually in motion, seeping through the layers of rock. How fast it moves depends largely on how steeply the aquifer slopes and how permeable the rocks are. Groundwater in some aquifers moves only a few centimeters a day. At that rate, the water moves about 10 meters a year—less than the length of a typical classroom. Groundwater may travel hundreds of kilometers and stay in an aquifer for thousands of years before coming to the surface again.

☑ *Checkpoint* *What factors affect how fast water moves in an aquifer?*

Bringing Groundwater to the Surface

Look at Figure 9 and notice how the level of the water table generally follows the shape of the underground rock layers. The depth of the water table can vary greatly even over a small area of land. Heavy rain or lots of melting snow raise the level of the water table. The level falls in dry weather.

Where the water table meets the ground surface, groundwater bubbles or flows out of cracks in the rock in places called **springs.** The groundwater may feed a stream or pond, or form a wetland. People can also bring groundwater to the surface.

Wells Since ancient times, people have brought groundwater to the surface for drinking and other everyday uses. **People can obtain groundwater from an aquifer by drilling a well below the water table.** Locate the well near the center of Figure 9. Because the bottom of the well is in the saturated zone, the well contains water. Notice the level of the bottom of the dry well in the diagram. Because this well does not reach below the water table, water cannot be obtained from it.

Long ago, people dug wells by hand. They lined the sides of the well with brick or stone to keep the walls from collapsing. To bring up water, they lowered and raised a bucket. Today, most wells are dug with well-drilling equipment. Pumps bring up the groundwater.

Pumping water out of an aquifer lowers the water level near the well. If too much water is pumped out too fast, the well may

Spring

Artesian well

Aquifer

Aquifer

Water table

Aquifer

Dry well

Well

Impermeable rock

Figure 9 Groundwater is pumped up to the surface through wells like the one near the center of the diagram. At the right, pressure causes water to spurt from an artesian well. Where an aquifer meets the ground surface, at the left, a spring may form.
Interpreting Diagrams Why does the dry well not contain any water?

run dry. It will be necessary either to dig deeper to reach the lowered water table, or to wait for rainfall to refill the aquifer. New water that enters the aquifer from the surface is called **recharge.**

Artesian Wells In some aquifers, groundwater is trapped between two layers of impermeable rock or sediment. This water is under great pressure from the weight of the water above it. If the top layer of rock is punctured, the pressure sends water spurting up through the hole. Water flows without pumping from a well dug in such an aquifer. A well in which water rises because of pressure within the aquifer is called an **artesian well** (ahr TEEZH uhn).

Section 3 Review

1. Describe what happens to water that soaks into the ground.
2. Why is it important to know the depth of an aquifer before drilling a well?
3. Draw a cross section of the ground that includes the following labeled features: permeable layer, saturated zone, unsaturated zone, impermeable layer, and water table.
4. **Thinking Critically** **Inferring** During the winter, a small spring flows on your property. Every summer, the spring dries up. What might be the reason for the change?

Check Your Progress

CHAPTER PROJECT

By now you should have chosen a building in your community to monitor. How will you determine the amount and type of water usage there? Are the building's water uses different from the water uses in your home? Be sure to check with your teacher before contacting anyone at the site. (*Hint:* A building manager often has information about water use. You may find it helpful to write down your questions before you interview the person.) Prepare a second data table and record this building's water-use data.

SOIL TESTING

In what type of soil is it best to site a well? This is a question that hydrologists, scientists who study groundwater, need to answer before new houses or other buildings can be constructed. In this lab, you will compare different soil types to learn more about their water-holding properties.

Problem

How fast does water move through sand, clay, and pebbles?

Skills Focus

observing, measuring, drawing conclusions

Materials (per group)

hand lens | 3 beakers, 100-mL
sand, 100 mL | water, 300 mL
stopwatch | pebbles, 100 mL
3 rubber bands
powdered potter's clay, 100 mL
3 squares of cheesecloth
3 large funnels or cut-off plastic soda bottle tops

Procedure

1. Copy the data table into your notebook.

HELP WANTED

Hydrologists to conduct soil tests for new housing development. Homes will have private wells. Engineers must test soil permeability to select best locations. Please send resumé and references to

2. Use a hand lens to observe each of the three material samples closely. Record your observations in your data table.

3. Place a piece of cheesecloth over the bottom of each funnel or bottle top and secure it with a rubber band.

4. Place the sand in one funnel, the pebbles in another, and the clay in another. Be sure that there is at least 5 cm of space above the material in each funnel.

5. Place each funnel on top of a beaker.

6. Slowly pour 100 mL of water into the funnel containing the sand. Do not let the water overflow the funnel.

7. Start the stopwatch when the water begins to flow or drip out of the bottom of the funnel.

DATA TABLE		
Material	Observations	Time for Water to Stop Dripping
Sand		
Clay		
Pebbles		

8. Stop the stopwatch when the water stops dripping out of the funnel or after 5 minutes. Record the time to the nearest second in your data table.

9. Repeat Steps 6 through 8 with the pebbles and then with the clay. When you are finished with this activity, dispose of your materials according to your teacher's instructions. Wash your hands thoroughly with soap.

Analyze and Conclude

1. Through which material did water move the fastest? The slowest?

2. What can you conclude about the permeability of the three materials?

3. Based on your observations of each sample, suggest an explanation for the differences in their permeability.

4. Based on the results of this lab, would you expect to get more water from a well dug in sand, pebbles, or clay? Explain.

5. **Apply** Why might gardeners and landscapers need to know about the permeability of different soil types?

More to Explore

Which of the soil samples that you tested do you think the soil of the grounds at your school most resembles? Design an experiment to test your hypothesis. With your teacher's permission, carry out your experiment.

SECTION 4 Wetland Systems

DISCOVER · ACTIVITY· · ·

Wet or Dry?

1. Soak a kitchen sponge under water. Then squeeze out the water until the sponge is just damp.

2. Place the damp sponge next to a dry sponge in a pan. The sponges represent areas of wet and dry land.

3. Pour water into two paper cups until each is half full.

4. Hold one cup in each hand so that the cups are about 10 centimeters above the pan. Pour the water onto both sponges at the same time.

Think It Over
Observing Which of the sponges absorbs water faster? How are your observations related to what might happen in areas of wet and dry land?

GUIDE FOR READING

◆ What are the parts of a wetland system?

◆ How do the properties of a wetland system differ from the properties of its parts?

◆ How are wetland systems important?

Reading Tip Before you read, write a short description of what you think a wetland is. As you read, add details and examples to your description.

Key Terms wetland • system

An Oregon marsh ▼

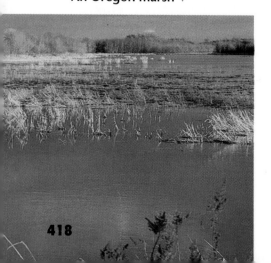

What image does the word *wetland* bring to mind? Do you think of a shallow pond filled with plants and animals? Or do you imagine a swamp with knobby cypress trees growing in still water?

A **wetland** is an area of land that is covered with a shallow layer of water during some or all of the year. Wetlands form in places where water is trapped in low areas or where groundwater seeps onto the surface of the land.

There are many different types of wetlands. Marshes, swamps, and bogs are three common types of freshwater wetlands. You can compare two types of wetlands in Figure 10. Wetlands along the coast usually contain both fresh and salt water.

What Is a Wetland System?

A wetland is not simply water and land. It includes many other parts that make up the total wetland system. A **system** is a group of parts that work together as a whole. More exactly, a wetland is an ecosystem—a system made up of all of the living things in a given area and their physical environment.

As in all ecosystems, the two main parts of a wetland system are the abiotic factors and the biotic factors. Recall from Chapter 8 that abiotic factors are the nonliving parts of an ecosystem. The living parts of an ecosystem are called biotic factors. The parts interact in many ways, affecting each other and changing the system as a whole. As you learn about the parts of a wetland ecosystem, you can better understand how they work together.

Abiotic Parts of a Wetland System

The abiotic factors, or nonliving parts, of an ecosystem include the water, temperature soil, oxygen, and sunlight. Each of these factors affects the types of life an ecosystem can support.

The layer of water covering a wetland can range from several centimeters to a few meters deep. The amount of precipitation and the temperature range greatly affect the amount of water available. Recall that water on Earth is part of the global water cycle. The water in the wetland ecosystem moves from the plants, animals, and land into the atmosphere through evaporation and transpiration, then falls back to the wetland as precipitation. This continuous cycling of water allows the wetland to maintain itself over a long time period.

The types of rock and soil as well as the slope and drainage of the land also help determine the type of wetland you will find. In some wetlands water flows through slowly; in others there is no drainage at all. Impermeable layers of rock or clay can prevent surface water from seeping into the ground.

The level of oxygen in the air, water, and ground is different for each wetland. Due to the lack of movement of water in many wetlands, there is often little oxygen. This affects the kinds of organisms that live there. The sunlight provides the energy that warms the air and water in a wetland, and enables plants to carry on photosynthesis. The sunlight also provides the energy for the water cycle.

Biotic Parts of a Wetland System

The biotic factors in an ecosystem include all of its producers, consumers, and decomposers. These organisms interact with each other and with the wetland's abiotic factors.

Producers The producers in a wetland ecosystem capture the energy of sunlight through photosynthesis and store it as chemical energy in food. The types of producers that exist in a particular wetland depend on the abiotic factors of the wetland.

Figure 10 Freshwater wetlands come in many forms. **(A)** In Montana, colorful flowers dot a bed of velvety moss in an alpine bog. **(B)** Spanish moss hangs from cypress trees in a swamp in Caddo Lake State Park, Texas.
Comparing and Contrasting How are these two environments similar? How are they different?

A great variety of plant life finds a place to grow and thrive in wetlands. For example, certain grasses and tall grasslike plants such as cattails can be found in a marsh. Trees that tolerate wet soils are found in swamps. Cypress trees grow in southern swamps in the United States. Willow and dogwood trees are found in northern parts of the country. Sphagnum moss often grows in a bog where the water is acidic. Over time layers of partly decayed moss compress to form a blackish-brown material called peat.

Consumers The consumers found in a wetland depend on the type of producers that thrive there. As in a pond, you will find waterfowl, frogs, turtles, raccoons, snakes, muskrats, and a variety of insects in many wetlands. In southern regions of the United States you can also find alligators and armadillos.

Birds nest in and around wetlands, feeding on the plants and insects there. Waterfowl rely on wetlands to provide temporary shelter as they migrate. Wetlands provide breeding grounds and nurturing waters for young organisms to develop. Many other animals find food and shelter among the wetland plants.

Figure 11 Many unusual species live in the freshwater wetland habitats of the Everglades.

Roseate spoonbills

Great egret

Snowy egret

Little blue heron

Sawgrass

Anhinga

Florida panther

Decomposers Decomposers such as bacteria and fungi break down the wastes and remains from the plants and animals. Dead leaves and other plant and animal material serve as natural fertilizer, adding nitrogen, phosphates and other nutrients to the water and soil.

Properties of Wetland Systems

The properties of a wetland ecosystem differ from the properties of its individual parts. Like all ecosystems, a wetland transforms energy, provides different habitats and niches for the organisms that live there, and maintains itself over time. A wetland captures an enormous amount of energy from sunlight. Living things use this energy directly to grow and reproduce. But incoming energy also affects the abiotic parts of a wetland. For example, sunlight warms the water, causing it to evaporate and to continue the water cycle.

Each part of the wetland offers different habitats and niches for living things. Some organisms may live on the wetland's trees, shrubs, and grasses. Others may live in the water, or beneath the water in a layer of mud.

Sharpen your Skills

Making Models

ACTIVITY

In one end of a loaf pan, build a sloping hill of damp soil. Add water to the other end of the pan to form a lake. Use a watering can to sprinkle water onto the hill to simulate rain. Observe the result. Next, empty the water out of the pan and rebuild the hill. Push a sponge into the soil across the bottom of the hill. Again, add water and sprinkle "rain." What happened to the soil with and without the sponge? What does the sponge represent in your model?

Everglades palm

White-tailed deer

Flamingos

Raccoon

Purple gallinule

American alligator

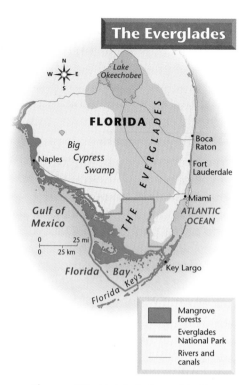

The Everglades

Figure 12 Habitats found in the Everglades include sawgrass marshes, cypress swamps, and mangrove forests.
Interpreting Maps In which area of the park would you expect to find mangrove trees?

A wetland ecosystem tends to remain stable unless it is disturbed by a change in its abiotic or biotic factors. For example, some bogs slowly dry up over many years. This gradually changes the types of organisms that can live in the bog.

The Everglades: A Unique Wetland System

Water is the key to the Everglades, a unique region of wetlands. A shallow layer of water moves slowly over the gently sloping land from Lake Okeechobee south to Florida Bay. Tall, sharp-edged blades of sawgrass grow in the water. The thick growth of sawgrass gave this region its Native American name, *Pa-hay-okee,* which means "river of grass." Low, tree-covered islands called hammocks are scattered throughout the sawgrass marsh.

As in other wetlands, water means life for many Everglades creatures. Fish and snakes gobble up tiny organisms in the warm, muddy water. Wading birds in a rainbow of colors—pink flamingoes, white egrets, and purple gallinules—stand on skinny legs in the water. A raccoon digs for alligator eggs, unaware of the alligator lying low in the sawgrass nearby.

Importance of Wetland Systems

Wetland ecosystems have important properties that benefit all living things. **Wetlands provide natural filtration and absorb water that might otherwise cause flooding.** As water moves slowly through a wetland, waste materials settle out. The thick network of plant roots traps silt and mud. Wetlands also help control floods by absorbing extra runoff from heavy rains. They act like giant sponges, storing water and gradually releasing it as it drains or evaporates. If wetlands are drained or paved over, the water cannot be absorbed, and flooding may result.

Section 4 Review

1. Give two examples of each: abiotic and biotic parts of a wetland system.
2. Pick one biotic or abiotic part of a wetland system. Explain how a change in this part of the system could change the properties of the wetland system.
3. Explain how wetlands help control floods.
4. **Thinking Critically Making Judgments** Some plans to restore the Everglades require millions of dollars and negatively affect local farmers. What information would you need to decide on a plan to save the Everglades?

Check Your Progress CHAPTER PROJECT

At this point, you should be ready to use the data in your water-use data tables to graph the results of tracking water use in your home and in another building in your community. Think about the type of graph that will best communicate your findings. Decide whether to draw your graphs by hand or to create them on the computer.

DISCOVER •••••••••••••••••••••••••••••••••••••••ACTIVITY••••

Can You Reach a Balance?

1. Fill a large measuring cup with water to represent a reservoir. Record the level of the water. One partner, the water supplier, should have a plastic dropper and a small bowl of water. The other partner, the water user, should have a spoon and an empty bowl.

2. Start a stopwatch. For two minutes, the water supplier should add water to the measuring cup one dropperful at a time. Each time the water supplier adds a dropperful of water, the water user should remove one spoonful of water from the reservoir.

3. At the end of two minutes, record the level of water in the cup.

4. Now increase the rate of water use by removing two spoonfuls of water for every dropperful added.

5. After another two minutes, record the level of water in the cup again.

Think It Over

Predicting What changes will you need to make so that the water level in the reservoir stays constant?

H as this ever happened to you? You're eating dinner with your family and you ask someone to pass the rolls. As the basket makes its way around the table, each person takes a roll. By the time it gets to you, there's nothing left in the basket but crumbs!

This scenario is an example of a limited resource, the rolls, being used by many people. The same thing can happen to a river! For example, the Colorado River holds a resource that is precious in the Southwest—water. In this desert region there is little precipitation to provide water for people's needs. As the river flows through seven states and into Mexico, it is tapped again and again to provide water for drinking, irrigation, and other uses. The river's mouth at the Gulf of California is now often only a dry riverbed.

GUIDE FOR READING

◆ What conditions can result in a water shortage?

◆ What are some ways industries can conserve water?

Reading Tip Before you read, write an explanation of what you think water conservation means. As you read, add to your explanation.

Key Terms drought
• conservation • desalination

Figure 13 Cracks appear in the dry soil of an empty riverbed.

423

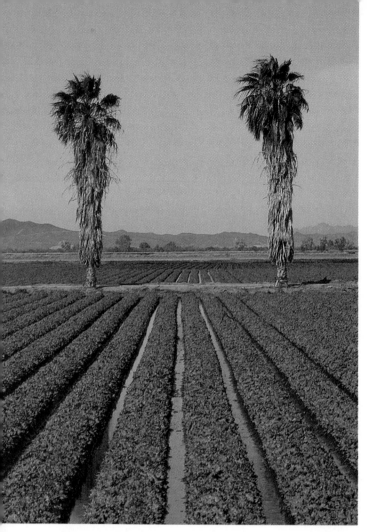

Figure 14 Farmers require large amounts of water to irrigate crops in the dry desert.
Relating Cause and Effect What are two factors that might result in a shortage of water available for irrigation?

Water Supply and Demand

States along a river such as the Colorado have to decide how much water each one can take from the river. The deserts of Nevada and Arizona are home to some of the fastest-growing cities in the country. As more people move to Las Vegas, Phoenix, and Tucson, these cities need more water. They increase their demand on already scarce water supplies. Meanwhile, farmers claim a large share to irrigate their fields. Mining companies use water to cool down machinery and flush out the mines they dig. The cities, farms, and mines compete for water rights—the legal right to take water from a particular source.

The Southwest is just one of many places in the world where there doesn't seem to be enough water to go around. As you know, the water cycle ensures that water is a renewable resource. However, the water supply in a specific area is only renewed when there is enough time for rainfall to replace what has been used. **A water shortage occurs when there is too little water or too great a demand in an area—or both.**

Drought Places that normally get enough precipitation may experience a few years of scarce rainfall, a condition known as a **drought.** A drought affects the supply of groundwater as well as surface water. Without precipitation to recharge the aquifer, the amount of groundwater in the aquifer decreases. What happens to a well as the level of the water table falls? Imagine trying to drink from a tall glass of milk through a straw the length of a toothpick. When the level of the milk falls below the bottom of the straw, you can no longer reach it to drink. In the same way, when the water table falls below the bottom of a well, the well runs dry.

Aquifer Overuse Even without droughts, the demands of

INTEGRATING TECHNOLOGY

growing populations can result in overuse of aquifers. When water is used up faster than the aquifer can be recharged, the aquifer is depleted, or emptied.

When too much water is pumped out of an aquifer, the ground above the aquifer can sink or collapse. The ground is no longer supported by the pressure of the water inside it. To prevent collapse, engineers can artificially recharge an aquifer. One method is to pump water from wastewater treatment plants or industrial cooling water into shallow ponds that feed the aquifer. Another method is to inject water down wells directly into the saturated zone. However, because these techniques require expensive equipment and additional water, it is a better solution not to overuse the aquifer.

✓ *Checkpoint* *How can a drought cause a well to run dry?*

Conserving Water

During a water shortage, people often pay more attention to how they use water. They look for ways to avoid wasting water both at home and at work. Using a resource wisely so that it will not be used up is called **conservation.**

In the Home Most people in the United States have access to as much clean, safe water as they want. As a result, it is often easy to use more water than needed without thinking much about it. But as Figure 15 shows, there are some simple things you can do to help conserve water around your home.

Sharpen your Skills

Predicting

ACTIVITY

Find a leaking faucet in your school or home, or turn on a faucet just enough to produce a very slow drip. How much water do you think will drip from the faucet in half an hour? Write down your prediction. Place a large measuring cup under the faucet. After half an hour, check the cup. How does the result compare with your prediction? How much water would you save per day if you fixed the leaking faucet?

Take shorter showers. If you take baths, fill the bathtub only halfway. ▼

If you have a lawn, water it early in the morning or late in the afternoon so the sun won't evaporate the water. ▼

▲ Turn off the faucet instead of letting the water run while you brush your teeth.

▲ Scrub vegetables in a basin of water, not under running water.

◄ Keep a pitcher of drinking water in the refrigerator instead of running the water till it gets cold.

◄ Only run the washing machine when you have a full load.

Figure 15 There are many simple ways to conserve water around the home. *Developing Hypotheses Which of these ideas do you think would save the most water per day in your home? How could you test your hypothesis?*

Laws regarding the use of water are a very old concept. Nearly 4,000 years ago in ancient Mesopotamia, now Iraq, a ruler named Hammurabi wrote in his code of laws:

> "If a man neglects the canal so that water floods a neighboring field, he shall repay the loss with his own grain."

In Your Journal

A river carries 10,000 liters of water a day through your village. Imagine that you are a member of the village council. Propose a fair way to assign water rights to the following people. (*Hint:* Think about which uses will return water to the river and which will not.)

- grain farmer who wants 4,000 liters a day for watering crops
- livestock owner who wants 600 liters a day for washing animals and 500 liters a day for animals to drink
- fisherman who needs to keep the river at least half full for the fish to survive
- miller who needs 3,500 liters a day to turn his water wheel

Can these suggestions really make a difference? Figure it out. How long do you stand under the shower? For every minute, you use about 18 liters of water. If you stand under the shower for 10 minutes, that's about 180 liters. But if you showered for 5 minutes instead, you would use only 90 liters. And if each student in a class of 25 showered for 5 minutes instead of 10, they would save a total of 2,250 liters of water—enough to fill 22 trash barrels! As you can see, small efforts by many individuals can add up to a lot of water savings.

In Agriculture The biggest use of water in the United States is for agriculture. Farmers have found new ways to use less water. When water is carried into fields in open canals or ditches, much of it is lost through evaporation. Using pipes to carry water reduces the time that water is exposed to the air. Two such methods are sprinkler irrigation and drip irrigation. Sprinkler irrigation sprays water onto crops from overhead pipes. Drip irrigation distributes water through pipes with tiny holes. The water drips directly onto the soil near the plants' roots so that very little is wasted.

In Industry Paper mills, oil refineries, chemical factories, and other industries have made changes in manufacturing processes to use less water. For example, in the 1950s it took about 227,000 liters of water to make 1,000 kilograms of writing paper. By the 1980s, paper mills needed only half that much water to produce the same amount of paper.

New water-saving techniques help industries save money in water costs and meet the requirements of environmental laws. **Reducing water use, recycling water, and reusing water are three major forms of water conservation by industries.** These approaches conserve water while also reducing the amount of wastewater that plants release. For example, some factories that use water to cool machinery are building lagoons on their property. The heated water cools off in the lagoons and then can be used again. Other factories are replacing water-cooling systems with cooling systems that use air. Another change is to use high-pressure water sprays to clean products and equipment instead of dipping the objects in large tanks of water.

Fresh Water for the Future

As the number of people in the world increases, so does the need for water. Where can people find new sources of water for the future? One obvious place would seem to be the other 97 percent of water on Earth—the salt water in the oceans. For thousands of years, people have tried different methods to make salty ocean water drinkable.

Desalination The process of obtaining fresh water

INTEGRATING CHEMISTRY from saltwater is **desalination.** One method of desalination, called distillation, is to boil water so that it evaporates, leaving the salt behind. The water vapor is then condensed to produce liquid fresh water. Another method involves freezing the water, which also leaves the salt behind. Still another method is to pump water at high pressure through a very fine filter. The filter separates out pure water and returns saltier water to the ocean.

Desalination is very expensive because of the energy and equipment it requires. In spite of the cost, however, Saudi Arabia, Kuwait, Israel, and other nations in the dry Middle East depend on this technology. A few cities in the United States, such as Santa Barbara, California, have also built desalination plants.

Icebergs Some people think that icebergs are another possible source of fresh water for dry regions. Tugboats could tow a wrapped iceberg from Antarctica to a coastal area of Africa or South America. An iceberg would provide millions of liters of pure water that could be piped to shore as the iceberg melted. However, such plans raise environmental questions: How would a huge mass of ice offshore affect local weather? What would happen to living things as the ice cooled the water around it? These questions need to be answered before icebergs can be seen as a solution to Earth's future water needs.

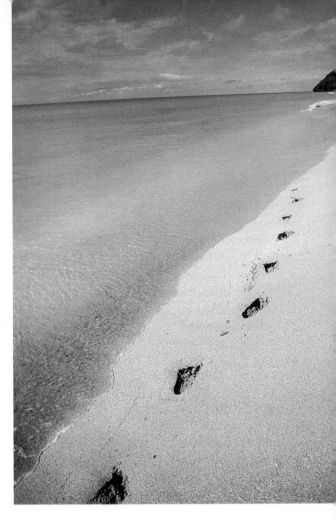

Figure 16 The ocean is one possible source of drinking water for the future. *Applying Concepts How can ocean water be made suitable for drinking?*

Section 5 Review

1. Describe a situation that could lead to a water shortage in a community.
2. Name three ways that industries can conserve water.
3. Describe the possible effects overpumping might have on an aquifer.
4. Explain how an iceberg might provide drinking water in the future.
5. **Thinking Critically Making Judgments** Do you think communities should be able to limit how often people water their lawns or wash their cars? Why or why not?

Science at Home

Water Use for Brushing Place a stopper over the drain in a sink. Ask a family member to brush his or her teeth over the sink, allowing the water to run until he or she is done. Mark the level of the water in the sink with a small piece of tape. Remove the stopper and let the water drain. Replace the stopper and have the person repeat the brushing, this time turning the water on only when needed. Mark the water level with another piece of tape. Point out the difference in the amount of water used in each case.

The Ogallala Aquifer

The Ogallala Aquifer lies beneath eight states of the Great Plains. It contains about 4 quadrillion liters of groundwater—about the amount of water in Lake Huron. Rainfall is scarce on the Great Plains. But by pumping water out of the aquifer, farmers can grow cotton, wheat, sorghum, and corn to feed cattle. More than one third of the nation's livestock are raised in this area.

Water in the Ogallala was trapped there during the last Ice Age, about 12,000 years ago. Now, due to the demands of irrigation, water levels are dropping much faster than the aquifer can recharge. In certain parts of the aquifer, water levels have fallen as much as 12 meters since 1980. Farmers recognize that the Ogallala cannot withstand this heavy use for long. However, not all agree on what should be done.

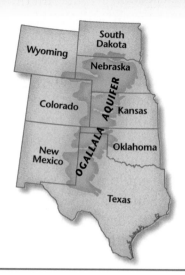

The Issues

Should Water Use Be Regulated? One way to reduce water use might be to charge people for water. But who owns the water and who would determine the cost? In most of the Great Plains, water has been free to anyone who dug a well on their land. To charge for water, local governments would need to construct a public water system as in most cities. This would be a very complex and costly task. Both farmers and consumers would be affected by the charge. Higher costs for growing crops would result in higher supermarket prices for grains and meat.

Should Farmers Change Their Practices? Farmers could switch to crops such as sunflowers and grains that need less water. These crops, however, are less valuable than others for producing food and for feeding livestock. As a result, they would be less profitable than traditional crops. Farmers could use water-saving methods of irrigation. Such methods are expensive to install but eventually save both water and money.

Another possibility is "dryland farming," a method that was used by pioneer farmers. This method involves keeping the soil moist using only rainwater. Because dryland farming depends on the amount of rainfall, it is unpredictable. It may not produce large harvests.

Should Current Use Continue? Many residents of the Great Plains depend on the aquifer for a living. Some people feel that farmers there must continue their present water use in order to compete with farmers elsewhere in the nation and around the world. They feel that people today should not have to suffer in order to preserve the aquifer for future generations. New sources of water may be discovered, or better methods of transporting water to the Great Plains may be developed. Better irrigation techniques that use less water may also be invented. But other people feel that since these possibilities are not certain, water use must be greatly reduced now to save the aquifer.

You Decide

1. Identify the Problem
In your own words, explain the problem facing the farmers on the Great Plains.

2. Analyze the Options
Make a chart of the solutions mentioned. List advantages and drawbacks of each. Who would benefit from each solution? Who would suffer?

3. Find a Solution
As a resident of the Great Plains, write a letter to the newspaper proposing a solution to the Ogallala problem.

SECTION 1 **The Water Cycle**

Key Ideas

◆ About 97 percent of Earth's water is salt water stored in the oceans. Less than 1 percent is usable fresh water.

◆ In the water cycle, water evaporates from Earth's surface into the atmosphere. The water forms clouds, then falls as precipitation. Energy from the sun drives the water cycle.

◆ All living things need water to carry out their life processes.

Key Terms

water vapor   evaporation   precipitation
groundwater   transpiration   irrigation
water cycle

 SECTION 2 **Surface Water**

Key Ideas

◆ Runoff from precipitation forms streams, which flow together to form rivers. The area drained by a river system is its watershed.

◆ Ponds and lakes are bodies of standing water that form when fresh water collects in depressions in the land.

Key Terms

tributary   divide   reservoir
watershed   levee

 SECTION 3 **Groundwater**

Key Ideas

◆ As water soaks into the ground, it moves through the pores between particles of soil and rock. Water moves easily through permeable materials, but does not move easily through impermeable materials.

◆ People dig wells to obtain groundwater from aquifers.

Key Terms

pore   water table   spring
permeable   unsaturated zone   recharge
impermeable   aquifer   artesian well
saturated zone

 SECTION 4 **Wetland Systems**

INTEGRATING LIFE SCIENCE

Key Ideas

◆ The two main parts of a wetland ecosystem are the abiotic factors, or nonliving parts, and the biotic factors, or living parts.

◆ A wetland ecosystem transforms energy, provides different habitats and niches for the organisms, and maintains itself over time.

◆ Wetland ecosystems provide natural filtration and absorb water that might otherwise cause flooding.

Key Terms

wetland   system

 SECTION 5 **Water Resources**

Key Ideas

◆ Water is scarce in many places, leading to competition for limited supplies.

◆ Water shortages can occur when there is too little water or too much demand in an area.

◆ Industries can conserve water by reducing water use, recycling water, and reusing water.

◆ Desalination of ocean water and icebergs are two possible future sources of fresh water.

Key Terms

drought   conservation   desalination

Organizing Information

Concept Map Copy the concept map about the water cycle onto a separate piece of paper, then complete it and add a title. (For more on concept maps, see the Skills Handbook.)

Reviewing Content

 Review key concepts online using
iText at www.phschool.com

Multiple Choice
Choose the letter of the best answer.

1. More than 97 percent of Earth's total water supply is found in
   a. ice sheets.
   b. the atmosphere.
   c. the oceans and salt lakes.
   d. groundwater.

2. The energy that drives the water cycle comes from the
   a. Earth.   b. sun.
   c. rain.   d. ocean.

3. One process used to obtain fresh water from salt water is
   a. irrigation.   b. filtration.
   c. recharge.   d. desalination.

4. More than two thirds of Earth's fresh water is found in
   a. rivers and streams.
   b. ponds and lakes.
   c. wetlands.
   d. glaciers and icebergs.

5. Groundwater is stored in
   a. wetlands.   b. water tables.
   c. aquifers.   d. impermeable layers.

True or False
If the statement is true, write true. If it is false, change the underlined word or words to make the statement true.

6. Most of Earth's liquid fresh water is found in the form of <u>lakes</u>.

7. In the water cycle, precipitation returns <u>salt water</u> to Earth.

8. A drought can cause wells to dry up if the level of the water table <u>rises</u>.

9. Water moves easily through <u>permeable</u> rock layers.

10. Wetland systems help to control <u>flooding</u> by absorbing water.

Checking Concepts

11. Explain why Earth is called the "water planet."

12. Describe two changes that occur during the water cycle.

13. Explain why so little of Earth's water is available for human use.

14. How is the water supplied to plants important for many other living things on Earth?

15. Describe one way that farmers can reduce the amount of water lost during irrigation.

16. What are the two major parts of a wetland ecosystem?

17. **Writing to Learn** Imagine that you are a molecule of water. Write a story about the changes you would experience as you go through the water cycle. Begin in the ocean, then describe each change that occurs, and return to the ocean at the end of your story.

Thinking Critically

18. **Making Generalizations** Explain why towns and cities are often located along bodies of water.

19. **Comparing and Contrasting** How is the variety of organisms you would find in the center of a pond different from those you would find in deep water at the center of a lake?

20. **Classifying** Determine which of the following materials are permeable and which are impermeable: aluminum foil, cotton, plastic wrap, glass, paper towel, and bread.

21. **Problem Solving** What effect would the draining of a wetland have on migrating birds?

22. **Relating Cause and Effect** Describe how one abiotic factor can affect many biotic factors in a wetland system.

Applying Skills

Use the diagram of underground layers to answer Questions 23–25.

23. **Drawing Conclusions** Would point D or point E be a better location to dig a well? Explain your reasoning.

24. **Inferring** At which location could you obtain groundwater without having to pump it up? What is such a place called?

25. **Predicting** Draw a simple diagram showing how this area might look during a very rainy season.

Present Your Project Now you are ready to share the data you have collected. Present your graph of your water-use data to the class. As a class, discuss any surprising results. How do your findings compare to those of your classmates?

Reflect and Record In your project notebook, reflect on the data collection process. What part of the project was the most difficult? How might you approach this task differently? Write a paragraph summarizing what your class discovered about how water is used in your community. Do you notice any similarities among buildings where a lot of water is used, or among those where little water is used?

Test Preparation

Use these questions to prepare for standardized tests.

Study the circle graph. Then answer Questions 26–29.

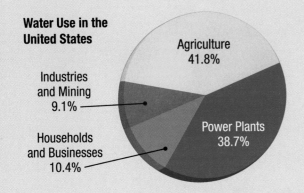

Water Use in the United States

Agriculture 41.8%
Industries and Mining 9.1%
Power Plants 38.7%
Households and Businesses 10.4%

26. Together the two largest categories of water users represent about what percentage of the total water used in the United States?
    A 19.5 percent   B 49.9 percent
    C 51.1 percent   D 80.5 percent

27. Which of the four categories of water users shown in the graph represents the largest use of water in the United States?
    F agriculture
    G households and businesses
    H industries and mining
    J power plants

28. If the total daily usage of water in the United States is 1,280 billion liters, about how many liters are used each day by power plants?
    A 38.7 billion   B 387 billion
    C 495 billion   D 49,500 billion

29. If farmers were able to reduce their water use by 10 percent, by about how much would total water use decrease in the United States?
    F 1.5 percent   G 4.2 percent
    H 10 percent   J 41.8 percent

CHAPTER 13 Earth's Atmosphere

WEB ACTIVITY www.phschool.com

SECTION 1 The Air Around You
Discover How Long Will the Candle Burn?
Real-World Lab How Clean Is the Air?

SECTION 2 Air Quality
Discover What's On the Jar?

SECTION 3 Air Pressure
Discover Does Air Have Mass?
Skills Lab Working Under Pressure

SECTION 4 Layers of the Atmosphere
Discover Is Air There?

Watching the Weather

The air is cool and clear—just perfect for a trip in a hot-air balloon. As you rise, a fresh breeze begins to move you along. Where will it take you? Hot-air balloon pilots need to know about the weather to plot their course.

In this chapter, you will learn about the air around you. As you learn about the atmosphere, you will use your senses to collect information about weather conditions. Even without scientific instruments it is possible to make many accurate observations about the weather.

Your Goal To observe weather conditions without using instruments and to look for hints about tomorrow's weather in the weather conditions today.

Your completed project must

◆ include a plan for observing and describing a variety of weather conditions over a period of two to three weeks
◆ show your observations in a daily weather log
◆ display your findings about weather conditions

Get Started Begin by discussing what weather conditions you can observe. Brainstorm how to use your senses to describe the weather. For example, can you describe the wind speed by observing the school flag? Can you describe the temperature based on what clothes you need to wear outside? Be creative.

Check Your Progress You'll be working on this project as you study this chapter. To keep your project on track, look for Check Your Progress boxes at the following points.

Section 1 Review, page 437: Collect and record observations.
Section 4 Review, page 456: Look for patterns in your data.

Present Your Project At the end of the chapter (page 459), use your weather observations to prepare a display for the class.

Hot-air balloons soar into the atmosphere at a balloon festival in Snowmass, Colorado.

TEKS

In addition to process TEKS, this chapter addresses these concept TEKS as they relate to the chapter's topics.

(6.14) The student knows the structures and functions of Earth systems.
The student is expected to:
(C) describe components of the atmosphere, including oxygen, nitrogen, and water vapor, and identify the role of atmospheric movement in weather change.

SECTION 1 The Air Around You

DISCOVER · ACTIVITY

How Long Will the Candle Burn?

1. Put on your goggles.

2. Stick a small piece of modeling clay onto an aluminum pie pan. Push a short candle into the clay. Carefully light the candle.

3. Hold a small glass jar by the bottom. Lower the mouth of the jar over the candle until the jar rests on the pie pan. As you do this, start a stopwatch or note where the second hand is on a clock.

4. Watch the candle carefully. How long does the flame burn?

5. Wearing an oven mitt, remove the jar. Relight the candle and then repeat Steps 3 and 4 with a larger jar.

Think It Over

Inferring How would you explain any differences between your results in Steps 4 and 5?

GUIDE FOR READING

◆ How is the atmosphere important to living things?

◆ What gases are present in Earth's atmosphere?

Reading Tip Before you read, preview Figure 2. As you read, write a sentence about each of the major gases in the atmosphere.

Key Terms weather
• atmosphere • ozone
• water vapor

As you walk home from school, the air is warm and still. The sky is full of thick, dark clouds. In the distance you see a bright flash. A few seconds later, you hear a crack of thunder. As you turn the corner onto your street, raindrops start to fall. You begin to run and reach your home just as the downpour begins. That was close! From the shelter of the entrance you pause to catch your breath and watch the storm.

Importance of the Atmosphere

Does the weather where you live change frequently, or is it fairly constant from day to day? **Weather** is the condition of Earth's atmosphere at a particular time and place. But what is the atmosphere? Earth's **atmosphere** (AT muh sfeer) is the layer of gases that surrounds the planet. To understand the relative size of the atmosphere, imagine that the planet Earth is the size of an apple.

Figure 1 When seen from space, Earth's atmosphere appears as a thin layer near the horizon. The atmosphere makes life on Earth possible.

If you breathe on the apple, a thin film of water will form on its surface. Earth's atmosphere is like that water on the apple— a thin layer of gases on Earth's surface.

Earth's atmosphere makes conditions on Earth suitable for living things. The atmosphere contains oxygen and other gases that you and other living things need to live. In turn, living things affect the atmosphere. The atmosphere is constantly changing, with atoms and molecules of gases moving around the globe and in and out of living things, the land, and the water.

Living things also need warmth and liquid water. By trapping energy from the sun, the atmosphere keeps most of Earth's surface warm enough for water to exist as a liquid. In addition, Earth's atmosphere protects living things from dangerous radiation from the sun. It also prevents Earth's surface from being hit by most meteoroids, or chunks of rock from outer space.

☑ *Checkpoint* *What would conditions on Earth be like without the atmosphere?*

Composition of the Atmosphere

The atmosphere is made up of a mixture of atoms and molecules of different kinds of gases. An atom is the smallest unit of a chemical element that can exist by itself. Molecules are made up of two or more atoms. **Earth's atmosphere is made up of nitrogen, oxygen, carbon dioxide, water vapor, and many other gases, as well as particles of liquids and solids.**

Nitrogen As you can see in Figure 2, nitrogen is the most abundant gas in the atmosphere. It makes up a little more than three fourths of the air we breathe. Each nitrogen molecule consists of two nitrogen atoms.

Other Gases	Percentage by Volume
Argon	0.93
Carbon dioxide	0.036
Neon	0.0018
Helium	0.00052
Methane	0.00015
Krypton	0.00011
Hydrogen	0.00005

Figure 2 Dry air in the lower atmosphere always has the same composition of gases.
Interpreting Data What two gases make up most of the air?

Breathe In, Breathe Out ACTIVITY

How can you detect carbon dioxide in the air you exhale?

1. Put on your goggles.
2. Fill a glass or beaker halfway with limewater.

3. Using a straw, slowly blow air through the limewater for about a minute. **CAUTION:** *Do not suck on the straw or drink the limewater.*
4. What happens to the limewater?

Developing Hypotheses What do you think would happen if you did the same experiment after jogging for 10 minutes? If you tried this, what might the results tell you about exercise and carbon dioxide?

Nitrogen is essential to living things. Proteins and other complex chemical substances in living things contain nitrogen. You and all other organisms must have nitrogen in order to grow and to repair body cells.

Most living things cannot obtain nitrogen directly from the air. Instead, some bacteria convert nitrogen into substances called nitrates. Plants then absorb the nitrates from the soil and use them to make proteins. To obtain proteins, animals must eat plants or other animals.

Oxygen Most oxygen molecules have two oxygen atoms. Even though oxygen is the second-most abundant gas in the atmosphere, it makes up less than one fourth of the volume. Plants and animals take oxygen directly from the air and use it to release energy from food in a usable form.

Oxygen is also involved in other important processes. Any fuel you can think of, from the gasoline in a car to the candles on a birthday cake, uses oxygen as it burns. Without oxygen, a fire will go out. Burning uses oxygen rapidly. During other processes, oxygen is used slowly. For example, steel in cars and other objects reacts slowly with oxygen to form iron oxide, or rust.

Have you ever noticed a pungent smell in the air after a thunderstorm? This is the odor of ozone, which forms when lightning interacts with oxygen in the air. **Ozone** is a form of oxygen that has three oxygen atoms in each molecule instead of the usual two.

Carbon Dioxide Each molecule of carbon dioxide has one atom of carbon and two atoms of oxygen. Even though the atmosphere contains only a small amount of carbon dioxide, it is essential to life. Plants must have carbon dioxide to produce food. Animals, on the other hand, give off carbon dioxide as a waste product.

When fuels such as coal and gasoline are burned, they release carbon dioxide. Burning these fuels increases the amount of carbon dioxide in the atmosphere. Rising carbon dioxide levels may be raising Earth's temperature.

Figure 3 To burn, these candles need oxygen, one of the gases in the atmosphere. *Predicting What would happen if the candles used up all of the oxygen around them?*

Other Gases Oxygen and nitrogen together make up 99 percent of dry air. Carbon dioxide and argon make up most of the other one percent. The remaining gases are called trace gases because only small amounts of them are present.

Water Vapor The composition of the air discussed so far has been for dry air. In reality, air is not dry because it contains water vapor. **Water vapor** is water in the form of a gas. Water vapor is invisible—it is not the same thing as steam, which is made up of tiny droplets of liquid water. Each water molecule contains two atoms of hydrogen and one atom of oxygen.

The amount of water vapor in the air varies greatly from place to place and from time to time. Air above a desert or polar ice sheet may contain almost no water vapor. In tropical rain forests, on the other hand, as much as five percent of the air may be water vapor.

Water vapor plays an important role in Earth's weather. Clouds form when water vapor condenses out of the air to form tiny droplets of liquid water or crystals of ice. If these droplets or crystals become large enough, they can fall as rain or snow.

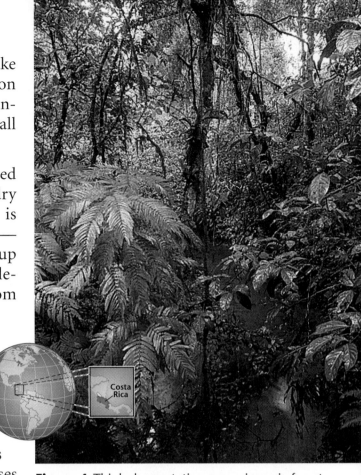

Figure 4 This lush vegetation grows in a rain forest in Costa Rica. The percentage of water vapor in the air in a rain forest may be as high as five percent.

Particles Pure air contains only gases. But pure air exists only in laboratories. In the real world, air also contains tiny solid and liquid particles of dust, smoke, salt, and other chemicals. Sometimes you can see particles in the air around you, but most of them are too small to see.

Section 1 Review

1. Describe two ways in which the atmosphere is important to life on Earth.
2. What are the four most common gases in dry air?
3. Why are the amounts of gases in the atmosphere usually shown as percentages of dry air?
4. **Thinking Critically Applying Concepts** How would the amount of carbon dioxide in the atmosphere change if there were no plants? If there were no animals?

Check Your Progress

CHAPTER PROJECT

Have you determined *how*, *where*, and *when*, you will make your observations? Organize a notebook to record them. Think of ways to compare weather conditions from day to day. Make your observations without weather instruments or TV weather reports. (*Hint:* You can estimate how much of the sky is covered by clouds.) For your own safety, do not try to make observations during storms.

How Clean Is the Air?

S ometimes you can actually see the atmosphere! How? Since air is normally transparent, it can only be visible because it contains particles. In this activity, you will use a vacuum cleaner to gather particles from the air.

Problem

How do weather factors affect the number of particles in the air?

Skills Focus

measuring, interpreting data

Materials

coffee filters   low-power microscope
rubber band   vacuum cleaner with
thermometer   intake hose (1 per class)
computer (optional)

Procedure

1. Predict what factors will affect the number of particles you collect. How might different weather factors affect your results?
2. In your notebook or on the computer, make a data table like the one below.

3. Place the coffee filter over the nozzle of the vacuum cleaner hose. Fasten the coffee filter securely to the hose with a rubber band. Draw a circle over the filter to show the area over the vacuum nozzle.
4. You will take air samples in the same place each day for five days. If possible, find a place outdoors. Otherwise, you can run the vacuum cleaner out a classroom window. **CAUTION:** *Do not use the vacuum cleaner outdoors on wet or rainy days.* If it is wet or rainy, collect the sample as soon as possible after it stops raining.
5. Hold the vacuum nozzle at least one meter above the ground each time you use the vacuum. Turn on the vacuum. Run the vacuum for 30 minutes.

DATA TABLE					
Date and Time	Temperature	Amount of Precipitation	Wind Direction	Wind Speed	Number of Particles

6. While the vacuum is running, observe the weather conditions. Measure the temperature. Estimate the amount of precipitation, if any, since the previous observation. Note the direction from which the wind, if any, is blowing. Also note whether the wind is heavy, light, or calm. Record your observations.

7. After 30 minutes, turn off the vacuum. Remove the coffee filter from the nozzle. Label the filter with the place, time, and date.

8. Place the coffee filter on the stage of a microscope (40 power). Be sure that the part of the filter that was over the vacuum nozzle is directly under the microscope lens. Without moving the coffee filter, count all the particles you see. Record the number in your data table.

9. Repeat Steps 3–8 each clear day.

Analyze and Conclude

1. Was there a day of the week when you collected more particles?

2. What factors changed during the week that could have caused changes in the particle count?

3. Did the weather have any effect on your day-to-day results? If so, which weather factor do you think was most important?

4. Make a list of some possible sources of the particles you collected. Are these sources natural, or did the particles come from manufactured products?

5. How could you improve your method to get more particles out of the air?

6. **Apply** Identify areas in or around your school where there may be high levels of dust and other particles. What can people do to protect themselves in these areas?

Design an Experiment

Do you think time of day will affect the number of particles you collect? Develop a hypothesis and a plan for testing it. Could you work with other classes to get data at different times of the day? Before carrying out your plan, get your teacher's approval.

2 Air Quality

DISCOVER

What's On the Jar?

1. Put on your goggles.
2. Put a small piece of modeling clay on a piece of aluminum foil. Push a candle into the clay. Light the candle.
3. Wearing an oven mitt, hold a glass jar by the rim so that the bottom of the jar is just above the flame.

Think It Over

Observing What do you see on the jar? Where did it come from?

GUIDE FOR READING

◆ What are the main sources of air pollution?

◆ How do photochemical smog and acid rain form?

Reading Tip As you read, look for evidence to support this statement: Most air pollution is caused by human activities. What facts support this statement? What facts do not support it?

Key Terms pollutant
• photochemical smog
• temperature inversion
• acid rain

One hundred years ago, the city of London, England, was dark and dirty. Factories burned coal, and most houses were heated by coal. The air was full of soot. In 1905, the term *smog* was created by combining the words *smoke* and *fog* to describe this type of air pollution. Today, people in London burn much less coal. As a result, the air in London now is much cleaner than it was 100 years ago.

Air Pollution

As you are reading this, you are breathing without even thinking about it. Breathing brings air into your lungs, where the oxygen you need is taken into your body. You may also breathe in tiny particles or even a small amount of harmful gases. In fact, these particles and gases are a concern to people everywhere.

If you live in a large city, you probably already know what air pollution is. You may have noticed a brown haze or an unpleasant smell in the air. Even if you live far from a city, the air around you may be polluted. Harmful substances in the air, water, or soil are known as **pollutants**. Figure 5 shows some of the effects of air pollution on human health.

Dizziness and headaches

Eye, nose, and throat irritation

Allergies

Cough

Lung diseases

Chest pains

Figure 5 Air pollution can cause many different problems. Some air pollutants are natural, but most are caused by human activities. *Interpreting Photographs* What parts of the body are most affected by air pollution?

Figure 6 These pollen grains from a ragweed flower have been greatly magnified to show detail. Pollen can cause people who are allergic to it to sneeze.

Some air pollution occurs naturally, but much of it is caused by human activities. **Most air pollution is the result of burning fossil fuels such as coal, oil, gasoline, and diesel fuel.** Almost half of the air pollution from human activities comes from cars and other motor vehicles. A little more than one fourth comes from factories and power plants that burn coal and oil. Burning fossil fuels produces a number of air pollutants, including particles and gases that can form smog and acid rain.

☑ *Checkpoint* *What are two sources of air pollution that you see every day?*

Particles

As you know, air contains particles along with gases. When you draw these particles deep into your lungs, the particles can be harmful. Particles in the air come from both natural sources and human activities.

Natural Sources Many natural processes add particles to the atmosphere. When ocean waves splash salt water against rocks, some of the water sprays into the air and evaporates. Tiny salt particles stay in the air. The wind blows particles of molds and plant pollen. Forest fires, soil erosion, and dust storms add particles to the atmosphere. Erupting volcanoes spew out clouds of dust and ashes along with poisonous gases.

INTEGRATING HEALTH Even fairly clean air usually contains particles of dust and pollen. Figure 6 shows pollen, a fine, powdery material produced by many plants. The wind carries pollen not only to other plants, but also to people. One type of allergy, popularly called "hay fever," is caused by pollen from plants such as ragweed. Symptoms of hay fever include sneezing, a runny nose, red and itchy eyes, and headaches. Weather reports often include a "pollen count," which is the average number of pollen grains in a cubic meter of air.

Human Activities When people burn fuels such as wood and coal, particles made mostly of carbon enter the air. These particles of soot are what gives smoke its dark color. Farming and construction also release large amounts of soil particles into the air.

Figure 7 These people in Pontianak, Indonesia, are being given dust masks to protect them from smoke caused by widespread forest fires. *Inferring What effects do you think this smoke might have had on the people who live in this area?*

Sharpen your Skills

Predicting ACTIVITY

Are the amounts of pollutants in the air always at the same level, or do they change from time to time? At what time of the day do you think the major sources of air pollution—cars, trucks, power plants, and factories— might produce the most pollution? Overall, do you think there is more air pollution in the morning or in the evening? On Mondays or on Fridays? On what did you base your prediction?

Smog

London-type smog forms when particles in coal smoke combine with water droplets in humid air. Fortunately, London-type smog is no longer common in the United States. Today sunny cities like Los Angeles often have another type of smog. The brown haze that forms in cities is called **photochemical smog**. The *photo-* in photochemical means "light." Photochemical smog is caused by the action of sunlight on chemicals.

INTEGRATING CHEMISTRY Photochemical smog is formed by a complex process. All fossil fuels contain hydrocarbons, which are substances composed of carbon and hydrogen. When fossil fuels are burned, some hydrocarbons are not burned completely and escape into the air. At the same time, the high temperatures that accompany burning cause some of the nitrogen in the air to react with oxygen to form nitrogen oxides. **The nitrogen oxides, hydrocarbons, and other air pollutants then react with one another in the presence of sunlight to form a mix of ozone and other chemicals called photochemical smog.** The ozone in photochemical smog irritates breathing passages, harms plants, and damages rubber, paint, and some plastics.

Temperature Inversion

Normally, air close to the ground is heated by Earth's surface. As the air warms, it rises into the cooler air above it. Pollutants are carried higher into the atmosphere where they blow away. But certain weather conditions cause a condition known as a temperature inversion. During a **temperature inversion,** a layer of warm air prevents the rising air from escaping. The polluted air is trapped and held close to Earth's surface. The smog becomes more concentrated and dangerous.

✓ *Checkpoint* *What happens during a temperature inversion?*

Figure 8 Normally, pollutants rise high in the air and blow away (left). But during a temperature inversion, a layer of warm air traps pollutants close to the ground (right).

Acid Rain

One result of air pollution is acid rain. The burning of coal that contains a lot of sulfur produces substances composed of oxygen and sulfur called sulfur oxides. **Acid rain forms when nitrogen oxides and sulfur oxides combine with water in the air to form nitric acid and sulfuric acid.**

Rain, sleet, snow, fog, and even dry particles carry these two acids from the air to trees, lakes, and buildings. Rain is naturally slightly acidic, but rain that contains more acid than normal is known as **acid rain.** Acid rain is sometimes strong enough to damage the surfaces of buildings and statues.

As Figure 9 shows, needle-leafed trees such as pines and spruce are especially sensitive to acid rain. It also harms lakes and ponds. Acid rain can make water so acidic that plants, amphibians, fish, and insects can no longer survive in it.

Improving Air Quality

The federal and state governments have passed a number of laws and regulations to reduce air pollution. For example, pollution-control devices are required equipment on cars. Factories and power plants must install filters in smokestacks to remove pollutants from smoke before they are released into the atmosphere.

Air quality in this country has improved over the past 30 years. The amounts of most major air pollutants have decreased. Newer cars cause less pollution than older models. Recently built power plants are less polluting than older power plants.

However, there are now more cars on the road and more power plants burning fossil fuels than in the past. Unfortunately, the air in many cities is still polluted. Many people think that stricter regulations are needed to control air pollution. Others argue that reducing air pollution is expensive.

Figure 9 This scientist is studying trees damaged by acid rain. Acid rain may make tree needles turn brown or fall off.

Section 2 Review

1. How is most air pollution produced?
2. Name two natural and two artificial sources of particles in the atmosphere.
3. How is photochemical smog formed? What kinds of harm does it cause?
4. What substances combine to form acid rain?
5. **Thinking Critically Inferring** Do you think that photochemical smog levels are higher during the winter or during the summer? Explain.

Science at Home

Air Particles It's easy to see particles in the air. Gather your family members in a dark room. Open a window shade or blind slightly, or turn on a flashlight. Can they see tiny particles suspended in the beam of light? Discuss with your family where the particles came from. What might be some natural sources? What might be some human sources?

SCIENCE AND SOCIETY

Cars and Clean Air

New technology and strict laws have brought cleaner air to many American cities. But in some places the air is still polluted. Cars and trucks still cause about half the air pollution in cities. And there are more cars on the road every year!

Worldwide, there are about 500 million cars. More cars will mean more pollution and more traffic jams. Unfortunately, cars stuck in traffic produce three times as much pollution as cars on the open road. What can people do to reduce air pollution by cars?

The Issues

Can Cars Be Made To Pollute Less?
In the past 20 years, cars have become more fuel-efficient and pollution levels have been lowered. Now engineers are running out of ways to make cars run more efficiently and produce less pollution. But technology does offer other answers.

Some vehicles use fuels other than gasoline. For instance, natural gas can power cars and trucks. Burning natural gas produces less pollution than burning gasoline.

Battery-powered electric cars produce no air pollution. However, the electricity to charge the batteries often comes from power plants that burn oil or coal. So electric cars still produce some pollution indirectly. Car makers have produced a few electric cars, but they are expensive and can make only fairly short trips.

Should People Drive Less? Many car trips are shorter than a mile—an easy distance for most people to walk. For longer trips, people might consider riding a bicycle. Many cars on the road carry just one person. Some people might consider riding with others in car pools or taking buses or subways.

Are Stricter Standards or Taxes the Answer? Some state governments have led efforts to reduce pollution. The state of California, for example, has strict anti-pollution laws. These laws set standards for gradually reducing pollutants released by cars. Stricter laws might make some old cars illegal.

Another approach is to make driving more expensive so that people use their cars less. That might mean higher gasoline taxes or fees for using the roads at busy times.

You Decide

1. **Identify the Problem**
   In your own words, explain why automobiles make it hard to improve air quality. What kinds of pollution are caused by automobiles?

2. **Analyze the Options**
   What are some ways to reduce the pollution caused by cars? Should these actions be voluntary, or should governments require them?

3. **Find a Solution**
   How would you encourage people to try to reduce the pollution from cars? Create a visual essay from newspaper and magazine clippings. Write captions to explain your solution.

3 Air Pressure

Does Air Have Mass?

1. Use a balance to find the mass of a deflated balloon.

2. Blow up the balloon and tie the neck closed. Do you think the mass of the inflated balloon will differ from the mass of the deflated balloon?

3. Find the mass of the inflated balloon. Compare this mass to the mass of the deflated balloon. Was your prediction correct?

Think It Over

Drawing Conclusions Did the mass of the balloon change after it was inflated? What can you conclude about whether air has mass?

One of the best parts of eating roasted peanuts is opening the jar. When a jar of peanuts is "vacuum packed," most of the air is pumped out, creating low pressure inside. When you break the seal, the "whoosh" you hear is air from the outside rushing into the jar. The "whoosh" is the result of a difference in pressure between the outside of the jar and the inside.

Properties of Air

It may seem to you that air has no mass. However, air consists of atoms and molecules, which have mass. So air must have mass. **Because air has mass, it also has other properties, including density and pressure.**

Density The amount of mass in a given volume of air is its **density**. You can calculate density by dividing mass by volume.

$$Density = \frac{Mass}{Volume}$$

If there are more molecules in a given volume of air, the density is higher. If there are fewer molecules, the density is lower.

Pressure The force pushing on an area or surface is known as **pressure**. A denser substance has more mass per unit volume than a less dense one. So denser air exerts more pressure than less dense air.

To understand pressure, think of carrying a heavy backpack. The weight presses the straps into your shoulders just as the pack does to the hiker in the photo.

445

When you take off a backpack, it feels as if all the pressure has been taken off your shoulders. But has it? The weight of the column of air above you remains, as shown in Figure 10.

Air pressure is the result of the weight of a column of air pushing down on an area. The weight of the column of air above your desk is about the same as the weight of a large school bus!

So why doesn't air pressure crush your desk? The reason is that the molecules in air push in all directions—down, up, and sideways. So the air pushing down on the top of your desk is balanced by the air pushing up on the bottom of the desk.

Measuring Air Pressure

Have you ever heard a weather report say that the air pressure is falling? Falling air pressure usually indicates that a storm is approaching. Rising air pressure usually means that the weather is clearing. A **barometer** (buh RAHM uh tur) is an instrument that is used to measure changes in air pressure. **There are two kinds of barometers: mercury barometers and aneroid barometers.**

Mercury Barometers The first barometers invented were mercury barometers. Figure 11 shows how a mercury barometer works. A **mercury barometer** consists of a glass tube open at the bottom end and partially filled with mercury. The space in the tube above the mercury is almost a vacuum—it contains no air. The open end of the tube rests in a dish of mercury. The air pressure pushing down on the surface of the mercury in the dish is equal to the

Figure 10 There is a column of air above you all the time. The weight of the air in the atmosphere causes air pressure.

Mercury

Air pressure   Air pressure

Mercury

Air pressure   Air pressure

Figure 11 Air pressure pushes down on the surface of the mercury in the dish, causing the mercury in the tube to rise. *Predicting What happens when the air pressure increases?*

446

Dial

Needle

Chain

Spring

Levers

Metal disc

Airtight
metal chamber

Figure 12 Changes in air pressure cause the walls of the airtight metal chamber to flex in and out. The needle on the dial indicates the air pressure.

weight of the column of mercury in the tube. At sea level the mercury column is about 76 centimeters high, on average.

When the air pressure increases, it presses down more on the surface of the mercury. Greater air pressure forces the column of mercury higher. What will happen to the column of mercury if the air pressure decreases? The column will fall.

Aneroid Barometers If you have a barometer on a desk or wall at home, it is probably an aneroid barometer. The word *aneroid* means "without liquid." An **aneroid barometer** (AN uh royd) has an airtight metal chamber, as shown in Figure 12. The metal chamber is sensitive to changes in air pressure. When air pressure increases, the thin walls of the chamber are pushed in. When the pressure drops, the walls bulge out. The chamber is connected to a dial by a series of springs and levers. As the shape of the chamber changes, the needle on the dial moves.

Aneroid barometers are smaller than mercury barometers and don't contain a liquid. Therefore, they are portable and often more practical for uses such as airplane instrument panels.

Units of Air Pressure Weather reports use several different units for air pressure. Most weather reports for the general public use inches of mercury. For example, if the column of mercury in a mercury barometer is 30 inches high, the air pressure is "30 inches of mercury" or just "30 inches."

National Weather Service maps indicate air pressure in millibars. One inch of mercury equals approximately 33.87 millibars, so 30 inches of mercury equals approximately 1,016 millibars.

☑ *Checkpoint* *Name two common units used to measure air pressure.*

Soda-Bottle Barometer

Here's how to build a device that shows changes in air pressure.

1. Fill a 2-liter soda bottle one-half full with water.

2. Lower a long straw into the bottle so that the end of the straw is in the water. Seal the mouth of the bottle around the straw with modeling clay.

3. Squeeze the sides of the bottle. What happens to the level of the water in the straw?

4. Let go of the sides of the bottle. Watch the level of the water in the straw.

Inferring Explain your results in terms of air pressure.

Increasing Altitude

The air pressure at the top of Alaska's Mount McKinley—more than 6 kilometers above sea level—is less than half the air pressure at sea level. **Altitude,** or elevation, is the distance above sea level, the average level of the surface of the oceans. **Air pressure decreases as altitude increases. As air pressure decreases, so does density.**

Altitude Affects Air Pressure Imagine a stack of ten books. Which book has more weight on it, the second book from the top or the book at the bottom? The second book from the top has only the weight of one book on top of it. The book at the bottom

Measuring

Working Under PRESSURE

Air pressure changes are related to changing weather conditions. In this lab, you will build and use your own barometer to measure air pressure.

Problem

How can a barometer detect changes in air pressure?

Materials

modeling clay   scissors
white glue   tape
pencil   wide-mouthed glass jar
metric ruler   rubber band
large rubber balloon
drinking straw, 12–15 cm long
cardboard strip, 10 cm x 25 cm

Procedure

1. Cut off the narrow opening of the balloon.
2. Fold the edges of the balloon outward. Carefully stretch the balloon over the open end of the glass jar. Use a rubber band to hold the balloon on the rim of the glass jar.

Glue   *Balloon*   *Straw*

High Pressure
5
4
3
2
1
0
Low Pressure

Rubber band

Tape

3. Place a small amount of glue on the center of the balloon top. Attach one end of the straw to the glue. Allow the other end to extend several centimeters beyond the edge of the glass jar. This is your pointer.

of the stack has the weight of all the other books pressing on it.

Air at sea level is like the bottom book. Recall that air pressure is the weight of the column of air pushing down on an area. Sea-level air has the weight of the whole atmosphere pressing on it. So air pressure is greatest at sea level. Air near the top of the atmosphere is like the second book from the top. There, the air has less weight pressing on it, and thus has lower air pressure.

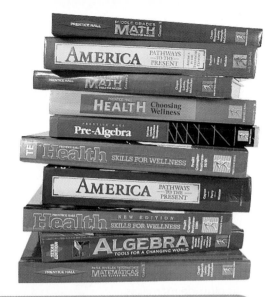

DATA TABLE

Date and Time	Air Pressure	Weather Conditions

4. While the glue dries, fold the cardboard strip lengthwise and draw a scale along the edge with marks 0.5 cm apart. Write "High pressure" at the top of your scale and "Low pressure" at the bottom.

5. After the glue dries, add a pea-sized piece of modeling clay to the end of the pointer. Place your barometer and its scale in a location that is as free from temperature changes as possible. Arrange the scale and the barometer as shown in the diagram. Note that the pointer of the straw must just reach the cardboard strip.

6. Tape both the scale and the barometer to a surface so they do not move during your experiment.

7. In your notebook, make a data table like the one at the left. Record the date and time. Note the level of the straw on the cardboard strip.

8. Check the barometer twice a day. Record your observations in your data table.

9. Record the weather conditions for each day.

Analyze and Conclude

1. What change in atmospheric conditions must occur to cause the free end of the straw to rise? What change must occur for it to fall?

2. According to your observations, what kind of weather is usually associated with high air pressure? With low air pressure?

3. If the balloon had a tiny hole in it, what would happen to the accuracy of your barometer?

4. **Think About It** What effect, if any, would a great temperature change have on the accuracy of your barometer?

More to Explore

Compare changes in air pressure shown by your barometer with high and low air pressure readings shown on newspaper weather maps during the same time period. How do your readings compare with the readings in the newspapers?

Figure 13 The density of air decreases as altitude increases. Air at sea level has more gas molecules in each cubic meter than air at the top of a mountain.

Air Pressure (inches of mercury)

2.2	18
5.7	12
9.1	9
14	6
21	3
30	0

Altitude (km)

Density at 8 kilometers

Density at sea level

Altitude Also Affects Density If you were near the top of Mount McKinley and tried to run, you would get out of breath quickly. Why would you have difficulty breathing at high altitudes?

INTEGRATING LIFE SCIENCE

As you go up through the atmosphere, the air pressure decreases. As air pressure decreases, the density of the air decreases. So density decreases as altitude increases, as shown in Figure 13.

Whether air is at sea level or at 6 kilometers above sea level, the air still contains 21 percent oxygen. However, since the air is less dense at a high altitude, there are fewer oxygen molecules to breathe in each cubic meter of air than there are at sea level. You are taking in less oxygen with each breath. That is why you get out of breath quickly.

Section 3 Review

1. What properties does air have? Why does it have these properties?
2. Describe how a mercury barometer measures air pressure.
3. Why is the air at the top of a mountain hard to breathe?
4. **Thinking Critically** **Predicting** What changes in air pressure would you expect to see if you carried a barometer down a mine shaft? Explain.

Science at Home

Under Pressure Here's how you can show your family that air has pressure. Fill a glass to the brim with water. Place a piece of heavy cardboard over the top of the glass. Hold the cardboard in place with one hand as you turn the glass upside down. **CAUTION:** *Be sure the cardboard does not bend.* Now remove your hand from the cardboard. What happens? Explain to your family that the cardboard doesn't fall because the air pressure pushing up on it is greater than the weight of the water pushing down.

SECTION 4 Layers of the Atmosphere

DISCOVER • ACTIVITY • • • •

Is Air There?

1. Use a heavy rubber band to tightly secure a plastic bag over the top of a wide-mouthed jar.

2. Gently try to push the bag into the jar. What happens? Is the air pressure higher inside or outside of the bag?

3. Remove the rubber band and line the inside of the jar with the plastic bag. Use the rubber band to tightly secure the edges of the bag over the rim of the jar.

4. Gently try to pull the bag out of the jar with your fingertips. What happens? Is the air pressure higher inside or outside of the bag?

Think It Over

Predicting Explain your observations in terms of air pressure. How do you think differences in air pressure would affect a weather balloon as it traveled up through the atmosphere?

Imagine taking a trip upward into the atmosphere in a hot-air balloon. You begin on a warm beach near the ocean, at an altitude of 0 kilometers.

You hear a roar as the balloon's pilot turns up the burner to heat the air in the balloon. The balloon begins to rise, and Earth's surface gets farther and farther away. As the balloon rises to an altitude of 3 kilometers, you realize that the air is getting colder. As you continue to rise, the air gets colder and colder. At 6 kilometers you begin to have trouble breathing. The air is becoming less dense. It's time to go back down.

What if you could have continued your balloon ride up through the atmosphere? As you rose farther up through the atmosphere, the air pressure and temperature would change dramatically. **The four main layers of the atmosphere are the troposphere, the stratosphere, the mesosphere, and the thermosphere. They are classified according to changes in temperature.**

The Troposphere

You live in the inner, or lowest, layer of Earth's atmosphere, the **troposphere** (TROH puh sfeer). *Tropo-* means "turning" or "changing"; conditions in the troposphere are more variable than in the other layers. The troposphere is where Earth's weather occurs.

GUIDE FOR READING

◆ What are the main layers of the atmosphere and how are they classified?

Reading Tip Before you read, preview *Exploring Layers of the Atmosphere*. Make a list of unfamiliar words. Look for the meanings of these words as you read.

Key Terms troposphere
• stratosphere • mesosphere
• thermosphere • ionosphere
• aurora borealis • exosphere

Figure 14 This weather balloon will carry a package of instruments to measure weather conditions high in the atmosphere.
Applying Concepts Which is the first layer of the atmosphere the balloon passes through on its way up?

Although hot-air balloons cannot travel very high into the troposphere, other types of balloons can. To measure weather conditions, scientists launch weather balloons that carry instruments up into the atmosphere. The balloons are not fully inflated before they are launched. Recall that air pressure decreases as you rise through the atmosphere. Leaving the balloon only partly inflated gives the gas inside the balloon room to expand as the air pressure outside the balloon decreases.

The depth of the troposphere varies from more than 16 kilometers above the equator to less than 9 kilometers above the North and South Poles. Even though it is the shallowest layer of the atmosphere, the troposphere contains almost all of the mass of the atmosphere.

As altitude increases in the troposphere, the temperature decreases. On average, for every 1-kilometer increase in altitude the air gets about 6.5 Celsius degrees cooler. At the top of the troposphere, the temperature stops decreasing and stays constant at about −60°C. Water here forms thin, feathery clouds of ice.

☑ *Checkpoint* Why are clouds at the top of the troposphere made of ice crystals instead of drops of water?

The Stratosphere

The **stratosphere** extends from the top of the troposphere to about 50 kilometers above Earth's surface. *Strato-* is similar to *stratum,* which means "layer" or "spreading out."

The lower stratosphere is cold, about −60°C. You might be surprised to learn that the upper stratosphere is warmer than the lower stratosphere. The upper stratosphere contains a layer of ozone, the three-atom form of oxygen. When the ozone absorbs energy from the sun, the energy is converted into heat, warming the air.

As a weather balloon rises through the stratosphere, the air pressure outside the balloon continues to decrease. The volume of the balloon increases. Finally, the balloon bursts, and the instrument package falls back to Earth's surface.

The Mesosphere

Above the stratosphere, a drop in temperature marks the beginning of the next layer, the **mesosphere.** *Meso-* means "middle," so the mesosphere is the middle layer of the atmosphere. The mesosphere begins 50 kilometers above Earth's surface and ends at 80 kilometers. The outer mesosphere is the coldest part of the atmosphere, with temperatures near −90°C.

EXPLORING *Layers of the Atmosphere*

The atmosphere is divided into four layers: the troposphere, the stratosphere, the mesosphere, and the thermosphere. The thermosphere is further divided into the ionosphere and the exosphere.

Exosphere
above 550 km

Phone calls and television pictures often reach you by way of communications satellites that orbit Earth in the exosphere.

Ionosphere
80 to 550 km

Ions in the ionosphere reflect radio waves back to Earth. The aurora borealis occurs in the ionosphere.

Thermosphere above 80 km

The thermosphere extends from 80 km above Earth's surface outward into space. It has no definite outer limit.

Mesosphere 50 to 80 km

Most meteoroids burn up in the mesosphere, producing meteor trails.

Stratosphere
12 to 50 km

The ozone layer in the stratosphere absorbs ultraviolet radiation.

Troposphere 0 to 12 km

Rain, snow, storms, and most clouds occur in the troposphere.

550 km

500 km

400 km

300 km

200 km

100 km

80 km

50 km

12 km

INTEGRATING SPACE SCIENCE If you watch a shooting star streak across the night sky, you are seeing a meteoroid burn up as it enters the mesosphere. The mesosphere protects Earth's surface from being hit by most meteoroids, which are chunks of stone and metal from space. What you see as a shooting star, or meteor, is the trail of hot, glowing gases the burning meteoroid leaves behind.

☑ *Checkpoint* *What is the depth of the mesosphere?*

The Thermosphere

Near the top of the atmosphere, the air is very thin. The air 80 kilometers above Earth's surface is only about 0.001 percent as dense as the air at sea level. It's as though you took a cubic

SCIENCE & History

Explorers of the Atmosphere

The atmosphere has been explored from the ground and from space.

1746

Franklin's Experiment with Electricity

American statesman and inventor Benjamin Franklin and some friends in Philadelphia experimented with electricity in the atmosphere. To demonstrate that lightning is a form of electricity, Franklin flew a kite in a thunderstorm. However, Franklin did not hold the kite string in his hand, as this historical print shows.

1600	1700	1800

1643

Torricelli Invents the Barometer

Italian physicist and mathematician Evangelista Torricelli improved existing scientific instruments and invented some new ones. In 1643 he invented the barometer, using a column of mercury 1.2 meters high.

1804

Gay-Lussac Studies the Upper Troposphere

French chemist Joseph-Louis Gay-Lussac ascended to a height of about 7 kilometers in a hydrogen balloon to study the upper troposphere. Gay-Lussac studied pressure, temperature, and humidity.

meter of air at sea level and expanded it into 100,000 cubic meters at the top of the mesosphere. The outermost layer of the atmosphere, the **thermosphere,** extends from 80 kilometers above Earth's surface outward into space. It has no definite outer limit. The atmosphere does not end suddenly at the outer edge of the thermosphere. Gas atoms and molecules there are so far apart that the air blends gradually with outer space.

The *thermo-* in thermosphere means "heat." Even though the air in the thermosphere is thin, it is very hot, up to 1,800°C. The temperature in the thermosphere is actually higher than the temperature in a furnace used to make steel! But why is the thermosphere so hot? Energy coming from the sun strikes the thermosphere first. Nitrogen and oxygen molecules convert energy from the sun into heat.

In Your Journal

Imagine you were one of the first people to go up into the atmosphere in a balloon. What would you need to take? Find out what the early explorers took with them in their balloons. Write at least two paragraphs about what you would take, and why.

1931
Piccard Explores the Stratosphere

Swiss-Belgian physicist Auguste Piccard made the first ascent into the stratosphere. He reached a height of about 16 kilometers in an airtight cabin attached to a huge hydrogen balloon. Piccard is shown here with the cabin.

1900   **2000**

1960
First Weather Satellite Launched

TIROS-1, the first weather satellite equipped with a camera to send data back to Earth, was put into orbit by the United States. As later weather satellites circled Earth, they observed cloud cover and recorded temperatures and air pressures in the atmosphere.

1994
Space Shuttle Investigates the Atmosphere

The NASA space shuttle *Atlantis* traveled to a height of 300 kilometers in the thermosphere. *Atlantis* carried the ATLAS–3 research program, which observed the sun's influence on the atmosphere.

Figure 15 The aurora borealis, seen from Fairbanks, Alaska, creates a spectacular display in the night sky.

Despite the high temperature, however, you would not feel warm in the thermosphere. An ordinary thermometer would show a temperature well below 0°C. Why is that? Temperature is the average amount of energy of motion of each molecule of a substance. The gas molecules in the thermosphere move very rapidly, so the temperature is very high. However, the molecules are spaced far apart in the thin air. And there are not enough of them to collide with a thermometer and warm it very much. So an ordinary thermometer would not detect the molecules' energy.

The Ionosphere The thermosphere is divided into two layers. The lower layer of the thermosphere, called the **ionosphere** (eye AHN uh sfeer), begins 80 kilometers above the surface and ends at 550 kilometers. Energy from the sun causes gas molecules in the ionosphere to become electrically charged particles called ions. Radio waves bounce off ions in the ionosphere and then bounce back to Earth's surface.

The brilliant light displays of the **aurora borealis**—the Northern Lights—also occur in the ionosphere. The aurora borealis is caused by particles from the sun that enter the ionosphere near the North Pole. These particles strike oxygen and nitrogen atoms in the ionosphere, causing them to glow.

The Exosphere *Exo-* means "outer," so the **exosphere** is the

INTEGRATING TECHNOLOGY

outer layer of the thermosphere. The exosphere extends from 550 kilometers outward for thousands of kilometers. When you make a long-distance phone call or watch television, the signal may have traveled up to a satellite orbiting in the exosphere and then back down to your home. Satellites are also used for watching the world's weather and carrying telescopes that look deep into space.

Section 4 Review

1. What property is used to classify the layers of the atmosphere?
2. Describe one characteristic of each of the four main layers of the atmosphere.
3. What is the aurora borealis? In which layer of the atmosphere does it occur?
4. **Thinking Critically** Drawing Conclusions Why is the mesosphere the coldest part of the atmosphere?

Check Your Progress CHAPTER PROJECT
At this point, review your weather log. What do you notice about the weather on one day that might allow you to predict the next day's weather? What weather conditions changed the most from day to day? Continue to record your observations and start thinking about how you will present them.

SECTION 1 · The Air Around You

Key Ideas

◆ Earth's atmosphere makes conditions on Earth suitable for living things.
◆ Earth's atmosphere is made up of molecules of nitrogen, oxygen, carbon dioxide, and water vapor, as well as some other gases and particles of liquids and solids.

Key Terms

weather   ozone
atmosphere   water vapor

SECTION 2 · Heat Transfer

INTEGRATING ENVIRONMENTAL SCIENCE

Key Ideas

◆ Most air pollution results from the burning of fossil fuels such as coal and oil.
◆ Nitrogen oxides, hydrocarbons, and other air pollutants react with one another in the presence of sunlight to form a mix of ozone and other chemicals called photochemical smog.
◆ Acid rain forms when nitrogen oxides and sulfur oxides combine with water in the air to form nitric acid and sulfuric acid.

Key Terms

pollutant   temperature inversion
photochemical smog   acid rain

SECTION 3 · Air Pressure

Key Ideas

◆ Properties of air include mass, density, and pressure.
◆ Air pressure is the result of the weight of a column of air pushing down on an area.
◆ Air pressure is measured with mercury barometers and aneroid barometers.
◆ Air pressure decreases as altitude increases. As air pressure decreases, so does density.

Key Terms

density   barometer   altitude
pressure   mercury barometer
air pressure aneroid barometer

SECTION 4 · Layers of the Atmosphere

Key Ideas

◆ The four main layers of the atmosphere are classified according to changes in temperature. These layers are the troposphere, the stratosphere, the mesosphere, and the thermosphere.
◆ Rain, snow, storms, and most clouds occur in the troposphere.
◆ Ozone in the stratosphere absorbs energy from the sun.
◆ Most meteoroids burn up in the mesosphere, producing meteor trails.
◆ The aurora borealis occurs in the ionosphere.
◆ Communications satellites orbit Earth in the exosphere.

Key Terms

troposphere   thermosphere   aurora borealis
stratosphere   ionosphere   exosphere
mesosphere

Organizing Information

Concept Map Copy the air pressure concept map onto a separate sheet of paper. Then complete it and add a title. (For more on concept maps, see the Skills Handbook.)

Reviewing Content

 Review key concepts online using iText at www.phschool.com

Multiple Choice

Choose the letter of the answer that best completes each statement.

1. The most abundant gas in the atmosphere is
   a. ozone.   b. carbon dioxide.
   c. oxygen.   d. nitrogen.
2. Most air pollution is caused by
   a. dust and pollen.
   b. acid rain.
   c. erupting volcanoes.
   d. the burning of fossil fuels.
3. A barometer is used to measure
   a. temperature.   b. smog.
   c. air pressure   d. density.
4. The layers of the atmosphere are classified according to changes in
   a. altitude.
   b. temperature.
   c. pressure.
   d. density.
5. The inner layer, or "weather layer," of the atmosphere is called the
   a. mesosphere.
   b. troposphere.
   c. thermosphere.
   d. stratosphere.

True or False

If the statement is true, write true. If it is false, change the underlined word or words to make the statement true.

6. Plants need <u>carbon dioxide</u> from the atmosphere to make food.
7. Burning fuels add <u>nitrogen</u> to the atmosphere.
8. When sulfur and nitrogen oxides mix with water in the air, they form <u>smog</u>.
9. If the mass of a fixed volume of air increases, it becomes <u>less</u> dense.
10. Air pressure <u>increases</u> as you climb from land at sea level to the top of a mountain.

Checking Concepts

11. Name two ways in which carbon dioxide is added to the atmosphere.
12. Explain why it is difficult to include water vapor in a graph that shows the percentages of various gases in the atmosphere.
13. What is the difference between photochemical smog and London-type smog?
14. Describe some of the problems caused by acid rain.
15. List the following layers of the atmosphere in order moving up from Earth's surface: thermosphere, stratosphere, troposphere, mesosphere.
16. Describe the temperature changes that occur as you move upward through the troposphere.
17. **Writing to Learn** You are a scientist who has a chance to join a research mission to explore the atmosphere. To win a place on this mission, write a persuasive letter telling which layer of the atmosphere you want to research and why you chose it.

Thinking Critically

18. **Predicting** Describe the changes in the atmosphere that you would experience while climbing a mountain four or more kilometers high. How might these changes affect you physically?
19. **Applying Concepts** Why can an aneroid barometer be used to measure elevation as well as air pressure?
20. **Relating Cause and Effect** How can burning high-sulfur coal in a power-generating plant harm a forest hundreds of kilometers away?
21. **Classifying** Which sources of air pollution occur naturally, and which are caused by humans?

Applying Skills

The table below shows the temperature at various altitudes above Omaha, Nebraska, on a day in January. Use the table to answer the questions that follow.

Altitude (kilometers)	0	1.6	3.2	4.8	6.4	7.2
Temperature (°C)	0	–4	–9	–21	–32	–40

22. Graphing Make a line graph of the data in the table. Put temperature on the horizontal axis and altitude on the vertical axis. Label your graph.

23. Interpreting Graphs At about what height above the ground was the temperature –15°C?

24. Interpreting Graphs What was the approximate temperature 2.4 kilometers over Omaha?

25. Calculating Suppose an airplane was about 6.8 kilometers above Omaha on this day. What was the approximate temperature at 6.8 kilometers? How much colder was the temperature at 6.8 kilometers above the ground than at ground level?

Performance ▼ CHAPTER PROJECT ▼ Assessment

Present Your Project For your class presentation, prepare a display of your weather observations. Include drawings, graphs, and tables that summarize the weather you observed. Practice presenting your project to your group. Do you need to make any improvements? If so, make them now.

Reflect and Record In your journal, write how you might improve your weather log. What weather conditions would you like to know more about? What factors could you have measured more accurately using instruments?

Test Preparation

Use these questions to prepare for standardized tests.

Study the graph. Then answer Questions 26–29.

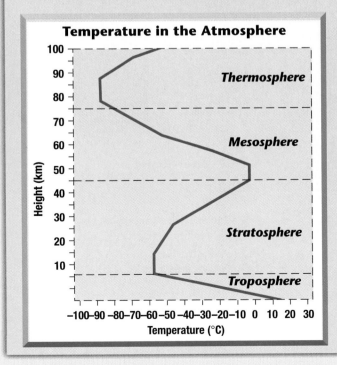

Temperature in the Atmosphere

26. Name the layer of the atmosphere that is closest to Earth's surface.
A thermosphere   B troposphere
C stratosphere   D mesosphere

27. Which layer of the atmosphere has the lowest temperature?
F thermosphere   G troposphere
H stratosphere   J mesosphere

28. The range of temperatures found in the stratosphere is about ____ Celsius degrees.
A 100   B 0
C 30   D 60

29. Which of the following best describes how temperature changes as altitude increases in the troposphere?
F steadily increases
G increases then decreases
H steadily decreases
J decreases then increases

CHAPTER
14 Weather Factors

WEB ACTIVITY www.phschool.com

Your Own Weather Station

Adrenching spring rain is just what the flowers need! As the weather gets warmer, the garden will bloom. Warm days, soft winds, and plenty of rain—all of these are weather factors that affect growing things. In this chapter, you will learn about a variety of weather factors, including air pressure, temperature, wind speed and direction, relative humidity, precipitation, and the amount and types of clouds.

Your Goal To measure and record weather conditions using instruments. You will look for patterns in your data that can be used to predict the next day's weather.

In completing your project, you will
◆ develop a plan for measuring weather factors
◆ record your data in a daily log
◆ display your data in a set of graphs
◆ use your data and graphs to try to predict the weather
◆ follow the safety guidelines in Appendix A

Get Started Begin by previewing the chapter to see what weather factors you want to measure. Discuss with a group of your classmates what instruments you might use. Brainstorm what observations you should make each day.

Check Your Progress You'll be working on the project as you study this chapter. To keep your project on track, look for Check Your Progress boxes at the following points.
Section 2 Review, page 471: Prepare to make observations.
Section 3 Review, page 480: Collect and record data.
Section 5 Review, page 490: Graph your data and look for patterns.

Present Your Project At the end of the chapter (page 493), present your weather observations and explain how well you predicted the weather.

Spring rains are an important factor in helping these tulips grow.

TEKS

In addition to process TEKS, this chapter addresses these concept TEKS as they relate to the chapter's topics.

(6.14) The student knows the structures and functions of Earth systems.
The student is expected to:
(C) describe components of the atmosphere, including oxygen, nitrogen, and water vapor, and identify the role of atmospheric movement in weather change.

SECTION 1 Energy in the Atmosphere

Does a Plastic Bag Trap Heat?

1. Record the initial temperatures on two thermometers. (You should get the same readings.)

2. Place one of the thermometers in a plastic bag. Put a small piece of paper in the bag so that it shades the bulb of the thermometer. Seal the bag.

3. Place both thermometers on a sunny window ledge or near a light bulb. Cover the bulb of the second thermometer with a small piece of paper. Predict what you think will happen.

4. Wait five minutes. Then record the temperatures on the two thermometers.

Think It Over

Measuring Were the two temperatures the same? How could you explain any difference?

GUIDE FOR READING

◆ In what form does energy from the sun travel to Earth?

◆ What happens to energy from the sun when it reaches Earth?

Reading Tip Before you read, skim the section for boldfaced words that are unfamiliar to you. As you read, find their meanings and write them down in your notebook.

Key Terms radiation
• electromagnetic waves
• infrared radiation
• ultraviolet radiation
• scattering • greenhouse effect

Think of a sunny summer day. When you get up in the morning, the sun is low in the sky and the air is cool. As the sun rises, the temperature increases. By noon it is quite hot. As you will see in this chapter, heat is a major factor in the weather. The movement of heat in the atmosphere causes temperatures to change, winds to blow, and rain to fall.

Energy from the Sun

 INTEGRATING PHYSICS Nearly all the energy in Earth's atmosphere comes from the sun. This energy travels to Earth as **electromagnetic waves,** a form of energy that can travel through space. Electromagnetic waves are classified according to wavelength, or distance between waves. The direct transfer of energy by electromagnetic waves is called **radiation.**

Most of the energy from the sun reaches Earth in the form of visible light and infrared radiation, and a small amount of ultraviolet radiation. Visible light is a mixture of all of the colors that you see in a rainbow: red, orange, yellow, green, blue, and violet. The different colors are the result of different wavelengths

Infrared · Red · Orange · Yellow · Green · Blue · Violet · Ultraviolet

Longer wavelengths   **Visible light**   **Shorter wavelengths**

of visible light. Red and orange light have the longest wavelengths, while blue and violet light have the shortest wavelengths.

Infrared radiation is a form of energy with wavelengths that are longer than red light. Infrared radiation is not visible, but can be felt as heat. Heat lamps used to keep food warm in restaurants give off both visible red light and invisible infrared radiation. The sun also gives off **ultraviolet radiation,** which has wavelengths that are shorter than violet light. Sunburns are caused by ultraviolet radiation. This radiation can also cause skin cancer and eye damage.

☑ *Checkpoint* *Which color of visible light has the longest wavelengths?*

Energy in the Atmosphere

Before the sun's rays can reach Earth's surface, they must pass through the atmosphere. The path of the sun's rays is shown in *Exploring Energy in the Atmosphere* on the following page.

Some of the energy from the sun is absorbed within the atmosphere. Water vapor and carbon dioxide absorb some infrared radiation. The ozone layer in the stratosphere absorbs most of the ultraviolet radiation. Clouds, dust, and other gases also absorb energy from the sun.

Some of the sun's rays are reflected. Clouds in the atmosphere act like mirrors, reflecting some solar energy back into space. In addition, dust particles and molecules of gases in the atmosphere reflect light from the sun in all directions.

Figure 1 Electromagnetic waves include infrared radiation, visible light, and ultraviolet radiation. *Interpreting Diagrams* *What type of radiation has wavelengths that are shorter than visible light? What type has wavelengths that are longer?*

Reflection of light in all directions is called **scattering.** When you look at the sky, the light you see has been scattered by gas molecules in the atmosphere. Gas molecules scatter short wavelengths of visible light (blue and violet) more than long wavelengths (red and orange). Scattered light is therefore bluer than ordinary sunlight, which is why the daytime sky looks blue.

When the sun is rising or setting, light from the sun passes through a greater thickness of the atmosphere than when the sun is higher in the sky. More light from the blue end of the spectrum is removed by scattering before it reaches your eyes. The remaining light from the sun contains mostly red and orange light. The sun looks red, and clouds around it become very colorful.

✓ *Checkpoint* *Why would particles from volcanic eruptions make sunsets and sunrises more red?*

EXPLORING *Energy in the Atmosphere*

Most of the energy that keeps Earth warm comes from the sun. Some of this energy is reflected or absorbed in the atmosphere. The rest of the energy reaches Earth's surface, where it is reflected or absorbed.

Solar energy is mostly visible light and infrared radiation, with a small amount of ultraviolet radiation.

Clouds, dust, and gases in the atmosphere reflect and scatter light.

Gases and particles in the atmosphere absorb solar energy.

Some energy that reaches the surface is reflected back into the atmosphere.

Earth's surface absorbs solar energy. This energy heats the land and water.

Some of the absorbed energy is then radiated back into the atmosphere.

Energy at Earth's Surface

Some of the sun's energy reaches Earth's surface and is reflected back into the atmosphere. Some of the energy, however, is absorbed by the land and water and changed into heat.

When Earth's surface is heated, it radiates some of the energy back into the atmosphere as infrared radiation. Most of this infrared radiation cannot travel all the way through the atmosphere back into space. Instead, much of it is absorbed by water vapor, carbon dioxide, methane, and other gases in the air. The energy from the absorbed radiation heats the gases in the air. These gases form a "blanket" around Earth that holds heat in the atmosphere. The process by which gases hold heat in the air is called the **greenhouse effect.**

Have you ever been inside a greenhouse during the winter? Even on a cold day, a greenhouse is warm. Greenhouses trap heat in two ways. First, infrared radiation given off in the interior cannot easily pass through glass and is trapped inside. Second, warm air inside the greenhouse cannot escape because the glass blocks the movement of air. What happens in Earth's atmosphere is similar to the first way that greenhouses trap heat.

The greenhouse effect is a natural process that keeps Earth's atmosphere at a temperature that is comfortable for most living things. Human activities over the last 200 years, however, have increased the amount of carbon dioxide in the atmosphere, which may be warming the atmosphere.

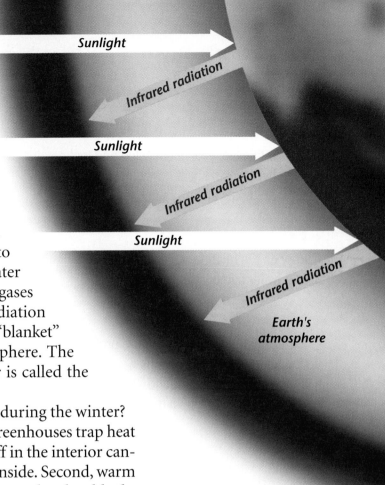

Sunlight

Infrared radiation

Sunlight

Infrared radiation

Sunlight

Infrared radiation

Earth's atmosphere

Figure 2 Sunlight travels through the atmosphere to Earth's surface. Earth's surface then gives off infrared radiation. Much of this energy is held by the atmosphere, warming it.

Section 1 Review

1. List three forms of radiation from the sun. How are these alike? How are they different?
2. What happens to the energy from the sun that is absorbed by Earth's surface?
3. Why is the sky blue? Why are sunsets often red?
4. **Thinking Critically Applying Concepts** What might conditions on Earth be like without the greenhouse effect?

Science at Home

Heating by Radiation With an adult family member, explore the role radiation plays in heating your home. Are some rooms warmer and sunnier in the morning? Are other rooms warmer and sunnier in the afternoon? How does opening and closing curtains or blinds affect the temperature of a room? Explain your observations to your family.

Heating Earth's Surface

Skills Lab

In this lab, you will develop and test a hypothesis about how quickly different materials absorb radiation.

Problem

How do the heating and cooling rates of sand and water compare?

Materials

2 thermometers or temperature probes
ring stand and 2 ring clamps

2 beakers, 400 mL	sand, 300 mL
water, 300 mL	lamp with 150-W bulb
metric ruler	clock or stopwatch
string	graph paper

Procedure

1. Do you think sand or water will heat up faster? Record your hypothesis. Then follow these steps to test your hypothesis.
2. Copy the data table into your notebook. Add enough rows to record data for 15 minutes.
3. Fill one beaker with 300 mL of dry sand.
4. Fill the second beaker with 300 mL of water at room temperature.
5. Arrange the beakers beneath the ring stand.
6. Place one thermometer in each beaker. If using temperature probes, see your teacher for instructions.
7. Suspend the thermometers from the ring stand with string. This will hold the thermometers in place so they do not fall.

8. Adjust the height of the clamp so that the bulb of each thermometer is covered by about 0.5 cm of sand or water in a beaker.
9. Position the lamp so that it is about 20 cm above the sand and water. There should be no more than 8 cm between the beakers. **CAUTION:** *Be careful not to splash water onto the hot light bulb.*
10. Record the temperature of the sand and water in your data table.
11. Turn on the lamp. Read the temperature of the sand and water every minute for 15 minutes. Record the temperatures in the Light On column in the data table.
12. Which material do you think will cool off more quickly? Record your hypothesis. Again, give reasons why you think your hypothesis is correct.
13. Turn the light off. Read the temperature of the sand and water every minute for another 15 minutes. Record the temperatures in the Light Off column (16–30 minutes).

DATA TABLE

Temperature with Light On (°C)			Temperature with Light Off (°C)		
Time (min)	Sand	Water	Time (min)	Sand	Water
Start			16		
1			17		
2			18		
3			19		
4			20		
5			21		

Analyze and Conclude

1. Draw two line graphs to show the data for the temperature change in sand and water over time. Label the horizontal axis from 0 to 30 minutes and the vertical axis in degrees Celsius. Draw both graphs on the same piece of graph paper. Use a dashed line to show the temperature change in water and a solid line to show the temperature change in sand.

2. Calculate the total change in temperature for each material.

3. Based on your data, which material had the greater increase in temperature?

4. What can you conclude about which material absorbed heat faster? How do your results compare with your hypothesis?

5. Review your data again. In 15 minutes, which material cooled faster?

6. How do these results compare to your second hypothesis?

7. **Think About It** If your results did not support either of your hypotheses, why do you think the results differed from what you expected?

8. **Apply** Based on your results, which do you think will heat up more quickly on a sunny day: the water in a lake or the sand surrounding it? Which will cool off more quickly after dark?

More to Explore

Do you think all solid materials heat up as fast as sand? For example, consider gravel, crushed stone, or different types of soil. Write a hypothesis about their heating rates as an "If . . . then . . ." statement. With the approval and supervision of your teacher, develop a procedure to test your hypothesis. Was your hypothesis correct?

SECTION 2 Heat Transfer

What Happens When Air Is Heated?

1. Use heavy scissors to cut the flat part out of an aluminum pie plate. Use the tip of the scissors to poke a small hole in the middle of the flat part.

2. Cut the part into a spiral shape, as shown in the photo. Tie a 30-centimeter piece of thread to the middle of the spiral.

3. Hold the spiral over a source of heat, such as a candle, hot plate, or incandescent light bulb.

Think It Over

Inferring What happened to the spiral? Why do you think this happened?

GUIDE FOR READING

◆ How is temperature measured?

◆ In what three ways is heat transferred?

Reading Tip As you read, make a list of the types of heat transfer. Write a sentence about how each type occurs.

Key Terms thermal energy
• temperature • thermometer
• heat • conduction
• convection

You know that energy from the sun is absorbed by Earth's surface. Some energy is then transferred from the surface to the atmosphere in the form of heat. The heat then moves from place to place within the atmosphere. But how does heat move in the atmosphere?

Energy and Temperature

Gases are made up of small particles, called molecules, that are constantly moving. The faster the molecules are moving, the more energy they have. Figure 3 shows how the motion of

Figure 3 The lemonade is cold, so the molecules move slowly. The herbal tea is hot, so the molecules move faster than the molecules in the lemonade. *Inferring* Which liquid has a higher temperature?

molecules is related to the amount of energy they hold. The total energy of motion in the molecules of a substance is called **thermal energy.** On the other hand, **temperature** is the *average* amount of energy of motion of each molecule of a substance. That means that temperature is a measure of how hot or cold a substance is.

Measuring Temperature

Ask someone what the weather is like. The answer will probably include the temperature. Temperature is one of the most important elements of weather. **Air temperature is usually measured with a thermometer.** A **thermometer** is a thin glass tube with a bulb on one end that contains a liquid, usually mercury or colored alcohol.

Thermometers work because liquids usually expand when they are heated and contract when they are cooled. When the air temperature increases, the liquid in the bulb expands and rises up the column. What happens when the temperature decreases? The liquid in the bulb contracts and moves down the tube.

Temperature is measured in units called degrees. The two most common scales are shown in Figure 4. Scientists use the Celsius scale. On the Celsius scale, the freezing point of pure water is 0°C (read "zero degrees Celsius"). The boiling point of pure water is 100°C. Weather reports in the United States use the Fahrenheit scale. On the Fahrenheit scale, the freezing point of water is 32°F and the boiling point is 212°F.

Figure 4 Scientists use the Celsius scale to measure temperature. However, weather reports often use the Fahrenheit scale. *Measuring According to this thermometer, what is the air temperature in degrees Celsius?*

☑ *Checkpoint* *How many degrees Celsius are there between the freezing point of water and the boiling point of water?*

How Heat Is Transferred

The energy transferred from a hotter object to a cooler one is referred to as **heat.** You can compare the different types of heat transfer in Figure 5 on page 471. **Heat is transferred in three ways: radiation, conduction, and convection.**

Radiation Have you ever felt the warmth of the sun's rays on your face? You were feeling energy coming directly from the sun as radiation. Recall that radiation is the direct transfer of energy by electromagnetic waves. The heat you feel from the sun or a campfire travels directly to you as infrared radiation. You cannot see infrared radiation, but you can feel it as heat.

Conduction Have you ever walked barefoot on hot sand? Your feet felt hot because heat moved directly from the sand into your feet. When a fast-moving molecule bumps into a nearby slower-moving molecule, it transfers some of its energy. The direct transfer of heat from one substance to another substance that it is touching is called **conduction.** The molecules that gain energy can in turn pass the energy along to other nearby molecules. When you walk on hot sand, the fast-moving molecules in the sand transfer heat into the slower-moving molecules in your feet.

The closer together the molecules in a substance are, the more effectively they can conduct heat. Conduction works well in some solids, such as metals, but not as well in liquids and gases. Air and water do not conduct heat very well.

Convection How can you dry your boots over a hot-air vent, even though the furnace is in another room? Air from the furnace carries the heat to your boots. In fluids (liquids and gases), molecules can move from place to place. As the molecules move, they take their heat along with them. The transfer of heat by the movement of a fluid is called **convection.**

☑ *Checkpoint* Give at least one example each of radiation, conduction, and convection in your daily life.

Heat Transfer in the Troposphere

Radiation, conduction, and convection work together to heat the troposphere. When Earth's surface absorbs solar energy during the day, the surface of the land becomes warmer than the air. Air near Earth's surface is warmed by radiation and conduction of heat from the surface to the air. However, heat is not easily conducted from one air molecule to another. Only the first few meters of the troposphere are heated by conduction. Thus, the air close to the ground is usually warmer than the air a few meters up.

Convection causes most of the heating of the troposphere. When the air near the ground is heated, the molecules have more energy. Because they have more energy, the molecules move

Heat transfer by convection

Heat transfer by radiation

Heat transfer by convection

Heat transfer by radiation

Heat transfer by conduction

Figure 5 All three types of heat transfer—radiation, convection, and conduction—occur near Earth's surface.

faster. As the molecules in the heated air move, they bump into each other and move farther apart. The air becomes less dense. Cooler, denser air sinks, forcing the warmer, less dense air to rise.

The upward movement of warm air and the downward movement of cool air form convection currents. Convection currents move heat throughout the troposphere.

 Section 2 Review

1. What is temperature? How is it usually measured?
2. Describe how a thermometer works.
3. Name three ways that heat can be transferred. Briefly explain how the three heat the troposphere.
4. **Thinking Critically** **Applying Concepts** When you light a fire in a fireplace, warm air rises by convection and goes up the chimney. How, then, does a fireplace heat a room? Why do only the people directly in front of the fireplace feel the warmth of the fire?

Check Your Progress **CHAPTER PROJECT**
Gather the instruments you will need to measure the weather factors. (*Hint:* Make sure you know how to take accurate measurements.) Plan when and where to measure weather factors. Be sure to take your measurements at the same location and at the same time of day.

DISCOVER • **ACTIVITY** • • • •

Which Way Does the Wind Turn?

Do this activity with a partner. Think of the ball as a model of Earth and the marker as representing wind.

1. Using heavy-duty tape, attach a pencil to a large smooth ball so that you can spin the ball from the top without touching it.

2. One partner should hold the pencil. Slowly turn the ball counterclockwise when seen from above.

3. While the ball is turning, the second partner should use a marker to try to draw a straight line from the "North Pole" to the "equator" of the ball. What shape does the line form?

Think It Over
Making Models If cold air were moving south from Canada into the United States, how would its movement be affected by Earth's rotation?

The highest point in the northeastern United States, at 1,917 meters above sea level, is Mount Washington in New Hampshire. On April 12, 1934, instruments at the weather observatory atop Mount Washington measured a wind speed of 370 kilometers per hour. That's the greatest wind speed ever measured at Earth's surface apart from a fierce storm such as a tornado. What causes this incredible force?

What Causes Winds?

Because air is a fluid, it can move easily from place to place. The force that makes air move is caused by a difference of air pressure. Fluids tend to move from areas of high pressure to areas of low pressure. A **wind** is the horizontal movement of air from an area of high pressure to an area of lower pressure. **All winds are caused by differences in air pressure.**

Most differences in air pressure are caused by unequal heating of the atmosphere. As you learned in the previous section, convection currents form when an area of Earth's surface is heated by the sun's rays. Air over the heated surface expands and becomes less dense. As the air becomes less dense, its air pressure decreases. If a nearby area is not heated as much, the air above the less-heated area will be cooler and denser. The cool, dense air has a higher air pressure so it flows underneath the warm, less dense air. This process forces the warm air to rise.

Measuring Wind

Winds are described by their direction and speed. Wind direction is determined with a wind vane. The wind swings the wind vane so that one end points into the wind. The name of a wind tells you where the wind is coming from. For example, a south wind blows from the south toward the north. A north wind blows to the south.

Wind speed is measured with an **anemometer** (an uh MAHM uh tur). An anemometer has three or four cups mounted at the ends of spokes that spin on an axle. The force of the wind against the cups turns the axle. A speedometer attached to the axle shows the wind speed.

A cool breeze can be very refreshing on a warm day. However, during the winter, a similar breeze can make you feel uncomfortably cold. The wind blowing over your skin removes body heat. The stronger the wind, the colder you feel. The increased cooling that a wind can cause is called the **wind-chill factor.** Thus a weather report may say, "The temperature is 20 degrees Fahrenheit. But with a wind speed of 30 miles per hour, the wind-chill factor makes it feel like 18 degrees below zero."

☑ *Checkpoint* *Toward what direction does a west wind blow?*

Build a Wind Vane
ACTIVITY

1. ✂ Use scissors to cut out a pointer and a slightly larger tail fin from construction paper.

2. Make a slit 1 cm deep in each end of a soda straw.

3. Slide the pointer and tail fin into place on the straw, securing them with small pieces of tape.

4. Hold the straw on your finger to find the point at which it balances.

5. Carefully push a pin through the balance point and into the eraser of a pencil. Move the wind vane back and forth to make sure it can spin freely.

6. Place your wind vane in the center of a magnetic compass to determine the direction the wind is blowing from.

Observing How can you use your wind vane to tell the direction of the wind?

Figure 6 The wind vane on the left points in the direction the wind is blowing from. The anemometer on the right measures wind speed.

Local Winds

Have you ever flown a kite at the beach on a hot summer day? Even if there is no wind inland, there may be a cool breeze blowing in from the water toward the beach. This breeze is an example of a local wind. **Local winds** are winds that blow over short distances. **Local winds are caused by unequal heating of Earth's surface within a small area.** Local winds form only when no winds are blowing from farther away.

You and Your Community

Where's the Wind?

Your city is planning to build a new community center. You and your classmates want to be sure that the doors will not be hard to open or close on windy days. You need to know which side of the building will be sheltered from the wind. You decide to measure wind speeds around a similar building.

Problem

How can you determine wind patterns around a building?

Skills Focus

measuring, interpreting data, drawing conclusions

Materials

pen
wind vane
meter stick
corrugated cardboard sheet, 15 cm x 20 cm
computer (optional)

round toothpick
2 wooden coffee stirrers
narrow masking tape

Procedure ✂

1. You'll begin by making a simple anemometer that uses wooden coffee stirrers to indicate wind speed. On your piece of cardboard, draw a

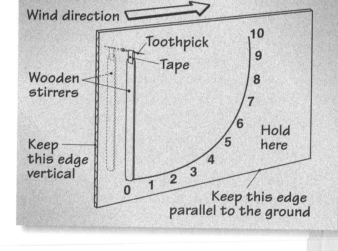

curved scale like the one shown in the diagram. Mark it in equal intervals from 0 to 10.

2. Carefully use the pen to make a small hole where the toothpick will go. Insert the toothpick through the hole.

3. Tape the wooden coffee stirrers to the toothpick as shown in the diagram, one on each side of the cardboard.

4. Copy the data table into your notebook or create the data table on the computer.

5. Take your anemometer outside the school. Stand about 2–3 m away from the building and away from any corners or large plants.

474

Unequal heating often occurs on land that is next to a large body of water. It takes more energy to warm up a body of water than it does to warm up an equal area of land. This means that as the sun heats Earth's surface during the day, the land warms up faster than the water. Therefore the air over the land becomes warmer than the air over the water. The warm air over the land expands and rises, creating a low-pressure area. Cool air blows inland from the water and moves underneath the warm air.

DATA TABLE		
Location	Wind Direction	Wind Speed

Analyze and Conclude

1. Was the wind stronger on one side of the school building than the other sides? How can you explain your observation?
2. Do your classmates' results agree with yours? What might account for any differences?
3. **Apply** Based on your data, which side of the building provides the best location for a door?

More to Explore

What effect do plants have on the wind speed in an area? Could bushes and trees be planted so that they reduce the wind speed near the doors? What measurements could you make to find out?

6. Use the wind vane to find out what direction the wind is coming from. Hold your anemometer so that the card is straight, vertical, and parallel to the wind direction. Observe which number the wooden stirrer is closest to. Record your data.
7. Repeat your measurements on all the other sides of the building. Record your data.

Warmer air rising

Warmer air rising

Cooler air moving to take warmer air's place

Cooler air moving to take warmer air's place

A

B

Figure 7 **(A)** During the day, cool air moves from the sea to the land, creating a sea breeze. **(B)** At night, cooler air moves from the land to the sea.
Forming Operational Definitions
What type of breeze occurs at night?

A wind that blows from an ocean or lake onto land is known as a **sea breeze** or a lake breeze. Figure 7A shows a sea breeze.

At night, the situation is reversed. Land cools more quickly than water, so the air over the land becomes cooler than the air over the water. As the warmer air over the water rises, cooler air moves from the land to take its place. The flow of air from land to a body of water is called a **land breeze.**

Monsoons

A process similar to land and sea breezes can occur over wider areas. In the summer in South and Southeast Asia, the land gradually gets warmer than the ocean. A large "sea breeze" blows steadily inland from the ocean all summer, even at night. In the winter, the land cools and becomes colder than the ocean. A "land breeze" blows steadily from the land to the ocean.

Sea and land breezes over a large region that change direction with the seasons are called **monsoons.** The summer monsoon in South Asia and Southeast Asia is very important for the crops grown there. The air blowing from the ocean during the rainy season is very warm and humid. As the humid air rises over the land, the air cools, producing heavy rains that supply the water needed by rice and other crops.

Figure 8 This heavy rain in Nepal is part of the summer monsoon, which blows from the ocean to the land. In the winter, the monsoon reverses and blows from the land to the ocean.

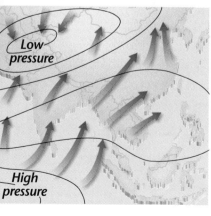

Summer Monsoon

Low pressure

High pressure

Winter Monsoon

High pressure

Low pressure

476

Global Winds

Winds that blow steadily from specific directions over long distances are referred to as **global winds.** Like local winds, global winds are created by unequal heating of Earth's surface. Refer to Figure 9 to see how sunlight strikes Earth's surface. In the middle of the day near the equator, the sun is almost directly overhead. The direct rays from the sun heat Earth's surface intensely. Near the North Pole or South Pole, the sun's rays strike Earth's surface at a lower angle, even at noon. The sun's energy is spread out over a larger area, so it heats the surface less. As a result, temperatures near the poles are much lower than they are near the equator.

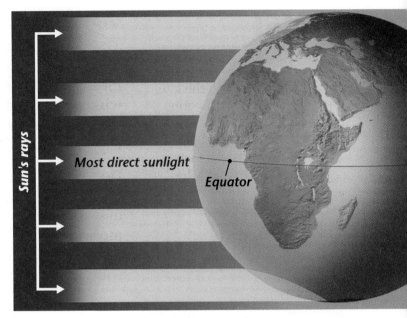

Figure 9 Near the equator, energy from the sun strikes Earth almost directly. Near the poles, the same amount of energy is spread out over a larger area.

Global Convection Currents Temperature differences between the equator and the poles produce giant convection currents in the atmosphere. Warm air rises at the equator, and cold air sinks at the poles. Therefore air pressure tends to be lower near the equator and greater near the poles, causing winds at Earth's surface to blow from the poles toward the equator. Higher in the atmosphere, air flows away from the equator toward the poles. **The movement of air between the equator and the poles produces global winds.**

The Coriolis Effect If Earth did not rotate, global winds would blow in a straight line from the poles toward the equator. Because Earth is rotating, global winds do not follow a straight path. As the winds move, Earth rotates from west to east underneath them, making it seem as if the winds have curved. The way Earth's rotation makes winds curve is called the **Coriolis effect** (kawr ee OH lis). It is named for the French mathematician who studied and explained it in 1835.

In the Northern Hemisphere, all global winds gradually turn toward the right. As you can see in Figure 10, a wind blowing toward the north gradually turns toward the northeast. In other words, a south wind gradually changes to a southwest wind. In the Southern Hemisphere, winds curve toward the left. A south wind becomes an southeast wind, and a north wind becomes a northwest wind.

Figure 10 As Earth rotates on its axis, the Coriolis effect turns winds in the Northern Hemisphere toward the right. *Interpreting Diagrams Which way do winds turn in the Southern Hemisphere?*

☑ *Checkpoint* *What happens to a wind blowing toward the south in the Northern Hemisphere? What would you call this wind?*

From colonial days to the late 1800s, American merchants traded new ships, lumber, cotton, tobacco, and furs for manufactured goods, such as textiles, from England. The eastbound voyage in the early 1800s took about three weeks. However, the westbound passage took almost twice as long—five to six weeks.

In Your Journal

Imagine that you are a sea captain making the voyage to England and back to America. Your family doesn't understand why your journey home takes almost twice as long as your journey to England. Write a letter to your family explaining why you have to travel farther south to take advantage of the prevailing winds on your return voyage.

Global Wind Belts

The Coriolis effect and other factors combine to produce a pattern of calm areas and wind belts around Earth. The calm areas include the doldrums and the horse latitudes. **The major global wind belts are the trade winds, the prevailing westerlies, and the polar easterlies.** As you read about each area, find it in *Exploring Global Winds.*

Doldrums Near the equator, the sun heats the surface strongly. Warm air rises steadily, creating an area of low pressure. Cool air moves into the area, but is warmed rapidly and rises before it moves very far. There is very little horizontal motion, so the winds near the equator are very weak. Regions near the equator with little or no wind are called the doldrums.

Horse Latitudes Warm air that rises at the equator divides and flows both north and south. **Latitude** is the distance from the equator, measured in degrees. At about 30° north and south latitudes, the air stops moving toward the poles and sinks. In each of these regions, another belt of calm air forms. Hundreds of years ago, sailors becalmed in these waters ran out of food and water for their horses and had to throw the horses overboard. Because of this, the latitudes 30° north and south of the equator are called the horse latitudes.

Trade Winds When the cold air over the horse latitudes sinks, it produces a region of high pressure. This high pressure causes surface winds to blow both toward the equator and away from it. The winds that blow toward the equator are turned west by the Coriolis effect. As a result, winds in the Northern Hemisphere between 30° north latitude and the equator blow generally from the northeast. In the Southern Hemisphere between 30° south latitude and the equator, the winds blow from the southeast. These steady easterly winds are called the trade winds. For hundreds of years, sailors relied on them to carry cargoes from Europe to the West Indies and South America.

Figure 11 The bark *Patriot*, built in 1809, carried goods to many parts of the world.
Applying Concepts How much effect do you think the prevailing winds have on shipping today?

EXPLORING Global Winds

A series of wind belts circles Earth. Between the wind belts are calm areas where air is rising or falling.

The horse latitudes are calm areas of falling air.

The prevailing westerlies blow away from the horse latitudes.

The doldrums are a calm area where warm air rises.

The trade winds blow from the horse latitudes toward the equator.

The cold polar easterlies blow away from the poles.

90° N

Polar easterlies

60° N

Prevailing westerlies

Horse latitudes

30° N

Trade winds

Equator 0°

Doldrums

Trade winds

30° S

Horse latitudes

Prevailing westerlies

60° S

90° S

Polar easterlies

N
W   E
S

Figure 12 By traveling east in a jet stream, pilots can save time and fuel.
Predicting What would happen if a plane flew west in a jet stream?

Prevailing Westerlies In the mid-latitudes, winds that blow toward the poles are turned toward the east by the Coriolis effect. Because they blow from the west to the east, they are called prevailing westerlies. The prevailing westerlies blow generally from the southwest between 30° and 60° north latitudes and from the northwest between 30° and 60° south latitudes. The prevailing westerlies play an important part in the weather of the United States.

Polar Easterlies Cold air near the poles sinks and flows back toward lower latitudes. The Coriolis effect shifts these polar winds to the west, producing winds called the polar easterlies. The polar easterlies meet the prevailing westerlies at about 60° north and 60° south latitudes, along a region called the polar front. The mixing of warm and cold air along the polar front has a major effect on weather changes in the United States.

☑ *Checkpoint* In what region do the polar easterlies meet the prevailing westerlies?

Jet Streams

About 10 kilometers above Earth's surface are bands of high-speed winds called **jet streams.** These winds are hundreds of kilometers wide but only a few kilometers deep. Jet streams blow from west to east at speeds of 200 to 400 kilometers per hour. As jet streams travel around Earth, they wander north and south along a wavy path.

Airplanes are aided by a jet stream when traveling east. Pilots can save fuel and time by flying east in a jet stream. However, airplanes flying at jet stream altitudes are slowed down when traveling west against the jet stream winds.

 Section 3 Review

1. How does the unequal heating of Earth's surface cause winds?
2. How are local winds and global winds similar? How are they different?
3. Name and draw the three major wind belts.
4. **Thinking Critically Applying Concepts** Imagine you are flying from Seattle to San Francisco, which is almost exactly due south of Seattle. Should the pilot set a course due south? Explain your answer.

Check Your Progress CHAPTER PROJECT
Check with your teacher to be sure you are using the weather instruments correctly. Are you recording units for each measurement? Collect and record measurements each day.

SECTION
4 Water in the Atmosphere

DISCOVER • **ACTIVITY** • • • •

How Does Fog Form?

1. Fill a narrow-necked plastic bottle with hot tap water. Pour out most of the water, leaving about 3 cm at the bottom. **CAUTION:** *Avoid spilling hot water. Do not use water that is so hot that you cannot safely hold the bottle.*

2. Place an ice cube on the mouth of the bottle. What happens?

3. Repeat Steps 1 and 2 using cold water instead of hot water. What happens?

Think It Over
Developing Hypotheses How can you explain your observations? Why is there a difference between what happens with the hot water and with the cold water?

During a rainstorm, the air feels moist. On a clear, cloudless day, the air may feel dry. As the sun heats the land and oceans, the amount of water in the atmosphere changes. Water is always moving between the atmosphere and Earth's surface.

As you learned in Chapter 12, this movement of water between the atmosphere and Earth's surface is called the water cycle. This cycle is shown in Figure 13. Water vapor enters the air by evaporation from the oceans and other bodies of water. **Evaporation** is the process by which water molecules in liquid water escape into the air as water vapor. Water vapor is also added to the air by living things. Water enters the roots of plants, rises to the leaves, and is released as water vapor.

As part of the water cycle, some of the water vapor in the atmosphere condenses to form clouds. Rain and other forms of precipitation fall from the clouds toward the surface. The water then runs off the surface, or moves through the ground, back into the oceans, lakes, and streams.

GUIDE FOR READING

◆ How is relative humidity measured?

◆ How do clouds form?

◆ What are the three main types of clouds?

Reading Tip Before you read, write a definition of "cloud." Revise your definition as you read about clouds.

Key Terms evaporation
• humidity • relative humidity
• psychrometer • condensation
• dew point • cumulus • stratus
• cirrus

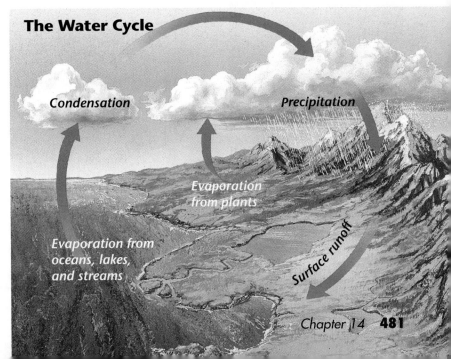

The Water Cycle

Condensation

Precipitation

Evaporation from plants

Evaporation from oceans, lakes, and streams

Surface runoff

Figure 13 In the water cycle, water moves from lakes and oceans into the atmosphere and falls back to Earth.

Humidity

Humidity is a measure of the amount of water vapor in the air. The percentage of water vapor in the air compared to the maximum amount the air could hold is the **relative humidity.** For example, at 10°C, 1 cubic meter of air can hold a maximum of 8 grams of water vapor. If there actually were 8 grams of water vapor in the air, then the relative humidity of the air would be 100 percent. If the air held 4 grams of water vapor, the relative humidity would be half, or 50 percent. The amount of water vapor that the air can hold depends on its temperature. Warm air can hold more water vapor than cool air.

INTEGRATING LIFE SCIENCE "It's not the heat, it's the humidity." What does this common expression mean? Even on a hot day, you can still feel comfortable if the air is dry. Evaporation of moisture from your skin removes heat and helps to keep your body's temperature comfortable. You feel less comfortable on a hot day if the relative humidity is high. When the relative humidity is high, evaporation slows down. Evaporation therefore has less cooling effect on your body.

Measuring Relative Humidity

Relative humidity can be measured with a psychrometer. A **psychrometer** (sy KRAHM uh tur) has two thermometers, a wet-bulb thermometer and a dry-bulb thermometer. The bulb of the wet-bulb thermometer has a cloth covering that is moistened with water. Air is then blown over both thermometers. Because the wet-bulb thermometer is cooled by evaporation, its reading drops below that of the dry-bulb thermometer.

Relative Humidity					
Dry-Bulb Reading (°C)	Difference Between Wet- and Dry-Bulb Readings (°C)				
	1	2	3	4	5
10	88	76	65	54	43
12	88	78	67	57	48
14	89	79	69	60	50
16	90	80	71	62	54
18	91	81	72	64	56
20	91	82	74	66	58
22	92	83	75	68	60
24	92	84	76	69	62
26	92	85	77	70	64
28	93	86	78	71	65
30	93	86	79	72	66

Figure 14 A sling psychrometer is used to measure relative humidity. First, find the wet-bulb and dry-bulb temperatures. Then find the dry-bulb temperature in the left column of the table. Find the difference between the wet- and dry-bulb temperatures across the top of the table. The number in the table where these two readings intersect indicates the relative humidity in percent.

If the relative humidity is high, the water on the wet bulb will evaporate slowly and the wet-bulb temperature will not change much. If the relative humidity is low, the water on the wet bulb will evaporate rapidly and the wet-bulb temperature will drop. The relative humidity can be found by comparing the temperatures of the wet-bulb and dry-bulb thermometers in a table like the one in Figure 14.

☑ *Checkpoint* *What is the difference between humidity and relative humidity?*

How Clouds Form

What do clouds remind you of? They can look like people, animals, countries, and a thousand other fanciful forms. Of course, not all clouds are fluffy and white. Storm clouds can be dark and cover the whole sky.

Clouds of all kinds form when water vapor in the air becomes liquid water or ice crystals. The process by which molecules of water vapor in the air become liquid water is called **condensation.** How does water condense? As you know, cold air can hold less water vapor than warm air. As air cools, the amount of water vapor it can hold decreases. Some of the water vapor in the air condenses to form droplets of liquid water.

The temperature at which condensation begins is called the **dew point.** If the dew point is below the freezing point, the water vapor may change directly into ice crystals. When you look at a cloud, you are seeing millions of tiny ice crystals or water droplets.

For water vapor to condense, tiny particles must be present so the water has a surface on which to condense. Most of these particles are salt crystals, dust from soil, and smoke. Sometimes water vapor condenses onto solid surfaces, such as blades of grass, instead of particles. Water that condenses from the air onto a cold surface is called dew. Frost is ice that has been deposited directly from the air onto a cold surface.

Clouds form whenever air is cooled to its dew point and particles are present. But why does the air cool? If air is warmed near the ground, it

Figure 15 Dew forms when water vapor condenses out of the air onto a solid surface, such as this flower.

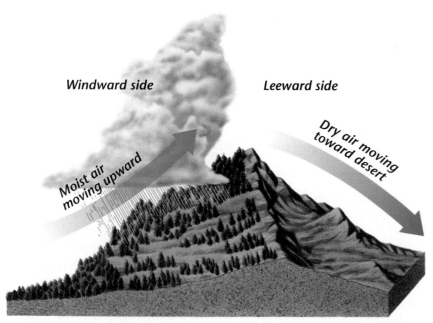

Windward side

Moist air moving upward

Leeward side

Dry air moving toward desert

Figure 16 Humid air cools as it is blown up the side of a mountain. *Predicting What happens when water vapor condenses out of the air?*

becomes less dense and rises in a convection current. When the rising air expands and becomes cooler, clouds may form.

When wind strikes the side of a hill or mountain, the air is forced upward. As the air rises along the slope, the air cools. Rain or snow falls on the windward side of the mountains, the side facing the on-coming wind.

By the time the air reaches the other side of the mountains, it has lost much of its water vapor. The air is cool and dry. The land on the leeward side of the mountains—downwind—is in a rain shadow. Just as very little light falls in a sun shadow, very little rain falls in a rain shadow. Not only has the air lost its water vapor while crossing the mountains, but the air has also grown warmer while flowing down the mountainside. This warm, dry air often creates a desert on the leeward side of the mountains.

✓ *Checkpoint* **Why are the tops of some mountains almost always covered by clouds?**

Types of Clouds

As you know, clouds come in different shapes. **Meteorologists classify clouds into three main types: cumulus, stratus, and cirrus.** Clouds are also classified by their altitude. Each type of cloud is associated with a different type of weather.

Clouds that look like fluffy, rounded piles of cotton are called **cumulus** (KYOO myuh lus) clouds. The word *cumulus* means "heap" or "mass." Cumulus clouds form less than 2 kilometers above the ground, but may grow in size and height until they extend upward as much as 18 kilometers. Cumulus clouds usually indicate fair weather. Towering clouds with flat tops, called cumulonimbus clouds, often produce thunderstorms. The suffix *-nimbus* comes from a Latin word meaning "rain."

Clouds that form in flat layers are called **stratus** (STRAT us) clouds. *Strato* means "spread out." Stratus clouds usually cover all or most of the sky. As stratus clouds thicken, they may produce drizzle, rain, or snow. They are then called nimbostratus clouds.

Wispy, feathery clouds are called **cirrus** (SEER us) clouds. Cirrus clouds form only at high levels, above about 6 kilometers, where temperatures are very low. As a result, cirrus clouds are made mostly of ice crystals.

EXPLORING Clouds

The main types of clouds are cumulus, stratus, and cirrus. A cloud's name contains clues about its height and structure.

Cirrus clouds
Cirrus, cirrostratus, and cirrocumulus clouds are made up mostly of ice crystals.

Cumulonimbus clouds
Thunderstorms come from cumulonimbus clouds. For this reason cumulonimbus clouds are also called thunderheads.

Nimbostratus clouds
Nimbostratus clouds may produce rain or snow.

Cumulus clouds
Cumulus clouds are usually a sign of fair weather.

Cirrus

Cirrocumulus

Altocumulus

Altostratus

Cumulonimbus

Nimbostratus

Stratus

Cumulus

Fog

Figure 17 Fog often forms at night over cool lakes.
Predicting *What will happen as the sun rises and warms the air above the lake?*

Cirrus clouds that have feathery "hooked" ends are sometimes called mare's tails. Cirrocumulus clouds, which look like rows of cotton balls, often indicate that a storm is on its way.

Part of a cloud's name may be based on its height. The names of clouds that form between about 2 and 6 kilometers above Earth's surface have the prefix *alto-*, which means "high." The two main types of these clouds are altocumulus and altostratus.

Clouds that form at or near the ground are called fog. Fog often forms when the ground cools at night after a warm, humid day. The ground cools the air just above the ground to the air's dew point. The next day the heat of the morning sun "burns" the fog off as its water droplets evaporate.

 Section 4 Review

1. What instrument is used to measure relative humidity? How does it work?
2. What conditions are needed for clouds to form?
3. Describe each of the three main types of clouds.
4. **Thinking Critically** **Classifying** Classify each of the following cloud types as low-level, medium-level, or high-level: altocumulus, altostratus, cirrostratus, cirrus, cumulus, fog, nimbostratus, and stratus.

Science at Home

Condensation on Glass Fill a large glass half-full with cold water. Show your family members what happens as you add ice cubes to the water. Explain to your family that the water that appears on the outside of the glass comes from water vapor in the atmosphere. Also explain why the water on the outside of the glass only appears after you add ice to the water in the glass.

SECTION 5 Precipitation

DISCOVER ········· ACTIVITY ····

How Can You Make Hail?

1. Put on your goggles.

2. 🔥 Put 15 g of salt into a beaker. Add 50 mL of water. Stir the solution until most of the salt is dissolved.

3. Put 15 mL of cold water in a clean test tube.

4. Place the test tube in the beaker.

5. Fill the beaker almost to the top with crushed ice. Stir the ice mixture every minute for six minutes.

6. Remove the test tube from the beaker and drop an ice chip into the test tube. What happens?

Think It Over

Inferring Based on your observation, what conditions are necessary for hail to form?

In Arica, Chile, the average rainfall is less than 1 millimeter per year. Many years pass with no precipitation at all. On the other hand, the average rainfall on Mount Waialeale on the island of Kauai in Hawaii is about 12 meters per year. That's more than enough to cover a three-story house! As you can see, rainfall varies greatly around the world.

Water evaporates into the air from every water surface on Earth and from living things. This water eventually returns to the surface as precipitation. **Precipitation** (pree sip uh TAY shun) is any form of water that falls from clouds and reaches Earth's surface.

Precipitation always comes from clouds. But not all clouds produce precipitation. For precipitation to occur, cloud droplets or ice crystals must grow heavy enough to fall through the air. One way that cloud droplets grow is by colliding and combining with other cloud droplets. As the droplets grow larger, they fall faster and collect more droplets. Finally, the droplets become heavy enough to fall out of the cloud as raindrops.

Types of Precipitation

In warm parts of the world, precipitation is almost always rain or drizzle. In colder regions, precipitation may fall as snow or ice. **Common types of precipitation include rain, sleet, freezing rain, hail, and snow.**

GUIDE FOR READING

◆ What are the main types of precipitation?

◆ How is rainfall measured?

Reading Tip As you read, make a list of the types of precipitation. Write a sentence describing how each type forms.

Key Terms precipitation • rain gauge • drought

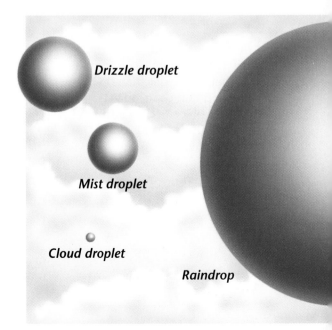

Drizzle droplet

Mist droplet

Cloud droplet

Raindrop

Figure 18 Droplets come in many sizes. Believe it or not, a raindrop has about one million times as much water in it as a cloud droplet.

Rain The most common kind of precipitation is rain. Drops of water are called rain if they are at least 0.5 millimeter in diameter. Precipitation made up of smaller drops of water is called mist or drizzle. Mist and drizzle usually fall from nimbostratus clouds.

Sleet Sometimes raindrops fall through a layer of air below 0°C, the freezing point of water. As they fall, the raindrops freeze into solid particles of ice. Ice particles smaller than 5 millimeters in diameter are called sleet.

Freezing Rain At other times raindrops falling through cold air near the ground do not freeze in the air. Instead, the raindrops freeze when they touch a cold surface. This is called freezing rain. In an ice storm, a smooth, thick layer of ice builds up on every surface. The weight of the ice may break tree branches onto power lines, causing power failures. Freezing rain and sleet can make sidewalks and roads slippery and dangerous.

Figure 19 (A) Snowflakes form in clouds that are colder than 0°C. (B) Freezing rain coats objects with a layer of ice. (C) Hailstones are formed inside clouds during thunderstorms.

Hail Round pellets of ice larger than 5 millimeters in diameter are called hailstones. Hail forms only inside cumulonimbus clouds during thunderstorms. A hailstone starts as an ice pellet inside a cold region of a cloud. Strong updrafts in the cloud carry the hailstone up and down through the cold region many times. Each time the hailstone goes through the cold region, a new layer of ice forms around the hailstone. Eventually the hailstone becomes heavy enough to fall to the ground. If you cut a hailstone in half, you can often see shells of ice, like the layers of an onion. Because hailstones can grow quite large before finally falling to the ground, hail can cause tremendous damage to crops, buildings, and vehicles.

Snow Often water vapor in a cloud is converted directly into ice crystals called snowflakes. Snowflakes have an endless number of different shapes and patterns, all with six sides or branches. Snowflakes often join together into larger clumps of snow in which the six-sided crystals are hard to see.

☑ *Checkpoint* *How do hailstones form?*

Measuring Precipitation

Meteorologists measure rainfall with a rain gauge. A **rain gauge** is an open-ended can or tube that collects rainfall. The amount of rainfall is measured by dipping a ruler into the water or by reading a marked scale. To increase the accuracy of the measurement, the top of a rain gauge may have a funnel that collects ten times as much rain as the tube alone. The funnel collects a greater depth of water that is easier to measure. But to get the actual depth of rain, it is necessary to divide by ten.

Snowfall is measured using a ruler or by melting collected snow and measuring the depth of water it produces. On average, 10 centimeters of snow contains about the same amount of water as 1 centimeter of rain. Of course, light, fluffy snow contains far less water than heavy, wet snow.

Collecting funnel

1 centimeter of rain

10 centimeters in measuring tube

Measuring tube $\frac{1}{10}$ *area of funnel*

Figure 20 A rain gauge measures the depth of rain that falls.
Observing How much rain was collected in the measuring tube of this rain gauge?

Controlling Precipitation

In some regions, there may be periods that are much drier than usual. Long periods of unusually low precipitation are called **droughts.** Droughts can cause great hardship. In the farming regions of the Midwest, for example, droughts may cause entire crops to fail. The farmers suffer from lost income and consumers suffer from high food prices. In some less-developed countries, droughts can cause widespread hunger, or famine.

 INTEGRATING TECHNOLOGY In recent years, scientists have been trying to produce rain during droughts. The most common method is called cloud seeding. In cloud seeding, tiny crystals of dry ice (solid carbon dioxide) and silver iodide are sprinkled into clouds from airplanes. Many clouds contain supercooled water droplets, which are actually below 0°C. The droplets don't freeze because there aren't enough particles around which ice crystals can form. Water vapor can condense on the particles of silver iodide, forming rain or snow. Dry ice works by cooling the droplets even further, so that they will freeze without particles being present.

Cloud seeding has also been used with some success to clear fog from airports. Dry ice is sprinkled into the fog, causing ice crystals to form. This removes some of the fog so pilots can see the runways. Unfortunately, cloud seeding clears only cold fogs, so its use for this purpose is limited.

Figure 21 The corn in this photo was damaged by a long drought. *Applying Concepts How can cloud seeding be used to reduce the effect of droughts?*

Section 5 Review

1. Name the five common types of precipitation.
2. What device is used to measure precipitation?
3. What must happen before precipitation can fall from a cloud?
4. What kind of cloud produces hail?
5. **Thinking Critically Applying Concepts** If two open cans of different diameters were left out in the rain, how would the amount of water they collected compare? How would the depth of water in the cans compare?

Check Your Progress
CHAPTER PROJECT

Now you should be ready to begin graphing your weather data. Look for patterns in your graphs. Use your data to predict what the next day's weather will be. Compare your predictions with what actually happens the next day. Are you able to predict the weather with confidence?

Energy in the Atmosphere

Key Ideas

◆ Energy from the sun travels to Earth as electromagnetic waves—mostly visible light, infrared radiation, and ultraviolet radiation.

◆ When Earth's surface is heated, it radiates some of the energy back into the atmosphere in the form of longer-wavelength radiation.

Key Terms

electromagnetic waves ultraviolet radiation
radiation scattering
infrared radiation greenhouse effect

 Heat Transfer

INTEGRATING PHYSICS

Key Ideas

◆ Temperature of the air is typically measured with a thermometer.

◆ Three forms of heat transfer—radiation, conduction, and convection—work together to heat the troposphere.

Key Terms

thermal energy thermometer conduction
temperature heat convection

 Winds

Key Ideas

◆ All winds are caused by differences in air pressure, which are the result of unequal heating of Earth's surface.

◆ Local winds are caused by unequal heating of Earth's surface within a small area.

◆ The movement of air between the equator and the poles produces global winds.

Key Terms

wind monsoon
anemometer global wind
wind-chill factor Coriolis effect
local wind latitude
sea breeze jet stream
land breeze

 Water in the Atmosphere

Key Ideas

◆ Relative humidity is the percentage of water vapor in the air compared to the amount of water vapor the air could hold. It can be measured with a psychrometer.

◆ Clouds of all kinds form when water vapor in the air becomes liquid water or solid ice.

◆ Meteorologists classify clouds into three main types: cumulus, stratus, and cirrus.

Key Terms

evaporation psychrometer cumulus
humidity condensation stratus
relative humidity dew point cirrus

Precipitation

Key Ideas

◆ Common types of precipitation include rain, sleet, freezing rain, hail, and snow.

◆ Rain is measured with a rain gauge.

◆ Scientists have used cloud seeding to produce rain and to clear fog from airports.

Key Terms
precipitation
rain gauge
drought

Organizing Information

Concept Map Construct a concept map about winds on a separate sheet of paper. Be sure to include the following terms: local winds, global winds, monsoons, sea breezes, land breezes, prevailing westerlies, polar easterlies, tradewinds, and the two types of monsoon. (For more on concept maps, see the Skills Handbook.)

Reviewing Content

 Review key concepts online using iText at www.phschool.com

Multiple Choice

Choose the letter of the best answer.

1. Energy from the sun travels to Earth's surface by
   a. radiation.
   b. convection.
   c. evaporation.
   d. conduction.

2. Rising warm air transports heat energy by
   a. conduction.
   b. convection.
   c. radiation.
   d. condensation.

3. A psychrometer is used to measure
   a. rainfall.
   b. relative humidity.
   c. temperature.
   d. humidity.

4. Clouds form because water vapor in the air
   a. warms.   b. conducts.
   c. condenses.   d. evaporates.

5. Rain, sleet, and hail are all forms of
   a. evaporation.
   b. condensation.
   c. precipitation.
   d. convection.

True or False

If the statement is true, write true. If it is false, change the underlined word or words to make the statement true.

6. Infrared radiation and <u>ultraviolet radiation</u> make up most of the energy Earth receives from the sun.

7. The process by which gases hold heat in the atmosphere is called the <u>wind-chill factor</u>.

8. Water molecules in liquid water escape into the atmosphere as water vapor in the process of <u>evaporation</u>.

9. The instrument used to measure wind speed is a <u>thermometer</u>.

10. Clouds that form near the ground are called <u>fog</u>.

Checking Concepts

11. What causes the greenhouse effect? How does it affect Earth's atmosphere?

12. What form of heat transfer is most important in heating the troposphere?

13. What are monsoons? How are they like land and sea breezes? How are they different?

14. Describe how the movements of hot air at the equator and cold air at the poles produce global wind patterns.

15. Why are deserts often found on the leeward side of mountain ranges?

16. Why do clouds usually form high in the air instead of near Earth's surface?

17. Describe sleet, hail, and snow in terms of how each one forms.

18. **Writing to Learn** Imagine you are a drop of water in the ocean. Write a diary describing your journey through the water cycle. How do you become a cloud? What type of conditions cause you to fall as precipitation? Use descriptive words to describe your journey.

Thinking Critically

19. **Relating Cause and Effect** What circumstances could cause a nighttime land breeze in a city near the ocean?

20. **Problem Solving** If you use a psychrometer and get the same reading on both thermometers, what is the relative humidity?

21. **Comparing and Contrasting** How are hail and sleet alike? How are they different?

22. **Classifying** Classify the different types of clouds by the kind of weather associated with each type.

23. **Relating Cause and Effect** What is the source of the energy that powers Earth's winds?

Applying Skills

Use the table below to answer Questions 24–27.

Average Monthly Rainfall

Month	Rainfall	Month	Rainfall
January	1 cm	July	49 cm
February	1 cm	August	57 cm
March	1 cm	September	40 cm
April	2 cm	October	20 cm
May	25 cm	November	4 cm
June	52 cm	December	1 cm

24. **Graphing** Use the information in the table to draw a bar graph that shows the rainfall each month at this location.
25. **Calculating** What is the total amount of rainfall each year at this location?
26. **Classifying** Which months of the year would you classify as "dry"? Which months would you classify as "wet"?

27. **Drawing Conclusions** The place represented by the rainfall data is in Southeast Asia. What do you think accounts for the extremely heavy rainfall that occurs during some months?

CHAPTER PROJECT

Performance ▼ **Assessment**

Present Your Project Develop a way to present your findings to the class. For example, you could put your graphs and predictions on a poster. Are your graphs neatly drawn and easy to understand? Practice your presentation and make any needed improvements.

Reflect and Record How could you improve the accuracy of your observations? What did you learn about how easy or difficult it is to predict the weather?

Test Preparation

Use these questions to prepare for standardized tests.

Study the graph. Then answer Questions 28–31.

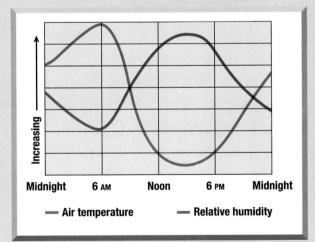

— Air temperature   — Relative humidity

28. The greatest change in air temperature occurred during the period from
    A midnight to 6 A.M.
    B 6 A.M. to noon.
    C noon to 6 P.M.
    D 6 P.M. to midnight.

29. The graph indicates that as air temperature increases, relative humidity
    F increases.
    G sometimes increases and sometimes decreases.
    H decreases.
    J stays about the same.

30. Condensation is most likely to occur at approximately
    A 6 A.M.   B noon.
    C 3 P.M.   D 6 P.M.

31. Assuming that the amount of water vapor in the air stayed constant through the day, one could infer from the graph that
    F cool air can hold more water vapor than warm air.
    G cool air can hold less water vapor than warm air.
    H cool air and warm air can hold the same amount of water vapor.
    J cool air cannot hold water vapor.

A lightning bolt tears
through the dark sky.

WEB ACTIVITY
www.phschool.com

The Weather Tomorrow

When the sky turns dark and threatening, it's not hard to predict the weather. A storm is on its way. But wouldn' you rather know about an approaching storm before it actually arrives?

In this chapter you will learn about weather patterns, including the kinds of patterns that cause strong thunderstorms like this one. As you work through this chapter, you will get a chance to make your own weather forecasts and compare them to the forecasts of professionals. Good luck!

Your Goal To predict the weather for your own community and two other locations in the United States.

To complete the project you will
- ◆ compare weather maps for several days at a time
- ◆ look for repeating patterns in the weather
- ◆ draw maps to show your weather predictions

Get Started Begin by previewing Section 4 to learn about weather maps and symbols. Start a project folder to hold daily national weather maps from your local newspaper and a description of the symbols used on the maps. Choose two locations in the United States that are at least 1,000 kilometers away from your community and from each other.

Check Your Progress You'll be working on this project as you study this chapter. To keep your project on track, look for Check Your Progress boxes at the following points.

Section 1 Review, page 502: Collect weather maps and look for patterns.
Section 3 Review, page 518: Predict the next day's weather.
Section 4 Review, page 525: Compare your predictions to professional forecasts and to the actual weather.

Present Your Project At the end of the chapter (page 529), you will present your weather maps and discuss how well you predicted the weather.

TEKS

In addition to process TEKS, this chapter addresses these concept TEKS as they relate to the chapter's topic

(6.14) The student knows the structures and functions of Earth systems.
The student is expected to:
(C) describe components of the atmosphere, including oxygen, nitrogen, and water vapor, and identify the role of atmospheric movement in weather change.

1 Air Masses and Fronts

How Do Fluids of Different Densities Behave?

1. Put on your apron. Place a cardboard divider across the middle of a plastic shoe box.

2. Add a few drops of red food coloring to a liter of warm water. Pour the red liquid, which represents low-density warm air, into the shoe box on one side of the divider.

3. Add about 100 mL of table salt and a few drops of blue food coloring to a liter of cold water. Pour the blue liquid, which represents high-density cold air, into the shoe box on the other side of the divider.

4. What do you think will happen if you remove the divider?

5. Now quickly remove the divider. Watch carefully from the side. What happens?

Think It Over

Developing Hypotheses Based on this activity, write a hypothesis stating what would happen if a mass of cold air ran into a mass of warm air.

GUIDE FOR READING

◆ What are the major types of air masses that affect the weather in North America?

◆ What are the main types of fronts?

◆ What are cyclones?

Reading Tip Before you read, use the headings to make an outline about air masses and fronts. Leave space to fill in details as you read.

Key Terms air mass • tropical • polar • maritime • continental • front • occluded • cyclone • anticyclone

Listen to the evening news and you may hear a weather forecast like this: "A huge mass of Arctic air is moving our way, bringing freezing temperatures." Today's weather is influenced by air from thousands of kilometers away—perhaps from Canada or the Caribbean Sea. A huge body of air that has similar temperature, humidity, and air pressure throughout it is called an **air mass.** A single air mass may spread over an area of millions of square kilometers and be up to 10 kilometers high.

Types of Air Masses

Scientists classify air masses according to two characteristics: temperature and humidity. Whether an air mass is warm or cold depends on the temperature of the region over which the air mass forms. **Tropical,** or warm, air masses form in the tropics and have low air pressure. **Polar,** or cold, air masses form north of 50° north latitude and south of 50° south latitude. Polar air masses have high air pressure.

Whether an air mass is humid or dry depends on whether it forms over water or land. **Maritime** air masses form over oceans. Water evaporates from the oceans, so the air can become very humid. **Continental** air masses form over land, in the middle of continents, and are dry.

Today

Four major types of air masses influence the weather in North America: maritime tropical, continental tropical, maritime polar, and continental polar. *Exploring North American Air Masses* on the next page shows where these air masses come from and what parts of North America they affect.

Maritime Tropical Warm, humid air masses form over oceans near the tropics. Maritime tropical air masses that form over the Gulf of Mexico and the Atlantic Ocean move first into the southeastern United States. These air masses then move north and northeast, where they influence weather in the central and eastern United States. In the west, maritime tropical air masses form over the Pacific Ocean. They affect mainly the weather on the West Coast. As they cross the coastal mountain ranges, the Pacific air masses lose moisture. They bring dry air to the eastern slopes.

In summer, maritime tropical air masses usually bring hot, humid weather. Most summer showers and thunderstorms in the United States develop in air masses that have formed over the Gulf of Mexico. In winter, a humid air mass can bring heavy rain or snow.

Maritime Polar Cool, humid air masses form over the icy cold North Pacific and North Atlantic oceans. Maritime polar air masses affect the West Coast more than the East Coast. Even in summer, these masses of cool, humid air often bring fog, rain, and cool temperatures to the West Coast.

Figure 1 This beach is on the southern Oregon coast. *Applying Concepts How does maritime polar air affect the weather at this location?*

EXPLORING North American Air Masses

Air masses can be warm or cold, and humid or dry. As an air mass moves into an area, it changes the weather there.

Maritime polar air masses from the Pacific Ocean bring cool, humid air to the West Coast.

Continental polar air masses from central and northern Canada bring cold air to the central and eastern United States.

Maritime polar air masses from the Atlantic Ocean are often pushed out to sea by westerly winds.

PACIFIC OCEAN

ATLANTIC OCEAN

Maritime tropical air masses from the Pacific Ocean bring warm, humid air to California and the Southwest.

Continental tropical air masses from the Southwest bring hot, dry air.

Gulf of Mexico

Maritime tropical air masses from the Gulf of Mexico bring warm, humid air to the eastern United States.

Continental Tropical Hot, dry air masses form only in summer over dry areas of the Southwest and northern Mexico. Continental tropical air masses cover a smaller area than other air masses. They occasionally move northeast, bringing hot, dry weather to the southern Great Plains.

Continental Polar Large continental polar air masses form over central and northern Canada and Alaska. As you would expect, continental polar air masses bring cool or cold air. In winter, continental polar air masses bring clear, cold, dry air to much of North America. Air masses that form near the Arctic Circle can bring bitterly cold weather with very low humidity. In summer, storms may occur when continental polar air masses move south and meet maritime tropical air masses moving north.

☑ *Checkpoint* *Where do continental polar air masses come from?*

How Air Masses Move

Recall that the prevailing westerlies are the major wind belts in the continental United States. The prevailing westerlies generally push air masses from west to east. For example, maritime polar air masses from the Pacific Ocean are blown onto the West Coast, bringing heavy rain or snow. Continental polar air masses from central Canada enter the United States between the Rocky Mountains and the Great Lakes. These cold, dry air masses are then blown east, where they affect the weather of the central and eastern United States.

Fronts

As huge masses of air move across the land and the oceans, they bump into each other. But the air masses do not easily mix. Why don't they? Think about a bottle of oil-and-vinegar salad dressing. The less dense oil floats on top of the more dense vinegar.

Something similar happens when two air masses with different temperatures and densities collide. The area where the air masses meet and do not mix becomes a **front.** The word *front*, which is borrowed from military language, means a battle area where opposing armies meet to fight. When air masses meet at a front, the collision often causes storms and changeable weather. A front may be 15 to 200 kilometers wide and extend as much as 10 kilometers up into the troposphere.

There are four types of fronts: cold fronts, warm fronts, stationary fronts, and occluded fronts. The kind of front that develops depends on the characteristics of the air masses and how they are moving. How does each type of front affect your local weather?

Figure 2 A cold front forms when cold air moves underneath warm air, forcing the warm air to rise.

Cold Fronts As you know, cold air is dense and tends to sink. Warm air is less dense and tends to rise. When a rapidly moving cold air mass runs into a slowly moving warm air mass, the denser cold air slides under the lighter warm air. The warm air is pushed upward, as shown in Figure 2. The front that forms is called a cold front.

As the warm air rises, it cools. Remember that warm air can hold more water vapor than cool air. The rising air soon reaches the dew point, the temperature at which the water vapor in the air condenses into droplets of liquid water. Clouds form. If there is a lot of water vapor in the warm air, heavy rain or snow may fall. What will happen if the warm air mass contains only a little water vapor? In this case, the cold front may be accompanied by only cloudy skies.

Cold fronts move quickly, so they can cause abrupt weather changes, including violent thunderstorms. After a cold front passes through an area, cool, dry air moves in, often bringing clear skies and cooler temperatures.

Warm Fronts Clouds, storms, and rain also accompany warm fronts. At a warm front, a moving warm air mass collides with a slowly moving cold air mass. Because cold air is more dense than warm air, the warm air moves over the cold air, as shown in Figure 3. If the warm air is humid, showers and light rain fall along the front where the warm and cold air meet. If the warm air is dry, scattered clouds form. Because warm fronts move more slowly than cold fronts, the weather may be rainy or foggy for several days. After a warm front passes through an area, the weather is likely to be warm and humid. In winter, warm fronts bring snow.

Figure 3 A warm front forms when warm air moves over cold air. *Interpreting Diagrams* *What kind of weather forms at a warm front?*

Direction of front

Warm air

Cold air

Warm front

Figure 4 When a cold air mass and a cool air mass come together, the warm air caught between them is forced upward. The result is an occluded front.

Cold air

Warm air

Cool air

Direction of front

Stationary Fronts Sometimes cold and warm air masses meet, but neither one has enough force to move the other. The two air masses face each other in a "standoff." In this case, the front is called a stationary front. Where the warm and cool air meet, water vapor in the warm air condenses into rain, snow, fog, or clouds. If a stationary front remains stalled over an area, it may bring many days of clouds and precipitation.

Occluded Fronts The most complex weather situation occurs at an occluded front, shown in Figure 4. At an occluded front, a warm air mass is caught between two cooler air masses. The denser cool air masses move underneath the less dense warm air mass and push it upward. The two cooler air masses meet in the middle and may mix. The temperature near the ground becomes cooler. The warm air mass is cut off, or **occluded,** from the ground. As the warm air cools and its water vapor condenses, the weather may turn cloudy and rainy or snowy.

✓ *Checkpoint* *What type of front forms when two air masses meet and neither one can move?*

Cyclones and Anticyclones

If you look at a weather map, you will see areas marked with an "L." The "L" is short for "low," and indicates an area of relatively low air pressure. A swirling center of low air pressure is called a **cyclone,** from a Greek word meaning "wheel."

As warm air at the center of a cyclone rises, the air pressure decreases. Cooler air blows toward this low-pressure area from nearby areas where the air pressure is higher. Winds spiral inward toward the center of the system. Recall that in the Northern Hemisphere, the Coriolis effect deflects winds to the right.

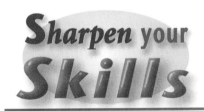

Classifying

At home, watch the weather forecast on television. Take note of each time the weather reporter mentions a front. Classify the fronts mentioned or shown as cold, warm, stationary, or occluded. Also note what type of weather is predicted to occur when the front arrives. Is each type of front always associated with the same type of weather?

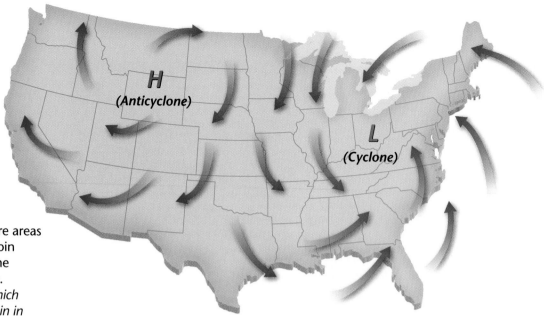

Figure 5 Cyclones are areas of low pressure that spin counterclockwise in the Northern Hemisphere.
Interpreting Maps Which way do anticyclones spin in the Northern Hemisphere?

H
(Anticyclone)

L
(Cyclone)

Because of this, winds in a cyclone spin counterclockwise in the Northern Hemisphere, as shown in Figure 5.

Cyclones play a large part in the weather of the United States. As air rises in a cyclone, the air cools, forming clouds and precipitation. **Cyclones and decreasing air pressure are associated with storms and precipitation.**

As its name suggests, an anticyclone is the opposite of a cyclone in most ways. **Anticyclones** are high-pressure centers of dry air. Anticyclones are also called "highs"—"H" on a weather map. Winds spiral outward from the center of an anticyclone, moving toward areas of lower pressure. Because of the Coriolis effect, winds in an anticyclone spin clockwise in the Northern Hemisphere. Because air moves out from the center of the anticyclone, cool air moves downward from higher in the troposphere. As the cool air falls, it warms up, so its relative humidity drops. The descending air in an anticyclone causes dry, clear weather.

Section 1 Review

1. What two main characteristics are used to classify air masses?
2. What is a front? Name and describe four types of fronts.
3. What is a cyclone? What type of weather does it bring?
4. Why do maritime polar air masses have more effect on the West Coast than the East Coast?
5. **Thinking Critically** **Classifying** Classify the four major types of air masses according to whether they are dry or humid.

Check Your Progress

CHAPTER PROJECT

Collect newspaper weather maps for about a week, and arrange them in order. Look carefully at how symbols on the map have moved from one day to the next. What patterns do you see from day to day in different weather factors? How does the weather in your community differ from the weather in the two other locations you selected?

2 Storms

ACTIVITY

Can You Make a Tornado?

1. Fill a large jar three-quarters full with water. Add a drop of liquid dish detergent and a penny or marble.

2. Put the lid on the jar tightly. Now move the jar in a circle until the water inside begins to spin.

Think It Over

Observing What happens to the water in the jar? Describe the pattern that forms. How is it like a tornado? Unlike a tornado?

Early in 1998, a series of powerful tornadoes roared through central Florida. With winds as high as 210 miles per hour, the tornadoes dropped cars into living rooms, crumpled trailers, and destroyed businesses and school buildings. They were the deadliest tornadoes ever to hit Florida. These tornadoes were not the only violent weather that year. In California the problem was rain. Record rainfalls brought devastating floods and mudslides.

What was causing these disasters? Meteorologists had an answer: El Niño. El Niño is a weather pattern related to the temperature of the water in the tropical Pacific Ocean. When temperatures there rise, they set off a series of events that can influence weather half a world away.

Have you ever experienced a tornado, hurricane, or other severe storm? When rain pours down, thunder crashes, or snow-drifts pile up, it may be hard to think about the actions of air pressure and air masses. Yet these are the causes of severe storms as well as the weather you experience every day.

A **storm** is a violent disturbance in the atmosphere. Storms involve sudden changes in air pressure, which in turn cause rapid air movements. Conditions that bring one kind of storm often cause other kinds of storms in the same area. For example, the conditions that cause thunderstorms can also cause tornadoes.

GUIDE FOR READING

◆ What are the main kinds of storms? How do they form?

◆ What measures can you take to ensure safety in a storm?

Reading Tip As you read, create a table comparing thunderstorms, tornadoes, hurricanes, and snowstorms. Include temperature, precipitation, and safety rules.

Key Terms storm • lightning • tornado • hurricane • storm surge • evacuate

Figure 6 Tornadoes caused tremendous damage in Florida and other parts of the southeastern United States in 1998.

Figure 7 The anvil shape of this cloud is typical of cumulonimbus clouds that produce thunderstorms. *Applying Concepts Why do cumulonimbus clouds often form along cold fronts?*

Thunderstorms

Do you find thunderstorms frightening? Exciting? A little of both? As you watch the brilliant flashes of lightning and listen to long rolls of thunder, you have probably wondered what caused them.

How Thunderstorms Form Thunderstorms are heavy rainstorms accompanied by thunder and lightning. **Thunderstorms form within large cumulonimbus clouds, or thunderheads.** Most cumulonimbus clouds and thunderstorms form when warm air is forced upward at a cold front. Cumulonimbus clouds also form on hot, humid afternoons in the spring and summer. In both cases, the warm, humid air rises rapidly. As the air rises, it cools, forming dense thunderheads. Heavy rain falls, sometimes along with hail.

Thunderstorms produce strong upward and downward winds—updrafts and downdrafts—inside clouds. When a downdraft strikes the ground, the air spreads out in all directions, producing bursts of wind called wind shear. Wind shear has caused a number of airplane accidents during takeoff or landing.

Lightning and Thunder During a thunderstorm, areas of positive and negative electrical charges build up in the storm clouds. **Lightning** is a sudden spark, or energy discharge, as these charges jump between parts of a cloud, between nearby clouds, or between a cloud and the ground. Lightning is similar to the shocks you sometimes feel when you touch a metal object on a very dry day, but on a much larger scale.

What causes thunder? A lightning bolt can heat the air near it to as much as 30,000°C, much hotter than the surface of the sun. The rapidly heated air expands suddenly and explosively. Thunder is the sound of the explosion. Because light travels faster than sound, you see lightning before you hear thunder.

Thunderstorm Safety When lightning strikes the ground, the hot, expanding air can start forest fires. When lightning strikes people or animals, it acts like a powerful electric shock. Being struck by lightning can cause unconsciousness, serious burns, or even heart failure.

What should you do to remain safe if you are caught outside during a thunderstorm? **During thunderstorms, avoid touching metal objects because they can conduct electricity from lightning into your body.** Lightning usually strikes the tallest nearby object, such as a tree, house, or flagpole. To protect buildings from lightning, people install metal lightning rods at the highest point on a roof. Lightning rods intercept a lightning stroke and conduct the electricity through cables safely into the ground.

In open spaces, such as a golf course, people can be in danger because they are the tallest objects in the area. It is equally dangerous to seek shelter under a tree, because lightning may strike the tree and you at the same time. Instead, find a low area away from trees, fences, and poles. Crouch with your head down and your hands on your knees. If you are swimming or in a boat, get to shore and find shelter away from the water.

If you are inside a house during a thunderstorm, avoid touching telephones, electrical appliances, or plumbing fixtures, all of which can conduct electricity into the house. It is usually safe to stay in a car with a hard top during a thunderstorm because the electricity will move along the metal skin of the car and jump to the ground. However, do not touch any metal inside the car.

☑ *Checkpoint* *Why is lightning dangerous?*

Figure 8 Lightning occurs when electricity jumps within clouds, between clouds, or between a cloud and the ground.

Tornadoes

A tornado is one of the most frightening and destructive types of storms. A **tornado** is a rapidly whirling, funnel-shaped cloud that reaches down from a storm cloud to touch Earth's surface. If a tornado occurs over a lake or ocean, it is known as a waterspout. Tornadoes are usually brief, but can be deadly. They may touch the ground for 15 minutes or less and be only a few hundred meters across, but wind speeds may approach 480 kilometers per hour.

How Tornadoes Form Tornadoes develop in low, heavy cumulonimbus clouds—the same type of clouds that brings thunderstorms. Tornadoes are most likely to occur when thunderstorms are likely—in spring and early summer, often late in the afternoon when the ground is warm. The Great Plains often have the kind of weather pattern that is likely to create tornadoes: a warm, humid air mass moves north from the Gulf of Mexico into the lower Great Plains. A cold, dry air mass moves south from Canada. When the air masses meet, the cold air moves under the warm air, which rises. A squall line of thunderstorms is likely to form, with storms traveling from southwest to northeast. A single squall line can cause 10 or more tornadoes.

Tornadoes occur more often in the United States than in any other country. About 800 tornadoes occur in the United States

SCIENCE & History

Weather That Changed History

Unanticipated storms have caused incredible damage, killed numbers of people, and even changed the course of history.

1281 Japan

In an attempt to conquer Japan, Kublai Khan, the Mongol emperor of China, sent a fleet of ships carrying a huge army. A hurricane from the Pacific brought high winds and towering waves that sank the ships. The Japanese named the storm *kamikaze,* meaning "divine wind."

1620 Massachusetts

English Pilgrims set sail for the Americas in the *Mayflower.* They had planned to land near the mouth of the Hudson River, but turned back north because of rough seas and storms. When the Pilgrims landed farther north, they decided to stay and so established Plymouth Colony.

1300	1400	1500	1600

1588 England

King Philip II of Spain sent the Spanish Armada, a fleet of 130 ships, to invade England. Strong winds in the English Channel trapped the Armada near shore. Some Spanish ships escaped, but storms wrecked most of them.

every year. Weather patterns on the Great Plains, shown on the next page in Figure 9, result in a "tornado alley" that runs from Texas across Oklahoma, Kansas, and Nebraska. However, tornadoes can and do occur in nearly every part of the United States.

☑ *Checkpoint* **Where do tornadoes form?**

Tornado Safety A tornado can level houses on one street, but leave neighboring houses standing. Tornado damage comes from both strong winds and flying debris. The low pressure inside the tornado sucks up dust and other objects into the funnel. Tornadoes can move large objects—sheds, trailers, cars—and scatter debris many miles away. One tornado tore off a motel sign in Broken Bow, Oklahoma, and dropped it 30 miles away in Arkansas!

INTEGRATING HEALTH

In Your Journal

Some of these events happened before forecasters had the equipment to predict weather scientifically. Choose one of the events in the time line. Write a paragraph describing how history might have been different if the people involved had had accurate weather predictions.

1869 Great Lakes

Learning that more than 1,900 boats had sunk in storms on the Great Lakes in 1869, Congress decided to set up a national weather service, the Army Signal Corps. In 1891, the job of issuing weather warnings and forecasts went to a new agency, the U.S. Weather Bureau.

| 1700 | 1800 | 1900 |

1837 North Carolina

The steamship *Home* sank during a hurricane off Ocracoke, North Carolina. In one of the worst storm-caused disasters at sea, 90 people died. In response, the U.S. Congress passed a law requiring seagoing ships to carry a life preserver for every passenger.

1915 Texas

When a hurricane struck the port city of Galveston in 1900, it killed 6,000 people and destroyed much of the city. As a result, a seawall 5 meters high and 16 kilometers long was built. When another hurricane struck in 1915, the seawall greatly reduced the amount of damage.

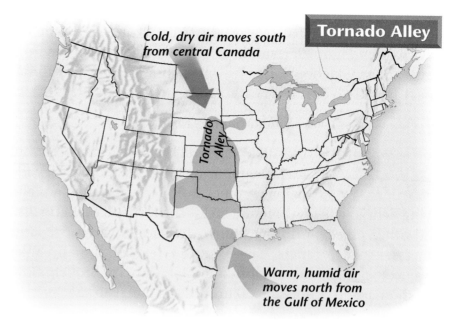

Cold, dry air moves south from central Canada

Tornado Alley

Warm, humid air moves north from the Gulf of Mexico

What should you do if a tornado is predicted in your area? A "tornado watch" is an announcement that tornadoes are possible in your area. You should watch for approaching thunderstorms. A "tornado warning" is an announcement that a tornado has been seen in the sky or on weather radar. If you hear a tornado warning, move to a safe area as soon as you can. Do not wait until you actually see the tornado.

The safest place to be during a tornado is in the basement of a well-built building. If the building you are in does not have a basement, move to the middle of the ground floor. Stay away from windows and doors that could break and fly through the air. Lie on the floor under a sturdy piece of furniture, such as a large table. If you are outdoors or in a car or mobile home, move to a building or lie flat in a ditch.

☑ *Checkpoint* *What is the difference between a tornado watch and a tornado warning?*

Hurricanes

Between June and November, people who live in the eastern United States hear weather reports much like this: "A hurricane warning has been issued for the Atlantic coast from Florida to North Carolina. Hurricane Michael has winds of over 160 kilometers per hour and is moving north at about 65 kilometers per hour." A **hurricane** is a tropical storm that has winds of 119 kilometers per hour or higher. A typical hurricane is about 600 kilometers across.

Hurricanes also form in the Pacific and Indian oceans. In the western Pacific Ocean, hurricanes are called typhoons. Although hurricanes may be destructive, they bring much-needed rainfall to South Asia and Southeast Asia.

Figure 9 A tornado can cause a lot of damage in a short period of time. The map shows where tornadoes are most likely to occur in the United States.
Interpreting Maps *Which states are partially located in "tornado alley"?*

How Hurricanes Form A typical hurricane that strikes the United States forms in the Atlantic Ocean north of the equator in August, September, or October. **A hurricane begins over warm water as a low-pressure area, or tropical disturbance.** If the tropical disturbance grows in size and strength, it becomes a tropical storm, which may then become a hurricane.

A hurricane gets its energy from the warm, humid air at the ocean's surface. As this air rises and forms clouds, more air is drawn into the system. As with other storm systems, winds spiral inward toward the areas of low pressure. Inside the storm are bands of very high winds and heavy rains. The lowest air pressure and warmest temperatures are at the center of the hurricane. The lower the air pressure at the center of a storm, the faster the winds blow toward the center. Hurricane winds may be as strong as 320 kilometers per hour.

The Eye of the Hurricane The center of a hurricane is a ring of clouds surrounding a quiet "eye," as shown in Figure 10. If you were in the path of a hurricane, you would notice that the wind gets stronger as the eye approaches. When the eye arrives, the weather changes suddenly. The winds grow calm and the sky may clear. After the eye passes, the storm resumes, but the wind blows from the opposite direction.

How Hurricanes Move Hurricanes last longer than other storms, usually a week or more. Hurricanes that form in the Atlantic Ocean are steered by easterly trade winds toward the Caribbean islands and the southeastern United States. After a hurricane passes over land, it no longer has warm, moist air to draw energy from. The hurricane gradually slows down and loses strength, although heavy rainfall may continue for a number of days.

Figure 10 In a hurricane, air moves rapidly around a low-pressure area called the eye. *Observing Where is the eye of the hurricane in the photograph?*

Cloud layer

Path of wind flow

Eye

Warm, moist air rises

Rain

Rain

Ocean surface

Hurricane Damage When a hurricane comes ashore, it brings high waves and severe flooding as well as wind damage. Hurricanes uproot trees, smash buildings, and destroy power lines.

One of the most dangerous features of a hurricane is the storm surge. The low pressure and high winds of the hurricane over the ocean raise the level of the water up to six meters above normal sea level. The result is a **storm surge,** a "dome" of water that sweeps across the coast where the hurricane lands. As the hurricane comes onshore, the water comes with it. Storm surges can cause great damage, washing away beaches and buildings.

Hurricane Safety Until the 1950s, a fast-moving hurricane

INTEGRATING HEALTH could strike with little warning. Since then, advances in communications and satellite tracking have made hurricanes less deadly. People now receive information well in advance of an approaching hurricane.

A "hurricane watch" is an announcement that hurricane conditions are *possible* in your area within the next 36 hours. People should be prepared to **evacuate** (ee VAK yoo ayt), or move away temporarily.

A "hurricane warning" means that hurricane conditions are *expected* within 24 hours. **If you hear a hurricane warning and are told to evacuate, leave the area immediately.** If you must stay in a house, move to the interior of the building, away from windows.

☑ *Checkpoint* **What is a storm surge?**

Winter Storms

In the winter in the northern United States, much precipitation falls as snow. **Snow falls when humid air cools below 0°C.** Heavy snowfalls can block roads, trapping people in their homes and making it hard for emergency vehicles to move.

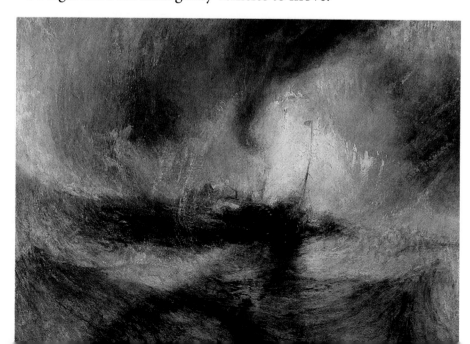

Figure 11 The British artist J.M.W. Turner painted "Snow Storm" in 1842.

Lake-Effect Snow Two of the snowiest cities in the United States are Buffalo and Rochester in upstate New York. On average, nearly three meters of snow falls on each of these cities every winter. Why do Buffalo and Rochester get so much snow?

Study Figure 12. Notice that Buffalo is located to the east of Lake Erie, and Rochester is located to the south of Lake Ontario. In the fall and winter, the land near these lakes cools much more rapidly than the water in the lakes. Although the water in these lakes is cold, it is still much warmer than the surrounding land and air. When a cold, dry air mass moves from central Canada southeast across one of the Great Lakes, it picks up water vapor and heat from the lake. As soon as the air mass reaches the other side of the lake, the air rises and cools again. The water vapor condenses and falls as snow, most often within 40 kilometers of the lake.

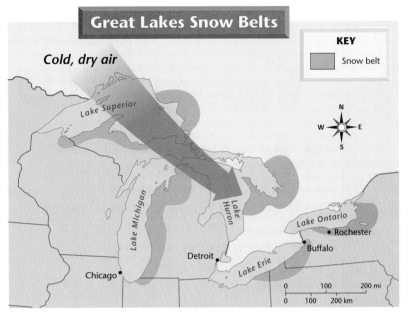

Great Lakes Snow Belts

KEY

Snow belt

Cold, dry air

Lake Superior

Lake Michigan

Lake Huron

Lake Ontario

• Rochester

Buffalo

Detroit •

Chicago •

Lake Erie

0   100   200 mi
0   100   200 km

Figure 12 As cold dry air moves across the warmer water, it picks up water vapor. When the air reaches land and cools, lake-effect snow falls. *Interpreting Maps Which two cities receive large amounts of snow?*

Snowstorm Safety Imagine being out in a snowstorm when **INTEGRATING HEALTH** the wind suddenly picks up. High winds can blow falling snow sideways or pick up snow from the ground and suspend it in the air. This situation can be extremely dangerous because the blowing snow makes it easy to get lost. Strong winds also cool a person's body rapidly. **If you are caught in a snowstorm, try to find shelter from the wind.** Cover exposed parts of your body and try to stay dry. If you are in a car, the driver should keep the engine running only if the exhaust pipe is clear of snow.

Section 2 Review

1. What weather conditions are most likely to cause thunderstorms and tornadoes?
2. What is the most common path for the hurricanes that strike the United States?
3. What safety precautions should you take if a tornado is predicted in your area? If a hurricane is predicted in your area?
4. **Thinking Critically** Applying Concepts In the winter, cool, humid air from the Pacific Ocean blows across the cold land of southern Alaska. What kind of storm do you think this causes?

Science at Home

Storm Experiences Interview a family member or other adult about a dramatic storm that he or she has experienced. Before the interview, make a list of questions you would like to ask. For example, how old was the person when the storm occurred? When and where did the storm occur? Write up your interview in a question-and-answer format, beginning with a short introduction.

Real-World Lab

Tracking a HURRICANE

Hurricane alert! You work at the National Hurricane Center. It is your job to track the paths of hurricanes and try to predict when and where a hurricane is likely to strike land. Then you must decide whether to warn people in the area to evacuate.

Problem

How can you predict when and where a hurricane will come ashore?

Skills Focus

interpreting data, predicting

Materials

ruler
red, blue, green, and brown pencils
tracing paper

Procedure

1. Look at the plotted path of the hurricane on the map. Each dot represents the location of the eye of the hurricane at six-hour intervals. The last dot shows where the hurricane was located at noon on August 30.

2. Predict the path you think the hurricane will take. Place tracing paper over the map below. Using a red pencil, place an X on your tracing paper where you think the hurricane will first reach land. Next to your X, write the date and time you think the hurricane will come ashore.

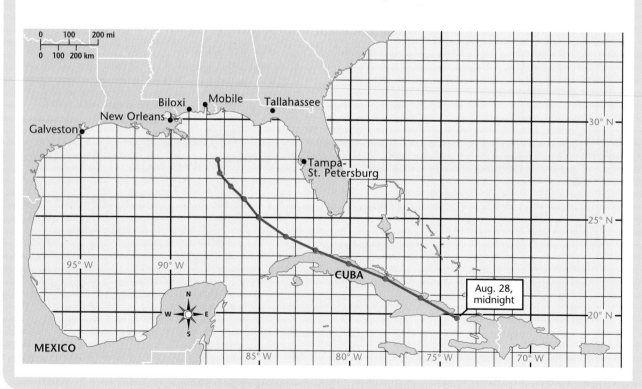

3. Hurricane warnings are issued for an area that is likely to experience a hurricane within 24 hours. On your tracing paper, shade in red the area for which you would issue a hurricane warning.

4. Using the following data table, plot the next five positions for the storm using a blue pencil. Use your ruler to connect the dots to show the hurricane's path.

Date and Time	Latitude	Longitude
August 30, 6:00 P.M.	28.3° N	86.8° W
August 31, midnight	28.4° N	86.0° W
August 31, 6:00 A.M.	28.6° N	85.3° W
August 31, noon	28.8° N	84.4° W
August 31, 6:00 P.M.	28.8° N	84.0° W

5. Based on the new data, decide if you need to change your prediction of where and when the hurricane will come ashore. Mark your new predictions in blue pencil on your tracing paper.

6. During September 1, you obtain four more positions. (Plot these points only after you have completed Step 5.) Based on these new data, mark in green pencil when and where you now think the hurricane will come ashore.

Date and Time	Latitude	Longitude
September 1, midnight	28.8° N	83.8° W
September 1, 6:00 A.M.	28.6° N	83.9° W
September 1, noon	28.6° N	84.2° W
September 1, 6:00 P.M.	28.9° N	84.8° W

7. The next day, September 2, you plot four more positions using a brown pencil. (Plot these points only after you have completed Step 6.)

Date and Time	Latitude	Longitude
September 2, midnight	29.4° N	85.9° W
September 2, 6:00 A.M.	29.7° N	87.3° W
September 2, noon	30.2° N	88.8° W
September 2, 6:00 P.M.	31.0° N	90.4° W

Analyze and Conclude

1. Describe in detail the complete path of the hurricane you tracked. Include where it came ashore and identify any cities that were in the vicinity.
2. How did your predictions in Steps 2, 5, and 6 compare to what actually happened?
3. What was unusual about your hurricane's path?
4. How do you think hurricanes with a path like this one affect the issuing of hurricane warnings?
5. Why do you have to be so careful when issuing warnings? What problems might be caused if you issued an unnecessary hurricane warning? What might happen if a hurricane warning were issued too late?
6. **Think About It** In this activity you only had data for the hurricane's position. If you were tracking a hurricane and issuing warnings, what other types of information would help you make decisions about the hurricane's path?

More to Explore

With your teacher's help, search the Internet for more hurricane tracking data. Map the data and try to predict where the hurricane will come ashore.

Hurricane Alert: To Stay or Not To Stay?

When a hurricane sweeps in from the ocean, the National Hurricane Center tracks the storm's course. Radio stations broadcast warnings. Sirens blow, and people in the storm path take steps to protect their homes and families.

State and local governments may try to keep people safe by closing state offices, setting up emergency shelters, and alerting the National Guard. As the danger increases, a state's governor can order the evacuation of people from dangerous areas. These actions are meant to protect public safety.

But not everyone wants to evacuate. Some people believe they have the right to stay. And officials cannot make people obey an evacuation order. How much can—or should—the government do to keep people safe?

The Issues

Why Play It Safe? Hurricanes can be extremely dangerous. High winds blow off roofs and shatter windows. Flash floods and storm surges can wash away houses. Even after the storm blows away, officials may need to keep people from returning home because of flooded sewers or broken power lines and gas mains.

In recent years, earlier and more accurate forecasts have saved lives. People now have time to prepare and to get out of the hurricane's path. Emergency officials urge people—especially the elderly, sick, or disabled—to leave early while the weather is still good. Most casualties happen when people are taken by surprise or ignore warnings. Those who decide to stay may later have to be rescued by boat or helicopter. These rescues add to the expense of the storm and may put the lives of rescuers in danger.

Why Ride Out the Storm? People have different reasons for not wanting to evacuate. Some want to protect their homes or businesses. Others don't want to leave pets or farm animals or go to public shelters. Store owners may stay open to sell disaster supplies. In addition, warnings may exaggerate the potential danger, urging people to leave when they might actually be safe. Since leaving can be expensive and disruptive, residents have to carefully evaluate the risks.

Is It a Matter of Rights? Should a government have the power to make people evacuate? Some citizens argue that the government should not tell them what to do as long as they are not harming others. They believe that individuals should have the right to decide for themselves. What do you think?

You Decide

1. Identify the Problem

In your own words, explain the controversy around hurricane evacuations.

2. Analyze the Options

Review and list the pros and cons of forcing people to evacuate. What people benefit? Who might be harmed? What more, if anything, should government officials do? What more could citizens do?

3. Find a Solution

Imagine that the radio has broadcast a hurricane warning. Write a dialogue in which you and members of your family discuss the options and decide whether or not to evacuate.

SECTION 3 Floods

DISCOVER •• **ACTIVITY**

What Causes Floods?

1. Fill a cup with water. Hold a funnel above a basin and pour the water very slowly into the funnel.

2. Refill the cup with the same amount of water you used in Step 1. Hold the funnel above the basin and this time pour the water rapidly into the funnel. What happens?

Think It Over

Inferring How is a funnel like a river valley? What do you think would happen if a large amount of water entered a river valley in a short period of time?

Antelope Canyon in the northern Arizona desert is only a few meters wide in places. On August 12, 1997, a group of 12 hikers entered the dry, narrow canyon. That afternoon a severe thunderstorm dropped several inches of rain on the Kaibeto Plateau, 24 kilometers away. Dry stream channels that drain into Antelope Canyon quickly filled with rainwater. The water rushed into the canyon, creating a wall of water over 3 meters high. Tourists at the top of the canyon watched in horror as the water swept the hikers away. Only one hiker survived.

Are you surprised that floods can occur in a desert? Actually, floods like this are more common in the dry Southwest than in areas with more rain.

GUIDE FOR READING

◆ What causes flooding?

◆ How can people protect themselves in a flood?

Reading Tip As you read, draw a flowchart showing what can happen during a flood and how people should respond to it.

Key Term flash flood

Figure 13 From the top, Antelope Canyon looks like a narrow slit in the ground.

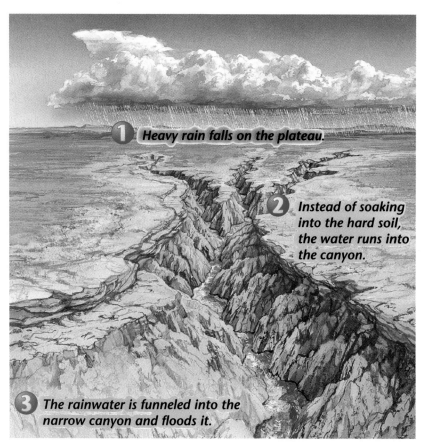

① *Heavy rain falls on the plateau.*

② *Instead of soaking into the hard soil, the water runs into the canyon.*

③ *The rainwater is funneled into the narrow canyon and floods it.*

Figure 14 Flash floods occur when large amounts of rain are funneled into a narrow valley. This drawing shows what happened in the Antelope Canyon flood.

Flash Floods

Although movies feature the violent winds of tornadoes and hurricanes, floods are the most dangerous weather-related events in the United States. **Floods occur when so much water pours into a stream or river that it overflows its banks and covers the land on either side of the channel.** People who live along certain rivers know that melting snow and spring rains are likely to bring floods.

Unexpected floods are the most dangerous. Floods like the Antelope Canyon flood are called flash floods because the water rises very rapidly—"in a flash"—after it begins to rain heavily. A **flash flood** is a sudden, violent flood that occurs within a few hours, or even minutes, of a storm.

Most flash floods are due to large amounts of rain. For example, a line of thunderstorms may remain over an area, dropping heavy rain for several hours or days. Hurricanes or tropical storms bring downpours that quickly fill stream channels. A flash flood can also be caused by a dam breaking, releasing millions of liters of water all at once. Similarly, if ice that has jammed a river breaks free, the sudden rush of water can cause a flash flood.

☑ *Checkpoint* *Why are flash floods so dangerous?*

Flood Safety Measures

If you've never been in a flood, it's hard to imagine the awesome power of rushing water. What can people do to protect themselves and their homes?

Predicting Floods Advance warnings can help reduce flood damage and loss of life. Weather satellites supply information about snow cover so that scientists can estimate how much water will run into rivers when the snow melts. Radar can track and measure the size of an approaching rainstorm. Scientists check river gauges that measure water levels. With this information, forecasters can predict flood heights at different points along a river. Their goal is to issue warnings early enough to help people prepare and evacuate if necessary.

The car stalls in the water.

Moving water pushes against the car.

As the water rises, the car begins to float.

Sixty centimeters of water can wash a car away.

Figure 15 These drawings show what can happen to a car in a flood. *Applying Concepts Why is it dangerous to stay in a car in a flood?*

A "flood watch" is an announcement describing the area in which flooding is possible. Stay alert for more news. A "flood warning" is an announcement that floods have already been reported or are about to occur. It's time to take action!

Emergency Safety What should *you* do in case of a flood? When the danger becomes too great or the water rises too high, people are usually evacuated. **The first rule of flood safety is to move to higher ground and stay away from flood waters.** Don't try to cross streams and rivers that look as if they're flooded. Playing in flood waters may look like fun, but it's dangerous. A few centimeters of fast-moving water can sweep you off your feet. Even the storm drain on a city street can draw you in.

If your family is in a car, the driver shouldn't try to drive on a flooded road. Sometimes less than 60 centimeters of fast-moving water can sweep a car away, as shown in Figure 15. Everyone should leave the car and move to higher ground.

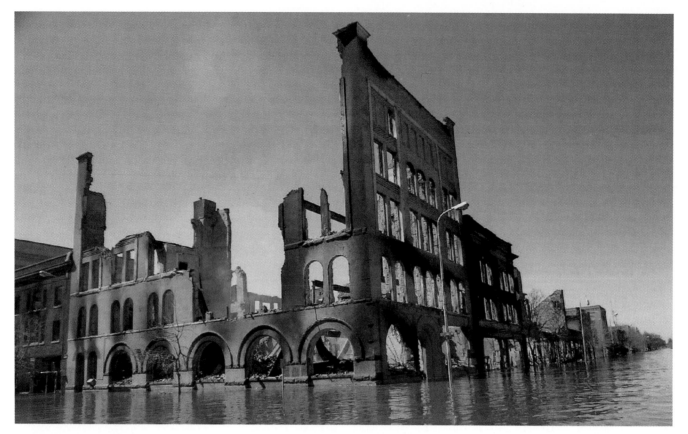

Figure 16 In the spring of 1997, the Red River of the North flooded regions of North Dakota and Minnesota. A large part of flooded downtown Grand Forks burned down because fire trucks could not get to the scene of the fire or connect to any fire hydrants.

Other Flood Hazards High water is not the only hazard in a flood. Floods can knock down electrical poles and wires, cutting off power supplies. Flood waters can also saturate soil, causing landslides or mudslides. If roads have been flooded or washed away, emergency vehicles such as fire trucks and ambulances may not be able to get through.

Flood waters can wash into wells and water treatment plants, polluting the water. Therefore, be careful with food and water that flood waters have touched. Boil water before drinking it to be sure it is safe.

 Section 3 Review

1. How can precipitation cause flooding?
2. How can you stay safe during a flood?
3. What is the difference between a flood watch and a flood warning?
4. Name three tools that supply information used in forecasting floods and providing flood information.
5. **Thinking Critically Predicting** Describe two weather situations in which you would expect floods to occur.

CHAPTER PROJECT

Check Your Progress

Now you are ready to predict tomorrow's weather. Look at today's weather map. Then predict tomorrow's weather both where you live and in the two other locations you selected. (*Project Hint:* Refer to the weather patterns you have been observing.) Decide what symbols you will need to use. Then, on an outline map of the United States, draw symbols to show what you think tomorrow's weather will be. Continue to make predictions every day for at least a week.

SECTION
4 Predicting Weather Change

DISCOVER ACTIVITY

What's the Weather?

1. Look at the weather report in your local newspaper. Note what weather conditions are predicted for your area today, including temperature, precipitation, and wind speed.

2. Look out the window or think about what it was like the last time you were outside. Write down the actual weather conditions where you are.

Think It Over

Observing Does the weather report match what you observe? What is the same? What is different?

For centuries, people have tried to predict the weather. Every nation's folklore includes weather sayings. Many of these sayings are based on long-term observations. Sailors, pilots, farmers, and others who work outdoors are usually careful observers of clouds, winds, and other signs of coming changes in the weather. Here are two examples:

> *Evening red and morning gray*
> *Will send the traveler on his way;*
> *Evening gray and morning red*
> *Will bring down rain upon his head.*
>
> *Red sky in morning,*
> *sailors take warning;*
> *Red sky at night, sailor's delight.*

GUIDE FOR READING

◆ How does technology help forecasters predict the weather?

◆ What types of information are shown on weather maps?

Reading Tip Before you read, preview Figure 19 and *Exploring Newspaper Weather Maps.* Write a list of any questions you have about weather maps.

Key Terms meteorologist • El Niño • isobar • isotherm

Why do these two weather sayings agree that a red morning sky means bad weather? Recall that in the United States, storms usually move from west to east. Clouds in the west may indicate an advancing low-pressure area, bringing stormy weather. If there are high clouds in the west in the morning, the rising sun in the east turns these clouds red. The reverse is true at sunset. As the sun sets in the west, it turns clouds in the east red. Clouds in the east may indicate that a storm is moving away to the east.

Weather Forecasting

You can make many predictions from your own observations. For example, if a barometer shows that the air pressure is falling, you can expect a change in the weather. Falling air pressure usually indicates an approaching low-pressure area, possibly bringing rain or snow.

You can read weather signs in the clouds too. Cumulus clouds often form on warm afternoons when warm air rises. If you see these clouds growing larger and taller, you can expect them to become cumulonimbus clouds, which may bring a thunderstorm. Thin cirrus clouds high in the sky may indicate that a low-pressure area is approaching.

Even careful weather observers often turn to professional meteorologists for television weather information. You may hear the person who gives the television weather report referred to as a meteorologist. Despite their name, meteorologists don't study meteors. **Meteorologists** (mee tee uh RAWL uh jists) are scientists who study the causes of weather and try to predict it.

Figure 17 These meteorologists are releasing a weather balloon. The box attached to the balloon contains instruments that will record weather data—such as temperature, pressure, and humidity—high in the troposphere.

Meteorologists interpret information from a variety of sources, including local weather observers, instruments carried by balloons, satellites, and weather stations around the world. They use maps, charts, and computers to analyze the data and to prepare weather forecasts. Meteorologists use radar to track areas of rain or snow, so that forecasters can follow the path of a storm system.

Where do television and radio weather reporters get their information? A lot of weather information comes from the National Weather Service. However, weather forecasts for the general public may not have enough detail to be useful to farmers and pilots. There are also private weather-forecasting services, many of which use advanced, high-technology equipment. Private forecasting services are useful to people who need to answer questions like these: "Will the frost hurt the oranges in my grove?" "Will the airport be fogged in?" "Will the trucks need to spread sand on the roads today?"

✓ *Checkpoint* *Where do meteorologists get weather information?*

Figure 18 This satellite photo shows an intense storm over the North Atlantic Ocean.
Observing *What weather-related information can you see in the photo?*

Warmer   Colder

Weather Technology

Techniques for predicting weather have changed rapidly in recent years. Short-range forecasts—forecasts for up to five days—are now fairly reliable. Meteorologists can also make long-range predictions that were once impossible. **Changes in technology have occurred in two areas: gathering weather data and using computers to make forecasts.**

Weather Balloons and Satellites As you learned in Chapter 13, weather balloons carry instruments high into the troposphere and stratosphere. The instruments measure temperature, air pressure, and humidity.

The first weather satellite was launched in 1960. Cameras on weather satellites in the exosphere can photograph Earth's surface, clouds, storms, and ice and snow cover. These images are then transmitted to meteorologists on Earth, who interpret the information.

Computer Forecasts Computers are widely used to help *INTEGRATING TECHNOLOGY* forecast weather. Instruments can now gather thousands of bits of data about temperature, air pressure, wind speed, and other factors. Computers process large amounts of information quickly to help forecasters make predictions. To make a forecast, the computer starts with weather conditions reported from weather stations over a large area. Conditions reported include wind speed and direction, humidity, sunlight, temperature, and air pressure. Then the computer works through thousands of calculations and makes forecasts for 12 hours, 24 hours, 36 hours, and so on. Each forecast builds on the previous forecast. When new weather data come in, the computer revises its forecasts.

El Niño

Some long-term weather patterns may be caused by changes in ocean currents and global winds. Periodically, a warm-water event known as **El Niño** occurs in the tropical Pacific Ocean. During an El Niño event, winds shift and push warm surface water toward the west coast of South America. The warm water replaces the cold water that usually rises from the deep ocean near the coast.

El Niño events occur once every two to seven years. They can cause dramatic climate changes around the Pacific Ocean and in other places. In the winter of 1997 and 1998, a strong El Niño current caused droughts in Asia and Brazil, heavy rains and floods in California and Peru, and tornadoes in Florida and other parts of the southeastern United States.

Scientists have looked for clues and warnings to help predict the return of El Niño. One signal is rising surface temperatures in the tropical part of the Pacific Ocean. Using data gathered during past El Niño events, scientists were able to predict many of the results of the 1997–1998 El Niño.

✓ *Checkpoint* *What evidence do scientists use to predict an El Niño?*

Reading Weather Maps

A weather map is a "snapshot" of conditions at a particular time over a large area. There are many different types of weather maps. Television forecasters often present maps generated by computers from radar information.

Weather Service Maps Data from more than 300 local weather stations all over the country are assembled into weather maps at the National Weather Service. The information collected by a typical reporting station is summarized in the key to Figure 19. The weather map, which has been simplified, includes most of the weather station data shown in the key.

On some weather maps, you see curved lines. These lines connect places where certain conditions—temperature or air pressure—are the same. **Isobars** are lines joining places on the map that have the same air pressure. (*Iso* means "equal" and *bar* means "pressure.") The numbers on the isobars are the pressure readings. Air pressure readings may be given in inches of mercury or in millibars or both. Figure 19 has isobars.

Isotherms are lines joining places that have the same temperature. The isotherm may be labeled with the temperature in degrees Fahrenheit, degrees Celsius, or both.

Sharpen your Skills

Interpreting Data

ACTIVITY

Use the key to Figure 19 to help you answer the questions about this weather station data.

1. What is the temperature at this station?
2. What is the wind speed?
3. Which way is the wind blowing?
4. What is the air pressure?
5. What percent of the sky is covered by clouds?
6. What type of precipitation, if any, is falling?

Weather Map

EXPLANATION OF FRONTS

▼▼▼ Cold Front
Boundary between a cold air mass and a warm air mass. Brings brief storms and cooler weather.

⌒⌒ Warm Front
Boundary between a warm air mass and a cold air mass. Usually accompanied by precipitation.

⌒▼ Stationary Front
Boundary between a warm air mass and a cold air mass when no movement occurs. Brings long periods of precipitation.

▲▲ Occluded Front
Boundary on which a warm front has been overtaken by a cold front. Brings precipitation.

Weather	Symbol
Drizzle	❟
Fog	≡
Hail	△
Haze	∞
Rain	●
Shower	▽
Sleet	⊿
Smoke	⌇
Snow	✳
Thunderstorm	⚡
Hurricane	❧

Wind Speed (mph)	Symbol
1–2	
3–8	
9–14	
15–20	
21–25	
26–31	
32–37	
38–43	
44–49	
50–54	
55–60	
61–66	
67–71	
72–77	

Cloud Cover (%)	Symbol
0	○
10	◐
20–30	◔
40	◑
50	◑
60	◕
70–80	◕
90	◕
100	●

How Symbols Are Used on a Weather Map

Amount of cloud cover (100%)
Atmospheric pressure (millibars)
Temperature (°F)
38   ● 1018
Wind direction (from the southwest)
Wind speed (21–25mph)

Figure 19 This weather map shows data collected from weather stations all over the country. Below the map is an explanation of what the symbols at each city mean.

Newspaper Weather Maps Maps in newspapers are simplified versions of maps produced by the National Weather Service. *Exploring Newspaper Weather Maps* shows a typical newspaper weather map. From what you have learned in this chapter, you can probably interpret most of the symbols on this map. **Standard symbols on weather maps show fronts, areas of high and low pressure, types of precipitation, and temperatures.** Note that the high and low temperatures are given in degrees Fahrenheit instead of Celsius.

The maps in Figure 20 show the path of a winter storm. If you study the maps carefully, you can track this storm and its effects. With practice, you can use information from weather maps to help you predict the weather in your area.

The Butterfly Effect

Even with current technology, weather forecasting is tricky. The main reason is that weather patterns do not follow an orderly, step-by-step process.

A forecast for the weather six days from now is based on forecasts for all the days between now and then. A small change in the weather today can mean a larger change in the weather a week later! This is the so-called butterfly effect. The name refers to a scientist's suggestion that even the flapping of a butterfly's wings causes a tiny disturbance in the atmosphere. This tiny event might cause a larger disturbance that could—eventually—grow into a hurricane.

DAY 1

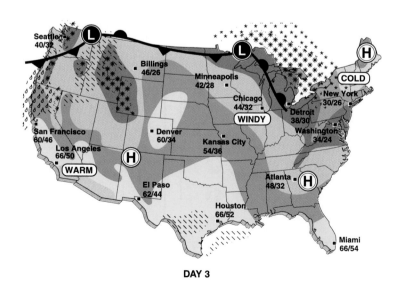

DAY 2

DAY 3

Figure 20 These weather maps show a storm moving from west to east over a three-day period.
Interpreting Diagrams *What were the high and low temperatures in Chicago on Day 2? On Day 3?*

EXPLORING Newspaper Weather Maps

Weather maps in newspapers use symbols to show fronts, high and low pressure areas, and precipitation. Color bands indicate different temperatures.

Major low-pressure areas are shown with an "L." High-pressure areas are shown with an "H."

Areas in the same temperature range are shown in the same color. For example, light green areas have high temperatures in the 40s.

Seattle 45/37

COLD

Billings 38/25

Minneapolis 32/26

Chicago 36/28

CHILLY

New York 44/34

Detroit 37/26

San Francisco 55/42

Denver 40/22

Kansas City 34/30

Washington 48/33

H

Los Angeles 60/48

DFW Metroplex 66/46

WINDY

El Paso 58/40

Houston 70/50

Atlanta 42/38

L

Miami 74/60

Symbols that look like raindrops or snowflakes show precipitation.

The triangles showing a cold front point in the direction the cold air is moving. The half-circles indicating a warm front show the direction the warm air is moving.

Section 4 Review

1. What kinds of technology do meteorologists use to help predict the weather?
2. Name at least three types of information you could get from a weather map of your area.
3. What lines on a weather map connect points that have the same temperature?
4. **Thinking Critically** **Predicting** If you observe that air pressure is rising, what kind of weather do you think is coming?

> **Check Your Progress** CHAPTER PROJECT
> After a week of predicting the weather, you are ready to compare your predictions to the actual weather that occurred. Then compare your predictions with those made by professional meteorologists. How accurate were your predictions? How accurate were the predictions made by professional meteorologists?

Skills Lab

Reading a Weather Map

I n this lab, you will interpret data from a weather map to describe weather conditions in various places.

Problem

How does a weather map communicate data?

Procedure

1. Examine the symbols on the weather map below. For more information about the symbols used on the map, refer to Figure 19 on page 523 and to *Exploring Newspaper Weather Maps* on page 525.
2. Observe the different colors on the weather map.
3. Find the symbols for snow and rain.
4. Locate the warm fronts and cold fronts.
5. Locate the symbols for high and low pressure.

Analyze and Conclude

1. What color represents the highest temperatures? What color represents the lowest temperatures?

2. What city has the highest temperature? What city has the lowest temperature?
3. Where on the map is it raining? Where on the map is it snowing?
4. How many different kinds of fronts are shown on the map?
5. How many areas of low pressure are shown on the map? How many areas of high pressure are shown on the map?
6. What season does this map represent? How do you know?
7. **Think About It** The triangles and semicircles on the front lines show which way the front is moving. What front is moving toward Minneapolis? What kind of weather do you think it will bring?

More to Explore

Compare this weather map with the weather map shown in a television news report. Which symbols on these maps are similar? Which symbols are different?

SECTION 1 Air Masses and Fronts

Key Ideas

- Four major types of air masses influence the weather in North America: maritime tropical, continental tropical, maritime polar, and continental polar.
- When air masses collide, they form four types of fronts: cold fronts, warm fronts, stationary fronts, and occluded fronts.
- Cyclones and decreasing air pressure are associated with storms and precipitation.

Key Terms

air mass	maritime	occluded
tropical	continental	cyclone
polar	front	anticyclone

SECTION 2 Storms

Key Ideas

- Thunderstorms and tornadoes form within large cumulonimbus clouds. During thunderstorms, avoid touching metal objects.
- A hurricane begins over warm water as a low-pressure area. If you hear a hurricane warning and are told to evacuate, leave the area immediately.
- Snow falls when humid air cools below 0°C. If you are caught in a snowstorm, try to find shelter from the wind.

Key Terms

storm	tornado	storm surge
lightning	hurricane	evacuate

SECTION 3 Floods

INTEGRATING HEALTH

Key Ideas

- Floods occur when so much water pours into a stream or river that it overflows its banks on either side of the channel.
- The first rule of flood safety is to move to higher ground and stay away from flood waters.

Key Term

flash flood

SECTION 4 Predicting Weather Change

Key Ideas

- Meteorologists interpret weather information from local weather observers, instruments carried by balloons, satellites, and weather stations around the world.
- Changes in weather technology have occurred in two areas: gathering weather data and using computers to make forecasts.
- Standard symbols on weather maps show fronts, areas of high and low pressure, types of precipitation, and temperatures.

Key Terms

meteorologist
El Niño
isobar
isotherm

Organizing Information

Compare/Contrast Table Copy the compare/contrast table about hurricanes and tornadoes onto a separate sheet of paper. Then fill in the empty spaces and add a title. (For more on compare/contrast tables, see the Skills Handbook.)

Type of Storm	Hurricane	Tornado
Where storm forms	Over warm ocean water	a. __?__
Size of storm	b. __?__	Several hundred meters
How long storm lasts	A week or more	c. __?__
Time of year	d. __?__	Spring, early summer
Safety rules	Evacuate or move inside a well-built building	e. __?__

Reviewing Content

 Review key concepts online using iText at www.phschool.com

Multiple Choice

Choose the letter of the answer that best completes each statement.

1. An air mass that forms over an ocean is called
   a. tropical.
   b. continental.
   c. maritime.
   d. polar.

2. Cool, clear weather is usually brought by a
   a. warm front.
   b. cold front.
   c. stationary front.
   d. occluded front.

3. Winds spiraling inward toward a center of low pressure form a(n)
   a. anticyclone.
   b. front.
   c. isobar.
   d. cyclone.

4. Very large tropical storms with high winds are called
   a. hurricanes.   b. tornadoes.
   c. thunderstorms. d. blizzards.

5. Most flash floods are caused by
   a. hailstorms.   b. heavy rainfall.
   c. high winds.   d. melting snow.

True or False

If the statement is true, write true. If it is false, change the underlined word or words to make it true.

6. Summers in the Southwest are hot and dry because of <u>maritime tropical</u> air masses.

7. A <u>cold front</u> over an area will bring many days of cloudy weather.

8. Foggy, rainy, or humid weather usually follows the passage of a <u>warm front</u> through an area.

9. Low cumulonimbus clouds may bring both thunderstorms and <u>tornadoes</u>.

10. On a weather map, <u>isobars</u> join places on the map with the same temperature.

Checking Concepts

11. What are the basic characteristics used to describe air masses?

12. Describe how wind patterns affect the movement of air masses in North America.

13. How does a cold front form?

14. Describe three hazards associated with floods.

15. What are some of the sources of information that meteorologists use to predict the weather?

16. What is El Niño? How does it influence the weather in certain regions?

17. **Writing to Learn** Imagine you are a meteorologist. Your assignment is to investigate a hurricane by flying into it with a large plane. Describe your experiences in a journal entry. Be sure to include descriptive words. How did the hurricane look? Sound? Feel?

Thinking Critically

18. **Classifying** Classify the major types of air masses that influence weather in the United States in two ways: by temperature and by where they form.

19. **Comparing and Contrasting** Compare and contrast cyclones and anticyclones. What type of weather is associated with each?

20. **Applying Concepts** Would you expect hurricanes to form over the oceans off the northeast and northwest coasts of the United States? Explain.

21. **Relating Cause and Effect** How do differences in air density influence the movement of cold and warm fronts?

22. **Making Judgments** What do you think is the most important thing people should do to reduce the dangers of storms?

Applying Skills

Use the map to answer Questions 23–26.

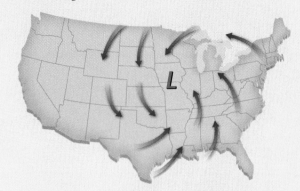

23. **Interpreting Maps** Does the map show a cyclone or an anticyclone? How can you tell?
24. **Interpreting Data** What do the arrows show about the movement of the winds in this pressure center? What else indicates wind direction?
25. **Making Models** Using this diagram as an example, draw a similar diagram to illustrate a high pressure area. Remember to indicate wind direction in your diagram.

26. **Posing Questions** If you saw a pressure center like this on a weather map, what prediction could you make about the weather? What questions would you need to ask in order to make a better prediction?

Performance ▼ CHAPTER PROJECT Assessment

Present Your Project Prepare your final report and arrange your maps for presentation. You may want to display each of your maps next to the actual newspaper weather map for that day. Practice your presentation, make any needed changes, and then present your report.

Reflect and Record In your journal, describe what you learned. Are there weather factors on the maps to which you should have paid more attention? Do meteorologists have information that isn't in the newspaper? How could you gather more information to improve your forecasting?

Test Preparation
Use these questions to prepare for standardized tests.

Read the passage. Then answer Questions 27–30.

As Hurricane Andrew roared toward the southern Florida coastline, millions of Florida residents evacuated the area, heading toward safety. It was 1992, and forecasters predicted that Andrew would make landfall sometime in the early morning of August 24. Andrew had been rapidly building speed and strength since it was first classified as a tropical storm on August 17. Andrew quickly advanced to a fierce Category 4 hurricane, with sustained wind speeds estimated at 145 m.p.h. The only type of hurricane that is stronger is a Category 5 hurricane—a very rare event.

Andrew pounded South Florida for several hours. In the end, this hurricane caused over $20 billion in damage to Florida, becoming the most expensive natural disaster in U.S. history to that point.

27. What is the best title for this selection?
    A Category 4 Hurricanes
    B August 24, 1992
    C Hurricane Andrew Pounds Florida
    D Hurricane Andrew Heads North

28. What kind of storm was Andrew before it was classified as a hurricane?
    F tropical storm   G thunderstorm
    H rainstorm   J monsoon

29. Which category of hurricanes has the greatest wind speed?
    A Category 1   B Category 4
    C Category 5   D none of the above

30. Why did Andrew cause so much damage?
    F because it traveled so fast
    G because it traveled in a northward direction
    H because it had very high wind speed
    J because it traveled over water

This artist's conception shows the *Cassini* space probe arriving near Saturn's rings in 2004.

WEB ACTIVITY
www.phschool.com

Model of the Solar System

If you could drive from Earth to the sun at 100 kilometers per hour, your trip would take 170 years. And most distances in the solar system are even greater! The *Cassini* space probe left Earth for Saturn in 1997 traveling much faster than highway speed, but will not arrive at Saturn's rings until 2004. Sizes in the solar system can be huge, too. Compared with some of the other planets in the solar system, Earth is very small. Saturn, for example, is about 10 times Earth's diameter.

In this chapter, you will get to know many of the objects in the solar system. To help you understand the huge distances and sizes, you will design three different scale models of the solar system.

Your Goal To design scale models of the solar system.

To complete this project, you will
◆ design a model to show the planets' distances from the sun
◆ design a model to show the planets' sizes relative to the sun
◆ test different scales to see if you can use the same scale for both size and distance in one model

Get Started Begin by previewing the tables with distances and diameters on pages 545 and 553. Brainstorm with a group of classmates how you will build your models. Prepare a data sheet to record your calculations of scaled-down distances and diameters.

Check Your Progress You will be working on this project as you study this chapter. To keep your project on track, look for Check Your Progress boxes at the following points.
Section 2 Review, page 542: Design a model to show distances.
Section 3 Review, page 551: Design a model to show diameters.
Section 4 Review, page 559: Design one scale model that shows both sizes and distances.

Present Your Project At the end of the chapter (page 573), you will present your design to the class.

TEKS

In addition to process TEKS, this chapter addresses these concept TEKS as they relate to the chapter's topics.

(6.5) Science concepts. The student knows that systems may combine with other systems to form a larger system. The student is expected to:
(A) identify and describe a system that results from the combination of two or more systems such as in the solar system.

(6.6) Science concepts. The student knows that there is a relationship between force and motion. The student is expected to:
(A) identify and describe the changes in position, direction of motion, and speed of an object when acted upon by force.

(6.13) Science concepts. The student knows components of our solar system. The student is expected to:
(A) identify characteristics of objects in our solar system including the Sun, planets, meteorites, comets, asteroids, and moons; and
(B) describe types of equipment and transportation needed for space travel.

SECTION 1 Describing the Solar System

DISCOVER

How Do Mass and Speed Affect an Object's Motion?

1. Have your partner push a toy truck across the table toward you. Stop the truck with your hands.

2. Repeat Step 1, but have your partner push the truck a little faster. Was it easier or harder to stop the truck than in Step 1?

3. Now add some rocks or other heavy objects to the truck and repeat Step 1. Your partner should push the truck at the same speed as in Step 1. How hard was it to stop the truck this time compared to Step 1?

4. Repeat Step 2 with the rocks still in the truck. How hard was it to stop the truck this time?

Think It Over

Predicting How hard would it be to stop the truck if your partner pushed it more slowly? If you added more mass to the truck?

GUIDE FOR READING

◆ How do the geocentric and heliocentric descriptions of the solar system differ?

◆ What two factors keep the planets in their orbits?

◆ What combines to form our solar system?

Reading Tip As you read, make a list of the evidence that supports the heliocentric system.

Key Terms geocentric system
• heliocentric system
• solar system • ellipse • inertia
• gravity

Have you ever lain outdoors on a starry night, gazing up at the stars? As you watch, the stars seem to move across the sky. The sky seems to be rotating right over your head. In fact, from the Northern Hemisphere, the sky appears to rotate around a point near Polaris, the North Star, once every 24 hours.

Now think about what you see every day. During the day, the sun appears to move across the sky. From here on Earth, it seems as if Earth is stationary and that the sun, moon, and stars are all moving around Earth. But is the sky really moving above you? Centuries ago, before there were space shuttles or even telescopes, there was no easy way to find out.

Figure 1 This photo was made by exposing the camera film for several hours. Each star appears as part of a circle, and all the stars seem to revolve around a single point.

Wandering Stars

When the ancient Greeks watched the stars move across the sky, they noticed that the patterns of most of the stars didn't change. Although the stars seemed to move, they stayed in the same position relative to one another.

As they observed the sky more carefully, the Greeks noticed something surprising. Five points of light seemed to wander among the stars. The Greeks called these objects *planets*, from the Greek word meaning "wandering star." The Greeks made very careful observations of the motions of the five planets they could see. You know these planets by the names the ancient Romans later gave them: Mercury, Venus, Mars, Jupiter, and Saturn.

Greek Ideas: Earth at the Center

When you look up at the sky, you can almost imagine that you are under a rotating dome with the stars pasted on it. The Greeks thought that they were inside a rotating dome they called the celestial sphere. Most Greek astronomers believed that the universe is perfect and unchangeable and that Earth is stationary in the center of the celestial sphere. Because *geo* is the Greek word for Earth, an Earth-centered system is known as a **geocentric** (jee oh SEN trik) **system. A system is a group of parts that work together as a unit. Earth is at the center of the revolving planets in a geocentric system.**

In A.D. 140, the Greek astronomer Ptolemy (TAHL uh mee) explained the motion of the planets in another way. Like the earlier Greeks, Ptolemy believed in a geocentric system with Earth at the center of the system of planets. Ptolemy also thought that the moon, Mercury, Venus, the sun, Mars, Jupiter, and Saturn revolve around Earth.

In Ptolemy's explanation, however, the planets move on little circles that move on bigger circles. Ptolemy thought that this explained why the planets seem to move at different speeds, and even backwards, among the stars. For the next 1,400 years, people believed that Ptolemy's ideas were correct.

Figure 2 In the 1500s, an astronomy book published this illustration of Ptolemy's system. *Interpreting Diagrams Where is Earth located in this illustration?*

☑ *Checkpoint* *What is a geocentric system?*

Copernicus's Idea: Sun at the Center

In the early 1500s, the Polish astronomer Nicolaus Copernicus developed another explanation for the motions of the planets. Copernicus thought that the sun is at the center of the system of planets. His sun-centered system is called a **heliocentric** (hee lee oh SEN trik) **system.** *Helios* is Greek for "sun." **In a heliocentric system, Earth and the other planets revolve around the sun.** Copernicus's explanation included the six planets he knew about: Mercury, Venus, Earth, Mars, Jupiter, and Saturn.

Galileo's Observations

In the 1500s and 1600s, most people still believed Ptolemy's geocentric explanation. However, the Italian astronomer Galileo Galilei, who lived nearly 100 years after Copernicus, thought that the heliocentric explanation was correct.

Galileo was the first scientist to use a telescope to look at objects in the sky. With his telescope, Galileo made two discoveries that supported the heliocentric model. First, Galileo saw four moons revolving around Jupiter. Galileo's observations of Jupiter's moons showed that not everything in the sky revolves around Earth.

Galileo's observations of Venus also supported Copernicus's heliocentric system. Galileo discovered that Venus goes through phases similar to those of Earth's moon. Galileo reasoned that the phases of Venus could not be explained if Earth were at the center of the system of planets. So Ptolemy's geocentric system could not be correct.

Galileo's evidence gradually convinced others that Copernicus's explanation was correct. Today, people refer to the **solar system** rather than the "Earth system." This shows that people accept Copernicus's idea that the sun is at the center of a system of planets.

☑ *Checkpoint* *What two discoveries made by Galileo supported the heliocentric description of the solar system?*

Brahe and Kepler

Copernicus and Galileo had correctly identified the sun as the center of the solar system. But Copernicus, like Ptolemy, assumed that the orbits of the planets are circles.

Copernicus's ideas were based on observations made by the ancient Greeks. In the late 1500s, Tycho Brahe (TEE koh BRAH uh), a Danish astronomer, made

Figure 3 From this observatory, Tycho Brahe made accurate observations of the planets for nearly 20 years. His data became the basis for many important discoveries.

much more accurate observations. Brahe carefully observed the positions of the planets for almost 20 years.

In 1600, a German mathematician, Johannes Kepler, went to work analyzing Brahe's data. Kepler tried to figure out the shape of the planets' orbits. At first, he assumed that the orbits are circles. When Kepler tried to figure out the exact orbit of Mars, however, no circle fit the observations.

Kepler had discovered that the orbit of each planet is an ellipse. An **ellipse** is an elongated circle, or oval shape. Kepler found that if he assumed that Mars's orbit is an ellipse, his calculations fit Brahe's observations better.

Inertia and Gravity

Kepler had discovered the correct shape of the planets' orbits. But he could not explain why the planets stay in orbit. The English scientist Isaac Newton did. **Newton concluded that two factors—inertia and gravity—combine to keep the planets in orbit.**

Galileo had discovered that a moving object will continue to move until some force acts to stop its motion. This tendency of a moving object to continue in a straight line or a stationary object to remain in place is the object's **inertia.** The more mass an object has, the more inertia it has. An object with greater inertia is more difficult to start or stop.

Isaac Newton picked up where Galileo had left off. Late in his life, Newton told the story of how watching an apple fall from a tree in 1665 had made him think about motion. He hypothesized that the same force that pulls the apple to the ground also pulls the moon toward Earth. This force, called **gravity,** attracts all objects toward one another. The strength of gravity depends on the masses of the objects and the distance between them.

A Loopy Ellipse

You can draw an ellipse.

1. ✂ Carefully stick two pushpins about 10 cm apart through a sheet of white paper on top of corrugated cardboard.

2. Tie the ends of a 30-cm piece of string together. Place the string around the pushpins.

3. Keeping the string tight, move a pencil around inside the string.

4. Now place the pushpins 5 cm apart. Repeat Step 3.

Predicting How does changing the distance between the pushpins affect the ellipse's shape? What shape would you draw if you used only one pushpin?

Figure 4 Newton was a man of many achievements. Among them was the invention of this telescope. *Relating Cause and Effect How did watching an apple fall from a tree lead Newton to his hypothesis about gravity?*

Mercury 58,000,000 km
Venus 108,000,000 km
Earth 150,000,000 km
Mars 228,000,000 km

Jupiter
778,000,000 km

Saturn
1,427,000,000 km

Newton figured out that Earth keeps pulling the moon toward it with gravity. At the same time, the moon keeps moving ahead because of its inertia. Earth curves away as the moon falls toward it, so the moon winds up in orbit around Earth.

In the same way, the planets are in orbit around the sun because the sun's gravity pulls on them while their inertia keeps them moving ahead. Therefore, the planets keep moving around the sun and end up in orbit.

Smaller Systems Inside

Since Newton's time, knowledge of the solar system has increased. Newton only knew about six planets—Mercury, Venus, Earth, Mars, Jupiter, and Saturn. Now astronomers know about three more planets—Uranus, Neptune, and Pluto. Just like Earth has a

Figure 5 If there were no force of gravity, inertia would make a planet travel in a straight line. But because gravity pulls the planet toward the sun, the planet actually travels in an elliptical orbit around the sun.
Interpreting Diagrams What would happen if a planet had no inertia?

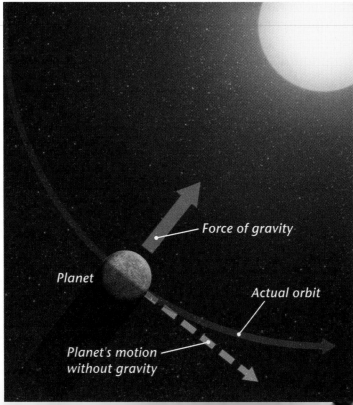

Force of gravity

Actual orbit

Planet

Planet's motion
without gravity

Uranus
2,871,000,000 km

Neptune
4,497,000,000 km

Pluto
5,913,000,000 km

Figure 6 This illustration shows the average distances of the planets from the sun. The sizes of the planets and the sun are not to scale.

moon orbiting around it, many other planets have moons that revolve around them. Each planet and its moons form a small system. These systems combine with each other to form the larger solar system. Astronomers have also identified many other objects in the solar system, such as comets and asteroids, that you will learn about later in this chapter. **The solar system is a large system that consists of a combination of many smaller systems and objects.**

Galileo and Brahe used telescopes on Earth to observe the smaller systems that make up the solar system. Astronomers still use telescopes on Earth, but they have also made close-up observations of the planets from space probes sent far into the solar system. Because of such exciting research, our understanding of the solar system continues to change. Who knows what new discoveries will be made in your lifetime!

Section 1 Review

1. How is Copernicus's description of the system of planets different from Ptolemy's description?
2. What two factors act together to keep the planets in orbit around the sun?
3. What smaller systems combine to make the solar system?
4. **Thinking Critically Applying Concepts** People usually say that the sun rises in the east, moves across the sky, and sets in the west. Is this description actually correct? Explain.

Science at Home

Heliocentric vs. Geocentric Use materials in your home, such as clay and straws, to make models of Ptolemy's geocentric solar system and Copernicus's heliocentric solar system. Use the models to explain the two hypotheses for a family member. Discuss how Galileo's observations supported Copernicus's idea of a heliocentric solar system.

SECTION 2 Characteristics of the Sun

DISCOVER ·······················ACTIVITY···

How Can You Safely Observe the Sun?

1. Clamp a pair of binoculars to a ring stand.

2. ✂ Cut a hole in a 20-cm by 28-cm sheet of thin cardboard so that it will fit over the binoculars, as shown in the photo. The cardboard should cover one lens, but allow light through the other lens. Tape the cardboard on securely. **CAUTION:** *Never look directly at the sun. You will hurt your eyes if you do.*

3. Use the binoculars to project an image of the sun onto a sheet of white paper. The cardboard will shade the paper. Change the focus and move the paper back and forth until you get a sharp image.

Think It Over

Observing Draw what you see on the paper. What do you see on the surface of the sun?

GUIDE FOR READING

◆ How does the sun get its energy?

◆ What are the layers of the sun's atmosphere?

◆ What are some features of the sun's surface?

Reading Tip As you read, write a sentence defining each boldfaced term in your own words.

Key Terms nuclear fusion
• core • photosphere
• chromosphere • corona
• solar wind • sunspot
• prominence • solar flare

The sun's gravity is by far the most powerful force in the solar system—strong enough to hold all of the planets and comets in orbit! The sun's gravity is so strong because the sun's mass is very large. In fact, 99.8 percent of the mass of the solar system is in the sun.

Like Earth, the sun has an interior and an atmosphere. Unlike Earth, however, the sun does not have a solid surface. The sun is a ball of glowing gas. About three fourths of the sun's mass is hydrogen, one fourth is helium, and very small amounts are other chemical elements.

The Sun's Interior

The interior of the sun is like a giant furnace. Like furnaces in houses, the sun produces energy. But the sun does not get its energy from burning fuels such as oil. **Instead, the sun's energy comes from nuclear fusion.** In the process of **nuclear fusion,** hydrogen atoms join together to form helium. Nuclear fusion occurs only under conditions of extremely high temperature and pressure. The temperature inside the sun's **core,** or center, reaches about 15 million degrees Celsius, high enough for nuclear fusion to occur.

The total mass of the helium produced by nuclear fusion is slightly less than the total mass of the hydrogen that goes into it. The change in mass occurs because some of the matter is converted into energy, including light and heat. The light and heat gradually move from the core of the sun to its atmosphere and escape into space. Some of this light and heat reach Earth, becoming Earth's main source of energy.

There is enough hydrogen fuel in the core of the sun to last for a total of 10 billion years. The sun is now only about 5 billion years old, so you don't have to worry about the sun "burning out" any time soon!

☑ *Checkpoint* *Where in the sun does nuclear fusion occur?*

The Sun's Atmosphere

The sun's atmosphere has three layers: the photosphere, the chromosphere, and the corona. There are no boundaries between the layers of the sun.

The Photosphere The inner layer of the sun's atmosphere is called the **photosphere** (FOH tuh sfeer). The Greek word *photo* means "light," so *photosphere* means the sphere that makes light. When you look at an image or photograph of the sun, you are looking at the photosphere.

The Chromosphere During a total solar eclipse, the moon blocks light from the photosphere. The photosphere no longer provides the glare that keeps you from seeing the sun's faint, outer layers. At the beginning and end of a total eclipse, you can see a reddish glow just around the photosphere. This glow comes from the middle layer of the sun's atmosphere, the **chromosphere.** The Greek word *chromo* means "color," so the chromosphere is the "color sphere."

The Corona In the middle of a total solar eclipse, the moon also blocks light from the chromosphere. At these times an even fainter layer of the sun becomes visible, as you can see in Figure 7. This outer layer, which looks like a white halo around the sun, is called the **corona,** which means "crown" in Latin. From Earth's surface, the corona is only visible during eclipses or from special telescopes. But astronomers can use telescopes in space to observe the corona all the time and to study how it changes.

Figure 7 During a total solar eclipse, you can see light from the corona, the outer layer of the sun's atmosphere. *Inferring Why is it easiest to photograph the sun's outer layers during a solar eclipse?*

Viewing Sunspots

ACTIVITY

You can observe changes in the number of sunspots.

1. Make a data table to record the average number of sunspots you see each day.

2. Decide on a time to look for sunspots each day.

3. View the sun in the way described in the Discover activity. **CAUTION:** *Never look directly at the sun. You will hurt your eyes if you do.*

4. Make and record your observations.

Interpreting Data How much did the average number of sunspots change from day to day?

The corona sends out a stream of electrically charged particles called **solar wind.** Normally Earth's atmosphere and magnetic field block these particles. However, near the North and South poles, the particles can enter Earth's atmosphere, where they hit gas molecules and cause them to glow. The result is rippling sheets of light in the sky called auroras.

☑ *Checkpoint* *During what event could you see the sun's corona?*

Features on the Sun

For hundreds of years, scientists have used telescopes to look at the sun. (To protect their eyes, they used a filter or projected the sun onto a white surface, as in the Discover activity.) The dark spots that they saw on the sun's surface became known as sunspots. The spots seemed to move across the sun's surface, which showed that the sun rotates on its axis, just as Earth does. **Features on or above the sun's surface include sunspots, prominences, and solar flares.**

Sunspots As you can see in Figure 8, sunspots look like small, dark areas on the sun's surface. But in fact, they can be as large as Earth. **Sunspots** are areas of gas on the sun that are cooler than the gases around them. Cooler gases don't give off as much light as hotter gases, which is why sunspots look darker than the rest of the photosphere.

Figure 8 Sunspots are areas of gas on the sun that are cooler than the gas around them. Many of the sunspots in these photos are about as large as Earth.

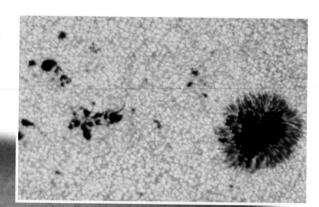

The number of sunspots on the sun varies over a period of 10 or 11 years. Some scientists have hypothesized that short-term changes in climate on Earth may be related to sunspot cycles. Satellites have recently collected data that show that the amount of energy the sun produces changes slightly from year to year. Some scientists think that these increases and decreases, which may be linked to the number of sunspots, may cause changes in Earth's temperature. Scientists need to make more observations in order to test this hypothesis.

EXPLORING *the Sun*

The diameter of the sun (not including the chromosphere and the corona) is 1.4 million kilometers.

Corona
Thickness: millions of kilometers
Temperature: about 2,000,000°C

Sunspots
Areas of cooler gases in the photosphere are called sunspots.

Chromosphere
Thickness: 2,000–3,000 km
Temperature: 5,000–10,000°C

Prominence
A prominence is a huge, looping mass of gas seen above the chromosphere.

Photosphere
Thickness: 400 km
Temperature: 5,000–8,000°C
The sunlight that reaches Earth comes from the photosphere.

Core
Temperature: as hot as 15,000,000°C, hot enough to convert hydrogen into helium by nuclear fusion, releasing

Figure 9 (A) Prominences are huge loops of gas that connect different parts of sunspot regions. (B) Solar flares on the sun release large amounts of energy. *Relating Cause and Effect How can solar flares affect communications on Earth?*

Prominences Sunspots usually occur in pairs or groups. Reddish loops of gas called **prominences** link different parts of sunspot regions. When a group of sunspots is near the edge of the sun as seen from Earth, these loops can stick out over the edge of the sun. If an eclipse hides the sun's photosphere, astronomers are able to see these loops. Prominences are about the same temperature as the sun's chromosphere, about 10,000 degrees Celsius.

Solar Flares Sometimes the loops in sunspot regions suddenly connect, releasing large amounts of energy. The energy heats gas on the sun to millions of degrees Celsius, causing the hydrogen gas to explode out into space. These explosions are known as **solar flares.**

Solar flares can greatly increase the solar wind from the corona, resulting in an increase in the number of particles reaching Earth's atmosphere. These solar wind particles can affect Earth's upper atmosphere, causing magnetic storms. Magnetic storms sometimes disrupt radio, telephone, and satellite signals. Magnetic storms can also cause electrical power problems for homes and businesses.

Section 2 Review

1. How is energy produced in the sun's core?
2. Name the layers of the sun's atmosphere.
3. Describe three features found on or above the surface of the sun.
4. Why do sunspots look darker than the rest of the sun's photosphere?
5. How does the number of sunspots change over time?
6. What is solar wind?
7. **Thinking Critically Comparing and Contrasting** What is the difference between a prominence and a solar flare?

Check Your Progress CHAPTER PROJECT
Begin by making a table that shows the distances of the planets from the sun. To help visualize the solar system, you can divide all the distances by the same amount: for example, divide all distances by 100,000 or 1,000,000. Record your calculations on your data sheet. Then choose a different scale and repeat your calculations. Which scale makes it easier to see the relative distances between the planets and the sun?

STORMY SUNSPOTS

Problem

How are magnetic storms on Earth related to sunspot activity?

Skills Focus

graphing, interpreting data

Materials

graph paper   pencil   straightedge
computer (optional)

Procedure

1. Use the data in the table to make a line graph of sunspot activity between 1967 and 1997. Create your graph on graph paper or on the computer.
2. On the graph, label the *x*-axis "Year." Use a scale with 2-year intervals, from 1967 to 1997.
3. Label the *y*-axis "Sunspot Number." Use a scale of 0 through 160 in intervals of 10.
4. Graph a point for the Sunspot Number for each year.
5. Complete your graph by connecting the points.

Sunspots			
Year	**Sunspot Number**	**Year**	**Sunspot Number**
1967	93.8	1983	66.6
1969	105.0	1985	17.9
1971	66.6	1987	29.4
1973	38.0	1989	157.6
1975	15.5	1991	145.7
1977	27.5	1993	54.6
1979	155.4	1995	17.5
1981	140.4	1997	23.4

Analyze and Conclude

1. Based on your graph, which years had the highest Sunspot Numbers? The lowest Sunspot Numbers?
2. How often does the cycle of maximum and minimum activity repeat?
3. When was the most recent maximum sunspot activity? The most recent minimum sunspot activity?
4. Compare your sunspot graph with the magnetic storms graph. What relationship can you infer between periods of high sunspot activity and magnetic storms? Explain.
5. **Apply** During which years do you think electrical disturbances on Earth were most common?

More to Explore

Using the pattern of sunspot activity you found, predict the number of peaks you would expect in the next 30 years. Around which years would you expect the peaks to occur?

SECTION 3 Characteristics of the Inner Planets

DISCOVER

How Does Mars Look From Earth?

1. Work in pairs. On a sheet of paper, draw a circle 20 cm across to represent Mars. Draw about 100 small lines, each about 1 cm long, at random places inside the circle.

2. Have your partner look at your drawing of Mars from the other side of the room. Your partner should draw what he or she sees.

3. Compare your original drawing with what your partner drew. Then look at your own drawing from across the room.

Think It Over

Observing Did your partner draw any connecting lines that were not actually on your drawing? What can you conclude about the accuracy of descriptions of other planets as observed from Earth?

GUIDE FOR READING

◆ What are the main characteristics of the inner planets?

Reading Tip As you read about each planet, write down the similarities and differences between that planet and Earth.

Key Terms terrestrial planet
• rotation • revolution
• retrograde rotation
• greenhouse effect

Picture a planet whose surface is hot enough to melt lead. How about a planet whose atmosphere has almost entirely leaked away? Some of the four planets closest to the sun have these characteristics. They are called the inner planets.

Earth and the other three inner planets of the solar system—Mercury, Venus, and Mars—are more similar to each other than they are to the five outer planets. **The four inner planets are small and have rocky surfaces.** These planets are often called the **terrestrial planets,** from the Latin word *terra*, which means "Earth." Figure 10 gives a summary of the characteristics of the inner planets. These characteristics include a planet's rotation and revolution. The **rotation** is the time it takes for a planet to spin once on its axis. The **revolution** is the time a planet takes to orbit the sun.

Earth

Our planet's atmosphere extends more than 100 kilometers above Earth's surface. The oxygen you need to live makes up about 20 percent of the gases in Earth's atmosphere. Almost all the rest is nitrogen gas, with a small amount of carbon dioxide. Earth's atmosphere also contains water vapor and clouds of water droplets. From space, astronauts can usually see past the clouds to Earth's surface.

Most of Earth, about 70 percent, is covered with water. Perhaps the planet should be named "Water" instead of "Earth"! No other planet in our solar system has oceans like Earth's.

Venus

Mercury

Earth

Mars

Characteristics of the Inner Planet Systems

Planet	Diameter (kilometers)	Period of Rotation (Earth days)	Average Distance From the Sun (kilometers)	Period of Revolution (Earth years)	Number of Moons
Mercury	4,878	59	58,000,000	0.24	0
Venus	12,104	243	108,000,000	0.62	0
Earth	12,756	1	150,000,000	1	1
Mars	6,794	1.03	228,000,000	1.9	2

Figure 10 The inner planets take up only a small part of the solar system. The diameter of the entire solar system is more than 25 times the diameter of Mars's orbit.

INTEGRATING EARTH SCIENCE As you recall from Chapter 10, Earth has three main layers—a crust, a mantle, and a core. The crust includes the solid rocky surface. Under the crust is the mantle, a layer of hot molten rock. When volcanoes erupt, this hot material rises to the surface. Earth has a dense inner core made up mainly of iron and nickel. The outer core is liquid, but the inner core is solid.

Scientists have been studying Earth for many years. They use what they know about Earth to make inferences about the other planets. For example, when astronomers find volcanoes on other planets, they infer that these planets have or once had hot material inside them. As we continue to learn more about our own planet, scientists will be able to apply that new knowledge to the study of the other planets.

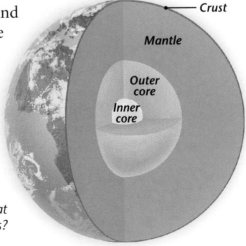

Crust

Mantle

Outer core

Inner core

Figure 11 Earth has a solid, rocky surface. *Interpreting Diagrams What are Earth's three main layers?*

Figure 12 This photo of Mercury and the closeup view of some of its craters (inset) were taken by the *Mariner 10* space probe.
Inferring Is there a connection between the thin atmosphere on Mercury and the craters on the surface of that planet? Explain.

Mercury

The planet system closest to the sun is Mercury. Mercury is not much larger than Earth's moon and has no moons of its own. Astronomers have been able to infer that the interior of Mercury is made up mainly of the dense metals iron and nickel.

Exploring Mercury Because Mercury is so close to the sun, people on Earth never get a good view of Mercury. Much of the knowledge that astronomers have about Mercury's surface came from a single space probe, *Mariner 10,* in 1974. *Mariner 10* photographed only half of Mercury's surface, so astronomers still don't know what the rest of Mercury is like.

Mariner 10's photographs show that, like the moon, Mercury has many flat plains and many craters on its surface. The craters on Mercury have been named for artists, writers, and musicians, including the composers Bach and Mozart.

Mercury's Atmosphere Mercury has an extremely thin atmosphere. Apparently the gases Mercury once had were heated so much that the gas particles moved very fast. Since they were moving so fast, the gas particles escaped from Mercury's weak gravity into space. However, astronomers have detected small amounts of sodium and other gases in Mercury's atmosphere.

Mercury is a planet of extremes. It is so close to the sun that during the day, the side facing the sun reaches temperatures of 430°C. Because Mercury has almost no atmosphere, at night all the heat escapes into space. The temperature drops to −170°C. Mercury thus has a greater range of temperatures than any other planet in the solar system.

☑ *Checkpoint Why is it difficult for astronomers to learn about Mercury?*

Venus

Whenever you see a bright object in the west after sunset, it is probably Venus. When Venus shines brightly like that, it is known as the "evening star," though of course it really isn't a star. Stars shine with their own light, while Venus shines because it is reflecting light from the sun, just as the other planets and moons do. At other times, you see Venus rise before the sun in the morning. It is then known as the "morning star." At still other times, Venus is too close to the sun in the sky for you to see it from Earth at all.

Venus is so similar in size to Earth that it is sometimes called Earth's twin. Astronomers also think that the density and internal structure of Venus are similar to Earth's. However, in many other ways, Venus is very different from Earth.

Venus's Rotation Venus takes about 7.5 Earth months to revolve around the sun. It takes about 8 months for Venus to rotate on its axis. Venus rotates so slowly that its "day" is longer than its "year." Oddly, Venus rotates from east to west, the opposite direction from most other planets and moons. This type of rotation is called **retrograde rotation,** from the Latin words for "moving backward." One hypothesis proposed by astronomers to explain this unusual rotation is that Venus was struck by a very large object billions of years ago. Such a collision could have caused the direction of its rotation to change.

Figure 13 The thick atmosphere of Venus makes the view from space a cloudy one.

Figure 14 The *Magellan* spacecraft used radar to penetrate Venus's clouds. This three-dimensional image of a volcano on Venus was created by a computer using radar data. The height of the mountains is exaggerated to make them stand out. *Inferring Why must radar be used to photograph the surface of Venus from space?*

Music CONNECTION

The English composer Gustav Holst, who lived from 1874 to 1934, composed a group of pieces for orchestra entitled *The Planets.* The seven pieces describe musically the planets Mars, Venus, Mercury, Jupiter, Saturn, Uranus, and Neptune.

In Your Journal

Listen to a recording of at least two of the pieces from *The Planets.* How did Holst use music to distinguish the planets from each other? What words would you use to describe what you heard?

Venus's Atmosphere The atmosphere of Venus is so thick that every day is a cloudy one. Venus never has a sunny day. From Earth, astronomers see only a smooth cloud cover over Venus all the time.

If you could stand on the surface of Venus, you would quickly be crushed by the weight of its atmosphere. The pressure of Venus's atmosphere is 90 times greater than the pressure of Earth's atmosphere. You could not breathe on Venus because its atmosphere is mostly carbon dioxide. Also, its clouds are partly made of sulfuric acid.

Because Venus is closer to the sun than Earth, it gets more solar energy than Earth does. Ordinary light from the sun can penetrate Venus's atmosphere and hit its surface. The surface heats up and then gives off heat. Carbon dioxide traps this heat in the atmosphere. So Venus's surface becomes hotter and hotter, until it is about 460°C—hot enough to melt lead. This trapping of heat by the atmosphere is called the **greenhouse effect.**

Exploring Venus About 20 spacecraft have visited Venus, more than have visited any other planet. Some have even penetrated its clouds and landed on its surface. The first spacecraft to land and send back information, *Venera 7,* landed in 1970 but transmitted for only 23 minutes. Later spacecraft were more durable and sent back pictures and other data from Venus's surface.

Scientists have learned most of what they now know about the surface of Venus from data collected by the *Magellan* probe.

The *Magellan* probe reached Venus in 1990, carrying radar instruments. Radar works through clouds, so *Magellan* was able to map Venus's entire surface.

The *Magellan* views are so detailed that computers can be used to figure out what Venus would look like if you could fly just above its surface. Figure 14 shows one of these radar images. Venus is covered with rock, similar to many rocky areas on Earth. Venus has volcanoes with lava flows, many craters, and strange domes not found on other planets.

☑ *Checkpoint* **Why is the surface of Venus so hot?**

Mars

Mars is called the "red planet" because it has a slightly reddish tinge when you see it in the sky. The atmosphere of Mars is mostly carbon dioxide and has only 1 percent the pressure of Earth's atmosphere. You could walk around on Mars, but you would have to wear an airtight suit and carry your own air, like a scuba diver. Mars has clouds but they are very thin compared to the clouds on Earth.

Canals on Mars? In 1877, an Italian astronomer, Giovanni Schiaparelli (sky ah puh REL ee), announced that he had seen long, straight lines on Mars. He called them *canale*, or channels. In the 1890s and the early 1900s, Percival Lowell, an American astronomer, convinced many people that these lines were canals that had been built by intelligent Martians to carry water. Astronomers now know that Schiaparelli and Lowell were mistaken. There are no canals on Mars, or even channels that can be seen from Earth.

However, astronomers have found that some water exists on Mars in the form of ice at its north pole, as shown in Figure 15. Mars' south pole has an ice cap made mostly of frozen carbon dioxide. Unlike Earth's ice caps, Mars' polar ice caps are covered by a layer of frozen carbon dioxide during each hemisphere's winter.

Figure 15 Because of its thin atmosphere and its distance from the sun, Mars is quite cold. Mars has ice caps at both poles.

Seasons on Mars Because the axis of Mars is tilted, Mars has seasons just as Earth does. As the seasons change on the dusty surface of Mars, wind storms arise and blow the dust around. Since the dust is blown off some regions, these regions look darker. A hundred years ago, some people thought these regions looked darker because plants were growing there. Astronomers now realize that it is just that wind storms blow dust off the surface.

Exploring Mars The United States has sent many spacecraft to Mars. The first ones, in the 1960s, seemed to show that Mars is barren and covered with craters like the moon. Later spacecraft showed that regions of Mars have giant volcanoes. Astronomers see signs that hot material flowed down the volcanoes in the past, but they don't think the volcanoes are active now.

In 1976, two NASA spacecraft, *Viking 1* and *Viking 2,* landed on Mars. They sent back close-up pictures from Mars's surface. The pictures showed that the rocks look red because they are covered with a rusty dust. Other parts of the *Viking* spacecraft went into orbit around Mars, sending back detailed pictures.

In 1997, *Mars Pathfinder* landed on Mars. As Figure 16 shows, close-up photographs from *Mars Pathfinder* show no oceans or even puddles of water. Photographs taken from space do show evidence that water flowed on Mars millions of years ago.

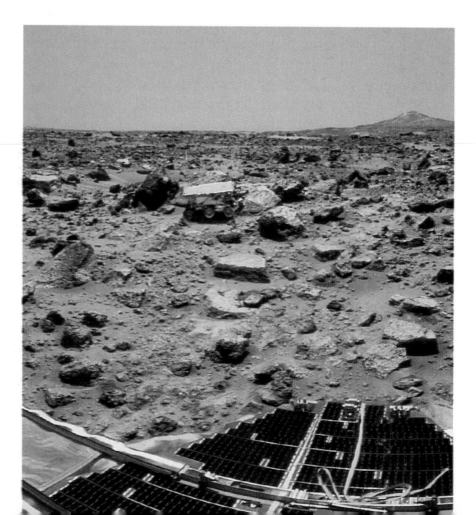

Figure 16 The surface of Mars is rugged and rocky. The object at the bottom of the photo is the *Mars Pathfinder* lander. You can see the remote-control rover *Sojourner* in the middle of the photo.

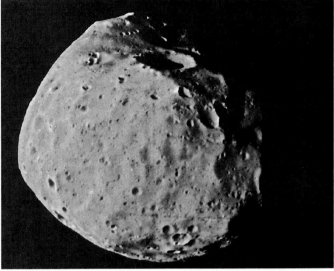

Figure 17 Phobos (left) and Deimos (right) are Mars's two small, crater-covered moons.

Mars Pathfinder carried a microwave-sized remote-control rover, called *Sojourner*, that investigated rocks on Mars. Also in 1997, another probe, *Mars Global Surveyor*, arrived in orbit around Mars, where it began mapping and photographing all of the planet's surface in detail.

Mars's Moons The Mars system has two very small moons that revolve around the planet. Phobos, the larger moon, is only 27 kilometers in diameter, about the distance a car can travel on the highway in 15 minutes. Deimos is even smaller, only 15 kilometers in diameter. Close-up views from space show that, like Earth's moon, Phobos and Deimos are covered with craters.

Section 3 Review

1. What characteristics do all of the inner planets have in common?
2. Why could Earth be called "The Water Planet"?
3. What is Mercury's atmosphere like? Explain.
4. Why can astronomers see the surface of Mars clearly, but not the surface of Venus?
5. How have astronomers been able to study the surface of Venus?
6. **Thinking Critically** Relating Cause and Effect Venus is much farther from the sun than is Mercury. Yet temperatures on Venus are as high as those on the sunny side of Mercury. Explain why.

Check Your Progress CHAPTER PROJECT

Now you will design a model that shows the relative diameters of the planets. Try several different scales to find one for which the smallest planet is clearly visible, but the sun would still fit into your classroom. Convert the sun's and planets' diameters to scaled-down diameters and record your results on your data sheet. Compare your scaled-down diameters to objects you are familiar with, such as coins. Include your comparisons in your data sheet.

Characteristics of the Outer Planets

How Large Are the Outer Planets?

The table shows the diameters of the outer planets compared to Earth. For example, Jupiter's diameter is 11 times Earth's diameter.

1. Measure the diameter of a quarter in millimeters. This represents Earth's diameter. Trace the quarter to represent Earth.

2. If Earth were the size of a quarter, calculate how large Jupiter would be. Now draw a circle to represent Jupiter.

3. Repeat Step 2 for each of the other outer planets.

Think It Over

Classifying List the planets in order from largest to smallest. Which outer planet is much smaller than Earth?

Planet Diameters	
Planet	**Diameter**
Earth	1
Jupiter	11
Saturn	9.4
Uranus	4.0
Neptune	3.9
Pluto	0.17

GUIDE FOR READING

◆ What are the main characteristics of the gas giant planets?

◆ How are Pluto and Charon different from the other outer planets?

Reading Tip Before you read, preview the photos and captions. Write down any questions you have. Look for answers as you read.

Key Term gas giant

Most of what astronomers know about the outer planet systems has come from NASA space probes. *Voyager 1* and *Voyager 2* reached Jupiter in 1979. *Voyager 1* went on to visit Saturn in 1980. *Voyager 2* also visited Saturn, and then explored Uranus and Neptune. In 1995, the spacecraft *Galileo* dropped a probe into Jupiter's atmosphere.

Characteristics of the Gas Giants

Compared to Earth, some planets are huge. The largest planet, Jupiter, has a diameter that is 11 times Earth's diameter. Jupiter's mass is more than 300 times Earth's mass. If you could put Earth next to Jupiter, Earth would look like a tiny Chihuahua next to an enormous Great Dane.

Jupiter and the other planets farthest from the sun, as seen in Figure 19, are called the outer planets. **The first four outer planets—Jupiter, Saturn, Uranus, and Neptune—are much larger than Earth, and do not have solid surfaces.** These four planets are all so large that they are also called the **gas giants.** The fifth outer planet, Pluto, is small and rocky like the terrestrial planets.

Figure 18 If the tiny Chihuahua were Earth's size, the Great Dane would be about half Jupiter's size.

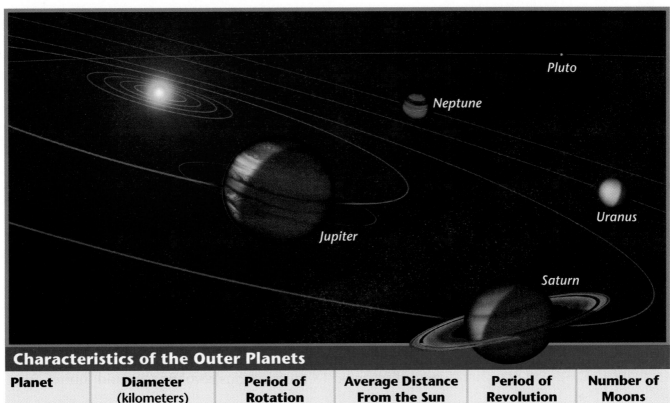

Characteristics of the Outer Planets

Planet	Diameter (kilometers)	Period of Rotation (Earth days)	Average Distance From the Sun (kilometers)	Period of Revolution (Earth years)	Number of Moons
Jupiter	142,800	0.41	778,000,000	12	17
Saturn	120,540	0.43	1,427,000,000	29	19
Uranus	51,200	0.72	2,871,000,000	84	18
Neptune	49,500	0.67	4,497,000,000	165	8
Pluto	2,200	6.4	5,913,000,000	248	1

Figure 19 The outer planets are much farther apart than the inner planets. At this scale, the inner planets are so small and close to the sun that they cannot be shown. *Observing Which outer planet is closest to the sun?*

Atmospheres Because the gas giants have so much mass, they exert a much stronger gravitational force than the terrestrial planets. The strong gravity keeps the giant planets' gases from escaping, so they have deep atmospheres. The composition of their atmospheres is similar to the gases in the sun. They average about 75 percent hydrogen, 24 percent helium, and 1 percent other elements.

None of the giant planets has a well-defined surface. If you could parachute into Jupiter's atmosphere, you would sink into denser and denser gas. You would be crushed by the enormous pressure long before you got to the center, or core, of the planet.

Solid Cores Astronomers think that each of the giant planets has a partly solid core made of rock, ice, frozen carbon dioxide, and other compounds. Each of these cores may have several times as much mass as Earth. But they are buried so deep inside the planets that it has been hard to find out much about them.

✓ *Checkpoint* *Why do the gas giants have large atmospheres?*

Jupiter

Jupiter is the most massive planet in the solar system. In fact, Jupiter is more than 300 times as massive as Earth.

Jupiter's Atmosphere Like all of the gas giant planets, Jupiter has a thick atmosphere made up mainly of hydrogen and helium. Jupiter's atmosphere contains many colorful bands and swirls of thick clouds. An especially interesting feature in Jupiter's atmosphere is its Great Red Spot, a giant area of swirling clouds many times bigger than Earth. The Great Red Spot, shown in Figure 20, appears to be an ongoing storm similar to a hurricane on Earth.

Jupiter's Moons Recall that the astronomer Galileo discovered four of Jupiter's moons. These moons are named Io (EYE oh), Europa, Ganymede, and Callisto. These four moons are Jupiter's largest. Three of them, Io, Ganymede, and Callisto, are larger than Earth's own moon. Since Galileo's time, astronomers have discovered 13 more moons revolving around Jupiter, for a total of 17.

The *Voyager* and *Galileo* probes sent back images that showed detailed views of Jupiter's moons. Jupiter's moons are very different from one another, as you can see in Figure 21.

Figure 20 The larger photo of Jupiter was taken by the *Voyager 1* spacecraft. The small objects in front of Jupiter are two of Jupiter's moons, Io (left) and Europa (right). The Great Red Spot, shown in the inset, is a giant storm much larger in size than Earth.

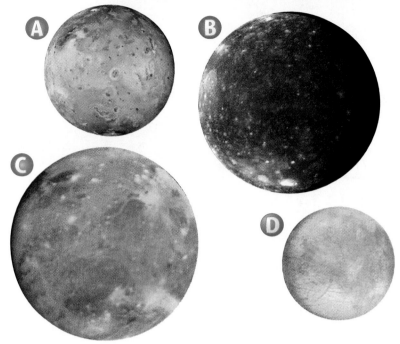

Figure 21 The astronomer Galileo discovered Jupiter's four largest moons. **(A)** Io's surface is covered with large, active volcanoes. **(B)** Callisto's surface is icy and covered with craters. **(C)** Ganymede is the largest of Jupiter's moons. **(D)** Europa's icy crust may have liquid water underneath.
Inferring Why was Galileo able to see only Jupiter's largest moons?

Io is covered with volcanoes. Over a dozen huge volcanoes are erupting all the time, so Io's surface changes from year to year because of the flows of hot material. The sulfur in the flows gives a variety of colors to Io's surface. From space, Io looks something like a giant pizza. In contrast, Europa has an icy crust that may have liquid water underneath.

Ganymede is the largest of Jupiter's moons and has about twice the mass of Earth's moon. Ganymede's surface is icy and partly covered with craters. Other parts of the surface show giant grooves in the ice. Callisto also has an icy surface. It is so heavily cratered that no part of its surface is free of craters.

☑ *Checkpoint* **What are Jupiter's four largest moons?**

Saturn

The second-largest planet in the solar system is Saturn. Saturn is slightly smaller than Jupiter, but including its beautiful rings it has a greater overall diameter. The *Voyager* probes showed that Saturn, like Jupiter, has a thick atmosphere made up mainly of hydrogen and helium. Saturn's atmosphere also contains clouds and storms, but they are less dramatic than those on Jupiter. Saturn is the only planet that is less dense than water.

Saturn's Rings When Galileo first looked at Saturn with a telescope, he saw something sticking out on the sides, but he didn't know what it was. A few decades later, another astronomer using a better telescope discovered that Saturn had rings around it. Astronomers later found that these rings are made of chunks of ice and rock, each traveling in its own orbit around Saturn. The rings are part of the Saturn system.

Model Saturn

Here's how you can build a scale model of Saturn. **ACTIVITY**

1. Use a plastic foam sphere 8 cm in diameter to represent Saturn.

2. ✂ Use an overhead transparency to represent Saturn's rings. Cut a circle 18 cm in diameter out of the transparency. Cut a hole 9 cm in diameter out of the center of the circle.

3. Stick five toothpicks into Saturn, spaced equally around its equator. Put the transparency on the toothpicks and tape it to them. Sprinkle baking soda on the transparency.

4. Use a peppercorn to represent Titan. Place the peppercorn 72 cm away from Saturn on the same plane as the rings.

Making Models What do the particles of baking soda represent?

Figure 22 Saturn's rings are made up of ice chunks and rocks of many different sizes. The smaller photo shows that there are actually many small rings. The colors in this photo have been added by a computer. *Observing Why might it be hard to see Saturn's rings when their edges are facing Earth?*

From Earth, it looks as though Saturn has only a few rings, and that they are divided from each other by narrow, dark regions. The *Voyager* spacecraft discovered that each of these obvious rings is divided into dozens of smaller rings. In all, Saturn has hundreds of rings.

Saturn's rings are broad and thin, like a compact disc. Sometimes the rings are tipped so that observers see them at an angle. Occasionally, they are on edge, and then, because they are so thin, astronomers can't see them at all.

In the last few decades, rings have been discovered around the other three gas giants as well. But the rings around Jupiter, Uranus, and Neptune are not as spectacular as Saturn's.

Saturn's Moons Saturn's largest moon, Titan, is larger than Earth's own moon. Titan was discovered in 1665 but was known only as a point of light until the *Voyagers* went by. The probes showed that Titan has an atmosphere so thick that little light can get through it. Astronomers studying Hubble Space Telescope images can barely see Titan's surface.

Four other moons of Saturn are each over 1,000 kilometers in diameter. They are named Tethys (TEE this), Iapetus (eye AP uh tus), Dione, and Rhea. *Voyager* images show craters and canyons on these moons.

☑ *Checkpoint* *What are Saturn's rings made of?*

Figure 23 This image of Saturn and six of its moons combines photos taken by *Voyager 1* and *Voyager 2*.

Uranus

Although the gas giant Uranus (YOOR uh nus) is about four times the diameter of Earth, it is still much smaller than Jupiter and Saturn. Uranus is twice as far from the sun as Saturn, so it is much colder. Uranus looks bluish because of traces of methane in its atmosphere.

Discovery of Uranus In 1781, Uranus became the first new planet discovered since ancient times. Astronomer William Herschel, in England, found an object in the sky that did not look like a star. At first he thought it might be a comet. But other astronomers soon calculated its orbit and realized that it was a planet beyond Saturn. The discovery made Herschel famous and started an era of solar system exploration.

Exploring Uranus In 1986, about 200 years after Herschel's discovery, *Voyager 2* arrived at Uranus and sent back our only close-up views of that giant planet. Images from *Voyager 2* show only a few clouds on Uranus's surface, but even these few allowed astronomers to calculate that Uranus rotates in about 17 hours.

Strangely, Uranus's axis is tilted at an angle of about 90° from the vertical, as shown in Figure 24. Viewed from Earth, Uranus is rotating from top to bottom instead of from side to side, the way most of the other planets do. Astronomers think that billions of years ago Uranus was hit by an object that knocked it on its side.

Uranus's Moons Photographs from *Voyager 2* showed that Uranus's five largest moons have icy, cratered surfaces. The craters show that the moons have been hit by rocks from space. Uranus's moons also have lava flows on their surfaces, suggesting that material has erupted from inside each moon. *Voyager 2* images revealed ten moons that had never been seen before. In 1999, astronomers discovered another moon, for a total of 18.

Figure 24 (A) This composite image of *Voyager 2* photos includes Uranus and five of its 18 moons. (B) Unlike most other planets, Uranus rotates on its side.

Figure 25 The Great Dark Spot was a giant storm in Neptune's atmosphere. The storm is now gone.

Figure 26 Neptune's largest moon, Triton, is covered with ridges and craters.

Neptune

Neptune is even farther from the sun than Uranus—in fact, it is 30 times Earth's distance from the sun. Unlike Uranus's nearly featureless blue atmosphere, the atmopshere of Neptune contains visible clouds.

Discovery of Neptune The planet Neptune was discovered as a result of a mathematical prediction. Uranus was not quite following the orbit astronomers predicted for it. Astronomers hypothesized that there must be another, unseen planet whose gravity was affecting Uranus's orbit. By 1846, mathematicians in both England and France had calculated the orbit of this new planet. A few months later, an observer in Germany saw an unknown object in the sky. It was the new planet, now called Neptune.

Exploring Neptune In 1989 *Voyager 2* flew by Neptune, where it photographed a Great Dark Spot, as shown in Figure 25, about the size of Earth. Like the Great Red Spot on Jupiter, the Great Dark Spot probably was a giant storm. But the storm didn't last long. Images from the Hubble Space Telescope taken five years later showed that the Great Dark Spot was gone. Other, smaller spots and regions of clouds on Neptune seem to come and go.

Neptune's Moons Astronomers have discovered eight moons revolving around Neptune. Neptune's largest moon is Triton. The *Voyager* photos show that the region near Triton's south pole is covered with a cap of ice, and that dark material is visible underneath the ice.

✓ *Checkpoint* Before they could see Neptune, what evidence led scientists to conclude that it existed?

Pluto and Charon

Pluto and its single moon Charon are very different from the gas giants. **Pluto and Charon have solid surfaces and masses much less than that of Earth.** In fact, Pluto is less than two thirds the size of Earth's moon. Since Charon is more than half the size of Pluto, astronomers sometimes consider them to be a double planet instead of a planet and a moon.

Pluto and Charon are so far from the sun that they revolve around the sun only once every 248 Earth years. Because Pluto and Charon are so small and far away, astronomers have been unable to learn much about them.

Discovery of Pluto and Charon The American astronomer Clyde Tombaugh discovered Pluto in 1930. He had been searching for a large object he thought might be affecting Neptune's orbit. Tombaugh spent 10 months looking at hundreds of thousands of images before he found Pluto. Charon was not discovered until 1978, by the astronomer James Christy. Christy was studying photographs of Pluto when he noticed that Pluto seemed to have a "bump." The bump turned out to be Charon.

Is Pluto Really a Planet? Pluto is so small that many astronomers do not think it should be called a planet at all. Pluto may be merely the largest of thousands of objects revolving around the sun out beyond Neptune. If astronomers had found these other objects before they found Pluto, they might not have called Pluto a planet.

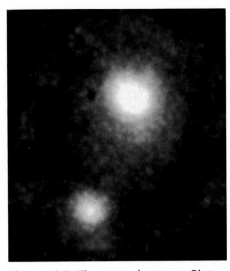

Figure 27 The space between Pluto and Charon was clearly seen from Earth in 1999, using new telescopes in Hawaii. This photo, taken with the Hubble Space Telescope, clearly shows them as two objects. *Inferring Why do astronomers sometimes call Pluto and Charon a double planet?*

Section 4 Review

1. How are the gas giants similar to each other? How are they different?
2. How is Pluto different from the gas giants?
3. What is the most prominent feature of Jupiter's surface? What causes this feature?
4. Why do astronomers think Uranus may have been hit by another object billions of years ago?
5. **Thinking Critically** **Predicting** Do you think astronomers have found all of the moons of the outer planets? Explain.

Check Your Progress CHAPTER PROJECT

Once you have models that show size and distance separately, design another scale model of the solar system. This time, use the same scale for both size and distance. If your chalkboard is the sun, which planets would be in your classroom? Where would the other planets be with respect to your classroom, school grounds, and town?

Discuss with classmates any problems that would come up in building a model using the same scale for both size and distance. Revise your model as needed.

SPEEDING AROUND THE SUN

In this lab, you will make and test a hypothesis about how a planet's distance from the sun is related to its period of revolution.

Problem

How does a planet's distance from the sun affect its period of revolution?

Materials

string, 1.5 m
plastic tube, 6 cm
meter stick

one-hole rubber stopper
stopwatch
weight or several washers

Procedure

1. What do you think is the relationship between a planet's distance from the sun and its period of revolution? Write your hypothesis in the form of an "If . . . then . . ." statement.

2. To test your hypothesis, you need to make a model planet.

   a. Thread the string through the rubber stopper hole. Tie the end of the string to the main part of the string. Pull tightly to make sure that the knot will not become untied.

   b. Thread the other end of the string through the plastic tube and tie a weight to that end. Have your teacher check both knots.

   c. Hold the plastic tube in your hand above your head. Swing the stopper around above your head. Practice keeping the stopper moving at a constant speed. The circle represents the planet's orbit. **CAUTION:** *Stand away from other students. Make sure the swinging stopper will not hit students or objects. Do not let go of the string.*

3. Before you try different distances for your model planet, copy the data table into your notebook.

DATA TABLE

Distance (cm)	Period of Revolution (seconds)			
	Trial 1	Trial 2	Trial 3	Average
20				
40				
60				

4. Pull the string so the stopper is 20 cm away from the plastic tube. Swing the stopper just fast enough to keep the stopper moving.

5. Have your partner time how long it takes for the stopper to make 10 revolutions. Divide by 10 to find the period of revolution. Record this number as Trial 1.

6. Repeat Steps 4–5 two more times. Record your results as Trials 2 and 3. Add the results of the three trials together and divide by three to find the average period of revolution.

7. If you pull the stopper out to 40 cm, do you think the period of revolution will increase or decrease? To find out, pull the stopper out to 40 cm and repeat Steps 4–6.

8. Based on your results in Step 7, do you want to revise your hypothesis? Make any needed changes. Then pull the stopper out to 60 cm and repeat Steps 4–6.

Analyze and Conclude

1. Which object in your model represented the sun? Which represented the planet?

2. What force did the pull on the string represent?

3. When you pulled the stopper out to make the orbit larger, did the string then represent a stronger or weaker force of gravity? Why?

4. What happened to the period of revolution when you made the orbit larger in Steps 7 and 8?

5. Did your observations support your hypothesis? Summarize your conclusions based on your observations.

6. Which planets take less time to revolve around the sun—those closer to the sun or those farther away? Use the model to support your answer.

7. **Think About It** What information did you consider when you made your hypothesis? How did having some experimental data help you modify your hypothesis?

Design an Experiment

Write a hypothesis relating the mass of a planet to its period of revolution. Then, using a stopper with a different mass, modify the activity to test your hypothesis. Before you swing the stopper, have your teacher check your knots.

DISCOVER · ACTIVITY · · ·

Which Way Do Comet Tails Point?

1. Form a small ball out of modeling clay to represent a comet.

2. Using a pencil point, push three 10-cm lengths of string into the ball. The strings represent the comet's tail. Stick the ball onto the pencil point, as shown in the photo.

3. Hold the ball about 1 m in front of a fan. The air from the fan represents the solar wind. Move the ball toward the fan, away from the fan, and from side to side.
CAUTION: *Keep your fingers away from the fan blades.*

Think It Over

Inferring How does moving the ball affect the direction in which the strings point? What determines which way the tail of a comet points?

GUIDE FOR READING

◆ **What are the characteristics of comets and asteroids?**

◆ **Where do meteoroids come from?**

Reading Tip As you read, make an outline of this section using the headings as the main topics.

Key Terms comet • asteroid • asteroid belt • meteroid • meteor • meteorite

---

Suppose you could watch a cosmic collision! That's exactly what happened in July 1994. Eugene and Carolyn Shoemaker and David Levy discovered a new comet in 1993 that had previously broken into pieces near Jupiter. In 1994, the fragments returned and crashed into Jupiter. On Earth, astronomers were fascinated to see the huge explosions—some were as large as Earth!

As this story shows, the sun, planets, and moons aren't the only objects in the solar system. There are also millions of smaller objects, most of which are classified as comets and asteroids.

Comet Systems

One of the most glorious things you can see in the night sky is a comet. A bright comet may be visible for days or weeks or months and is well worth seeing. In April 1997, for example, Comet Hale-Bopp and its bright dust tail were clearly visible even without a telescope.

Like each planet, each comet is a small system within the large solar system. You can think of a **comet** as a "dirty snowball" about the size of a mountain on Earth. **Comets are large chunks of ice and dust whose orbits are usually very long, narrow ellipses.**

◀ A dark ring on Jupiter caused by comet Shoemaker-Levy 9

562

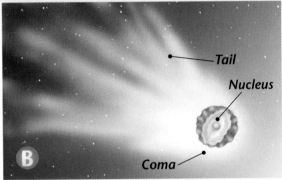

Figure 28 (A) Most comet systems revolve around the sun in very long, narrow orbits. (B) The main parts of a comet system are the nucleus, the coma, and the tail.
Observing What shape is a comet's orbit?

Because their orbits are so elliptical, few comet systems pass near Earth. The ones that do can usually be seen only briefly. When a comet system gets close enough to the sun, the energy in the sunlight turns the ice into gas, releasing dust. The gas and dust form an outer layer called the coma. Figure 28 shows the inner layer of the comet, which is then called the nucleus. The brightest part of a comet, the comet's head, is made up of the nucleus and coma.

Remember that the sun's corona produces a stream of particles called the solar wind. Solar wind pushes the gas from a comet away from the sun. Gas and dust form the comet's tail. The tail looks like hair; in fact, the name *comet* means "long-haired star" in Greek.

A comet's tail can be hundreds of millions of kilometers long and stretch across most of the sky. The material is stretched out very thinly, however, so there actually isn't much mass in the tail of a comet.

In 1705, Edmond Halley, an English astronomer, calculated the orbits of 24 comets that people had observed over hundreds of years. Halley realized that several of the comets seemed to have the same orbit and suggested that they were part of the same comet system. Halley calculated that this comet system appeared about every 76 years, and then predicted that it would reappear in 1758. When this prediction came true, the comet was named Halley's Comet. In 1986, the last time Halley's Comet appeared in our sky, the European Space Agency's *Giotto* spacecraft flew within a few hundred kilometers of it.

 Checkpoint **How did Halley's Comet get its name?**

Figure 29 The asteroid belt (left) lies between Mars and Jupiter. Asteroids come in many sizes and shapes, as shown in this artist's depiction (center). NASA's *Near Earth Asteroid Rendezvous* mission photographed the asteroid Mathilde (right) in 1997.

Frequency

The frequency of an event is how often the event occurs in a given time period. Meteors streak across the sky with a certain frequency during a meteor shower. For example, if you see 1 meteor streak per minute for an hour, the frequency of meteor streaks is 60 streaks per hour. At another time, you might see 1 meteor streak every 10 minutes for an hour. In this case, the frequency of streaks is 6 streaks per hour.

Asteroids

Between 1801 and 1807, astronomers discovered four small objects between the orbits of Mars and Jupiter. They named the objects Ceres, Pallas, Juno, and Vesta. Over the next 80 years, astronomers found 300 more. These objects, called **asteroids,** are too small and too numerous to be considered full-fledged planets. **Most asteroids revolve around the sun between the orbits of Mars and Jupiter.** This region of the solar system, shown in Figure 29, is known as the **asteroid belt.** The asteroid belt is another small system within the solar system.

Astronomers have discovered more than 10,000 asteroids, and more are found every month. Ceres, Pallas, Juno, and Vesta are among the dozen that are over 250 kilometers across.

INTEGRATING EARTH SCIENCE Some asteroids come near the orbit of Earth. Near Earth asteroids could hit Earth. When a large asteroid hit Earth 65 million years ago, it exploded, making a crater 200 kilometers in diameter near the Yucatán Peninsula of Mexico. The explosion almost certainly raised trillions of tons of dust into the atmosphere, blocking the light from the sun for months. Debris from the explosion probably started huge fires that destroyed much of Earth's forests and grass. Scientists hypothesize that as a result many species of organisms, including the dinosaurs, became extinct.

Meteors

Suppose you are outside on a clear night, looking up at the sky. Suddenly, you see a streak of light flashing across the sky. Within seconds, you see another streak. For an hour or so, meteors streak with a frequency of at least one per minute. You are watching a meteor shower. Meteor showers happen regularly, several times a year.

Even when there is no meteor shower, you can see meteors if you are far from city lights and the sky is free of clouds. On average, a meteor streaks overhead with a frequency of one every 10 minutes.

A **meteoroid** is a chunk of rock or dust in space. **Meteoroids usually come from comets or asteroids.** Comets leave dust behind as they move through the solar system. When Earth passes through one of these dust clouds, bits of dust enter Earth's atmosphere.

When a meteoroid enters Earth's atmosphere, friction makes it burn up and produce the streak of light you see in the sky—a **meteor.** If the meteoroid is large, it may not burn up completely. Meteoroids that pass through the atmosphere and hit Earth's surface are called **meteorites.** The craters on the moon and on other objects in the solar system were caused by meteoroids.

Meteorites fall all over Earth. Most of them look just like stones, so nobody notices them. A few meteorites are made almost entirely of iron and nickel, and so are unusually heavy for their size. This makes them more likely to be identified as meteorites than as Earth rocks.

Figure 30 (A) Meteor Crater in Arizona is the best-known meteorite crater on Earth. It was formed when a meteorite hit Earth about 40,000 years ago. (B) Meteoroids make streaks of light, like the one above, as they burn up in the atmosphere.

Section 5 Review

1. What is a comet made of?
2. Where are most asteroids found?
3. What are the main sources of meteoroids?
4. What is the difference between a meteor and a meteorite?
5. **Thinking Critically** **Predicting** Describe what might happen if an asteroid the size of the one that hit Earth 65 million years ago hit Earth today.

Science at Home

Watch a Meteor Shower Meteor showers occur regularly on specific dates. (The Perseids meteor shower, for example, occurs every August 12.) Look in the newspaper or almanac for information about the next meteor shower. With adult family members, go outside on that night and look for meteors. Explain to your family what causes the glow.

SECTION 6 Traveling in Space

How Do Rockets Work?

1. Put on your goggles. Blow up a balloon and hold its neck closed with your fingers.

2. Point the balloon toward an area where there are no people. Put your free hand behind the neck of the balloon, so the air will push against your hand. Let go of the balloon.

3. Repeat Steps 1 and 2 without your free hand behind the balloon.

Think It Over

Observing In which direction does the air rush out? In which direction does the balloon go? Does the balloon need to push against something in order to move? Explain your answer.

GUIDE FOR READING

◆ How do rockets travel in space?

◆ What type of equipment is needed in space?

Reading Tip Before you read, rewrite the headings in the section as *how, why,* or *what* questions. As you read, look for answers to those questions.

Key Terms satellite
• geosynchronous orbit

Curiosity about Earth's "neighborhood" in space has led to moon missions, space shuttle missions, space stations, and Mars missions. But without rockets, none of these accomplishments would have been possible.

Transportation in Space

It is not very easy to get into space. It is even more difficult to get back to Earth. Rockets transport astronauts and equipment into space and back.

How Rockets Work A rocket works in much the way that a balloon is propelled through the air by releasing gas. **A rocket moves forward when gases shot out the back of the rocket push it in the opposite direction.** This is because for every force, or action, an equal and opposite force, or reaction, happens. Therefore, the force of the air being forced out the back of a balloon is an action force. An equal force, the reaction, pushes the balloon forward. In a rocket, fuel is burned to make a hot gas. This hot gas is forced out of narrow nozzles in the back of the rocket, propelling the rocket forward.

Action

Reaction

Figure 31 The force of the rocket engine's hot gas in one direction (action) produces an opposing force (reaction) that propels the rocket forward.

4b Lunar vehicle proceeds to lunar orbit.

3b Third stage ignites.

4a Third stage is discarded.

3a Second stage separates and falls to Earth.

2b Second stage ignites and continues with third stage.

Figure 32 Multistage rockets have three stages, or sections. *Interpreting Diagrams According to this diagram, which stage, or section, of the rocket reaches the destination? What happens to the other stages?*

2a First stage separates and falls to Earth.

Multistage Rockets

Multistage Rockets Early rockets, built by the Chinese around the year 1000, used gunpowder as fuel. But gunpowder burns quickly and explosively. A rocket designed to travel out of Earth's atmosphere needs a different sort of fuel, one that burns slowly and continuously. The American scientist Robert H. Goddard experimented with liquid fuels in the 1920s. He showed that a liquid fuel can provide continuous power.

However, a rocket can carry only so much fuel. Once the fuel is used up, the rocket falls back to Earth. In 1903, the Russian Konstantin Tsiolkovsky came up with the idea of a multistage rocket. As each stage, or section, of a rocket uses up its fuel, the empty fuel container drops off. Then the next stage ignites and continues powering the rocket upward. The development of powerful multistage rockets in the 1950s and 1960s made it possible to send rockets to the moon and farther into space. Figure 32 shows a rocket similar to the one that carried the astronauts to the moon.

In the late 1970s, the National Aeronautics and Space Administration (NASA) developed reusable space shuttles. They are called shuttles because they can go back and forth, or shuttle, between Earth and space. Since the first shuttle was launched in 1981, space shuttles have been the main way that the United States has launched astronauts and equipment into space.

Artificial Satellites

The Soviet Union launched the first artificial satellite into orbit around Earth on October 4, 1957. A **satellite** is any natural or artificial object that revolves around an object in space. This satellite, *Sputnik 1*, revolved around Earth every 96 minutes. Three months later, the United States launched *Explorer 1* into orbit. On April 12, 1961, Yuri Gagarin, a Soviet cosmonaut, orbited Earth, becoming the first person in space.

Third stage

Second stage

First stage

1 Heavy first stage provides thrust for launch.

Be a Rocket Scientist

You can build a rocket. **ACTIVITY**

1. Use a plastic or paper cup as the rocket body. Cut out a paper nose cone and tape it to the closed end of the cup.

2. Obtain an empty film canister with a lid that snaps on inside the canister. Go outside to do Steps 3–5.

3. Fill the canister about one-quarter full with water.

4. Put on your goggles. Now add half of a fizzing antacid tablet to the film canister and quickly snap on the lid.

5. Place the canister on the ground with the lid down. Place your rocket over the canister and stand back.

Observing
What action happened inside the film canister? What was the reaction of the rocket?

Since 1957, thousands of artificial satellites, including space stations, have been launched into orbit. Satellites and space stations are used for communications, navigation, collecting weather data, and research.

Satellites Artificial satellites are used to relay telephone calls, to measure Earth's atmosphere, and to photograph weather systems, crops, and ships. In addition, two dozen Global Positioning Satellites give off signals that a small receiver on Earth can pick up. The receiver can then pinpoint your position on Earth's surface.

Some satellites are in **geosynchronous orbits,** which means they revolve around Earth at the same rate that Earth rotates. Geosynchronous satellites above the equator seem to hover over a given point on Earth. Geosynchronous satellites are used to relay television signals and to map weather patterns.

Space Stations A space station is a large satellite in which people can live for long periods. The first space station, the Soviet Union's *Salyut,* was launched in 1971. In 1973, the United States launched *Skylab,* which carried a series of telescopes and medical, geological, and astronomical experiments. The former Soviet Union, of which Russia was part, launched the *Mir* space station in 1986. The word *mir* is Russian for "peace." Astronauts from many countries, including Americans, have visited *Mir.* Sixteen countries, including the United States and Russia, are now cooperating to build the International Space Station.

☑ *Checkpoint* **What is a geosynchronous orbit?**

Figure 33 The International Space Station is a cooperative project involving 16 countries, including the United States, Russia, Japan, and Canada. This is an artist's conception of the station in orbit over Florida.

Figure 34 The Space Shuttle *Discovery* is launched into space by its own rockets as well as by rockets attached to it. *Inferring What is one advantage of a reusable space vehicle?*

Equipment Needed in Space

Astronauts need special equipment such as space suits and computers to work in space. The space suits help them adapt to the changes their bodies experience as they leave Earth. Each suit adjusts air pressure and oxygen levels for the astronaut wearing it. It also includes a helmet, communication system, and parachute.

Once in space, computers monitor the conditions on the shuttle, including air pressure, temperature, and the oxygen in the air. All this information is sent to computers on Earth, linking the shuttle with NASA scientists here.

When the astronauts leave the shuttle to work in space, they must take along a life-supporting environment. Space suits are portable work environments. They supply the oxygen the astronauts need to breathe. They also have built-in radios that allow astronauts to communicate with others. The suits are made of a material that protects astronauts from the sun's radiation and the extreme temperature changes in space.

Section 6 Review

1. How does a rocket move?
2. What do astronauts need to live and work in space?
3. Which stage of a multistage rocket reaches the final destination?
4. **Thinking Critically** **Applying Concepts** Explain why space suits are among the most important pieces of equipment for an astronaut.

Science at Home

Landmarks in Space Flight Interview someone who remembers the space programs of the 1950s and 1960s. Prepare your questions in advance, such as: How did you feel when *Sputnik* was in orbit? How did you feel when the first Americans went into space? Did you watch any of the rocket launches on television? You may want to record your interview, then write it out in a question-and-answer format.

Space Exploration—Is It Worth the Cost?

Imagine that your spacecraft has just landed on Mars after a two-month journey from Earth. You've spent years planning for this moment. Canyons, craters, and distant plains stretch out before you. You check your spacesuit and prepare to step out onto the rocky red surface of Mars.

Is such a trip likely? Would it be worthwhile? How much is space flight really worth to human society? Scientists and politicians have already started to debate such questions. Space exploration can help us learn more about the universe. But exploration is risky and expensive. Sending people into space costs billions of dollars and risks human lives. How can we balance the costs and benefits of space exploration?

The Issues

Should Humans Travel Into Space? Many Americans think that Neil Armstrong's walk on the moon in 1969 was one of the great moments in history. Also, learning how to keep people alive in space has led to improvements in everyday life. Safer equipment for firefighters, easier ways to package frozen food, and effective heart monitors have all come out of space program research.

What Are the Alternatives? Space exploration can involve a project to put a person on Mars. It also can involve a more limited use of scientific instruments near Earth, such as the Hubble Space Telescope. Instead of sending people, we could send space probes like *Mars Pathfinder* to other planets.

Is Human Space Exploration Worth the Cost? Scientists who favor human travel into space say that only people can collect certain kinds of information. And using simpler space vehicles that are cheaper to build can also save money. But no one knows if research in space really provides information quicker than research that can be done on Earth. Many critics of space research think that other needs are more important. One United States senator said, "Every time you put money into the space station, there is a dime that won't be available for our children's education or for medical research."

You Decide

1. **Identify the Problem**
   In your own words, list the costs and benefits of space exploration.

2. **Analyze the Options**
   Make a chart of three different approaches to space exploration: sending humans to another planet, doing only Earth-based research, and one other option. What are the benefits and drawbacks of each approach?

3. **Find a Solution**
   Imagine that you are a member of Congress who has to vote on a new budget. There is a fixed amount of money to spend, so you have to decide which needs are most important. Make a list of your top ten priorities. Explain your decisions.

SECTION 1 Describing the Solar System

Key Ideas
- ◆ Descriptions of the solar system have changed from a geocentric model to a heliocentric model.
- ◆ Newton concluded that two factors—inertia and gravity—combine to keep the planets in orbit.
- ◆ Many smaller systems exist within the larger system that is our solar system.

Key Terms

geocentric system	ellipse
heliocentric system	inertia
solar system	gravity

SECTION 2 Characteristics of the Sun

Key Ideas
- ◆ The sun's energy comes from nuclear fusion.
- ◆ The sun has three layers: the photosphere, the chromosphere, and the corona.
- ◆ Features on or above the sun's surface include sunspots, prominences, and solar flares.

Key Terms

nuclear fusion	chromosphere	sunspot
core	corona	prominence
photosphere	solar wind	solar flare

SECTION 3 Characteristics of the Inner Planets

Key Idea
- ◆ Mercury, Venus, Earth, and Mars are small and have rocky surfaces.

Key Terms

terrestrial planet	retrograde rotation
rotation	greenhouse effect
revolution	

SECTION 4 Characteristics of the Outer Planets

Key Ideas
- ◆ Jupiter, Saturn, Uranus, and Neptune are much larger than Earth, and are not solid.
- ◆ Pluto and Charon have solid surfaces.

Key Term
gas giant

SECTION 5 Comets, Asteroids, and Meteors

Key Ideas
- ◆ Comets are chunks of ice and dust that usually have long, elliptical orbits.
- ◆ Most asteroids revolve around the sun between the orbits of Mars and Jupiter.
- ◆ Most meteoroids are comets and asteroids.

Key Terms

comet	asteroid belt	meteor
asteroid	meteoroid	meteorite

SECTION 6 Traveling in Space

INTEGRATING TECHNOLOGY

Key Ideas
- ◆ Rockets move forward as gas is pushed from the back of the rocket.
- ◆ Astronauts need space suits and computers to survive in space.

Key Terms

satellite	geosynchronous orbit

Organizing Information

Compare/Contrast Table On a separate piece of paper, make a table comparing and contrasting the geocentric and heliocentric systems. Include information on the following: object at the center of the system; objects that move around the center; whom the system was first proposed by; and who supported the system. (For more on compare/contrast tables, see the Skills Handbook.)

Reviewing Content

 Review key concepts online using iText at www.phschool.com

Multiple Choice

Choose the letter of the answer that best completes each statement.

1. Copernicus thought that the solar system was
   a. celestial.
   b. elliptical.
   c. geocentric.
   d. heliocentric.

2. The part of the sun where nuclear fusion occurs is the
   a. photosphere.   b. chromosphere.
   c. corona.   d. core.

3. Planets with atmospheres composed mostly of carbon dioxide include
   a. Earth and Mercury.
   b. Venus and Mercury.
   c. Venus and Mars.
   d. Mercury and Mars.

4. The Great Red Spot is a huge storm on
   a. Jupiter.   b. Neptune.
   c. Saturn.   d. Pluto.

5. Most asteroids orbit the sun
   a. between the sun and Mercury.
   b. between Earth and Mars.
   c. between Mars and Jupiter.
   d. between Neptune and Pluto.

True or False

If the statement is true, write true. If it is false, change the underlined word or words to make the statement true.

6. The shape of the orbit of each planet is a <u>circle</u>.

7. Sunspots are regions of <u>cooler</u> gases on the sun.

8. The atmosphere of Venus has <u>higher</u> pressure than the atmosphere of Earth.

9. Aside from the sun, <u>Saturn</u> is the largest source of gravity in the solar system.

10. A <u>meteorite</u> is any natural or manmade object that revolves around an object in space.

Checking Concepts

11. How did Galileo's observations support the idea of a heliocentric system?

12. How did Newton's work on orbits add to the work Kepler had done?

13. Why is it usually impossible to see the sun's corona?

14. What are sunspots?

15. Why does Mercury have only a thin atmosphere?

16. How do astronomers explain that Venus rotates in the opposite direction from most planets and moons?

17. What are the major characteristics of the terrestrial planets? How do they differ from the gas giants?

18. Why do some astronomers think that Pluto should not be called a planet?

19. Why does a comet's tail always stream away from the sun?

20. Why would it be useful to have a satellite that relays television signals in a geosynchronous orbit?

21. **Writing to Learn** Imagine you are an astronaut on a mission to explore the solar system. Write a trip journal telling the story of your trip from Earth to another terrestrial planet and to a gas giant. Include a description of each planet.

Thinking Critically

22. **Relating Cause and Effect** How would Earth move if the sun (including its gravity) suddenly disappeared? Explain your answer.

23. **Applying Concepts** Explain why Venus is hotter than it would be without its atmosphere.

24. **Comparing and Contrasting** Compare and contrast meteoroids, meteors, and meteorites.

25. **Making Generalizations** How could the construction of an International Space Station help with the further exploration of the solar system?

Applying Skills

Use the diagram of an imaginary, newly discovered planetary system around Star X to answer Questions 26–28. The periods of revolution of Planets A, B, and C are 75 Earth days, 200 Earth days, and 300 Earth days.

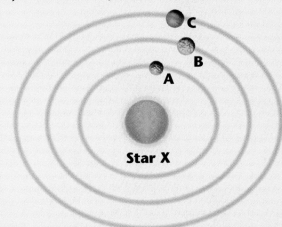

Star X

26. Interpreting Data Which planet in this new planetary system revolves around Star X in the shortest amount of time?

27. Making Models In 150 days, how far will each planet have revolved around Star X? Copy the diagram and sketch the positions of the three planets to find out. How far will each planet have revolved around Star X in 400 days? Sketch their positions.

28. Drawing Conclusions Can Planet C ever be closer to Planet A than to Planet B? Study your drawings to figure this out.

Performance ▼ CHAPTER PROJECT Assessment

Present Your Project Present your solar system. Explain how you worked with large distances. Display your data tables and your calculations. Show how you checked them for accuracy. Compare the distances in your models to distances inside and outside your classroom.

Reflect and Record In your journal, explain what you would do to improve the model. How effectively did you use computers or calculators to get the data?

Test Preparation
Use these questions to prepare for standardized tests.

Study the table. Then answer Questions 29–32.

Planet	Period of Rotation (Earth days)	Period of Revolution (Earth years)	Average Distance From the Sun (million kilometers)
Mars	1.03	1.9	228
Jupiter	0.41	12	778
Saturn	0.43	29	1,427
Uranus	0.72	84	2,871
Neptune	0.67	165	4,497

29. Which of these planet's orbits is farthest from Earth's orbit?

  A Mars   **B** Jupiter
  C Uranus   **D** Neptune

30. Which planet has a "day" that is most similar in length to a day on Earth?

  F Mars   **G** Jupiter
  H Uranus   **J** Neptune

31. Light takes about 8 minutes and 20 seconds to travel from the sun to Earth, 150 million kilometers away. About how long does it take light to travel from the sun to Jupiter?

  A 10 minutes   **B** 25 minutes
  C 43 minutes   **D** 112 minutes

32. Which one of the following conclusions about planets is supported by the information in the table?

  F As distance from the sun increases, period of rotation increases.

  G As distance from the sun increases, period of revolution increases.

  H As distance from the sun increases, period of revolution decreases.

  J There is no relationship between distance from the sun and period of revolution.

THE MISSISSIPPI

What would you name a river that—

◆ *carries about 420 million metric tons of cargo a year,*

◆ *drains 31 states and 2 Canadian provinces,*

◆ *looks like a tree that has a thin top trunk and 2 strong branches,*

◆ *flows at about 18,100 cubic meters of water per second?*

Native Americans called the river *misi sipi,* **an Algonquin word meaning "big water," or "father of waters."**

Have you ever traveled on a river or lake that feeds into the mighty Mississippi River? Perhaps you have but did not realize it. The map below shows the watershed of this great river. From the west, the Missouri River — the "Big Muddy"— carries soft silt eroded from the Great Plains. The Missouri joins the Mississippi near St. Louis, turning the river's clear water to muddy brown. From the east, the Ohio River flows in from the rocky Appalachian plateau, nearly doubling the volume of water in the river. In all, the huge Mississippi watershed drains about 40 percent of the United States.

The Mississippi River starts at Lake Itasca and flows through 10 states to the Gulf of Mexico. The river is a drainage point for hundreds of tributaries in the vast Mississippi watershed. ▶

The Mississippi River Watershed

574

A National Trade Route

Since Native Americans settled in villages along the Mississippi around 1,200 years ago, the river has served as a water highway for trade and travel.

In the late 1600s, French explorers, fur traders, and soldiers arrived in the Mississippi Valley. They chose strategic sites for forts and fur-trading posts — Prairie du Chien, St. Louis, and St. Genevieve. At first, traders used canoes, rafts, and flatboats to carry goods downstream. But traveling up the river was difficult. Crews had to use long poles to push narrow keelboats upstream against the current.

In 1811, the arrival of *The New Orleans,* the first steamboat on the Mississippi River, changed the river forever. Within 40 years, there were hundreds more steamboats and many new river towns. On the upper Mississippi, the city of Minneapolis grew up around flour mills near the falls. Farther downstream, Memphis became a center for transporting cotton. Later, it was a stopping point for showboats and musicians. New Orleans quickly became a world port. It received cotton, tobacco, and sugar cane from southern plantations and exported corn, wheat and indigo to Europe. Imported luxury items, such as soap, coffee, shoes, and textiles, traveled upstream from the port of New Orleans. Up and down the river townspeople eagerly waited for the cry, "Steamboat comin'!"

▲ St. Anthony Falls is the northernmost point of navigation on the Mississippi.

▲ Crews in flatboats rode the river currents, steering with long oars.

▲ New Orleans has been a major trading port since its founding in 1718.

Social Studies Activity

Use the map to choose a city on the Mississippi River to learn about. Imagine that you are an early settler in the city. Write a letter to persuade relatives to move to your city. Before writing, learn about the history, founding, and trade of the city. Look for answers to the following questions:

◆ Who founded the city? When was the city founded? Why did settlers decide to move there? Where did they come from?

◆ What part did the Mississippi River play in the city's founding?

◆What other physical features were important to the city?

◆ Where did the city's name come from?

◆ What products were grown, bought, or sold there?

Taming the River

Navigating the sandbars, shallow water, and rocky rapids on the upper Mississippi River was treacherous for captains of ships and barges in the 1800s. To make traveling easier, engineers in the early 1900s built a "water staircase," a series of 29 locks and dams between Minneapolis, Minnesota, and Alton, Illinois, above St. Louis. A lock is an enclosed basin, with gates at each end. Locks allow engineers to raise or lower the water level in a certain area of the river. Between the locks on the upper Mississippi, the river forms wide pools of quiet water, maintaining a channel deep enough for large boats.

Use the diagrams to trace how a boat "locks through" as it travels upstream. This technology allowed boats to travel to cities on the upper Mississippi. ▶

① The lock gate opens. Your boat moves in and you tie up to the wall.

Gate open
Upstream water level
Valve closed
Direction of river flow
Downstream water level

Gate closed
Upstream water level
Valve open
Downstream water level

② The gate closes, and water pours in. As water fills the lock—like a bathtub filling—it lifts the boat a meter or more. When the water in the lock is even with the water level upstream, the gates at the upstream end open. You untie your boat and move out into the river.

If you were going downstream, you would "lock through" in reverse. The water would empty out of the lock, lowering the water level to match the level downstream.

Science Activity

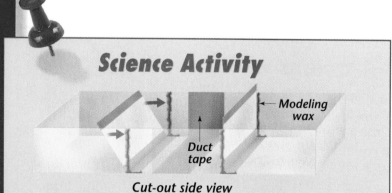

← Modeling wax
↑ Duct tape

Cut-out side view

Use a cardboard milk container to build a working model of a lock. Set up your lock following the illustration. Then demonstrate how your lock works, using a cork or pen cap as your ship and sailing it through the lock.

All Aboard

The whistle blows. The gleaming white steamboat pulls away from the dock just below Fort Snelling, Minnesota. You head downstream toward New Orleans. As you watch the paddlewheel splashing in the water, you think of the old-time steamboats that carried passengers up and down the Mississippi River in the 1800s.

Today you are cruising at a speed of 11.3 kilometers per hour. You want to stay awake until you enter Lock 3 at Red Wing, Minnesota. It's 4:30 P.M. on Monday now. You know that it's about 78.8 kilometers to Red Wing. It should take about 7 hours to reach the lock. So you'll be there at 11:30 P.M. and through the lock by midnight.

As your boat travels along the river, it will follow the schedule you see on this page. The highlight of your trip will be Mark Twain's hometown of Hannibal, Missouri. You will arrive there on Friday.

Look at the Upper Mississippi River schedule to answer the questions below. Distances are given from Fort Snelling.

◆ What is your average speed between Dubuque and Hannibal? Use the following equation:

$$speed = \frac{distance}{time}$$

Round to the nearest tenth.

◆ How long will you spend in Prairie du Chien?

◆ About how long does it take to travel from Prairie du Chien to Dubuque?

MISSISSIPPI RIVERBOAT
SCHEDULE
MAY to SEPTEMBER

UPPER MISSISSIPPI RIVERBOAT SCHEDULE

Port	Arrival Time	Departure Time	Distance From Fort Snelling
Fort Snelling, MN		4:30 P.M. Mon.	0 km
Lock 3, Red Wing, MN	11:30 P.M. Mon.	12:00 midnight	78.8 km
Prairie du Chien, WI	11:00 P.M. Tues.	10:30 A.M. Wed.	337.8 km
Dubuque, IA	6:30 P.M. Wed.	7:00 P.M. Wed.	426.3 km
Hannibal, MO	1:00 A.M. Fri.	———	863.9 km

LOWER MISSISSIPPI RIVERBOAT SCHEDULE

Port	Arrival Time	Departure Time	Distance From Fort Snelling
Hannibal, MO		6 P.M. Fri.	863.9 km
Lock 26 at Alton, IL	a. ?	b. ?	1033 km
St. Louis, MO	c. ?	d. ?	1070.7 km
Cape Girardeau, MO	6:30 A.M. Sun.	———	e. ?

Math Activity

Now complete the riverboat schedule for the Lower Mississippi. Your boat will leave Hannibal at 6 P.M. Friday and will travel at a speed of 14.7 kilometers per hour for the rest of the journey.

◆ When will you arrive at Lock 26?

◆ You spend 34 minutes in the lock. When will you depart from Lock 26? Your boat travels on. When will it arrive in St. Louis?

◆ The boat will spend 4 hours in St. Louis and head to Cape Girardeau, arriving at 6:30 A.M. Sunday. How far is it from St. Louis to Cape Girardeau?

Mark Three! Mark Twain!

To steer a boat on the Mississippi, early riverboat pilots had to memorize landmarks at every bend and curve of the river, going both upstream and down. They had to know where the channel was deep enough for the boat, where the current was strong, where there were sandbars or sunken logs.

When Samuel Clemens was growing up in the small river town of Hannibal, Missouri, his ambition was to become a Mississippi River steamboat pilot. He was a pilot for a while. Later he became one of America's most famous writers, using the pen name Mark Twain. In the passage below from his book *Life on the Mississippi*, Twain describes a lesson he learned from an experienced pilot, Mr. Bixby.

What's in a Name?

Mark Twain's name comes from a term that steamboat crews used to measure the depth of river water. *Twain* means "two." Dropping a weighted line, they would call out the depth: "Mark twain!"—2 fathoms deep; "Mark three!"—3 fathoms deep. (Note: One fathom equals 1.8 meters.)

"My boy," [Bixby said] "you've got to know the shape of the river perfectly. It is all there is left to steer by on a very dark night. Everything else is blotted out and gone. But mind you, it hasn't the same shape in the night that it has in the daytime."

"How on earth am I ever going to learn it, then?"

"How do you follow a hall at home in the dark? Because you know the shape of it. You can't see it."

"Do you mean to say that I've got to know all the million trifling variations of shape in the banks of this interminable [endless] river as well as I know the shape of the front hall at home?"

"On my honor, you've got to know them better than any man ever did know the shapes of the halls in his own house."

"I wish I was dead!"

"Now I don't want to discourage you, but —. . . . You see, this has got to be learned; there isn't any getting around it. . . .

The river is a very different shape on a pitch-dark night from what it is on a starlight night. All shores seem to be straight lines, then, and mighty dim ones, too; and you'd run them for straight lines, only you know better. . . . Then there's your gray mist. You take a night when there's one of these grisly, drizzly gray mists, and then there isn't any particular shape to a shore. A gray mist would tangle the head of the oldest man that ever lived. Well, then, different kinds of moonlight change the shape of the river in different ways. You see —"

"Oh, don't say any more, please! Have I got to learn the shape of the river according to all these five hundred thousand different ways? If I tried to carry all that cargo in my head, it would make me stoop-shouldered."

"No! You only learn the shape of the river; and you learn it with such absolute certainty that you can always steer by the shape that's in your head, and never mind the one that's before your eyes."

Language Arts Activity

Read the excerpt, focusing on what the dialogue tells you about the characters of Mark Twain and Mr. Bixby.

◆ What lesson does Mark Twain learn?

◆ How does Mr. Bixby feel about the Mississippi River? How can you tell?

Now, use dialogue to write an ending to this riverboat excerpt. Before you begin writing, think carefully about the characters, setting, and your conclusion.

Riverboat captains were licensed to navigate the river. ▶

Tie It Together

Celebrate the River

Plan a class fair featuring cities on the Mississippi River today, such as St. Louis (above). Set up a booth for each city and create a travel brochure to persuade people to visit.

As a team, choose a city to represent. Then divide up tasks so different members find information on the following topics:

◆ Interesting attractions and events that your city offers—zoos, museums, parks, sports events, music festivals, and so on.

◆ Influences of different groups on the city's food, customs, music, and architecture.

◆ Physical features of the area around the city.

◆ Famous people—writers, political figures, entertainers—who lived there.

◆ Historic places to visit, such as monuments, houses, battlefields, and statues.

◆ Illustrations and pictures of special attractions.

◆ Maps of walking tours and historic areas.

◆ Native plants and animals in the area.

Before starting your brochure, decide which attractions to highlight. Think of a slogan for your travel campaign. If you wish, make a poster. Celebrate life on the river today.

Think Like a Scientist

*A*lthough you may not know it, you think like a scientist every day. Whenever you ask a question and explore possible answers, you use many of the same skills that scientists do. Some of these skills are described on this page.

Observing

When you use one or more of your five senses to gather information about the world, you are **observing.** Hearing a dog bark, counting twelve green seeds, and smelling smoke are all observations. To increase the power of their senses, scientists sometimes use microscopes, telescopes, or other instruments that help them make more detailed observations.

An observation must be an accurate report of what your senses detect. It is important to keep careful records of your observations in science class by writing or drawing in a notebook. The information collected through observations is called evidence, or data. Evidence can be either direct or indirect.

Inferring

When you interpret an observation, you are **inferring,** or drawing an inference. For example, if you hear your dog barking, you may infer that someone is at your front door. To draw this inference, you combine the evidence—the barking dog—and your experience or knowledge—you know that your dog barks when strangers approach—to reach a logical conclusion.

Notice that an inference is not a fact; it is only one of many possible interpretations of an observation. For example, your dog may be barking because it wants to go for a walk. An inference may turn out to be incorrect even if it is based on accurate observations and logical reasoning. The only way to find out if an inference is correct is to investigate further.

Predicting

When you listen to the weather forecast, you may hear predictions about future weather—what the temperature will be, whether it will rain, and how windy it will be. Weather forecasters use observations and knowledge of weather patterns to predict the weather and weather trends. The skill of **predicting** involves making an inference about a future event based on current evidence.

Because a prediction is an inference, it may prove to be false. In science class, you can test some of your predictions by doing experiments. For example, suppose you predict that larger paper airplanes can fly farther than smaller airplanes. How could you test your prediction?

ACTIVITY Use the photograph to answer the questions below.

Observing Look closely at the photograph. List at least three observations.

Inferring Use your observations to make an inference about what has happened. What experience or knowledge did you use to make the inference?

Predicting Predict what will happen next. On what evidence or experience do you base your prediction?

Classifying

Could you imagine searching for a book in the library if the books were shelved in no particular order? Your trip to the library would be an all-day event! Luckily, librarians group together books on similar topics or by the same author. Grouping together items that are alike in some way is called **classifying.** You can classify items in many ways: by size, by shape, by use, and by other important characteristics.

Like librarians, scientists use the skill of classifying to organize information and objects. When things are sorted into groups, the relationships among them become easier to understand.

Classify the objects in the photograph into two groups based on any characteristic you choose. Then use another characteristic to classify the objects into three groups. **ACTIVITY**

Making Models

This student is using a model to demonstrate what causes day and night on Earth. What do the flashlight and the tennis ball in the model represent? What are the model's limitations? **ACTIVITY**

Have you ever drawn a picture to help someone understand what you were saying? Such a drawing is one type of model. A model is a picture, diagram, computer image, or other representation of a complex object or process. **Making models** helps people understand things that they cannot observe directly.

Scientists use models to represent very large or very small things, such as the planets in the solar system, or the parts of a cell. Such models are physical models—drawings or three-dimensional structures that look like the real thing. Other models are mental models—mathematical equations or words that describe how something works. All models have limitations.

Communicating

Whenever you talk on the phone, write a letter, or listen to your teacher at school, you are communicating. **Communicating** is the process of sharing ideas and information with other people. Communicating effectively requires many skills, including writing, reading, speaking, listening, and making models.

Scientists communicate to share results, information, and opinions. Scientists often communicate about their work in journals, over the telephone, in

letters, and on the Internet. They also attend scientific meetings where they share their ideas with one another in person.

On a sheet of paper, write out clear, detailed directions for tying your shoe. Then exchange directions with a partner. Follow your partner's directions exactly. How successful were you at tying your shoe? How could your partner have communicated more clearly? **ACTIVITY**

581

Making Measurements

When scientists make observations, it is not sufficient to say that something is "big" or "heavy." Instead, scientists use instruments to measure just how big or heavy an object is. By measuring, scientists can express their observations more precisely and communicate more information about what they observe.

Measuring in SI

The standard system of measurement used by scientists around the world is known as the International System of Units, which is abbreviated as SI (in French, *Système International d'Unités*). SI units are easy to use because they are based on multiples of 10. Each unit is ten times larger than the next smallest unit and one tenth the size of the next largest unit. The table lists the prefixes used to name the most common SI units.

Common SI Prefixes

Prefix	Symbol	Meaning
kilo-	k	1,000
hecto-	h	100
deka-	da	10
deci-	d	0.1 (one tenth)
centi-	c	0.01 (one hundredth)
milli-	m	0.001 (one thousandth)

Length To measure length, or the distance between two points, the unit of measure is the **meter (m).** The distance from the floor to a doorknob is approximately one meter. Long distances, such as the distance between two cities, are measured in kilometers (km). Small lengths are measured in centimeters (cm) or millimeters (mm). Scientists use metric rulers and meter sticks to measure length.

Common Conversions

1 km = 1,000 m
1 m = 100 cm
1 m = 1,000 mm
1 cm = 10 mm

The larger lines on the metric ruler in the picture show centimeter divisions, while the smaller, unnumbered lines show millimeter divisions. How many centimeters long is the shell? How many millimeters long is it? **ACTIVITY**

Liquid Volume To measure the volume of a liquid, or the amount of space it takes up, you will use a unit of measure known as the **liter (L).** One liter is the approximate volume of a medium-sized carton of milk. Smaller volumes are measured in milliliters (mL). Scientists use graduated cylinders to measure liquid volume.

Common Conversion

1 L = 1,000 mL

The graduated cylinder in the picture is marked in milliliter divisions. Notice that the water in the cylinder has a curved surface. This curved surface is called the *meniscus.* To measure the volume, you must read the level at the lowest point of the meniscus. What is the volume of water in this graduated cylinder? **ACTIVITY**

Mass To measure mass, or the amount of matter in an object, you will use a unit of measure known as the **gram (g).** One gram is approximately the mass of a paper clip. Larger masses are measured in kilograms (kg). Scientists use a balance to find the mass of an object.

Common Conversion

1 kg = 1,000 g

The mass of the apple in the picture is measured in kilograms. What is the mass of the apple? Suppose a recipe for applesauce called for one kilogram of apples. About how many apples would you need?

ACTIVITY

Temperature
To measure the temperature of a substance, you will use the **Celsius scale.** Temperature is measured in degrees Celsius (°C) using a Celsius thermometer. Water freezes at 0°C and boils at 100°C.

ACTIVITY

What is the temperature of the liquid in degrees Celsius?

Converting SI Units

To use the SI system, you must know how to convert between units. Converting from one unit to another involves the skill of **calculating,** or using mathematical operations. Converting between SI units is similar to converting between dollars and dimes because both systems are based on multiples of ten.

Suppose you want to convert a length of 80 centimeters to meters. Follow these steps to convert between units.

1. Begin by writing down the measurement you want to convert—in this example, 80 centimeters.

2. Write a conversion factor that represents the relationship between the two units you are converting. In this example, the relationship is *1 meter = 100 centimeters.* Write this conversion factor as a fraction, making sure to place the units you are converting from (centimeters, in this example) in the denominator.

3. Multiply the measurement you want to convert by the fraction. When you do this, the units in the first measurement will cancel out with the units in the denominator. Your answer will be in the units you are converting to (meters, in this example).

Example

80 centimeters = _____?_____ meters

$$80 \text{ centimeters} \times \frac{1 \text{ meter}}{100 \text{ centimeters}} = \frac{80 \text{ meters}}{100}$$

$$= 0.8 \text{ meters}$$

Convert between the following units.

ACTIVITY

1. 600 millimeters = _?_ meters
2. 0.35 liters = _?_ milliliters
3. 1,050 grams = _?_ kilograms

Conducting a Scientific Investigation

In some ways, scientists are like detectives, piecing together clues to learn about a process or event. One way that scientists gather clues is by carrying out experiments. In an experiment, scientists test an idea in a careful, orderly manner. Although experiments do not all follow the same steps in the same order, many follow a pattern similar to the one described here.

Asking Questions

Experiments begin by asking a scientific question. A scientific question is one that can be answered by gathering evidence. For example, the question "Which freezes faster—fresh water or salt water?" is a scientific question because you can carry out an investigation and gather information to answer the question.

Formulating a Hypothesis

The next step is to form a hypothesis. A **hypothesis** is a possible explanation for a set of observations or answer to a scientific question. In science, a hypothesis must be something that can be tested. A hypothesis can be worded as an *If... then...* statement. For example, a hypothesis might be *"If I add salt to fresh water, then the water will take longer to freeze."* A hypothesis worded this way serves as a rough outline of the experiment you should perform.

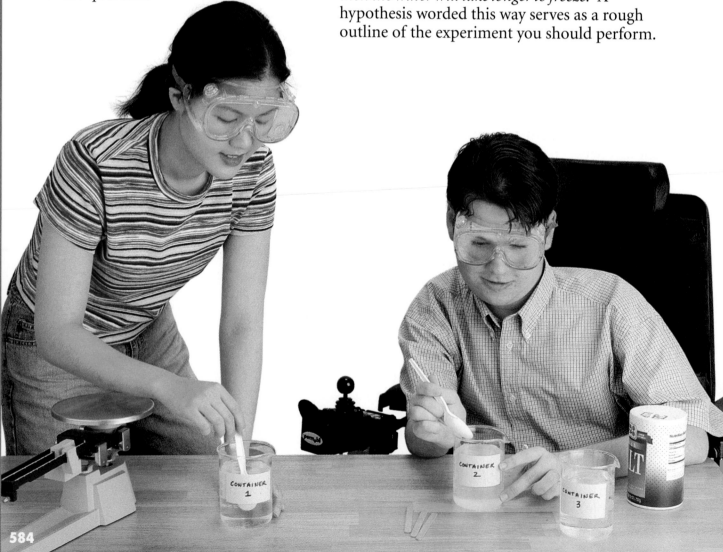

Designing an Experiment

Next you need to plan a way to test your hypothesis. Your plan should be written out as a step-by-step procedure and should describe the observations or measurements you will make.

Two important steps involved in designing an experiment are controlling variables and forming operational definitions.

Controlling Variables

In a well-designed experiment, you need to keep all variables the same except for one. A **variable** is any factor that can change in an experiment. The factor that you change is called the **manipulated variable.** In this experiment, the manipulated variable is the amount of salt added to the water. Other factors, such as the amount of water or the starting temperature, are kept constant.

The factor that changes as a result of the manipulated variable is called the responding variable. The **responding variable** is what you measure or observe to obtain your results. In this experiment, the responding variable is how long the water takes to freeze.

An experiment in which all factors except one are kept constant is a **controlled experiment.** Most controlled experiments include a test called the control. In this experiment, Container 3 is the control. Because no salt is added to Container 3, you can compare the results from the other containers to it. Any difference in results must be due to the addition of salt alone.

Forming Operational Definitions

Another important aspect of a well-designed experiment is having clear operational definitions. An **operational definition** is a statement that describes how a particular variable is to be measured or how a term is to be defined. For example, in this experiment, how will you determine if the water has frozen? You might decide to insert a stick in each container at the start of the experiment. Your operational definition of "frozen" would be that the stick can no longer move.

EXPERIMENTAL PROCEDURE

1. Fill 3 containers with 300 milliliters of cold tap water.

2. Add 10 grams of salt to Container 1; stir. Add 20 grams of salt to Container 2; stir. Add no salt to Container 3.

3. Place the 3 containers in a freezer.

4. Check the containers every 15 minutes. Record your observations.

Interpreting Data

The observations and measurements you make in an experiment are called data. At the end of an experiment, you need to analyze the data to look for any patterns or trends. Patterns often become clear if you organize your data in a data table, chart, or graph. Then think through what the data reveal. Do they support your hypothesis? Do they point out a flaw in your experiment? Do you need to collect more data?

Drawing Conclusions

A conclusion is a statement that sums up what you have learned from an experiment. When you draw a conclusion, you need to decide whether the data you collected support your hypothesis or not. You may need to repeat an experiment several times before you can draw any conclusions from it. Conclusions often lead you to pose new questions and plan new experiments to answer them.

Is a ball's bounce affected by the height from which it is dropped? Using the steps just described, plan a controlled experiment to investigate this problem. ACTIVITY

Thinking Critically

Has a friend ever asked for your advice about a problem? If so, you may have helped your friend think through the problem in a logical way. Without knowing it, you used critical-thinking skills to help your friend. Critical thinking involves the use of reasoning and logic to solve problems or make decisions. Some critical-thinking skills are described below.

Comparing and Contrasting

When you examine two objects for similarities and differences, you are using the skill of **comparing and contrasting.** Comparing involves identifying similarities, or common characteristics. Contrasting involves identifying differences. Analyzing objects in this way can help you discover details that you might otherwise overlook.

ACTIVITY Compare and contrast the two animals in the photo. First list all the similarities that you see. Then list all the differences.

Applying Concepts

When you use your knowledge about one situation to make sense of a similar situation, you are using the skill of **applying concepts.** Being able to transfer your knowledge from one situation to another shows that you truly understand a concept. You may use this skill in answering test questions that present different problems from the ones you've reviewed in class.

ACTIVITY You have just learned that water takes longer to freeze when other substances are mixed into it. Use this knowledge to explain why people need a substance called antifreeze in their car's radiator in the winter.

Interpreting Illustrations

Diagrams, photographs, and maps are included in textbooks to help clarify what you read. These illustrations show processes, places, and ideas in a visual manner. The skill called **interpreting illustrations** can help you learn from these visual elements. To understand an illustration, take the time to study the illustration along with all the written information that accompanies it. Captions identify the key concepts shown in the illustration. Labels point out the important parts of a diagram or map, while keys identify the symbols used in a map.

Upper blood vessel
Reproductive organs
Arches
Brain
Mouth
Bristles
Digestive tract
Lower blood vessel
Nerve cord
Waste-removal organs
Intestine

▲ Internal anatomy of an earthworm

ACTIVITY Study the diagram above. Then write a short paragraph explaining what you have learned.

Relating Cause and Effect

If one event causes another event to occur, the two events are said to have a cause-and-effect relationship. When you determine that such a relationship exists between two events, you use a skill called **relating cause and effect.** For example, if you notice an itchy, red bump on your skin, you might infer that a mosquito bit you. The mosquito bite is the cause, and the bump is the effect.

It is important to note that two events do not necessarily have a cause-and-effect relationship just because they occur together. Scientists carry out experiments or use past experience to determine whether a cause-and-effect relationship exists.

> **ACTIVITY**
> You are on a camping trip and your flashlight has stopped working. List some possible causes for the flashlight malfunction. How could you determine which cause-and-effect relationship has left you in the dark?

Making Generalizations

When you draw a conclusion about an entire group based on information about only some of the group's members, you are using a skill called **making generalizations.** For a generalization to be valid, the sample you choose must be large enough and representative of the entire group. You might, for example, put this skill to work at a farm stand if you see a sign that says, "Sample some grapes before you buy." If you sample a few sweet grapes, you may conclude that all the grapes are sweet—and purchase a large bunch.

> **ACTIVITY**
> A team of scientists needs to determine whether the water in a large reservoir is safe to drink. How could they use the skill of making generalizations to help them? What should they do?

Making Judgments

When you evaluate something to decide whether it is good or bad, or right or wrong, you are using a skill called **making judgments.** For example, you make judgments when you decide to eat healthful foods or to pick up litter in a park. Before you make a judgment, you need to think through the pros and cons of a situation, and identify the values or standards that you hold.

> **ACTIVITY**
> Should children and teens be required to wear helmets when bicycling? Explain why you feel the way you do.

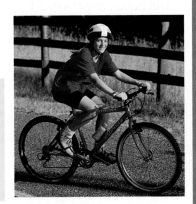

Problem Solving

When you use critical-thinking skills to resolve an issue or decide on a course of action, you are using a skill called **problem solving.** Some problems, such as how to convert a fraction into a decimal, are straightforward. Other problems, such as figuring out why your computer has stopped working, are complex. Some complex problems can be solved using the trial and error method—try out one solution first, and if that doesn't work, try another. Other useful problem-solving strategies include making models and brainstorming possible solutions with a partner.

Organizing Information

As you read this textbook, how can you make sense of all the information it contains? Some useful tools to help you organize information are shown on this page. These tools are called **graphic organizers** because they give you a visual picture of a topic, showing at a glance how key concepts are related.

Concept Maps

Concept maps are useful tools for organizing information on broad topics. A concept map begins with a general concept and shows how it can be broken down into more specific concepts. In that way, relationships between concepts become easier to understand.

A concept map is constructed by placing concept words (usually nouns) in ovals and connecting them with linking words. Often, the most general concept word is placed at the top, and the words become more specific as you move downward. Often the linking words, which are written on a line extending between two ovals, describe the relationship between the two concepts they connect. If you follow any string of concepts and linking words down the map, it should read like a sentence.

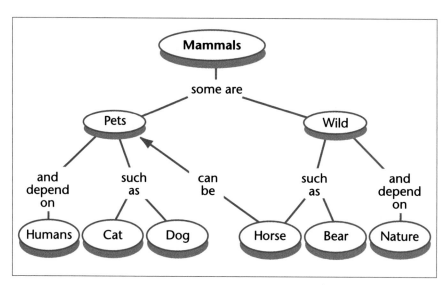

Some concept maps include linking words that connect a concept on one branch of the map to a concept on another branch. These linking words, called cross-linkages, show more complex interrelationships among concepts.

Compare/Contrast Tables

Compare/contrast tables are useful tools for sorting out the similarities and differences between two or more items. A table provides an organized framework in which to compare items based on specific characteristics that you identify.

To create a compare/contrast table, list the items to be compared across the top of a table. Then list the characteristics that will form the basis of your comparison in the left-hand

Characteristic	Baseball	Basketball
Number of Players	9	5
Playing Field	Baseball diamond	Basketball court
Equipment	Bat, baseball, mitts	Basket, basketball

column. Complete the table by filling in information about each characteristic, first for one item and then for the other.

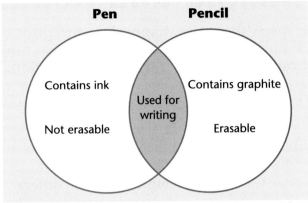

Venn Diagrams

Another way to show similarities and differences between items is with a Venn diagram. A Venn diagram consists of two or more circles that partially overlap. Each circle represents a particular concept or idea. Common characteristics, or similarities, are written within the area of overlap between the two circles. Unique characteristics, or differences, are written in the parts of the circles outside the area of overlap.

To create a Venn diagram, draw two overlapping circles. Label the circles with the names of the items being compared. Write the unique characteristics in each circle outside the area of overlap. Then write the shared characteristics within the area of overlap.

Flowcharts

A flowchart can help you understand the order in which certain events have occurred or should occur. Flowcharts are useful for outlining the stages in a process or the steps in a procedure.

To make a flowchart, write a brief description of each event in a box. Place the first event at the top of the page, followed by the second event, the third event, and so on. Then draw an arrow to connect each event to the one that occurs next.

Preparing Pasta

Boil water
↓
Cook pasta
↓
Drain water
↓
Add sauce

Cycle Diagrams

A cycle diagram can be used to show a sequence of events that is continuous, or cyclical. A continuous sequence does not have an end because, when the final event is over, the first event begins again. Like a flowchart, a cycle diagram can help you understand the order of events.

To create a cycle diagram, write a brief description of each event in a box. Place one event at the top of the page in the center. Then, moving in a clockwise direction around an imaginary circle, write each event in its proper sequence. Draw arrows that connect each event to the one that occurs next, forming a continuous circle.

Steps in Scientific Inquiry

Pose a question → Develop a hypothesis → Design an experiment → Interpret data → Draw conclusions → Pose a question

Making and Reading Maps

Maps show the shape, size, and position of Earth's features. To understand the information that maps convey, you must learn about the symbols and other conventions that mapmakers use.

A Map's Scale

A map is a flat model that shows all or part of Earth's surface as it looks from above. Of course, the size of a feature on a map differs from the real size of the feature on Earth. The same is true of a globe, which is a sphere that represents Earth's entire surface. Both maps and globes include a **scale,** which relates distances on the map to the corresponding distances on Earth's surface.

A scale is sometimes given as a ratio. For example, one unit on a map may equal 100,000 units on the ground. This means that 1 centimeter on the map represents 100,000 centimeters, 1 kilometer, on Earth. Similarly, 1 inch on the map represents 100,000 inches, 1.58 miles, on Earth.

This scale, "one to one-hundred thousand" is written "1 : 100,000." The three types of map scales are shown below.

Ratio scale 1:100,000

Bar scale

| 0 | 1 | 2 | 3 | 4 | 5 km |

| 0 | | 1 | | 2 | 3 mi |

Equivalent units scale

1 cm = 1 km   1 inch = 1.58 miles

Compass Rose

Maps also include a compass rose. The compass rose relates directions on the map to directions on Earth. North is usually located at the top of a map.

Make a map of your classroom, school, or neighborhood. Be sure to include a scale, compass rose, and key explaining the symbols you used.

ACTIVITY

Map Symbols

Mapmakers use a variety of symbols to show where important landmarks and other features are located. The symbols are explained in a section of the map called the key, or legend. The table below shows some of the most common symbols often found on maps.

Commonly Used Map Symbols

Building	■ □ ▨ ▨	Primary highway	━━━━━	Airport	✕
Building		Primary highway		Airport	
School; church	⚑ ⚑	Secondary highway	━ ━	Body of water	〰
Campground; picnic area	⛺ ⛱	Divided highway	═══	Waterfall or rapids	
Cemetery	⌐Cem¬	Railroad tracks	┼┼┼┼	Woods or parks	

Latitude and Longitude

To find a point on Earth's surface, mapmakers use a reference system similar to the grid of squares on a checkerboard. The grid is made up of two types of imaginary lines. Lines of **latitude** run east-to-west around the globe, while lines of **longitude** run north-to-south.

Lines of latitude are sometimes called parallels because they run parallel to each other. In the middle of the globe is a parallel known as the equator. The **equator** divides Earth into two halves—the Northern and Southern hemispheres.

The equator is the starting line for measuring distances north or south. Distances are measured in units called degrees. The equator is 0° latitude. The farthest distance north of the equator is 90° north latitude, the location of the North Pole. The farthest distance south of the equator is 90° south latitude, the location of the South Pole.

If you look on a globe, you can see that, unlike lines of latitude, lines of longitude are not parallel lines. Lines of longitude run north-to-south and meet at the poles. The

prime meridian is a line of longitude that passes through Greenwich, England. Places east of the prime meridian are in the Eastern hemisphere. Places west of the prime meridian are in the Western hemisphere.

The prime meridian is at 0° longitude, the starting line for measuring longitude. Longitude lines in each hemisphere are numbered up to 180°.

Every point on Earth's surface has a particular latitude and longitude. By finding the point where a latitude line crosses a longitude line, you can determine where a given place is located.

Where in the World? ACTIVITY

Using a globe, determine what city is found at each of the following points:

a. 2° S, 79° W   **d.** 34° S, 58° W
b. 38° N, 9° W   **e.** 55° N, 3° W
c. 34° N, 135° E   **f.** 1° N, 103° E

What word is spelled by the first letters of these city names?

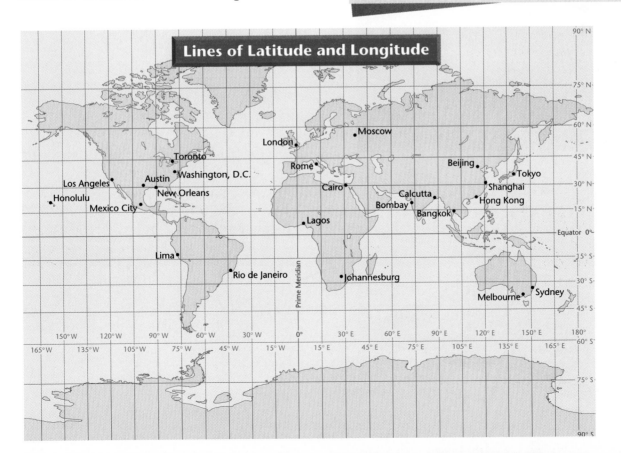

Lines of Latitude and Longitude

Topographic Maps

Some maps include information about a region's **topography,** or its physical features, such as mountains, hills, and valleys. These maps use symbols to show the land's elevation, or height above sea level.

A topographic map is a map that uses symbols known as contour lines to show the physical features of a region. On a topographic map, a **contour line** connects points of equal elevation. The change in elevation from one contour line to the next is called the **contour interval.** The contour interval for a given map is always the same. For example, the map below has a contour interval of 200 feet. If you start at one contour line and count up five contour lines, you have reached an elevation 1,000 feet above where you started. Usually every fifth contour line is darker and heavier than the others. This contour line is called the index contour. This line is labeled with the elevation in round units, such as 1,600 or 2,000 feet above sea level.

You are planning to hike up Mt. Monadnock. Use the topographic map to find the difference in elevation between the park headquarters and the summit. Also, determine which route is steeper: the White Arrow Trail or the Pumpelly Trail. How do you know?

ACTIVITY

In addition to showing elevation, contour maps also show other features, such as bodies of water, roads, and buildings. The topographic map below, which shows part of Tennessee, was made by the United States Geological Survey (USGS). Note that contour maps, like all maps, include a scale. You can use the scale to figure out the size of the whole area or the distance between any two points on the map.

Contour lines *Closely spaced contour lines indicate steep slopes. Widely spaced contour lines indicate gentle slopes.*

Depression *A closed loop with dashes inside indicates a depression.*

Index contour *To find the elevation of a feature, begin at the labeled index contour, which is a heavier line than regular contour lines.*

Hilltop *A contour line that forms a closed loop with no other contour lines inside it indicates a hilltop.*

V-Shaped contours *V-shaped contour lines pointing downhill indicate a ridge line. V-shaped contour lines pointing uphill indicate a valley. A stream in the valley flows toward the open end of the V.*

Scale

0 — 1 Mile

0 — 1 Kilometer

Contour interval = 20 feet

593

Creating Data Tables and Graphs

How can you make sense of the data in a science experiment? The first step is to organize the data to help you understand them. Data tables and graphs are helpful tools for organizing data.

Data Tables

You have gathered your materials and set up your experiment. But before you start, you need to plan a way to record what happens during the experiment. By creating a data table, you can record your observations and measurements in an orderly way.

Suppose, for example, that a scientist conducted an experiment to find out how many Calories people of different body masses burn while doing various activities. The data table shows the results.

Notice in this data table that the manipulated variable (body mass) is the heading of one column. The responding variable (for Experiment 1, the number of Calories burned while bicycling) is the heading of the next column. Additional columns were added for related experiments.

CALORIES BURNED IN 30 MINUTES OF ACTIVITY

Body Mass	Experiment 1 Bicycling	Experiment 2 Playing Basketball	Experiment 3 Watching Television
30 kg	60 Calories	120 Calories	21 Calories
40 kg	77 Calories	164 Calories	27 Calories
50 kg	95 Calories	206 Calories	33 Calories
60 kg	114 Calories	248 Calories	38 Calories

Bar Graphs

To compare how many Calories a person burns doing various activities, you could create a bar graph. A bar graph is used to display data in a number of separate, or distinct, categories. In this example, bicycling, playing basketball, and watching television are three separate categories.

To create a bar graph, follow these steps.

1. On graph paper, draw a horizontal, or *x*-, axis and a vertical, or *y*-, axis.
2. Write the names of the categories to be graphed along the horizontal axis. Include an overall label for the axis as well.
3. Label the vertical axis with the name of the responding variable. Include units of measurement. Then create a scale along the axis by marking off equally spaced numbers that cover the range of the data collected.
4. For each category, draw a solid bar using the scale on the vertical axis to determine the

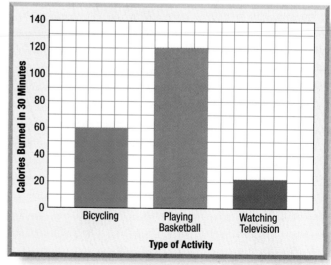

Calories Burned by a 30-kilogram Person in Various Activities

appropriate height. For example, for bicycling, draw the bar as high as the 60 mark on the vertical axis. Make all the bars the same width and leave equal spaces between them.

5. Add a title that describes the graph.

Line Graphs

To see whether a relationship exists between body mass and the number of Calories burned while bicycling, you could create a line graph. A line graph is used to display data that show how one variable (the responding variable) changes in response to another variable (the manipulated variable). You can use a line graph when your manipulated variable is *continuous*, that is, when there are other points between the ones that you tested. In this example, body mass is a continuous variable because there are other body masses between 30 and 40 kilograms (for example, 31 kilograms). Time is another example of a continuous variable.

Line graphs are powerful tools because they allow you to estimate values for conditions that you did not test in the experiment. For example, you can use the line graph to estimate that a 35-kilogram person would burn 68 Calories while bicycling.

To create a line graph, follow these steps.
1. On graph paper, draw a horizontal, or *x*-, axis and a vertical, or *y*-, axis.
2. Label the horizontal axis with the name of the manipulated variable. Label the vertical axis with the name of the responding variable. Include units of measurement.
3. Create a scale on each axis by marking off equally spaced numbers that cover the range of the data collected.
4. Plot a point on the graph for each piece of data. In the line graph above, the dotted lines show how to plot the first data point (30 kilograms and 60 Calories). Draw an imaginary vertical line extending up from the horizontal axis at the 30-kilogram mark. Then draw an imaginary horizontal line extending across from the vertical axis at the 60-Calorie mark. Plot the point where the two lines intersect.

Effect of Body Mass on Calories Burned While Bicycling

5. Connect the plotted points with a solid line. (In some cases, it may be more appropriate to draw a line that shows the general trend of the plotted points. In those cases, some of the points may fall above or below the line. Also, not all graphs are linear. It may be more appropriate to draw a curve to connect the points.)
6. Add a title that identifies the variables or relationship in the graph.

ACTIVITY

Create line graphs to display the data from Experiment 2 and Experiment 3 in the data table.

ACTIVITY

You read in the newspaper that a total of 4 centimeters of rain fell in your area in June, 2.5 centimeters fell in July, and 1.5 centimeters fell in August. What type of graph would you use to display these data? Use graph paper to create the graph.

595

Circle Graphs

Like bar graphs, circle graphs can be used to display data in a number of separate categories. Unlike bar graphs, however, circle graphs can only be used when you have data for *all* the categories that make up a given topic. A circle graph is sometimes called a pie chart because it resembles a pie cut into slices. The pie represents the entire topic, while the slices represent the individual categories. The size of a slice indicates what percentage of the whole a particular category makes up.

The data table below shows the results of a survey in which 24 teenagers were asked to identify their favorite sport. The data were then used to create the circle graph at the right.

Sports That Teens Prefer

FAVORITE SPORTS

Sport	Number of Students
Soccer	8
Basketball	6
Bicycling	6
Swimming	4

To create a circle graph, follow these steps.

1. Use a compass to draw a circle. Mark the center of the circle with a point. Then draw a line from the center point to the top of the circle.

2. Determine the size of each "slice" by setting up a proportion where x equals the number of degrees in a slice. (NOTE: A circle contains 360 degrees.) For example, to find the number of degrees in the "soccer" slice, set up the following proportion:

$$\frac{\text{students who prefer soccer}}{\text{total number of students}} = \frac{x}{\text{total number of degrees in a circle}}$$

$$\frac{8}{24} = \frac{x}{360}$$

Cross-multiply and solve for x.

$$24x = 8 \times 360$$
$$x = 120$$

The "soccer" slice should contain 120 degrees.

3. Use a protractor to measure the angle of the first slice, using the line you drew to the top of the circle as the 0° line. Draw a line from the center of the circle to the edge for the angle you measured.

4. Continue around the circle by measuring the size of each slice with the protractor. Start measuring from the edge of the previous slice so the wedges do not overlap. When you are done, the entire circle should be filled in.

5. Determine the percentage of the whole circle that each slice represents. To do this, divide the number of degrees in a slice by the total number of degrees in a circle (360), and multiply by 100%. For the "soccer" slice, you can find the percentage as follows:

$$\frac{120}{360} \times 100\% = 33.3\%$$

6. Use a different color to shade in each slice. Label each slice with the name of the category and with the percentage of the whole it represents.

7. Add a title to the circle graph.

ACTIVITY

In a class of 28 students, 12 students take the bus to school, 10 students walk, and 6 students ride their bicycles. Create a circle graph to display these data.

Laboratory Safety

Safety Symbols

These symbols alert you to possible dangers in the laboratory and remind you to work carefully.

Safety Goggles Always wear safety goggles to protect your eyes in any activity involving chemicals, flames or heating, or the possibility of broken glassware.

Lab Apron Wear a laboratory apron to protect your skin and clothing from damage.

Breakage You are working with materials that may be breakable, such as glass containers, glass tubing, thermometers, or funnels. Handle breakable materials with care. Do not touch broken glassware.

Heat-resistant Gloves Use an oven mitt or other hand protection when handling hot materials. Hot plates, hot glassware, or hot water can cause burns. Do not touch hot objects with your bare hands.

Heating Use a clamp or tongs to pick up hot glassware. Do not touch hot objects with your bare hands.

Sharp Object Pointed-tip scissors, scalpels, knives, needles, pins, or tacks are sharp. They can cut or puncture your skin. Always direct a sharp edge or point away from yourself and others. Use sharp instruments only as instructed.

Electric Shock Avoid the possibility of electric shock. Never use electrical equipment around water, or when the equipment is wet or your hands are wet. Be sure cords are untangled and cannot trip anyone. Disconnect the equipment when it is not in use.

Corrosive Chemical You are working with an acid or another corrosive chemical. Avoid getting it on your skin or clothing, or in your eyes. Do not inhale the vapors. Wash your hands when you are finished with the activity.

Poison Do not let any poisonous chemical come in contact with your skin, and do not inhale its vapors. Wash your hands when you are finished with the activity.

Physical Safety When an experiment involves physical activity, take precautions to avoid injuring yourself or others. Follow instructions from your teacher. Alert your teacher if there is any reason you should not participate in the activity.

Animal Safety Treat live animals with care to avoid harming the animals or yourself. Working with animal parts or preserved animals also may require caution. Wash your hands when you are finished with the activity.

Plant Safety Handle plants in the laboratory or during field work only as directed by your teacher. If you are allergic to certain plants, tell your teacher before doing an activity in which those plants are used. Avoid touching harmful plants such as poison ivy, poison oak, or poison sumac, or plants with thorns. Wash your hands when you are finished with the activity.

Flames You may be working with flames from a lab burner, candle, or matches. Tie back loose hair and clothing. Follow instructions from your teacher about lighting and extinguishing flames.

No Flames Flammable materials may be present. Make sure there are no flames, sparks, or other exposed heat sources present.

Fumes When poisonous or unpleasant vapors may be involved, work in a ventilated area. Avoid inhaling vapors directly. Only test an odor when directed to do so by your teacher, and use a wafting motion to direct the vapor toward your nose.

Disposal Chemicals and other laboratory materials used in the activity must be disposed of safely. Follow the instructions from your teacher.

Hand Washing Wash your hands thoroughly when finished with the activity. Use antibacterial soap and warm water. Lather both sides of your hands and between your fingers. Rinse well.

General Safety Awareness You may see this symbol when none of the symbols described earlier appears. In this case, follow the specific instructions provided. You may also see this symbol when you are asked to develop your own procedure in a lab. Have your teacher approve your plan before you go further.

Science Safety Rules

To prepare yourself to work safely in the laboratory, read over the following safety rules. Then read them a second time. Make sure you understand and follow each rule. Ask your teacher to explain any rules you do not understand.

Dress Code

1. To protect yourself from injuring your eyes, wear safety goggles whenever you work with chemicals, burners, glassware, or any substance that might get into your eyes. If you wear contact lenses, notify your teacher.
2. Wear a lab apron or coat whenever you work with corrosive chemicals or substances that can stain.
3. Tie back long hair to keep it away from any chemicals, flames, or equipment.
4. Remove or tie back any article of clothing or jewelry that can hang down and touch chemicals, flames, or equipment. Roll up or secure long sleeves.
5. Never wear open shoes or sandals.

General Precautions

6. Read all directions for an experiment several times before beginning the activity. Carefully follow all written and oral instructions. If you are in doubt about any part of the experiment, ask your teacher for assistance.
7. Never perform activities that are not assigned or authorized by your teacher. Obtain permission before "experimenting" on your own. Never handle any equipment unless you have specific permission.
8. Never perform lab activities without direct supervision.
9. Never eat or drink in the laboratory.
10. Keep work areas clean and tidy at all times. Bring only notebooks and lab manuals or written lab procedures to the work area. All other items, such as purses and backpacks, should be left in a designated area.
11. Do not engage in horseplay.

First Aid

12. Always report all accidents or injuries to your teacher, no matter how minor. Notify your teacher immediately of any fires.
13. Learn what to do in case of specific accidents, such as getting acid in your eyes or on your skin. (Rinse acids from your body with lots of water.)
14. Be aware of the location of the first-aid kit, but do not use it unless instructed by your teacher. In case of injury, your teacher should administer first aid. Your teacher may also send you to the school nurse or call a physician.
15. Know the location of emergency equipment, such as the fire extinguisher and fire blanket, and know how to use it.
16. Know the location of the nearest telephone and whom to contact in an emergency.

Heating and Fire Safety

17. Never use a heat source, such as a candle, burner, or hot plate, without wearing safety goggles.
18. Never heat anything unless instructed to do so. A chemical that is harmless when cool may be dangerous when heated.
19. Keep all combustible materials away from flames. Never use a flame or spark near a combustible chemical.
20. Never reach across a flame.
21. Before using a laboratory burner, make sure you know proper procedures for lighting and adjusting the burner, as demonstrated by your teacher. Do not touch the burner. It may be hot. And never leave a lighted burner unattended!
22. Chemicals can splash or boil out of a heated test tube. When heating a substance in a test tube, make sure that the mouth of the tube is not pointed at you or anyone else.
23. Never heat a liquid in a closed container. The expanding gases produced may blow the container apart.
24. Before picking up a container that has been heated, hold the back of your hand near it. If you can feel heat on the back of your hand, the container is too hot to handle. Use an oven mitt to pick up a container that has been heated.

Using Chemicals Safely

25. Never mix chemicals "for the fun of it." You might produce a dangerous, possibly explosive, substance.

26. Never put your face near the mouth of a container that holds chemicals. Never touch, taste, or smell a chemical unless you are instructed by your teacher to do so. Many chemicals are poisonous.

27. Use only those chemicals needed in the activity. Read and double-check labels on supply bottles before removing any chemicals. Take only as much as you need. Keep all containers closed when chemicals are not being used.

28. Dispose of all chemicals as instructed by your teacher. To avoid contamination, never return chemicals to their original containers. Never simply pour chemicals or other substances into the sink or trash containers.

29. Be extra careful when working with acids or bases. Pour all chemicals over the sink or a container, not over your work surface.

30. If you are instructed to test for odors, use a wafting motion to direct the odors to your nose. Do not inhale the fumes directly from the container.

31. When mixing an acid and water, always pour the water into the container first, and then add the acid to the water. Never pour water into an acid.

32. Take extreme care not to spill any material in the laboratory. Wash chemical spills and splashes immediately with plenty of water. Immediately begin rinsing with water any acids that get on your skin or clothing, and notify your teacher of any acid spill at the same time.

Using Glassware Safely

33. Never force glass tubing or thermometers into a rubber stopper or rubber tubing. Have your teacher insert the glass tubing or thermometer if required for an activity.

34. If you are using a laboratory burner, use a wire screen to protect glassware from any flame. Never heat glassware that is not thoroughly dry on the outside.

35. Keep in mind that hot glassware looks cool. Never pick up glassware without first checking to see if it is hot. Use an oven mitt. See rule 24.

36. Never use broken or chipped glassware. If glassware breaks, notify your teacher and dispose of the glassware in the proper broken-glassware container. Never handle broken glass with your bare hands.

37. Never eat or drink from lab glassware.

38. Thoroughly clean glassware before putting it away.

Using Sharp Instruments

39. Handle scalpels or other sharp instruments with extreme care. Never cut material toward you; cut away from you.

40. Immediately notify your teacher if you cut your skin when working in the laboratory.

Animal and Plant Safety

41. Never perform experiments that cause pain, discomfort, or harm to mammals, birds, reptiles, fishes, or amphibians. This rule applies at home as well as in the classroom.

42. Animals should be handled only if absolutely necessary. Your teacher will instruct you as to how to handle each animal species brought into the classroom.

43. If you know that you are allergic to certain plants, molds, or animals, tell your teacher before doing an activity in which these are used.

44. During field work, protect your skin by wearing long pants, long sleeves, socks, and closed shoes. Know how to recognize the poisonous plants and fungi in your area, as well as plants with thorns, and avoid contact with them.

45. Never eat any part of an unidentified plant or fungus.

46. Wash your hands thoroughly after handling animals or the cage containing animals. Wash your hands when you are finished with any activity involving animal parts, plants, or soil.

End-of-Experiment Rules

47. After an experiment has been completed, clean up your work area and return all equipment to its proper place.

48. Dispose of waste materials as instructed by your teacher.

49. Wash your hands after every experiment.

50. Always turn off all burners or hot plates when they are not in use. Unplug hot plates and other electrical equipment. If you used a burner, check that the gas-line valve to the burner is off as well.

Using the Microscope

The microscope is an essential tool in the study of life science. It allows you to see things that are too small to be seen with the unaided eye.

You will probably use a compound microscope like the one you see here. The compound microscope has more than one lens that magnifies the object you view.

Typically, a compound microscope has one lens in the eyepiece, the part you look through. The eyepiece lens usually magnifies 10 ×. Any object you view through this lens would appear 10 times larger than it is.

The compound microscope may contain one or two other lenses called objective lenses. If there are two objective lenses, they are called the low-power and high-power objective lenses. The low-power objective lens usually magnifies 10 ×. The high-power objective lens usually magnifies 40 ×.

To calculate the total magnification with which you are viewing an object, multiply the magnification of the eyepiece lens by the magnification of the objective lens you are using. For example, the eyepiece's magnification of 10 × multiplied by the low-power objective's magnification of 10 × equals a total magnification of 100 ×.

Use the photo of the compound microscope to become familiar with the parts of the microscope and their functions.

The Parts of the Compound Microscope

Eyepiece
Contains a lens that magnifies about 10 ×

Body tube
Separates the eyepiece lens from the objective lens

Coarse adjustment knob
Moves the body tube for focusing with the low-power objective lens

Nosepiece
Holds the low-power and high-power objective lenses; allows the lenses to rotate for viewing

Fine adjustment knob
Moves the body tube for focusing with the high-power objective lens

High-power objective lens
Magnifies about 40 ×

Arm
Supports the body tube

Stage
Supports the slide being used

Low-power objective lens
Magnifies about 10 ×

Stage clip
Holds the slide in place

Diaphragm
Controls the amount of light passing through the opening of the stage

Base
Supports the microscope

Mirror
Reflects light upward through the diaphragm

Using the Microscope

Use the following procedures when you are working with a microscope.

1. To carry the microscope grasp the microscope's arm with one hand. Place your other hand under the base.
2. Place the microscope on a table with the arm toward you.
3. Turn the coarse adjustment knob to raise the body tube.
4. Revolve the nosepiece until the low-power objective lens clicks into place.
5. Adjust the diaphragm. While looking through the eyepiece, also adjust the mirror until you see a bright white circle of light. **CAUTION:** *Never use direct sunlight as a light source.*
6. Place a slide on the stage. Center the specimen over the opening on the stage. Use the stage clips to hold the slide in place. **CAUTION:** *Glass slides are fragile.*
7. Look at the stage from the side. Carefully turn the coarse adjustment knob to lower the body tube until the low-power objective almost touches the slide.
8. Looking through the eyepiece, very slowly turn the coarse adjustment knob until the specimen comes into focus.
9. To switch to the high-power objective lens, look at the microscope from the side. Carefully revolve the nosepiece until the high-power objective lens clicks into place. Make sure the lens does not hit the slide.
10. Looking through the eyepiece, turn the fine adjustment knob until the specimen comes into focus.

Making a Wet-Mount Slide

Use the following procedures to make a wet-mount slide of a specimen.

1. Obtain a clean microscope slide and a coverslip. **CAUTION:** *Glass slides and coverslips are fragile.*
2. Place the specimen on the slide. The specimen must be thin enough for light to pass through it.
3. Using a plastic dropper, place a drop of water on the specimen.
4. Gently place one edge of the coverslip against the slide so that it touches the edge of the water drop at a 45° angle. Slowly lower the coverslip over the specimen. If air bubbles are trapped beneath the coverslip, tap the coverslip gently with the eraser end of a pencil.
5. Remove any excess water at the edge of the coverslip with a paper towel.

Using a Laboratory Balance

The laboratory balance is an important tool in scientific investigations. You can use a balance to determine the masses of materials that you study or experiment with in the laboratory.

Different kinds of balances are used in the laboratory. One kind of balance is the triple-beam balance. The balance that you may use in your science class is probably similar to the balance illustrated in this Appendix. To use the balance properly, you should learn the name, location, and function of each part of the balance you are using. What kind of balance do you have in your science class?

The Triple-Beam Balance

The triple-beam balance is a single-pan balance with three beams calibrated in grams. The back, or 100-gram, beam is divided into ten units of 10 grams each. The middle, or 500-gram, beam is divided into five units of 100 grams each. The front, or 10-gram, beam is divided into ten major units of 1 gram each. Each of these units is further divided into units of 0.1 gram. What is the largest mass you could find with a triple-beam balance?

The following procedure can be used to find the mass of an object with a triple-beam balance:

1. Place the object on the pan.
2. Move the rider on the middle beam notch by notch until the horizontal pointer drops below zero. Move the rider back one notch.
3. Move the rider on the back beam notch by notch until the pointer again drops below zero. Move the rider back one notch.
4. Slowly slide the rider along the front beam until the pointer stops at the zero point.
5. The mass of the object is equal to the sum of the readings on the three beams.

Triple-Beam Balance

List of Chemical Elements

Name	Symbol	Atomic Number	Atomic Mass[†]
Actinium	Ac	89	227.028
Aluminum	Al	13	26.982
Americium	Am	95	(243)
Antimony	Sb	51	121.75
Argon	Ar	18	39.948
Arsenic	As	33	74.922
Astatine	At	85	(210)
Barium	Ba	56	137.327
Berkelium	Bk	97	(247)
Beryllium	Be	4	9.012
Bismuth	Bi	83	208.980
Bohrium	Bh	107	(262)
Boron	B	5	10.811
Bromine	Br	35	79.904
Cadmium	Cd	48	112.411
Calcium	Ca	20	40.078
Californium	Cf	98	(251)
Carbon	C	6	12.011
Cerium	Ce	58	140.115
Cesium	Cs	55	132.905
Chlorine	Cl	17	35.453
Chromium	Cr	24	51.996
Cobalt	Co	27	58.933
Copper	Cu	29	63.546
Curium	Cm	96	(247)
Dubnium	Db	105	(262)
Dysprosium	Dy	66	162.50
Einsteinium	Es	99	(252)
Erbium	Er	68	167.26
Europium	Eu	63	151.965
Fermium	Fm	100	(257)
Fluorine	F	9	18.998
Francium	Fr	87	(223)
Gadolinium	Gd	64	157.25
Gallium	Ga	31	69.723
Germanium	Ge	32	72.61
Gold	Au	79	196.967
Hafnium	Hf	72	178.49
Hassium	Hs	108	(265)
Helium	He	2	4.003
Holmium	Ho	67	164.930
Hydrogen	H	1	1.008
Indium	In	49	114.818
Iodine	I	53	126.904
Iridium	Ir	77	192.22
Iron	Fe	26	55.847
Krypton	Kr	36	83.80
Lanthanum	La	57	138.906
Lawrencium	Lr	103	(260)
Lead	Pb	82	207.2
Lithium	Li	3	6.941
Lutetium	Lu	71	174.967
Magnesium	Mg	12	24.305
Manganese	Mn	25	54.938
Meitnerium	Mt	109	(266)
Mendelevium	Md	101	(258)
Mercury	Hg	80	200.659
Molybdenum	Mo	42	95.94

Name	Symbol	Atomic Number	Atomic Mass[†]
Neodymium	Nd	60	144.2
Neon	Ne	10	20.180
Neptunium	Np	93	237.048
Nickel	Ni	28	58.69
Niobium	Nb	41	92.906
Nitrogen	N	7	14.007
Nobelium	No	102	(259)
Osmium	Os	76	190.23
Oxygen	O	8	15.999
Palladium	Pd	46	106.42
Phosphorus	P	15	30.974
Platinum	Pt	78	195.08
Plutonium	Pu	94	(244)
Polonium	Po	84	(209)
Potassium	K	19	39.098
Praseodymium	Pr	59	140.908
Promethium	Pm	61	(145)
Protactinium	Pa	91	231.036
Radium	Ra	88	226.025
Radon	Rn	86	(222)
Rhenium	Re	75	186.207
Rhodium	Rh	45	102.906
Rubidium	Rb	37	85.468
Ruthenium	Ru	44	101.07
Rutherfordium	Rf	104	(261)
Samarium	Sm	62	150.36
Scandium	Sc	21	44.956
Seaborgium	Sg	106	(263)
Selenium	Se	34	78.96
Silicon	Si	14	28.086
Silver	Ag	47	107.868
Sodium	Na	11	22.990
Strontium	Sr	38	87.62
Sulfur	S	16	32.066
Tantalum	Ta	73	180.948
Technetium	Tc	43	(98)
Tellurium	Te	52	127.60
Terbium	Tb	65	158.925
Thallium	Tl	81	204.383
Thorium	Th	90	232.038
Thulium	Tm	69	168.934
Tin	Sn	50	118.710
Titanium	Ti	22	47.88
Tungsten	W	74	183.85
Ununbium	Uub	112	(272)
Ununhexium	Uuh	116	*
Ununnilium	Uun	110	(269)
Unununium	Uuu	111	(272)
Ununoctium	Uuo	118	*
Ununquadium	Uuq	114	*
Uranium	U	92	238.029
Vanadium	V	23	50.942
Xenon	Xe	54	131.29
Ytterbium	Yb	70	173.04
Yttrium	Y	39	88.906
Zinc	Zn	30	65.39
Zirconium	Zr	40	91.224

[†]Numbers in parentheses give the mass number of the most stable or common isotope.

*Newly discovered

Periodic Table of the Elements

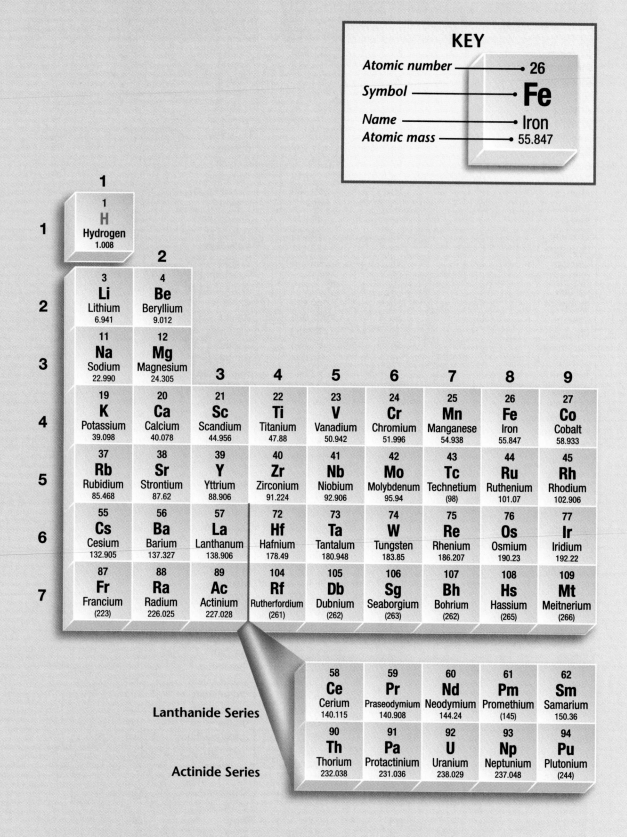

KEY

Atomic number —— 26

Symbol —— **Fe**

Name —— Iron

Atomic mass —— 55.847

1

1
H
Hydrogen
1.008

2

3	4
Li	**Be**
Lithium	Beryllium
6.941	9.012

11	12
Na	**Mg**
Sodium	Magnesium
22.990	24.305

3   **4**   **5**   **6**   **7**   **8**   **9**

19	20	21	22	23	24	25	26	27
K	**Ca**	**Sc**	**Ti**	**V**	**Cr**	**Mn**	**Fe**	**Co**
Potassium	Calcium	Scandium	Titanium	Vanadium	Chromium	Manganese	Iron	Cobalt
39.098	40.078	44.956	47.88	50.942	51.996	54.938	55.847	58.933

37	38	39	40	41	42	43	44	45
Rb	**Sr**	**Y**	**Zr**	**Nb**	**Mo**	**Tc**	**Ru**	**Rh**
Rubidium	Strontium	Yttrium	Zirconium	Niobium	Molybdenum	Technetium	Ruthenium	Rhodium
85.468	87.62	88.906	91.224	92.906	95.94	(98)	101.07	102.906

55	56	57	72	73	74	75	76	77
Cs	**Ba**	**La**	**Hf**	**Ta**	**W**	**Re**	**Os**	**Ir**
Cesium	Barium	Lanthanum	Hafnium	Tantalum	Tungsten	Rhenium	Osmium	Iridium
132.905	137.327	138.906	178.49	180.948	183.85	186.207	190.23	192.22

87	88	89	104	105	106	107	108	109
Fr	**Ra**	**Ac**	**Rf**	**Db**	**Sg**	**Bh**	**Hs**	**Mt**
Francium	Radium	Actinium	Rutherfordium	Dubnium	Seaborgium	Bohrium	Hassium	Meitnerium
(223)	226.025	227.028	(261)	(262)	(263)	(262)	(265)	(266)

Lanthanide Series

58	59	60	61	62
Ce	**Pr**	**Nd**	**Pm**	**Sm**
Cerium	Praseodymium	Neodymium	Promethium	Samarium
140.115	140.908	144.24	(145)	150.36

Actinide Series

90	91	92	93	94
Th	**Pa**	**U**	**Np**	**Pu**
Thorium	Protactinium	Uranium	Neptunium	Plutonium
232.038	231.036	238.029	237.048	(244)

Mass numbers in parentheses are those of the most stable or common isotope.

C	Solid	Br	Liquid	H	Gas
	Metal		Metalloid		Nonmetal

Discovered recently

18

					2 **He** Helium 4.003

13	**14**	**15**	**16**	**17**	
5 **B** Boron 10.811	**6** **C** Carbon 12.011	**7** **N** Nitrogen 14.007	**8** **O** Oxygen 15.999	**9** **F** Fluorine 18.998	**10** **Ne** Neon 20.180
13 **Al** Aluminum 26.982	**14** **Si** Silicon 28.086	**15** **P** Phosphorus 30.974	**16** **S** Sulfur 32.066	**17** **Cl** Chlorine 35.453	**18** **Ar** Argon 39.948

10	**11**	**12**						
28 **Ni** Nickel 58.69	**29** **Cu** Copper 63.546	**30** **Zn** Zinc 65.39	**31** **Ga** Gallium 69.723	**32** **Ge** Germanium 72.61	**33** **As** Arsenic 74.922	**34** **Se** Selenium 78.96	**35** **Br** Bromine 79.904	**36** **Kr** Krypton 83.80
46 **Pd** Palladium 106.42	**47** **Ag** Silver 107.868	**48** **Cd** Cadmium 112.411	**49** **In** Indium 114.818	**50** **Sn** Tin 118.710	**51** **Sb** Antimony 121.75	**52** **Te** Tellurium 127.60	**53** **I** Iodine 126.904	**54** **Xe** Xenon 131.29
78 **Pt** Platinum 195.08	**79** **Au** Gold 196.967	**80** **Hg** Mercury 200.59	**81** **Tl** Thallium 204.383	**82** **Pb** Lead 207.2	**83** **Bi** Bismuth 208.980	**84** **Po** Polonium (209)	**85** **At** Astatine (210)	**86** **Rn** Radon (222)
110 **Uun** Ununnilium (269)	**111** **Uuu** Unununium (272)	**112** **Uub** Ununbium (272)		**114** **Uuq** Ununquadium		**116** **Uuh** Ununhexium		**118** **Uuo** Ununoctium

63 **Eu** Europium 151.965	**64** **Gd** Gadolinium 157.25	**65** **Tb** Terbium 158.925	**66** **Dy** Dysprosium 162.50	**67** **Ho** Holmium 164.930	**68** **Er** Erbium 167.26	**69** **Tm** Thulium 168.934	**70** **Yb** Ytterbium 173.04	**71** **Lu** Lutetium 174.967
95 **Am** Americium (243)	**96** **Cm** Curium (247)	**97** **Bk** Berkelium (247)	**98** **Cf** Californium (251)	**99** **Es** Einsteinium (252)	**100** **Fm** Fermium (257)	**101** **Md** Mendelevium (258)	**102** **No** Nobelium (259)	**103** **Lr** Lawrencium (260)

The symbols shown for elements 110–118 are being used temporarily until names for these elements can be agreed upon.

Physical Map: Texas

COLORADO

KANSAS

MISSOURI

NEW MEXICO

HIGH PLAINS

Canadian R.

OKLAHOMA

ARKANSAS

Amarillo

Red R.

L L A N O   E S T A C A D O

Lubbock

Red R.

Dallas

Fort Worth

Sabine R.

T E X A S

Colorado R.

Brazos R.

Trinity R.

LOUISIANA

Guadalupe Pk.
2667m

El Paso

Guadalupe
Mountains
National Park

Pecos R.

Rio Grande

DAVIS
MTS.

Mt Livermore
2554m

Chinati Pk.
2356m

Big Bend
National
Park

CHISOS
MTS.

Emory Pk.
2385m

EDWARDS
PLATEAU

Austin

B A L C O N E S   E S C A R P M E N T

San Antonio

Colorado R.

Beaumont

Houston

G U L F   C O A S T A L   P L A I N

Galveston
Bay

MEXICO

Nueces R.

Matagorda Bay
Matagorda Island

Laredo

Corpus Christi

N
W   E
S

*Padre
Island*

Rio Grande

Brownsville

*Laguna
Madre*

*Gulf of
Mexico*

KEY

Elevation in meters

Over 2000
1000–2000
500–1000
200–500
0–200

0   50   100 mi

0   50   100 km

Identifying Common Minerals

GROUP 1
Metallic Luster, Mostly Dark-Colored

Mineral/ Formula	Hardness	Density (g/cm³)	Luster	Streak	Color	Other Properties/Remarks
Pyrite FeS_2	6–6.5	5.0	Metallic	Greenish, brownish black	Light yellow	Harder than chalcopyrite and pyrrhotite; called "fool's gold," but harder than gold and very brittle
Magnetite Fe_3O_4	6	5.2	Metallic	Black	Iron black	Very magnetic; important iron ore; some varieties known as "lodestone"
Hematite Fe_2O_3	5.5–6.5	4.9–5.3	Metallic or earthy	Red or red brown	Reddish brown to black; also steel gray crystals	Most important ore of iron; known as "red ocher"; often used as red pigment in paint.
Pyrrhotite FeS	4	4.6	Metallic	Gray black	Brownish bronze	Less hard than pyrite: slightly magnetic
Sphalerite ZnS	3.5–4	3.9–4.1	Resinous	Brown to light yellow	Brown to yellow	Most important zinc ore
Chalcopyrite $CuFeS_2$	3.5–4	4.1–4.3	Metallic	Greenish black	Golden yellow, often tarnished	Most important copper ore; softer than pyrite and more yellow; more brittle than gold
Bornite Cu_5FeS_4	3	4.9–5.4	Metallic	Gray black	Copper, brown; turns to purple and black	Important copper ore; known as "peacock ore" because of iridescent purple color when exposed to air for a time
Copper Cu	2.5–3	8.9	Metallic	Copper red	Copper red to black	Can be pounded into various shapes and drawn into wires; used in making electrical wires, coins, pipes
Gold Au	2.5–3	19.3	Metallic	Yellow	Rich yellow	Can be pounded into various shapes and drawn into wires; does not tarnish; used in jewelry, coins, dental fillings
Silver Ag	2.5–3	10.0–11.0	Metallic	Silver to light gray	Silver white, tarnishes to black	Can be pounded into various shapes and drawn into wires; used in jewelry, coins, electrical wire
Galena PbS	2.5	7.4–7.6	Metallic	Lead gray	Lead gray	Main ore of lead; used in shields against radiation
Graphite C	1–2	2.3	Metallic to dull	Black	Black	Feels greasy; very soft; used as pencil "lead" and as a lubricant

GROUP 2
Nonmetallic Luster, Mostly Dark-Colored

Mineral/Formula	Hardness	Density (g/cm³)	Luster	Streak	Color	Other Properties/Remarks
Corundum Al_2O_3	9	3.9–4.1	Brilliant to glassy	White	Usually brown	Very hard; used as an abrasive; transparent crystals used as gems called "ruby" (red) and "sapphire" (blue and other colors)
Garnet $(Ca,Mg,Fe)_3$ $(Al,Fe,Cr)_2(SiO_4)_3$	7–7.5	3.5–4.3	Glassy to resinous	White, light brown	Red, brown, black, green	A group of minerals used in jewelry, as a birthstone, and as an abrasive
Olivine $(Mg,Fe)_2SiO_4$	6.5–7	3.3–3.4	Glassy	White or gray	Olive green	Found in igneous rocks; sometimes used as a gem
Augite $Ca(Mg,Fe,Al)$ $(AlSi)_2O_6$	5–6	3.2–3.4	Glassy	Greenish gray	Dark green to black	Found in igneous rocks
Hornblende $NaCa_2(Mg,Fe,Al)_5$ $(Si,Al)_8O_{22}(OH)_2$	5–6	3.0–3.4	Glassy, silky	White to gray	Dark green to brown, black	Found in igneous and metamorphic rocks
Apatite $Ca_5(PO_4)_3F$	5	3.1–3.2	Glassy	White	Green, brown, red, blue, violet, yellow	Sometimes used as a gem; source of the phosphorus needed by plants
Azurite $Cu_3(CO_3)_2(OH)_2$	3.5–4	3.8	Glassy to dull	Pale blue	Intense blue	Ore of copper; used as a gem
Biotite $K(Mg,Fe)_3AlSiO_{10}$ $(OH)_2$	2.5–3	2.8–3.4	Glassy or pearly	White to gray	Dark green, brown, or black	A type of mica, sometimes used as a lubricant
Serpentine $Mg_6Si_4O_{10}(OH)_8$	2–5	2.2–2.6	Greasy, waxy, silky	White	Usually green	Once used in insulation but found to cause cancer; used in fireproofing; can be in the form of asbestos
Limonite Mixture of hydrous iron oxides	1–5.5	2.8–4.3	Glassy to dull	Yellow brown	Brown black to brownish yellow	Ore of iron, also known as "yellow ocher," a pigment; a mixture that is not strictly a mineral
Bauxite Mixture of hydrous aluminum oxides	1–3	2.0–2.5	Dull to earthy	Colorless to gray	Brown, yellow, gray, white	Ore of aluminum, smells like clay when wet; a mixture that is not strictly a mineral

GROUP 3
Nonmetallic Luster, Mostly Light-Colored

Mineral/ Formula	Hardness	Density (g/cm³)	Luster	Streak	Color	Other Properties/Remarks
Diamond C	10	3.5	Brilliant	White	Colorless and varied	Hardest known substance; used in jewelry; as an abrasive; in cutting instruments
Topaz $Al_2SiO_4(F,OH)_2$	8	3.5–3.6	Glassy	White	Straw yellow, pink, bluish, greenish	Valuable gem
Quartz SiO_2	7	2.6	Glassy, greasy	White	Colorless, white; any color when not pure	The second most abundant mineral; many varieties are gems (amethyst, cat's-eye, bloodstone, agate, jasper, onyx); used in making glass
Feldspar (K,Na,Ca) $(AlSi_3O_8)$	6	2.6	Glassy	Colorless, white	Colorless, white, various colors	As a family, the most abundant of all minerals; the different types of feldspar make up over 60 percent of Earth's crust
Fluorite CaF_2	4	3.0–3.3	Glassy	Colorless	Purple, light, green, yellow, bluish green, other colors	Some types are fluorescent (glow when exposed to ultraviolet light); used in making steel
Dolomite $CaMg(CO_3)_2$	3.5–4	2.8	Glassy or pearly	White	Colorless, white, pinkish, or light tints	Used in making concrete and cement; fizzes slowly in dilute hydrochloric acid
Calcite $CaCO_3$	3	2.7	Glassy	White to grayish	Colorless, white, pale tints	Easily scratched; bubbles in dilute hydrochloric acid; frequently fluorescent
Halite $NaCl$	2.5	2.1–2.6	Glassy	White	Colorless or white	Occurs as perfect cubic crystals; has salty taste
Gypsum $CaSO_4 \cdot 2H_2O$	2	2.3	Glassy, pearly, silky	White	Colorless, white, light tints	Very soft; used in manufacture of plaster of Paris; form known as alabaster used for statues
Sulfur S	2	2.0–2.1	Resinous to greasy	White	Yellow to yellowish brown	Used in making many medicines, in production of sulfuric acid, and in vulcanizing rubber
Talc $Mg_3Si_4O_{10}(OH)_2$	1	2.7–2.8	Pearly to greasy	White	Gray, white, greenish	Very soft; used in talcum powder; found mostly in metamorphic rocks; also called "soapstone"

Glossary

A

aa A slow-moving type of lava that hardens to form rough chunks; cooler than pahoehoe. (p. 378)

abdomen The region of an organism, such as an insect, that contains its reproductive organs and part of its digestive tract. (p. 232)

abiotic factor A nonliving part of an ecosystem. (p. 268)

acceleration The rate at which velocity changes. (p. 102)

acid rain Rain that is more acidic than normal, caused by the release of molecules of sulfur dioxide and nitrogen oxide into the air. (pp. 425, 443)

active transport The movement of materials through a cell membrane using energy. (p. 161)

active Said of a volcano that is erupting or shows signs of eruption in the near future. (p. 380)

adaptation A characteristic that helps an organism survive in its environment or reproduce. (p. 219)

air mass A huge body of air that has similar temperature, pressure, and humidity throughout. (p. 496)

air pressure A force that is the result of the weight of a column of air pushing down on an area. (p. 446)

altitude Elevation above sea level. (p. 448)

amorphous solid A solid made up of particles that are not arranged in a regular pattern. (p. 58)

anemometer An instrument used to measure wind speed. (p. 473)

aneroid barometer An instrument that measures changes in air pressure without using a liquid. Changes in the shape of an airtight metal box cause a needle on the barometer dial to move. (p. 447)

anticline An upward fold in rock formed by compression of Earth's crust. (p. 364)

anticyclone A high-pressure center of dry air. (p. 502)

anus The opening at the end of an organism's digestive system through which wastes are eliminated. (p. 226)

aquifer An underground layer of rock or soil that holds water. (p. 414)

arachnid An arthropod with two body sections. (p. 234)

artesian well A well in which water rises because of pressure within the aquifer. (p. 415)

arthropod An invertebrate that has an external skeleton, a segmented body, and jointed attachments called appendages. (p. 230)

asexual reproduction The reproductive process that involves only one parent and produces offspring that are identical to the parent. (p. 150)

asteroid belt The region of the solar system between the orbits of Mars and Jupiter, where many asteroids are found. (p. 564)

asteroids Objects revolving around the sun that are too small and too numerous to be considered planets. (p. 564)

atmosphere The mixture of gases that surrounds Earth. The outermost of the four spheres into which scientists divide Earth. (p. 484)

atom The smallest particle of an element. (p. 42)

atrium Each of the two upper chambers of the heart that receives blood coming into the heart. (p. 241)

aurora borealis A colorful, glowing display in the sky caused when particles from the sun strike oxygen and nitrogen atoms in the ionosphere; also called the Northern Lights. (p. 456)

autotroph An organism that makes its own food. (p. 128)

B

balanced forces Equal forces acting on an object in opposite directions. (p. 99)

barometer An instrument used to measure changes in air pressure. (p. 446)

batholith A mass of rock formed when a large body of magma cooled inside the crust. (p. 387)

bilateral symmetry Line symmetry; the quality of being divisible into two halves that are mirror images. (p. 221)

binary fission A form of asexual reproduction in which one cell divides to form two identical cells. (p. 192)

binomial nomenclature The naming system for organisms in which each organism is given a two-part name—a genus name and a species name. (p. 185)

biomass The living or formerly living material in an ecosystem. (p. 286)

biomass fuel Fuel made from things that once were alive. (p. 303)

biotic factor A living part of an ecosystem. (p. 267)

bird An endothermic vertebrate that has feathers and a four-chambered heart, and lays eggs. (p. 247)

birth rate The number of births in a population in a certain amount of time. (p. 275)

boiling Vaporization that occurs on and below the surface of a liquid. (p. 77)

boiling point The temperature at which a substance changes from a liquid to a gas. (p. 77)

Boyle's law The relationship between the pressure and volume of a gas at constant temperature; when volume increases, pressure decreases. (p. 64)

budding A form of asexual reproduction in which a new organism grows out of the body of a parent. (p. 203)

C

caldera The large hole at the top of a volcano formed when the roof of a volcano's magma chamber collapses. (p. 390)

carnivore An animal that eats only other animals. (p. 219)

carrying capacity The largest population that an area can support. (p. 277)

cartilage A connective tissue that is more flexible than bone and that gives support to some parts of the body. (p. 239)

Celsius scale The temperature scale on which zero and 100 are the temperatures at which water freezes and boils. (p. 583)

cell The basic unit of structure and function in organisms. (p. 123)

cell cycle The regular sequence of growth and division that cells undergo. (p. 171)

cell membrane The outside boundary of a cell; controls which substances can enter or leave the cell. (p. 140)

cell theory A widely accepted explanation of the relationship between cells and living things. (p. 134)

cell wall A rigid layer of nonliving material that surrounds the cells of plants and some other organisms. (p.139)

Charles's law The relationship between the temperature and volume of a gas at constant pressure; when temperature increases, volume increases. (p. 66)

chemical bond The force that holds two atoms together. (p. 44)

chemical change A change in matter that produces new substances. (p. 31)

chemical property A characteristic that is observed when a substance interacts with another substance. (p. 26)

chemistry The study of the properties of matter and how matter changes. (p. 25)

chlorophyll A substance that gives chloroplasts their green color and captures light energy during photosynthesis. (p. 163)

chloroplast A structure in the cells of plants and some other organisms that captures energy from sunlight and uses it to produce food. (p. 144)

chromatid One of the pair of the identical rods of a chromosome. (p.172)

chromatin Material in cells that contains DNA and carries genetic information. (p.141)

chromosome A rod-shaped cellular structure made of condensed chromatin; contains DNA, which carries the genetic information that controls inherited characteristics such as eye color and blood type. (p. 172)

chromosphere The middle layer of the sun's atmosphere. (p. 539)

cilia The hairlike projections on the outside of cells that move in a wavelike manner. (p. 198)

cinder cone A steep, cone-shaped hill or mountain made of volcanic ash, cinders, and bombs piled up around a volcano's opening. (p. 388)

cirrus Wispy, feathery clouds made of mostly ice crystals that form at high levels, above about 6 kilometers. (p. 484)

classification The process of grouping things based on their similarities. (p. 184)

cleavage A mineral's ability to split easily along flat surfaces. (p. 335)

cnidarians Animals that use stinging cells to capture prey and defend themselves, and take food into a hollow central cavity. (p. 224)

combustion A rapid reaction between oxygen and fuel that produces thermal energy. (p. 293)

comet A ball of ice and dust whose orbit is a long, narrow ellipse. (p. 563)

community All the different populations that live together in an area. (p. 270)

composite volcano A tall, cone-shaped mountain in which layers of lava alternate with layers of ash and other volcanic materials. (p. 388)

composting The process by which the wastes and remains of living things decay in the soil. (p. 286)

compound A substance made of two or more elements chemically combined in a set ratio. (p. 28)

compound microscope A light microscope that has more than one lens. (p. 132)

compression Stress that squeezes rock until it folds or breaks. (p. 359)

condensation The change from the gaseous to the liquid state of matter; also, the process by which a gas, such as water vapor, changes to a liquid, such as water. (pp. 77, 483)

conduction The transfer of heat by movements of a fluid. (p. 470)

conjugation The process in which a unicellular organism transfers some of its genetic material to another unicellular organism. (p. 192)

conservation The process of using a resource wisely so it will not be used up. (p. 421)

consumer An organism that obtains energy by feeding on other organisms. (p. 281)

continental (air mass) A dry air mass that forms over land. (p. 496)

contour line A line on a topographic map that connects points of equal elevation. (p. 592)

control rods Cadmium rod used in a nuclear reactor to absorb neutrons from fission. (p. 309)

controlled experiment An experiment in which all of the variables except for one remain the same. (p. 12)

convection The transfer of heat by movement of currents within a fluid. (p. 470)

convex lens A lens that is thicker in the center than at the edges. (p. 136)

core The central part of the sun, where nuclear fusion occurs. (p. 538)

Coriolis effect The way Earth's rotation makes winds in the Northern Hemisphere curve to the right and winds in the Southern Hemisphere curve to the left. (p. 477)

corona The outer layer of the sun's atmosphere. (p. 539)

cotyledon A seed leaf that stores food. (p. 208)

crater A bowl-shaped area that forms around a volcano's central opening. (p. 375)

crop A bird's internal storage tank that allows it to store food inside its body after swallowing the food. (p. 248)

crust The layer of rock that forms Earth's outer surface. (p. 226)

crustacean An arthropod that has two or three body sections, five or more pairs of legs, two pairs of antennae, and usually three pairs of appendages for chewing. (p. 234)

crystal A solid in which the atoms are arranged in a pattern that repeats again and again. (p. 332)

crystalline solid A substance that is made of crystals in which the particles are arranged in a regular, repeating pattern. (p. 58)

cumulus Clouds that form less than 2 kilometers above the ground and look like fluffy, rounded piles of cotton. (p. 484)

cyclone A swirling center of low air pressure. (p. 501)

cytokinesis The final stage of the cell cycle, in which the cell's cytoplasm divides, distributing the organelles into each of the two new cells. (p. 173)

cytoplasm The region of a cell located inside the cell membrane (in prokaryotes) or between the cell membrane and nucleus (in eukaryotes); contains a gel-like material and cell organelles. (p. 141)

data The facts, figures, and other evidence collected in an experiment. (p. 13)

death rate The number of deaths in a certain amount of time. (p. 275)

decomposer An organism that breaks down large chemicals from dead organisms into small chemicals and returns important materials to the soil and water. (pp. 193, 282)

deformation A change in the volume or shape of the Earth's crust. (p. 359)

delta A landform made of sediment that is deposited where a river flows into an ocean or lake. (p. 111)

density The measurement of how much mass of a sustance is contained in a given volume. (pp. 335, 445)

deposition The process by which sediment settles out of the water or wind that is carrying it, and is deposited in a new location. (pp. 108, 343)

desalination The process of obtaining fresh water from salt water by removing the salt. (p. 423)

dew point The temperature at which condensation begins. (p. 483)

diaphragm A large, dome-shaped muscle that has an important function in breathing. (p. 252)

diffusion The process by which molecules move from an area in which they are highly concentrated to an area in which they are less concentrated. (p. 159)

dike A slab of volcanic rock formed when magma forces itself across rock layers. (p. 387)

directly proportional A term used to describe the relationship between two variables whose graph is a straight line passing through the point (0,0). (p. 70)

divide A ridge of land that separates one drainage basin or watershed from another. (p. 405)

DNA (*Deoxyribo Nucleic Acid*) The genetic material that carries information about an organism and is passed from parent to offspring. (p. 150)

dormant Said of a volcano that does not show signs of erupting in the near future. (p. 380)

drought A water shortage caused by long periods of low precipitation in a particular area. (p. 490)

earthquake The shaking that results from the movement of rock beneath Earth's surface. (p. 358)

echinoderm A radially symmetrical invertebrate that lives on the ocean floor and has a spiny internal skeleton. (p. 235)

ecology The study of how living things interact with each other and with their environment. (p. 270)

ecosystem All the living and nonliving things that interact in an area. (p. 266)

ectotherm An animal whose body does not produce much internal heat. (p. 238)

efficiency The percentage of energy that is used by a device to perform work. (p. 314)

egg A female sex cell. (p. 150)

El Niño An abnormal climate event that occurs every 2 to 7 years in the Pacific Ocean, causing changes in winds, currents, and weather patterns that can lead to dramatic climate changes. (p. 522)

electrode A metal strip that gains or loses electrons during electrolysis. (p. 48)

electrolysis A process by which an electric current breaks chemical bonds. (p. 48)

electromagnetic wave A form of energy that can travel through space. (p. 462)

element A substance that cannot be broken down into other substances by chemical or physical means. (p. 27)

ellipse An elongated circle, or oval shape; the shape of the planets' orbits. (p. 535)

embryo The young organism that develops from a zygote. (p. 208)

emigration Leaving a population. (p. 276)

endoplasmic reticulum A cell structure that forms a maze of passageways in which proteins and other materials are carried from one part of the cell to another. (p. 144)

endoskeleton An internal skeleton. (p. 235)

endospore A small, rounded, thick-walled, resting cell that forms inside a bacterial cell. (p. 192)

endotherm An animal whose body controls and regulates its temperature by controlling the internal heat it produces. (p. 238)

energy The ability to do work or cause change. (p. 25)

energy conservation The practice of reducing energy use. (p. 313)

energy transformation Any change from one form of energy to another. (p. 292)

epicenter The point on Earth's surface directly above an earthquake's focus. (p. 368)

equator An imaginary line halfway between the North and South poles that circles the Earth. (p. 591)

erosion The process by which water, ice, wind, or gravity moves fragments of rock and soil. (p. 108, 343)

estimate An approximation of a number, based on reasonable assumptions. (p. 274)

eukaryote An organism with cells that contain nuclei and other cell structures. (p. 145)

evacuate To move away temporarily. (p. 510)

evaporation The process that occurs when vaporization takes place only on the surface of a liquid; also, the process by which molecules at the surface of a liquid, such as water, absorb enough energy to change to a gaseous state, such as water vapor. (pp. 76, 398, 481)

exoskeleton An outer skeleton. (p. 231)

exosphere The outer layer of the thermosphere, extending outward into space. (p. 456)

external stimulus A change in an organism's surroundings that causes the organism to react. (p. 124)

extinct Describes a type of organism that no longer exists anywhere on Earth; also, a volcano that is unlikely to erupt again. (p. 380)

extrusive rock Igneous rock that forms from lava on Earth's surface. (p. 342)

fault A break or crack in Earth's lithosphere along which rocks move. (p. 360)

fault-block mountain A mountain that forms where a normal fault uplifts a block of rock. (p. 362)

fermentation The process by which cells break down molecules to release energy without using oxygen. (p. 167)

fertilization The joining of a sperm cell and an egg cell. (p. 208)

flagellum A long, whiplike structure that helps a unicellular organism move. (p. 191)

flash flood A sudden, violent flood that occurs within a few hours, or even minutes, of a heavy rainstorm. (p. 516)

flood The overflowing of a river's channel due to the increase of the volume of water in the river. (pp. 111, 406)

flood plain A broad, flat valley through which a river flows. (p. 109)

flower The reproductive structure of an angiosperm. (p. 209)

focus The point beneath Earth's surface where rock breaks under stress resulting in an earthquake. (p. 368)

fold A bend in rock that forms where part of Earth's crust is compressed. (p. 363)

food chain The series of events in which one organism eats another, resulting in a flow of energy among the organisms involved. (p. 282)

food web The pattern of overlapping food chains in an ecosystem. (p. 284)

footwall The block of rock that forms the lower half of a fault. (p. 360)

force A push or a pull exerted on an object. (p. 98)

fossil fuel An energy-rich substance (such as coal, oil, or natural gas) formed from the remains of organisms. (p. 295)

fracture The way a mineral looks when it breaks apart in an irregular way. (p. 335)

freezing The change in state from a liquid to a solid. (p. 76)

front The area where air masses meet and do not mix. (p. 499)

fruit The ripened ovary and other structures that enclose one or more seeds of an angiosperm. (p. 210)

fuel A material that releases energy when it burns. (p. 293)

fuel rod The uranium rod that undergoes fission in a nuclear reactor. (p. 308)

G

gamete A sperm cell or an egg cell. (p. 208)

gas A state of matter with no definite shape or volume. (p. 60)

gas giants The name given to the first four outer planets: Jupiter, Saturn, Uranus, and Neptune. (p. 552)

gemstone A hard, colorful mineral that has a brilliant or glassy luster. (p. 336)

gene A segment of DNA on a chromosome that codes for a specific trait. (p. 150)

genus A classification grouping that consists of a number of similar, closely related species. (p. 185)

geocentric system A description of the solar system in which all of the planets revolve around Earth. (p. 533)

geologist A scientist who studies the forces that make and shape planet Earth. (p. 327)

geology The study of the solid Earth. (p. 327)

geosynchronous orbit The orbit of a satellite that revolves around Earth at the same rate that Earth rotates. (p. 568)

geothermal energy Heat energy in Earth's interior from water or steam that has been heated by magma. (pp. 303, 382)

gestation period The length of time between fertilization and the birth of a mammal. (p. 254)

geyser A type of hot spring that builds up pressure underground and erupts at regular intervals as a fountain of water and steam. (p. 382)

gill An organism's breathing organ that removes oxygen from water. (p. 228)

gizzard The thick-walled, muscular part of a bird's stomach that squeezes and grinds partially digested food. (p. 248)

global winds Winds that blow steadily from specific directions over long distances. (p. 477)

Golgi body A structure in a cell that receives proteins and other newly formed materials from the endoplasmic reticulum, packages them, and distributes them to other parts of the cell. (p. 144)

grain A particle of mineral or other rock that gives a rock its texture. (p. 341)

graph A diagram that shows how two variables are related. (p. 68)

gravity The force that pulls objects toward each other. (p. 535)

greenhouse effect The process by which heat is trapped in the atmosphere by water vapor, carbon dioxide, methane, and other gases that form a "blanket" around the earth. (pp. 465, 548)

H

habitat The place where an organism lives and that provides the things it needs to survive. (p. 267)

hanging wall The block of rock that forms the upper half of a fault. (p. 360)

headwaters The many small streams that come together at the source of a river. (p. 109)

heat The movement of thermal energy from one substance to another. (p. 469)

heliocentric system A description of the solar system in which all of the planets revolve around the sun. (p. 534)

herbivore An animal that eats only plants. (p. 219)

heredity The passing of traits from parents to offspring. (p. 149)

heterotroph An organism that cannot make its own food. (p. 128)

homeostasis The process by which an organism's internal environment is kept stable in spite of changes in its external environment. (p. 129)

hormone The chemical product of an endocrine gland that speeds up or slows down the activities of an organ or tissue; also, a chemical that affects a plant's growth and development. (p. 210)

host An organism that provides a source of energy or a suitable environment for a virus or for another organism to live. (p. 110)

humidity A measure of the amount of water vapor in the air. (p. 482)

hurricane A tropical storm that has winds of 119 kilometers per hour or higher; typically about 600 kilometers across. (p. 508)

hydrocarbon A compound that contains carbon and hydrogen atoms. (p. 295)

hydroelectric power Electricity produced by flowing water moving over a waterfall or dam. (p. 302)

hypothesis A possible explanation for a set of observations or answer to scientific question; must be testable. (p. 12)

I

igneous rock A type of rock that forms from the cooling of molten rock at or below the surface of Earth. (p. 342)

immigration Moving into a population. (p. 276)

impermeable Characteristic of materials through which water does not easily pass, such as clay or granite. (p. 413)

inertia The tendency of a moving object to continue in a straight line or a stationary object to remain in place. (p. 535)

inexhaustible resources Any living or nonliving thing in the environment for which there is a limitless supply. (p. 299)

inference An interpretation of an observation based on evidence and prior knowledge. (p. 11)

infrared radiation A form of energy with wavelengths that are longer than visible light. (p. 463)

inner core A dense sphere of solid iron and nickel in the center of Earth. (p. 328)

insect An arthropod with three body sections, six legs, one pair of antennae, and usually one or two pairs of wings. (p. 232)

insulation A building material that blocks heat transfer between the air inside and the air outside. (p. 315)

internal stimulus A change from within an organism, such as hunger and thirst, that causes the organism to respond. (p. 124)

International System of Units A system of measurement based on multiples of ten and on established measures of mass, length, and time. (p. 35)

interphase The stage of the cell cycle that takes place before cell division occurs; during this stage, the cell grows, copies its DNA, and prepares to divide. (p. 171)

intrusive rock Igneous rock that forms when magma hardens beneath Earth's surface. (p. 342)

invertebrate An animal without a backbone. (p. 220)

ionosphere The lower part of the thermosphere, where electrically charged particles called ions are found. (p. 456)

irrigation The process of supplying water to areas of land to make them suitable for growing crops. (p. 400)

isobars Lines on a map joining places that have the same air pressure. (p. 522)

isotherms Lines on a map joining places that have the same temperature. (p. 522)

jet streams Bands of high-speed winds about 10 kilometers above Earth's surface. (p. 480)

Kelvin scale The temperature scale on which zero is the temperature at which no more energy can be removed from matter. (p. 110)

kidney A major organ of the excretory system; eliminates urea, excess water, and other waste materials from the body. (p. 243)

land breeze The flow of air from land to a body of water. (p. 476)

larva The immature form of an animal that looks very different from the adult. (p. 234)

latitude The distance north or south from the equator, measured in degrees. (p. 478)

lava Magma that reaches the surface; also the rock formed when liquid lava hardens. (p. 335)

lava flow The area covered by lava as it pours out of a volcano's vent. (p. 375)

leaf The organ of a vascular plant where photosynthesis occurs. (p. 205)

levee A long ridge formed by deposits of sediment alongside a river channel. (pp. 112, 407)

lightning A sudden spark, or energy discharge, caused when electrical charges jump between parts of a cloud or between a cloud and the ground. (p. 504)

limiting factor An environmental factor that prevents a population from increasing. (p. 277)

linear The term used to describe the relationship between variables whose graph is a straight line. (p. 105)

liquid A state of matter that has a definite volume but no definite shape. (p. 58)

lithosphere A rigid layer made up of the uppermost part of Earth's mantle and crust. One of four spheres into which scientists divide Earth. (p. 329)

local wind Wind that blows over short distances. (p. 474)

luster The way a mineral reflects light from its surface. (p. 334)

lysosome A small rounded cell structure that contains chemicals that break down large food particles into smaller ones. (p. 145)

magma The molten mixture of rock-forming substances, gases, and water that makes up part of Earth's mantle. (p. 335)

magma chamber The pocket beneath a volcano where magma collects. (p. 375)

magnification The ability to make things look larger than they are. (p. 136)

magnitude The measurement of an earthquake's strength based on seismic waves and movement along faults. (p. 371)

mammary gland The organ that produces the milk with which mammals feed their young. (p. 253)

manipulated variable The one factor that a scientist changes during an experiment; also called independent variable. (p. 12)

mantle The layer of hot, solid material between Earth's crust and core. (p. 328)

maritime (air mass) A humid air mass that forms over oceans. (p. 496)

marsupial A mammal whose young are born alive at an early stage of development, and then usually continue to develop in a pouch on their mother's body. (p. 254)

mass A measure of how much matter is in an object. (p. 35)

matter Anything that has mass and occupies space. (p. 24)

meander A looping curve formed in a river as it winds through its flood plain. (p. 111)

meltdown A dangerous condition caused by overheating inside a nuclear reactor. (p. 309)

melting The change from the solid to the liquid state of matter. (p. 75)

melting point The temperature at which a substance changes from a solid to a liquid. (p. 58)

Mercalli scale A scale that rates earthquakes according to their intensity and how much damage they cause. (p. 371)

mercury barometer An instrument that measures changes in air pressure, consisting of a glass tube partly filled with mercury, with its open end resting in a dish of mercury. Air pressure pushing on the mercury in the dish forces the mercury in the tube higher. (p. 446)

mesosphere The middle layer of Earth's atmosphere; the layer in which most meteoroids burn up. (p. 452)

metamorphic rock A type of rock that forms from an existing rock that is changed by heat, pressure, or chemical reactions. (p. 345)

metamorphosis A process in which an animal's body undergoes dramatic changes during its life cycle. (p. 234)

meteor A streak of light in the sky produced by the burning of a meteoroid in Earth's atmosphere. (p. 565)

meteorite A meteoroid that has hit Earth's surface. (p. 565)

meteoroid A chunk of rock or dust in space. (p. 565)

meteorologist A scientist who studies the causes of weather and tries to predict it. (p. 520)

microscope An instrument that makes small objects look larger. (p. 132)

mineral A naturally occurring inorganic solid that has a crystal structure and a definite chemical composition. (p. 331)

mitochondria Rod-shaped cell structures that produce most of the energy needed to carry out the cell's functions. (p. 141)

mitosis The stage of the cell cycle during which the cell's nucleus divides into two new nuclei and one copy of the DNA is distributed into each daughter cell. (p. 172)

mixture Two or more substances that are mixed together but not chemically combined. (p. 28)

molecule A particle made of two or more atoms bonded together. (p. 44)

mollusk An invertebrate with a soft, unsegmented body; most are protected by hard outer shells. (p. 227)

moment magnitude scale A scale that rates earthquakes by estimating the total energy released by an earthquake. (p. 372)

monotreme A mammal that lays eggs. (p. 254)

monsoons Sea and land breezes over a large region that change direction with the seasons. (p. 476)

motion The state in which one object's distance from another is changing. (p. 87)

mouth The point at which a river flows into another body of water. (p. 111)

net force The overall force on an object when all the individual forces acting on an object are added together. (p. 99)

nitrogen fixation The process of changing free nitrogen gas into a usable form. (p. 285)

nonlinear The term used to describe a relationship between variables whose graph is not a straight line. (p. 105)

nonrenewable resource A natural resource that is not replaced as it is used. (p. 295)

normal fault A type of fault where the hanging wall slides downward; caused by tension in the crust. (p. 360)

nuclear fission The splitting of an atom's nucleus into two smaller nuclei. (p. 307)

nuclear fusion The combining of two atomic nuclei to produce a single larger nucleus as when two hydrogen atoms join together to form helium, releasing energy. (pp. 310, 538)

nucleus The control center of the cell that directs the cells' activities and determines the cell's characteristics; also, the central core of an atom containing protons and usually neutrons. (pp. 140, 307)

nymph A stage of gradual metamorphosis that usually resembles the adult insect. (p. 234)

observation The process of using one or more senses to gather information. (p. 11)

occluded Cut off, as the warm air mass at an occluded front is cut off from the ground by cooler air beneath it. (p. 501)

omnivore An animal that eats both plants and animals. (p. 219)

organ A structure in the body that is composed of different kinds of tissue. (p. 147)

organ system A group of organs that work together to perform a major function in the body. (p. 147)

organelle A tiny cell structure that carries out a specific function within the cell. (p. 139)

organism A living thing. (p. 122)

osmosis The diffusion of water molecules through a selectively permeable membrane. (p. 160)

outer core A layer of molten iron and nickel that surrounds the inner core of Earth. (p. 328)

ovary An organ of female reproductive system in which eggs and estrogen are produced; also, a protective structure in plants that encloses the developing seeds (p. 209)

ovule A plant structure in seed plants that contains an egg cell. (p. 209)

oxbow lake The crescent-shaped, cutoff body of water that remains after a river carves a new channel. (p. 111)

ozone A form of oxygen that has three oxygen atoms in each molecule instead of the usual two. (p. 436)

P wave A type of seismic wave that compresses and expands the ground. (p. 369)

pahoehoe A hot, fast-moving type of lava that hardens to form smooth, ropelike coils. (p. 378)

Pangaea The name of the single landmass that broke apart 225 million years ago and gave rise to today's continents. (p. 355)

parasite An organism that lives on or in a host and causes harm to the host. (p. 199)

passive transport The movement of materials through a cell membrane without using energy. (p. 161)

permeable Characteristic of materials such as sand and gravel which allow water to pass easily through them. (p. 413)

pesticide A chemical intended to kill insects and other organisms that damage crops. (p. 426)

petrochemical A compound made from oil. (p. 297)

petroleum Liquid fossil fuel; oil. (p. 296)

photochemical smog A brownish haze that is a mixture of ozone and other chemicals, formed when nitrogen oxides, hydrocarbons, and other pollutants react with one another in the presence of sunlight. (p. 442)

photosphere The inner layer of the sun's atmosphere. (p. 539)

photosynthesis The process by which plants and some other organisms capture light energy and use it to make food from carbon dioxide and water. (p. 163)

physical change A change that alters the form or appearance of a substance but does not make the material into another substance. (p. 30)

physical property A characteristic of a substance that can be observed without changing the substance into something else. (p. 26)

pipe A long tube through which magma moves from the magma chamber to Earth's surface. (p. 375)

placenta A membrane that becomes the link between the developing embryo or fetus and the mother. (p. 255)

placental mammal A mammal that develops inside its mother's body until its body systems can function independently. (p. 255)

plate boundary A crack in the lithosphere where two of Earth's plates meet. (p. 356)

plate A section of the lithosphere that slowly moves over the asthenosphere, carrying pieces of continental and oceanic crust. (p. 354)

plateau A landform that has a more or less level surface and is elevated high above sea level. (p. 365)

polar (air mass) A cold air mass that forms north of 50° north latitude and south of 50° south latitude and has high air pressure. (p. 496)

pollen Tiny particles produced by plants that contain the microscopic cells that later become sperm cells. (p. 209)

pollutant A harmful substance in the air, water, or soil. (p. 440)

population All the members of one species in a particular area. (p. 269)

population density The number of individuals in a specific area. (p. 273)

pores Tiny openings in and between particles of rock and soil which may contain air or water. (p. 413)

precipitation Forms of water such as rain, snow, sleet, or hail that fall from clouds and reach Earth's surface. (pp. 398, 487)

predator A carnivore that hunts and kills other animals for food and has adaptations that help it capture the animals it preys upon. (p. 219)

pressure The force pushing on an area or surface; also, the force of a gas's outward push divided by the area of the walls of the container. (pp. 63, 445)

prey An animal that a predator feeds upon. (p. 219)

prime meridian The line that makes a half-circle from the North pole to the South pole, passing through Greenwich, England. (p. 663)

producer An organism that can make its own food. (p. 281)

prokaryote An organism whose cells lack a nucleus and some other cell structures. (p. 145)

prominence A loop of gas that protrudes from the sun's surface, linking parts of sunspot regions. (p. 542)

protozoan An animal-like protist. (p. 197)

pseudopod A "false foot" or temporary bulge of the cell membrane used for feeding and movement in some protozoans. (p. 197)

psychrometer An instrument used to measure relative humidity, consisting of a wet-bulb thermometer and a dry-bulb thermometer. (p. 482)

pupa The second stage of complete metamorphosis, in which an insect is enclosed in a protective covering and gradually changes from a larva to an adult. (p. 234)

pyroclastic flow The expulsion of ash, cinders, bombs, and gases during an explosive volcanic eruption. (p. 379)

radial symmetry The quality of having many lines of symmetry that all pass through a central point. (p. 221)

radiation The direct transfer of energy through empty space by electromagnetic waves. (p. 462)

radula A flexible ribbon of tiny teeth in mollusks. (p. 228)

rain gauge An instrument used to measure the amount of precipitation, consisting of an open-ended container topped by a collecting funnel and having a collecting tube and measuring scale inside. (p. 489)

reactor vessel The part of a nuclear reactor where nuclear fission occurs. (p. 308)

recharge New water that enters an aquifer from the surface. (p. 110)

reference point A place or object used for comparison to determine if an object is in motion. (p. 88)

refinery A factory where crude oil is separated into fuels and other products. (p. 297)

relative humidity The percentage of water vapor in the air compared to the maximum amount the air can hold at that temperature. (p. 482)

renewable resource A resource that is naturally replaced in a relatively short time. (p. 299)

replication The process by which a cell makes a copy of the DNA in its nucleus. (p. 171)

reproduce The production of offspring that are similar to the parents. (p. 125)

reserve A known deposit of fuels. (p. 298)

reservoir A natural or artificial lake that stores water for human use. (p. 410)

resolution The ability to clearly distinguish the individual parts of an object. (p. 137)

respiration The process by which cells break down simple food molecules to release the energy they contain. (p. 166)

responding variable The factor that changes as a result of changes to the manipulated variable in an experiment. (p. 12)

response An action or change in behavior that occurs as a result of a stimulus. (p. 125)

retrograde rotation The spinning motion of a planet from east to west, opposite to the direction of rotation of most planets and moons. (p. 547)

reverse fault A type of fault where the hanging wall slides upward; caused by compression in the crust. (p. 361)

revolution The movement of an object around another object. (p. 544)

ribosome A tiny structure in the cytoplasm of a cell where proteins are made. (p. 144)

Richter scale A scale that rates seismic waves as measured by a mechanical seismograph. (p. 371)

river A large stream. (p. 404)

rock The material that forms Earth's hard surface. (pp. 326, 340)

rock cycle A series of processes on the surface and inside earth that slowly changes rocks from one kind to another. (p. 346)

root The underground part of any plant which anchors the plant in the ground and absorbs water and nutrients from the soil. (p. 208)

rotation The spinning motion of a planet about its axis. (p. 544)

S waves A type of seismic wave that moves the ground up and down or side to side. (p. 369)

satellite Any object that revolves around another object in space. (p. 567)

saturated zone A layer of permeable rock or soil in which the cracks and pores are completely filled with water. (p. 413)

scale Relates distance on a map to the corresponding distance on Earth's surface. (p. 662)

scattering Reflection of light in all directions. (p. 464)

science A way of learning about the natural world. (p. 10)

scientific inquiry The diverse ways in which scientists study the natural world. (p. 10)

scientific law A statement that describes what scientists expect to happen every time under a particular set of conditions. (p. 16)

scientific theory A well-tested scientific concept that explains a wide range of observations. (p. 10)

sea breeze The flow of air from an ocean or lake to the land. (p. 476)

sediment Small, solid particles of material from rocks or organisms which are moved by water or wind, resulting in erosion and deposition. (pp. 108, 343)

sedimentary rock A type of rock that forms when particles from other rocks or the remains of plants and animals are pressed and cemented together. (p. 343)

seed The plant structure that contains a young plant inside a protective covering. (p. 208).

seismic wave A vibration that travels through Earth carrying the energy released during an earthquake. (pp. 327, 368)

seismograph A device that records ground movements caused by seismic waves as they move through Earth. (p. 370)

selective breeding The process of selecting a few organisms with desired traits to serve as parents of the next generation. (p. 151).

selectively permeable A property of cell membranes that allows some substances to pass through, while others cannot. (p. 158)

sexual reproduction The reproductive process that involves two parents who combine their genetic material to produce a new organism, which differs from both parents. (p. 150)

shearing Stress that pushes a mass of rock in opposite directions. (p. 359)

shield volcano A wide, gently sloping mountain made of layers of lava and formed by quiet eruptions. (p. 388)

silica A material that is formed from the elements oxygen and silicon; silica is found in magma. (p. 377)

sill A slab of volcanic rock formed when magma squeezes between layers of rock. (p. 387)

solar energy Energy from the sun. (p. 299)

solar flare An explosion of hydrogen gas from the sun's surface that occurs when loops in sunspot regions suddenly connect. (p. 542)

solar system A large planetary system that consists of a combination of many smaller planetary systems and objects. (p. 534)

solar wind A stream of electrically charged particles produced by the sun's corona. (p. 540)

solid A state of matter that has a definite volume and a definite shape. (p. 57)

species A group of similar organisms whose members can mate with one another and produce fertile offspring. (p. 185)

speed The distance an object travels in one unit of time. (p. 90)

sperm cell A male sex cell. (p. 150)

spontaneous generation The mistaken idea that living things arise from nonliving sources. (p. 125)

spore A tiny cell that is able to grow into a new organism. (p. 201)

spring A place where groundwater bubbles or flows out of cracks in the rock. (p. 414)

stamen The male reproductive parts of a flower. (p. 209)

stem The stalk-like organ that supports a plant and that connects the roots to the leaves. (p. 208)

stimulus A change in an organism's surroundings that causes the organism to respond. (p. 124)

stomata The small openings on the undersides of most leaves through which oxygen and carbon dioxide can move. (p. 205)

storm A violent disturbance in the atmosphere. (p. 503)

storm surge A "dome" of water that sweeps across the coast where the hurricane lands. (p. 510)

stratosphere The second lowest layer of Earth's atmosphere; the ozone layer is located in the upper stratosphere. (p. 452)

stratus Clouds that form in flat layers. (p. 484)

streak The color of a mineral's powder. (p. 334)

stress The reaction of a person's body and mind to threatening, challenging, or disturbing events. (p. 358)

strike-slip fault A type of fault where rocks on either side move past each other sideways with little up-or-down motion. (p. 360)

sublimation The change in state from a solid directly to a gas without passing through the liquid state. (p. 78)

substance A single kind of matter that has distinct physical and chemical properties. (p. 25)

sunspot A dark, cooler region on the surface of the sun. (p. 540)

surface waves A type of seismic wave that forms when P waves and S waves reach Earth's surface. (p. 370)

syncline A downward fold in rock formed by compression in Earth's crust. (p. 364)

taxonomy The scientific study of how living things are classified. (p. 185)

temperature The average amount of energy of motion in the molecules of a substance. (pp. 62, 469)

temperature inversion A layer of warm air between two cooler layers that prevents the air close to Earth from escaping. (p. 442)

tension Stress that stretches rock so that it becomes thinner in the middle. (p. 359)

terrestrial planets The name given to the four inner planets: Mercury, Venus, Earth and Mars. (p. 544)

texture The size, shape, and pattern of a rock's grains. (p. 341)

theory of plate tectonics The theory that pieces of Earth's lithosphere are in constant motion, driven by convection currents in the mantle. (p. 356)

thermal energy The total energy of a substance's particles due to their movement or vibration; also, the energy of motion in the molecules of a substance. (pp. 74, 469)

thermometer An instrument used to measure temperature, consisting of a thin, glass tube with a bulb on one end that contains a liquid, usually mercury or alcohol. (p. 469)

thermosphere The outermost layer of Earth's atmosphere. (p. 455)

thorax An insect's mid-section, to which its wings and legs are attached. (p. 232)

tissue A group of similar cells that perform a specific function in an organism. (p. 146)

tornado A rapidly whirling, funnel-shaped cloud that reaches down from a storm cloud to touch Earth's surface, usually leaving a destructive path. (p. 505)

trait A characteristic that an organism can pass onto its offspring through its genes. (p. 149)

transpiration The process by which water is lost through a plant's leaves. (p. 398)

tributary A stream or small river that flows into a larger stream. (p. 404)

tropical (air mass) A warm air mass that forms in the tropics and has low air pressure. (p. 496)

tropism The growth response of a plant toward or away from a stimulus. (p. 210)

troposphere The lowest layer of Earth's atmosphere; where weather occurs. (p. 451)

ultraviolet radiation A form of energy with wavelengths that are shorter than visible light. (p. 463)

unbalanced force A nonzero net force that changes an object's motion. (p. 99)

unsaturated zone A layer of rocks and soil above the water table in which the pores contain air as well as water. (p. 413)

vacuole A water-filled sac inside a cell that acts as a storage area. (p. 145)

vaporization The change from the liquid to the gaseous state of matter. (p. 76)

vary inversely A term used to describe the relationship between two variables whose graph forms a curve that slopes downward from left to right. (p. 71)

vascular tissue The internal transporting tissue in some plants that is made up of tube-like structures. (p. 205)

vein A blood vessel that carries blood back to the heart. (p. 336)

velocity Speed in a given direction. (p. 93)

vent An opening through which molten rock and gas leave a volcano. (p. 375)

ventricle A lower chamber of the heart that pumps blood out to the lungs and body. (p. 241)

vertebrae The bones that make up the backbone of an animal. (p. 237)

vertebrate An animal with a backbone. (p. 220)

viscosity The resistance of a liquid to flowing. (p. 59)

volcanic neck A deposit of hardened magma in a volcano's pipe. (p. 387)

volume The amount of space that matter occupies. (p. 35)

water cycle The continuous process by which water moves from Earth's surface to the atmosphere and back passing through the living and nonliving parts of the environment. (p. 398)

water pollution The addition of any substance that has a negative effect on water or the living things that depend on the water. (p. 424)

water table The top of the saturated zone, or depth to the groundwater in an aquifer. (p. 413)

water vapor The invisible, gaseous form of water. (p. 437)

watershed The land area that supplies water to a river system. (p. 405)

weather The condition of Earth's atmosphere at a particular time and place. (p. 484)

weight A measure of the force of gravity on an object. (p. 35)

wind The horizontal movement of air from an area of high pressure to an area of lower pressure. (p. 472)

wind-chill factor Increased cooling caused by the wind. (p. 473)

zygote A fertilized egg, produced by the joining of a sperm cell and egg cell. (p. 208)

Spanish Glossary

A

aa/malpaís Tipo lento de lava que al solidificarse forma bloques ásperos; menos caliente que la lava cordada. (pág. 378)

abdomen/abdomen Región del cuerpo de algunos organismos, como los insectos, donde se encuentran los órganos reproductores y parte del canal digestivo. (pág. 232)

abiotic factor/factor abiótico Parte sin vida de un ecosistema. (pág. 268)

acceleration/aceleración Ritmo de cambio de velocidad. (pág. 102)

acid rain/lluvia ácida Lluvia más ácida de lo normal, producida por la liberación en el aire de moléculas de dióxido de azufre y óxido de nitrógeno. (págs. 425, 443)

active/activo Se dice del volcán que entra en erupción o da señales de poder hacerlo en un futuro próximo. (pág. 380)

active transport/transporte activo Movimiento de materiales a través de la membrana celular, usando energía para ello. (pág. 61)

adaptation/adaptación Característica que ayuda a un organismo a sobrevivir en su entorno o a reproducirse. (pág. 219)

air mass/masa de aire Enorme volumen de aire cuya temperatura, presión y humedad son uniformes. (pág. 496)

air pressure/presión atmosférica Fuerza que ejerce el peso de una columna de aire sobre una zona. (pág. 446)

altitude/altitud Elevación sobre el nivel del mar. (pág. 448)

amorphous solid/sólido amorfo Sólido formado por partículas que no están ordenadas según un patrón regular. (pág. 58)

anemometer/anemómetro Instrumento usado para medir la velocidad del viento. (pág. 473)

aneroid barometer/barómetro aneroide Instrumento que mide los cambios en la presión atmosférica sin usar líquido. Las alteraciones en la forma de la caja metálica hermética hacen que se mueva la aguja indicadora de este aparato. (pág. 447)

anticline/anticlinal Pliegue hacia arriba de las rocas debido a la compresión de la corteza terrestre. (pág. 364)

anticyclone/anticiclón Centro de alta presión de aire seco. (pág. 502)

anus/ano Abertura al final del aparato digestivo por la cual se eliminan los desechos del organismo. (pág. 226)

aquifer/acuífero Capa subterránea de roca o tierra donde se acumula agua. (pág. 414)

arachnid/arácnido Artrópodo cuyo cuerpo tiene dos secciones. (pág. 234)

artesian well/pozo artesiano Pozo donde el agua sube debido a la presión del interior del acuífero. (pág. 415)

arthropod/artrópodo Invertebrado con esqueleto externo, cuerpo dividido en segmentos y apéndices articulados. (pág. 230)

asexual reproduction/reproducción asexual Proceso por el cual un solo organismo produce descendientes idénticos a él. (pág. 150)

asteroid belt/cinturón de asteroides Región del sistema solar situada entre las órbitas de Marte y Júpiter, donde se encuentran muchos asteroides. (pág. 564)

asteroids/asteroides Objetos que giran alrededor del Sol, demasiado pequeños y numerosos como para ser considerados planetas. (pág. 564)

atmosphere/atmósfera Mezcla de gases que rodea la Tierra; la más externa de las cuatro esferas en que los científicos dividen al planeta. (pág. 484)

atom/átomo La partícula más pequeña de un elemento. (pág. 42)

atrium/aurícula Cada una de las dos cavidades superiores del corazón que reciben la sangre que entra en él. (pág. 241)

aurora borealis/aurora boreal Despliegue brillante de colores en el cielo, provocado por el choque en la ionosfera de partículas solares con átomos de oxígeno y nitrógeno; también se le llama luces del norte. (pág. 456)

autotroph/autótrofo Organismo que elabora sus propios alimentos. (pág. 128)

B

balanced forces/fuerzas equilibradas Fuerzas iguales que actúan sobre un objeto en sentidos opuestos. (pág. 99)

barometer/barómetro Instrumento usado para medir los cambios en la presión atmosférica. (pág. 446)

batholith/batolito Masa rocosa que se forma al enfriarse un gran volumen de magma en el interior de la corteza. (pág. 387)

bilateral symmetry/simetría bilateral Simetría lineal; capacidad de ser divisible en dos mitades que son reflejos exactos entre sí. (pág. 221)

binary fission/fisión binaria Forma de reproducción asexual en la que una célula se divide en otras dos idénticas. (pág. 192)

binomial nomenclature/nomenclatura binomial Sistema de denominación en el que cada organismo recibe un nombre formado por dos palabras, una para el género y otra para la especie. (pág. 185)

biomass/biomasa Material vivo o sus restos que haya en un ecosistema. (pág. 286)

biomass fuel/combustible de biomasa Combustible formado a partir de lo que fueron seres vivos. (pág. 303)

biotic factor/factor biótico Parte viva de un ecosistema. (pág. 267)

bird/ave Vertebrado endotérmico con plumas y corazón de cuatro cavidades, y que pone huevos. (pág. 247)

birth rate/índice de natalidad Número de nacimientos ocurridos en una población durante un período de tiempo determinado. (pág. 275)

boiling/ebullición Vaporización que ocurre sobre y bajo la superficie de un líquido. (pág. 77)

boiling point/punto de ebullición Temperatura a la que una sustancia pasa del estado líquido al gaseoso. (pág. 77)

Boyle's law/ley de Boyle Relación entre la presión y el volumen de un gas, a una temperatura constante; al aumentar el volumen, disminuye la presión. (pág. 64)

budding/gemación Modo de reproducción asexual en el que un nuevo organismo se forma separándose del cuerpo del progenitor. (pág. 203)

caldera/caldera Depresión grande en la parte superior de un volcán, formada al colapsarse el techo de la cámara magmática. (pág. 390)

carnivore/carnívoro Animal que se alimenta sólo de otros animales. (pág. 219)

carrying capacity/capacidad portadora Población máxima que una zona puede soportar. (pág. 277)

cartilage/cartílago Tejido conjuntivo más elástico que el hueso y que sirve de soporte a ciertas partes del cuerpo. (pág. 239)

cell/célula Unidad básica de estructura y función de los organismos. (pág. 123)

cell cycle/ciclo celular Secuencia normal de crecimiento y división que experimentan las células. (pág. 171)

cell membrane/membrana celular Borde exterior de una célula; regula la entrada y salida de sustancias de la célula. (pág. 140)

cell theory/teoría celular Explicación ampliamente aceptada de las relaciones entre las células y los seres vivos. (pág. 134)

cell wall/pared celular Capa rígida de material no vivo que rodea las células vegetales y las de algunos otros organismos. (pág. 139)

Celsius scale/escala Celsius Escala de temperaturas donde cero y 100 son las temperaturas a las que el agua se congela o hierve. (pág. 583)

Charles's law/ley de Charles Relación entre la temperatura y el volumen de un gas, a una presión constante; al aumentar la temperatura, aumenta el volumen. (pág. 66)

chemical bond/enlace químico Fuerza que une dos átomos. (pág. 44)

chemical change/cambio químico Transformación en la materia que produce nuevas sustancias. (pág. 31)

chemical property/propiedad química Característica que se observa cuando una sustancia interactúa con otra. (pág. 26)

chemistry/química Estudio de las propiedades y las transformaciones de la materia. (pág. 25)

chlorophyll/clorofila Sustancia que da su color verde a los cloroplastos y atrapa energía luminosa durante la fotosíntesis. (pág. 163)

chloroplast/cloroplasto Estructura de las células de las plantas y de algunos otros organismos que atrapa la energía de la luz solar y la utiliza para producir el alimento. (pág. 144)

chromatid/cromátida Cada uno de los dos bastones idénticos de un cromosoma. (pág. 172)

chromatin/cromatina Material celular que contiene ADN y transmite información genética. (pág. 141)

chromosome/cromosoma Estructura celular en forma de bastones, compuesta de cromatina condensada; contiene ADN, portador de la información genética que controla las características heredadas como son el color de los ojos y el grupo sanguíneo. (pág. 172)

chromosphere/cromosfera Capa intermedia de la atmósfera del Sol. (pág. 539)

cilia/cilios Estructuras de forma capilar que se prolongan por el exterior de las células y se mueven por ondas. (pág. 198)

cinder cone/cono de escorias Colina o montaña inclinada de forma cónica, compuesta de cenizas, escorias y bombas acumuladas alrededor de la abertura de un volcán. (pág. 388)

cirrus/cirros Nubes tenues y plumosas compuestas principalmente de cristales de hielo y formadas a grandes alturas, aproximadamente a más de 6 kilómetros de la tierra. (pág. 484)

classification/clasificación Proceso de agrupar objetos basándose en sus semejanzas. (pág. 184)

cleavage/exfoliación Capacidad de un mineral para fracturarse fácilmente en superficies planas. (pág. 335)

cnidarians/cnidarios Animales que usan células urticantes para capturar sus presas y defenderse, e ingieren sus alimentos por una cavidad central hueca. (pág. 224)

combustion/combustión Reacción rápida entre el oxígeno y un combustible, la cual produce energía térmica. (pág. 293)

comet/cometa Bola de hielo y polvo cuya órbita es una elipse larga y estrecha. (pág. 563)

community/comunidad Todas las diferentes poblaciones que conviven en una zona. (pág. 270)

composite volcano/volcán compuesto Montaña elevada y de forma cónica en la que las capas de lava se alternan con las de cenizas y otros materiales volcánicos. (pág. 388)

composting/compostaje Proceso mediante el cual los desechos y restos de seres vivos se descomponen en el suelo. (pág. 286)

compound/compuesto Sustancia formada por dos o más elementos combinados químicamente según una razón establecida. (pág. 28)

compound microscope/microscopio compuesto Microscopio de luz dotado de más de una lente. (pág. 132)

compression/compresión Tipo de esfuerzo que oprime las rocas hasta doblarlas o fragmentarlas. (pág. 359)

condensation/condensación Paso de la materia del estado gaseoso al líquido; también, proceso por el cual un gas, como el vapor de agua, se transforma en un líquido, como el agua. (págs. 77, 483)

conduction/conducción Transferencia de calor mediante los movimientos de un líquido. (pág. 470)

conjugation/conjugación Proceso en el que un organismo unicelular transfiere a otro parte de su material genético. (pág. 192)

conservation/conservación Uso racional de un recurso para evitar que se agote. (pág. 421)

consumer/consumidor Organismo que obtiene energía alimentándose de otros organismos. (pág. 281)

continental (air mass)/masa de aire continental Masa de aire seco que se forma sobre la tierra. (pág. 496)

contour line/curva de nivel Línea que une en un mapa topográfico los puntos de igual elevación. (pág. 592)

control rods/barras de control Varillas de cadmio usadas en los reactores nucleares para absorber los neutrones de la fisión. (pág. 309)

controlled experiment/experimento controlado Experimento donde todas las variables menos una se mantienen iguales. (pág. 12)

convection/convección Transferencia de calor mediante los movimientos de las corrientes de un fluido. (pág. 470)

convex lens/lente convexa Lente que tiene el centro más grueso que los bordes. (pág. 136)

core/núcleo Parte central del Sol donde se produce la fusión nuclear. (pág. 538)

Coriolis effect/efecto Coriolis Forma en que la rotación terrestre desvía hacia la derecha la dirección de los vientos del hemisferio norte y hacia la izquierda la de los vientos del hemisferio sur. (pág. 477)

corona/corona Capa externa de la atmósfera del Sol. (pág. 539)

cotyledon/cotiledón Hoja que sale de la semilla y en la que se almacena el alimento. (pág. 208)

crater/cráter Zona con forma de tazón que se origina alrededor de la abertura principal de un volcán. (pág. 375)

crop/buche Depósito interno de las aves donde almacenan los alimentos una vez tragados. (pág. 248)

crust/corteza Capa rocosa que forma la superficie externa de la Tierra. (pág. 226)

crustacean/crustáceo Artrópodo con dos o tres secciones corporales, cinco o más pares de patas, dos pares de antenas y normalmente tres pares de apéndices para masticar. (pág. 234)

crystal/cristal Sólido cuyos átomos están dispuestos según un patrón que se repite una y otra vez. (pág. 332)

crystalline solid/sólido cristalino Sustancia compuesta de cristales cuyas partículas están dispuestas según un patrón regular que se repite. (pág. 58)

cumulus/cúmulos Nubes que se forman a menos de 2 kilómetros de la tierra y parecen montones de algodón redondos y esponjosos. (pág. 484)

cyclone/ciclón Remolino de aire con centro de baja presión. (pág. 501)

cytokinesis/citocinesis Etapa final del ciclo celular en la que el citoplasma se divide y distribuye los organelos a cada una de las dos nuevas células. (pág. 173)

cytoplasm/citoplasma Región celular situada dentro de la membrana (en las procariotas) o bien entre ésta y el núcleo (en las eucariotas); contiene un material gelatinoso y los organelos. (pág. 141)

data/datos Hechos, cifras y otras evidencias recogidos en un experimento. (pág. 13)

death rate/índice de mortalidad Número de muertes ocurridas durante un período de tiempo determinado. (pág. 275)

decomposer/descomponedor Organismo que separa las grandes sustancias químicas de los seres muertos en otras más pequeñas, devolviendo a la tierra y al agua materiales importantes. (págs. 193, 282)

deformation/deformación Cambio en el volumen o la forma de la corteza terrestre. (pág. 359)

delta/delta Forma del relieve compuesta por los sedimentos que los ríos depositan al llegar a un océano o un lago. (pág. 111)

density/densidad Medida de la cantidad de masa de una sustancia que ocupa un volumen determinado. (págs. 335, 445)

deposition/sedimentación Proceso por el cual los sedimentos dejan el agua o el viento que los traslada, depositándose en un nuevo lugar. (págs. 108, 343)

desalination/desalinización Proceso de obtener agua dulce a partir del agua del mar extrayéndole la sal. (pág. 423)

dew point/punto de condensación Temperatura a la que se inicia la condensación. (pág. 483)

diaphragm/diafragma Músculo grande y con forma de bóveda que tiene una importante función en la respiración. (pág. 252)

diffusion/difusión Proceso por el que las moléculas pasan de una zona de alta concentración a otra de concentración menor. (pág. 159)

dike/dique Bloque de roca volcánica que se forma cuando el magma atraviesa los estratos rocosos. (pág. 387)

directly proportional/directamente proporcionales Término empleado para describir la relación entre dos variables cuya gráfica es una línea recta que pasa por el punto (0,0). (pág. 70)

divide/divisoria Elevación de tierra que separa un área de drenaje o cuenca hidrográfica de otra. (pág. 405)

DNA (*DeoxyriboNucleic Acid*)/ADN (*Acido DesoxirriboNucleico*) Material genético que contiene la información de un organismo y se transmite de padres a hijos. (pág. 150)

dormant/atenuado Se dice del volcán que no da señales de entrar en erupción en un futuro próximo. (pág. 380)

drought/sequía Escasez de agua ocasionada por períodos prolongados de bajas precipitaciones en una zona determinada. (pág. 490)

earthquake/terremoto Sacudidas producidas por los movimientos de las rocas debajo de la superficie terrestre. (pág. 358)

echinoderm/equinodermo Invertebrado de simetría radial y con esqueleto interno espinoso que vive en el fondo oceánico. (pág. 235)

ecology/ecología Estudio de las interacciones de los seres vivos entre sí y con su medio ambiente. (pág. 270)

ecosystem/ecosistema Todas las cosas vivas o no que interactúan en una zona. (pág. 266)

ectotherm/ectotermo Animal cuyo cuerpo no produce suficiente calor interno. (pág. 238)

efficiency/eficiencia Porcentaje de energía usada por un aparato para realizar un trabajo. (pág. 314)

egg/óvulo Célula sexual femenina. (pág. 150)

El Niño/el Niño Fenómeno climático anormal que tiene lugar en períodos de 2 a 7 años en el océano Pacífico, causando cambios en los vientos, las corrientes y los patrones meteorológicos que pueden dar origen a transformaciones climáticas dramáticas. (pág. 522)

electrode/electrodo Lámina de metal que adquiere o pierde electrones durante la electrólisis. (pág. 48)

electrolysis/electrólisis Proceso por el cual una corriente eléctrica rompe los enlaces químicos. (pág. 48)

electromagnetic wave/onda electromagnética Forma de energía que puede propagarse a través del espacio. (pág. 462)

element/elemento Sustancia que no puede descomponerse en otras por medios químicos o físicos. (pág. 27)

ellipse/elipse Círculo alargado o de forma ovalada; forma de la órbita de los planetas. (pág. 535)

embryo/embrión Organismo en desarrollo que se forma a partir de un cigoto. (pág. 208)

emigration/emigración Abandono de una población. (pág. 276)

endoplasmic reticulum/retículo endoplásmico Estructura celular que forma un laberinto de pasadizos en el que las proteínas y otros materiales son trasladados de una parte de la célula a otra. (pág. 144)

endoskeleton/endoesqueleto Esqueleto interno. (pág. 235)

endospore/endospora Célula inactiva pequeña, redondeada y de paredes gruesas que se forma en el interior de las células de las bacterias. (pág. 192)

endotherm/endotermo Animal cuyo cuerpo regula su temperatura controlando el calor interno que produce. (pág. 238)

energy/energía Capacidad para realizar un trabajo o producir cambios. (pág. 25)

energy conservation/conservación de la energía Proceso de reducir el consumo de energía. (pág. 313)

energy transformation/transformación de la energía Cualquier cambio de una forma de energía a otra. (pág. 292)

epicenter/epicentro Lugar de la superficie terrestre situado exactamente sobre el foco de un terremoto. (pág. 368)

equator/ecuador Línea imaginaria que circunda la Tierra a medio camino entre los polos norte y sur. (pág. 591)

erosion/erosión Proceso por el cual el agua, el hielo, el viento o la gravedad desplazan fragmentos de roca y tierra. (págs. 108, 343)

estimate/estimación Cálculo aproximado de un número basándose en supuestos razonables. (pág. 274)

eukaryote/eucariota Organismo cuyas células contienen un núcleo y otras estructuras. (pág. 145)

evacuate/evacuar Abandonar temporalmente un lugar. (pág. 510)

evaporation/evaporación Proceso en el que la vaporización sólo ocurre en la superficie de un líquido; también, proceso por el cual las moléculas de la superficie de un líquido, como el agua, absorben suficiente energía como para pasar al estado gaseoso, como el vapor de agua. (págs. 76, 398, 481)

exoskeleton/exoesqueleto Esqueleto externo. (pág. 231)

exosphere/exosfera Capa exterior de la termosfera que se extiende hacia el espacio. (pág. 456)

external stimulus/estímulo externo Cambio producido en el entorno de un organismo, provocándole una reacción. (pág. 124)

extinct/extinto Se aplica al tipo de organismo que ya no existe en el planeta; también se dice del volcán que tiene pocas probabilidades de entrar de nuevo en erupción. (pág. 380)

extrusive rock/roca efusiva Roca ígnea que se forma a partir de la lava de la superficie terrestre. (pág. 342)

fault/falla Fractura o grieta en la litosfera terrestre a lo largo de la cual se desplazan las rocas. (pág. 360)

fault-block mountain/montaña de bloques fallados Montaña formada en el lugar donde una falla normal levanta un bloque rocoso. (pág. 362)

fermentation/fermentación Proceso por el cual las células degradan las moléculas para liberar energía sin usar oxígeno. (pág. 167)

fertilization/fecundación Unión de un espermatozoide y un óvulo. (pág. 208)

flagellum/flagelo Estructura larga y con forma de látigo que sirve a los organismos unicelulares para moverse. (pág. 191)

flash flood/inundación repentina Inundación súbita y violenta que ocurre a pocas horas o incluso minutos de una fuerte tormenta de lluvia. (pág. 516)

flood/inundación Desbordamiento del cauce de un río debido al aumento del volumen de sus aguas. (págs. 111, 406)

flood plain/llanura aluvial Valle extenso y plano por el cual discurre un río. (pág. 109)

flower/flor Estructura reproductora de las angiospermas. (pág. 209)

focus/foco Zona situada debajo de la superficie terrestre donde las rocas sometidas a esfuerzo se rompen, provocando un terremoto. (pág. 368)

fold/pliegue Doblez de las rocas que se produce en lugares donde se comprime parte de la corteza terrestre. (pág. 363)

food chain/cadena alimenticia Secuencia de sucesos en la que un organismo se alimenta de otro, dando lugar a un flujo de energía entre los organismos afectados. (pág. 282)

food web/red alimenticia Patrón de cadenas alimenticias superpuestas de un ecosistema. (pág. 284)

footwall/labio inferior Bloque rocoso que compone la mitad inferior de una falla. (pág. 360)

force/fuerza Impulso o atracción ejercido sobre un objeto. (pág. 98)

fossil fuel/combustible fósil Sustancia rica en energía (como el carbón, el petróleo o el gas natural), formada a partir de restos de organismos. (pág. 295)

fracture/fractura Aspecto de un mineral al romperse de forma irregular. (pág. 335)

freezing/congelación Paso del estado líquido al sólido. (pág. 76)

front/frente Zona donde dos masas de aire se encuentran sin mezclarse. (pág. 499)

fruit/fruto En las angiospermas, ovario maduro y otras estructuras que encierran una o más semillas. (pág. 210)

fuel/combustible Material que libera energía cuando arde. (pág. 293)

fuel rod/barra de combustible Varilla de uranio sometida a fisión en un reactor nuclear. (pág. 308)

gamete/gameto Espermatozoide u óvulo. (pág. 208)

gas/gas Estado de la materia que carece de forma y volumen definidos. (pág. 60)

gas giants/gigantes gaseosos Nombre dado a los primeros cuatro planetas exteriores: Júpiter, Saturno, Urano y Neptuno. (pág. 552)

gemstone/gema Mineral duro y colorido de brillo intenso o vítreo. (pág. 336)

gene/gen Segmento de ADN de un cromosoma que lleva codificado un rasgo específico. (pág. 150)

genus/género Agrupamiento clasificatorio que comprende varias especies semejantes y de parentesco cercano. (pág. 185)

geocentric system/sistema geocéntrico Descripción del sistema solar en la que todos los planetas giran alrededor de la Tierra. (pág. 533)

geologist/geólogo Científico que estudia las fuerzas que forman y configuran el planeta Tierra. (pág. 327)

geology/geología Estudio de la masa terrestre. (pág. 327)

geosynchronous orbit/órbita geosíncrona Órbita de un satélite que gira alrededor de la Tierra al ritmo de rotación de ésta. (pág. 568)

geothermal energy/energía geotérmica Energía del calor del interior de la Tierra traída por el agua o el vapor que ha sido calentado por el magma. (págs. 303, 382)

gestation period/período de gestación Lapso de tiempo transcurrido entre la fecundación y el nacimiento de un mamífero. (pág. 254)

geyser/géiser Tipo de manantial termal que, debido a que aumenta la presión subterránea, arroja de forma intermitente un surtidor de agua y vapor. (pág. 382)

gill/branquia Órgano respiratorio de ciertos organismos que extrae oxígeno del agua. (pág. 228)

gizzard/molleja Parte musculosa y de paredes gruesas del estómago de las aves donde se estrujan y trituran los alimentos parcialmente digeridos. (pág. 248)

global winds/vientos globales Vientos constantes que soplan desde direcciones específicas a través de largas distancias. (pág. 477)

Golgi body/aparato de Golgi Estructura celular que recibe del retículo endoplásmico proteínas y otras sustancias recién formadas, las empaqueta y las distribuye a otras partes de la célula. (pág. 144)

grain/grano Partícula de un mineral u otra roca que caracteriza su textura. (pág. 341)

graph/gráfica Diagrama que muestra la relación entre dos variables. (pág. 68)

gravity/gravedad Fuerza que atrae objetos entre sí. (pág. 535)

greenhouse effect/efecto invernadero Proceso mediante el cual el calor es atrapado en la atmósfera por el vapor de agua, el dióxido de carbono, el metano y otros gases que forman un "cobertor" alrededor de la Tierra. (págs. 465, 548)

habitat/hábitat Lugar donde vive un organismo y que le proporciona lo que necesita para sobrevivir. (pág. 267)

hanging wall/labio superior Bloque rocoso que compone la mitad superior de una falla. (pág. 360)

headwaters/cabecera Conjunto de los numerosos y pequeños cursos de agua que confluyen en el nacimiento de un río. (pág. 109)

heat/calor Desplazamiento de energía térmica de una sustancia a otra. (pág. 469)

heliocentric system/sistema heliocéntrico Descripción del sistema solar en la que todos los planetas giran alrededor del Sol. (pág. 534)

herbivore/herbívoro Animal que se alimenta sólo de plantas. (pág. 219)

heredity/herencia Transmisión de rasgos de padres a hijos. (pág. 149)

heterotroph/heterótrofo Organismo incapaz de sintetizar su propio alimento. (pág. 128)

homeostasis/homeostasis Proceso mediante el cual el entorno interno del organismo se mantiene estable a pesar de los cambios producidos en el ambiente externo. (pág. 129)

hormone/hormona Producto químico de una glándula endocrina que acelera o desacelera las actividades de un órgano o tejido; también, sustancia química que afecta al crecimiento y desarrollo de las plantas. (pág. 210)

host/huésped Organismo que proporciona una fuente de energía o un ambiente adecuado para la vida de un virus u otro organismo. (pág. 110)

humidity/humedad Medida de la cantidad de vapor de agua presente en el aire. (pág. 482)

hurricane/huracán Tormenta tropical con vientos mínimos de 119 kilómetros por hora y generalmente de unos 600 kilómetros de diámetro. (pág. 508)

hydrocarbon/hidrocarburo Compuesto que contiene átomos de carbono y de hidrógeno. (pág. 295)

hydroelectric power/energía hidroeléctrica Electricidad producida por el movimiento del agua al descender por una cascada o presa. (pág. 302)

hypothesis/hipótesis Explicación posible a una serie de observaciones o respuesta a una pregunta científica; capaz de ser verificada. (pág. 12)

igneous rock/roca ígnea Tipo de roca que se forma al enfriarse las rocas fundidas en o debajo de la superficie terrestre. (pág. 342)

immigration/inmigración Traslado a una población. (pág. 276)

impermeable/impermeable Característica del material que no puede ser atravesado fácilmente por el agua, como la arcilla o el granito. (pág. 413)

inertia/inercia Tendencia de un objeto en movimiento a avanzar en línea recta o de un objeto estacionario a quedarse en el mismo sitio. (pág. 535)

inexhaustible resources/recursos inagotables Cualquier cosa viva o no del medio ambiente que no puede agotarse. (pág. 299)

inference/inferencia Interpretación de una observación basándose en evidencias y conocimientos previos. (pág. 11)

infrared radiation/radiación infrarroja Forma de energía cuya longitud de onda es mayor que la de la luz visible. (pág. 463)

inner core/núcleo interior Densa esfera de hierro y níquel sólidos del centro de la Tierra. (pág. 328)

insect/insecto Artrópodo cuyo cuerpo tiene tres secciones, seis patas, un par de antenas y normalmente uno o dos pares de alas. (pág. 232)

insulation/aislante Material de construcción que impide la transferencia de calor entre el aire interior y el exterior. (pág. 315)

internal stimulus/estímulo interno Cambio producido en el interior de un organismo, como el hambre o la sed, que le provoca una reacción. (pág. 124)

International System of Units/Sistema Internacional de Unidades Sistema de medidas basado en múltiplos de diez y en medidas establecidas de masa, longitud y tiempo. (pág. 35)

interphase/interfase Etapa del ciclo celular que ocurre antes de la división; en ella, la célula crece, copia el ADN y se prepara para dividirse. (pág. 171)

intrusive rock/roca intrusiva Roca ígnea que se forma al solidificarse el magma bajo la superficie terrestre. (pág. 342)

invertebrate/invertebrado Animal sin columna vertebral. (pág. 220)

ionosphere/ionosfera Parte inferior de la termosfera donde se encuentran partículas cargadas eléctricamente llamadas iones. (pág. 456)

irrigation/riego Proceso de suministrar agua a la tierra para que sea apta para el cultivo agrícola. (pág. 400)

isobars/isobaras Líneas que unen en un mapa los lugares que tienen igual presión atmosférica. (pág. 522)

isotherms/isotermas Líneas que unen en un mapa los lugares que tienen igual temperatura. (pág. 522)

jet streams/corrientes de chorro Bandas de vientos de alta velocidad a unos 10 kilómetros de la superficie terrestre. (pág. 480)

Kelvin scale/escala Kelvin Escala de temperaturas donde cero es la temperatura a la que no puede extraerse más energía de la materia. (pág. 110)

kidney/riñón Órgano principal del aparato excretor; elimina del cuerpo la urea, el exceso de agua y algunos otros materiales de desecho. (pág. 243)

land breeze/brisa terrestre Corriente de aire que va desde la tierra hasta una masa de agua. (pág. 476)

larva/larva Forma inmadura de un animal de aspecto muy distinto al del adulto. (pág. 234)

latitude/latitud Distancia expresada en grados al norte o al sur del ecuador. (pág. 478)

lava/lava Magma que llega a la superficie; también, rocas formadas al solidificarse la lava líquida. (pág. 335)

lava flow/colada de lava Zona que cubre la lava al salir de la boca de un volcán. (pág. 375)

leaf/hoja Órgano de las plantas vasculares donde se realiza la fotosíntesis. (pág. 205)

levee/dique Muro alargado formado por los sedimentos depositados junto al cauce de un río. (págs. 112, 407)

lightning/rayo Chispa repentina o descarga de energía provocada por cargas eléctricas que saltan entre distintas partes de una nube o entre una nube y la tierra. (pág. 504)

limiting factor/factor limitante Elemento ambiental que impide el crecimiento de una población. (pág. 277)

linear/lineal Término empleado para describir la relación entre variables cuya gráfica es una línea recta. (pág. 105)

liquid/líquido Estado de la materia que tiene su volumen definido, pero no su forma. (pág. 58)

lithosphere/litosfera Capa rígida formada por la parte superior del manto y la corteza terrestres; una de las cuatro esferas en que los científicos dividen la Tierra. (pág. 329)

local wind/viento local Viento que recorre distancias cortas. (pág. 474)

luster/brillo Forma en que un mineral refleja la luz que recibe sobre su superficie. (pág. 334)

lysosome/lisosoma Estructura celular pequeña y esférica que contiene sustancias químicas capaces de separar grandes partículas de alimento en otras más pequeñas. (pág. 145)

magma/magma Mezcla fundida de gases, agua y sustancias que forman las rocas; compone parte del manto terrestre. (pág. 335)

magma chamber/cámara magmática Cavidad del interior de un volcán donde se acumula el magma. (pág. 375)

magnification/aumento Capacidad de hacer que los objetos parezcan más grandes de lo que son. (pág. 136)

magnitude/magnitud Medida de la fuerza de un terremoto según las ondas sísmicas y los movimientos a lo largo de las fallas. (pág. 371)

mammary gland/glándula mamaria Órgano que produce la leche con la que los mamíferos alimentan a sus crías. (pág. 253)

manipulated variable/variable manipulada Único factor que un científico cambia durante un experimento; también se llama variable independiente. (pág. 12)

mantle/manto Capa de material sólido y caliente situada entre la corteza y el núcleo de la Tierra. (pág. 328)

maritime (air mass)/masa de aire marítimo Masa de aire húmedo que se forma sobre los océanos. (pág. 496)

marsupial/marsupial Mamífero cuyas crías nacen en un estado de desarrollo temprano que normalmente completan en una bolsa del cuerpo de la madre. (pág. 254)

mass/masa Medida de la cantidad de materia que hay en un objeto. (pág. 35)

matter/materia Todo lo que tiene masa y ocupa un sitio. (pág. 24)

meander/meandro Curva muy cerrada formada en el curso sinuoso de un río en la llanura aluvial. (pág. 111)

meltdown/fusión del núcleo de un reactor Estado peligroso ocasionado por el sobrecalentamiento del interior de un reactor nuclear. (pág. 309)

melting/fusión Paso de la materia del estado sólido al líquido. (pág. 75)

melting point/punto de fusión Temperatura a la cual una sustancia pasa de sólida a líquida. (pág. 58)

Mercalli scale/escala de Mercalli Escala que evalúa los terremotos según la intensidad y los daños causados. (pág. 371)

mercury barometer/barómetro de mercurio Instrumento que mide los cambios en la presión atmosférica. Consta de un tubo de cristal cerrado en uno de sus extremos y parcialmente lleno de mercurio, y en el que el extremo abierto se encuentra inmerso en un plato con mercurio. La presión atmosférica empuja al mercurio del plato, haciendo que suba por el tubo. (pág. 446)

mesosphere/mesosfera Capa intermedia de la atmósfera terrestre en la que la mayoría de los meteoroides se consumen. (pág. 452)

metamorphic rock/roca metamórfica Tipo de roca que se forma a partir de otra roca preexistente modificada por el calor, la presión o las reacciones químicas. (pág. 345)

metamorphosis/metamorfosis Proceso en el cual el cuerpo de un animal sufre cambios radicales durante su ciclo vital. (pág. 234)

meteor/meteoro Rayo de luz en el cielo, producto de la combustión de un meteoroide en la atmósfera terrestre. (pág. 565)

meteorite/meteorito Meteoroide que alcanza la superficie terrestre. (pág. 565)

meteoroid/meteoroide Pedazo de roca o polvo en el espacio. (pág. 565)

meteorologist/meteorólogo Científico que estudia las causas del estado del tiempo y trata de predecirlo. (pág. 520)

microscope/microscopio Instrumento que amplifica la imagen de objetos pequeños. (pág. 132)

mineral/mineral Sólido inorgánico de origen natural que tiene estructura de cristal y composición química definida. (pág. 331)

mitochondria/mitocondrias Estructuras celulares con forma de bastón que producen gran parte de la energía necesaria para efectuar las funciones celulares. (pág. 141)

mitosis/mitosis Etapa del ciclo celular durante la cual el núcleo se divide en dos y una copia del ADN se reparte a cada célula hija. (pág. 172)

mixture/mezcla Asociación de dos o más sustancias pero sin combinarlas químicamente. (pág. 28)

molecule/molécula Partícula formada por dos o más átomos unidos entre sí. (pág. 44)

mollusk/molusco Invertebrado de cuerpo blando y no segmentado; la mayoría se protege con conchas exteriores duras. (pág. 227)

moment magnitude scale/escala de magnitud de momento sísmico Escala que evalúa los terremotos estimando la energía total que liberan. (pág. 372)

monotreme/monotrema Mamífero que pone huevos. (pág. 254)

monsoons/monzones Brisas marinas y terrestres que soplan sobre una región extensa y cambian de dirección según las estaciones. (pág. 476)

motion/movimiento Estado en el que cambia la distancia entre un objeto y otro. (pág. 87)

mouth/desembocadura Lugar donde un río se encuentra con otra masa de agua. (pág. 111)

net force/fuerza neta Fuerza total ejercida sobre un objeto cuando se suman todas las fuerzas individuales que actúan sobre él. (pág. 99)

nitrogen fixation/fijación del nitrógeno Proceso de conversión del gas nitrógeno libre en una forma aprovechable. (pág. 285)

nonlinear/no lineal Término empleado para describir la relación entre variables cuya gráfica no es una línea recta. (pág. 105)

nonrenewable resource/recurso no renovable Recurso natural que no es reemplazado una vez utilizado. (pág. 295)

normal fault/falla normal Tipo de falla donde el labio superior se desliza hacia abajo; está provocada por la tensión de la corteza. (pág. 360)

nuclear fission/fisión nuclear División del núcleo de un átomo en dos más pequeños. (pág. 307)

nuclear fusion/fusión nuclear Unión de dos núcleos atómicos para producir uno más grande, como ocurre al unirse dos átomos de hidrógeno para formar helio, liberando energía. (págs. 310, 538)

nucleus/núcleo Centro de control que dirige las actividades de la célula y determina las características de ésta; también, parte central del átomo que contiene protones y normalmente neutrones. (págs. 140, 307)

nymph/ninfa Etapa de la metamorfosis gradual en la que el organismo normalmente se parece al insecto adulto. (pág. 234)

O

observation/observación Uso de al menos uno de los cinco sentidos para obtener información. (pág. 11)

occluded/ocluido Aislado o cerrado, como cuando la masa de aire cálido de un frente ocluido queda aislada de la tierra por el aire inferior más fresco. (pág. 501)

omnivore/omnívoro Animal que se alimenta tanto de plantas como de animales. (pág. 219)

organ/órgano Estructura corporal compuesta por diferentes clases de tejidos. (pág. 147)

organ system/sistema de órganos Grupo de órganos que realizan conjuntamente una función principal del cuerpo. (pág. 147)

organelle/organelo Estructura celular minúscula que efectúa una función determinada en la célula. (pág. 139)

organism/organismo Ser vivo. (pág. 122)

osmosis/ósmosis Difusión de moléculas del agua a través de una membrana selectivamente permeable. (pág. 160)

outer core/núcleo exterior Capa de hierro y níquel fundidos que rodea el núcleo interior de la Tierra. (pág. 328)

ovary/ovario Órgano del sistema reproductor femenino donde se producen los óvulos y el estrógeno; también en las plantas, estructura protectora que contiene las semillas en desarrollo. (pág. 209)

ovule/óvulo Estructura de las plantas con semillas que contiene una célula sexual femenina. (pág. 209)

oxbow lake/meandro abandonado Masa de agua aislada y de forma semilunar que permanece tras crear un río un nuevo cauce. (pág. 111)

ozone/ozono Forma de oxígeno que tiene tres átomos en cada molécula en lugar de los dos habituales. (pág. 436)

P

P wave/onda P Tipo de onda sísmica que comprime y expande el suelo. (pág. 369)

pahoehoe/cordada Tipo caliente y rápido de lava que al solidificarse forma tubos lisos con forma de cuerda. (pág. 378)

Pangaea/Pangea Nombre de una única masa continental que se fragmentó hace 225 millones de años, dando origen a los continentes actuales. (pág. 355)

parasite/parásito Organismo que vive en la superficie o en el interior de un huésped, provocándole daños. (pág. 199)

passive transport/transporte pasivo Movimiento de materiales a través de la membrana celular sin usar energía. (pág. 161)

permeable/permeable Característica del material que deja pasar el agua con facilidad, como la arena o la grava. (pág. 413)

pesticide/pesticida Sustancia química cuyo fin es destruir insectos y otros organismos que dañan los cultivos. (pág. 426)

petrochemical/producto petroquímico Compuesto obtenido del petróleo. (pág. 297)

petroleum/petróleo Combustible fósil líquido. (pág. 296)

photochemical smog/smog fotoquímico Bruma pardusca, mezcla de ozono y otras sustancias químicas, que se forma cuando los óxidos de nitrógeno, los hidrocarburos y otros contaminantes reaccionan entre sí en presencia de luz solar. (pág. 442)

photosphere/fotosfera Capa interior de la atmósfera del Sol. (pág. 539)

photosynthesis/fotosíntesis Proceso por el cual las plantas y algunos otros organismos atrapan la energía luminosa y la utilizan para elaborar su alimento a partir del dióxido de carbono y del agua. (pág. 163)

physical change/cambio físico Cambio que altera la forma o el aspecto de un material, pero sin transformarlo en otra sustancia. (pág. 30)

physical property/propiedad física Característica de un material que puede observarse sin necesidad de transformarlo en otra sustancia. (pág. 26)

pipe/chimenea Tubo alargado por el que se desplaza el magma desde la cámara magmática hasta la superficie terrestre. (pág. 375)

placenta/placenta Membrana que representa el nexo entre el embrión o feto en desarrollo y la madre. (pág. 255)

placental mammal/mamífero placentario Mamífero que se desarrolla en el cuerpo de la madre hasta que sus sistemas corporales pueden funcionar independientemente. (pág. 255)

plate/placa Sección de la litosfera que se desplaza lentamente sobre la astenosfera, llevando consigo fragmentos de la corteza continental y oceánica. (pág. 354)

plate boundary/borde de placas Grieta en la litosfera donde dos placas terrestres se cruzan. (pág. 356)

plateau/meseta Forma del relieve que tiene una superficie bastante llana y se encuentra muy por encima del nivel del mar. (pág. 365)

polar (air mass)/masa de aire polar Masa de aire frío de alta presión atmosférica que se forma al norte de los 50° de latitud norte o al sur de los 50° de latitud sur. (pág. 496)

pollen/polen Partículas diminutas producidas por las plantas y que contienen las células microscópicas que posteriormente se convierten en células sexuales masculinas. (pág. 209)

pollutant/contaminante Sustancia dañina del aire, agua o suelo. (pág. 440)

population/población Todos los miembros de una especie de una zona determinada. (pág. 269)

population density/densidad de población Número de individuos que habitan un lugar específico. (pág. 273)

pores/poros Aberturas diminutas en o entre las partículas de roca y tierra que pueden contener aire o agua. (pág. 413)

precipitation/precipitación Formas del agua como lluvia, nieve, aguanieve o granizo que proceden de las nubes y llegan a la superficie terrestre. (págs. 398, 487)

predator/depredador Carnívoro que caza y mata otros animales para alimentarse de ellos y que cuenta con adaptaciones que le ayudan a capturar sus presas. (pág. 219)

pressure/presión Fuerza que se ejerce sobre una zona o superficie; también, fuerza del empuje de un gas hacia el exterior dividida entre el área de las paredes del recipiente. (págs. 63, 445)

prey/presa Animal del que se alimenta un depredador. (pág. 219)

prime meridian/primer meridiano Línea que traza un medio círculo desde el polo norte al polo sur pasando por Greenwich, Inglaterra. (pág. 663)

producer/productor Organismo que puede elaborar su propio alimento. (pág. 281)

prokaryote/procariota Organismo cuyas células carecen de núcleo y de otras estructuras. (pág. 145)

prominence/protuberancia Arco de gas que sobresale de la superficie solar, enlazando diferentes zonas de las regiones con manchas solares. (pág. 542)

protozoan/protozoario Protista con características animales. (pág. 197)

pseudopod/pseudópodo "Pie falso" o proyección temporal de la membrana celular que emplean algunos protozoarios para desplazarse y alimentarse. (pág. 197)

psychrometer/psicrómetro Instrumento usado para medir la humedad relativa; consta de un termómetro de cubeta húmeda y otro de cubeta seca. (pág. 482)

pupa/pupa Segunda etapa de la metamorfosis completa en la que el insecto, envuelto en una cubierta protectora, se transforma gradualmente de larva en adulto. (pág. 234)

pyroclastic flow/flujo piroclástico Expulsión de cenizas, escorias, bombas y gases durante una erupción volcánica explosiva. (pág. 379)

radial symmetry/simetría radial Cualidad de poseer muchos ejes de simetría que pasan por un punto central. (pág. 221)

radiation/radiación Transferencia directa de energía a través del espacio vacío por medio de ondas electromagnéticas. (pág. 462)

radula/rádula Cinta flexible de dientes minúsculos de los moluscos. (pág. 228)

rain gauge/pluviómetro Instrumento usado para medir la cantidad de precipitaciones; consta de una lata que tiene en su extremo abierto un embudo colector y en su interior un tubo de acumulación y una escala medidora. (pág. 489)

reactor vessel/nave del reactor Parte del reactor nuclear donde tiene lugar la fisión. (pág. 308)

recharge/recarga Nueva aportación de agua que recibe el acuífero desde la superficie. (pág. 110)

reference point/punto de referencia Objeto o lugar que se usa como punto de comparación para determinar si un objeto está en movimiento. (pág. 88)

refinery/refinería Planta donde el petróleo bruto se separa en combustibles y otros productos. (pág. 297)

relative humidity/humedad relativa Porcentaje de vapor de agua que hay en el aire frente a la cantidad máxima que éste puede contener a esa temperatura. (pág. 482)

renewable resource/recurso renovable Recurso restituido de manera natural en un período de tiempo relativamente corto. (pág. 299)

replication/replicación Proceso por el cual una célula hace una copia del ADN de su núcleo. (pág. 171)

reproduce/reproducir Procrear descendientes parecidos a los progenitores. (pág. 125)

reserve/reserva Depósito conocido de combustibles. (pág. 298)

reservoir/embalse Lago natural o artificial donde se almacena agua para el aprovechamiento humano. (pág. 410)

resolution/resolución Capacidad de diferenciar con claridad cada una de las partes de un objeto. (pág. 137)

respiration/respiración Proceso por el cual las células degradan las moléculas simples de los alimentos para liberar la energía que contienen. (pág. 166)

responding variable/variable de respuesta Factor que se altera como resultado de los cambios producidos en la variable manipulada de un experimento. (pág. 12)

response/respuesta Acto o cambio de conducta que siguen a un estímulo. (pág. 125)

retrograde rotation/rotación retrógrada Movimiento giratorio de un planeta de este a oeste, en sentido opuesto al de la rotación de la mayoría de los planetas y las lunas. (pág. 547)

reverse fault/falla inversa Tipo de falla donde el labio superior se desliza hacia arriba; está provocada por la compresión de la corteza. (pág. 361)

revolution/revolución Movimiento de un objeto alrededor de otro. (pág. 544)

ribosome/ribosoma Estructura diminuta del citoplasma celular en la que se elaboran las proteínas. (pág. 144)

Richter scale/escala de Richter Escala que evalúa las ondas sísmicas según las mediciones de un sismógrafo mecánico. (pág. 371)

river/río Corriente grande de agua. (pág. 404)

rock/roca Material que forma la superficie dura de la Tierra. (págs. 326, 340)

rock cycle/ciclo de las rocas Serie de procesos ocurridos en la superficie y en el interior de la Tierra que transforman lentamente rocas de una clase en otra. (pág. 346)

root/raíz Parte vegetal subterránea que fija las plantas al suelo y absorbe agua y nutrientes de éste. (pág. 208)

rotation/rotación Movimiento giratorio de un planeta alrededor de su eje. (pág. 544)

S waves/ondas S Tipo de ondas sísmicas que mueven el suelo de arriba a abajo o de un lado a otro. (pág. 369)

satellite/satélite Cualquier objeto que gira alrededor de otro en el espacio. (pág. 567)

saturated zone/zona saturada Capa de roca o tierra permeables en la que las grietas y los poros están totalmente llenos de agua. (pág. 413)

scale/escala Relaciona la distancia en el mapa con la correspondiente de la superficie terrestre. (pág. 662)

scattering/dispersión Reflexión de la luz en todas las direcciones. (pág. 464)

science/ciencia Estudio del mundo natural. (pág. 10)

scientific inquiry/investigación científica Diversidad de métodos con los que los científicos estudian el mundo natural. (pág. 10)

scientific law/ley científica Afirmación que describe lo que los científicos esperan que ocurra cada vez que se dan una serie determinada de condiciones. (pág. 16)

scientific theory/teoría científica Concepto científico comprobado que explica una gran variedad de observaciones. (pág. 10)

sea breeze/brisa marina Corriente de aire que va desde un océano o lago hasta la tierra. (pág. 476)

sediment/sedimentos Partículas sólidas y pequeñas de material procedente de rocas u organismos que son trasladadas por el agua o el viento, dando origen a la erosión y la sedimentación. (págs. 108, 343)

sedimentary rock/roca sedimentaria Tipo de roca que se forma cuando las partículas de otras rocas o los restos vegetales y animales se comprimen y cementan entre sí. (pág. 343)

seed/semilla Estructura vegetal que contiene una planta en desarrollo envuelta en una cubierta protectora. (pág. 208)

seismic wave/onda sísmica Vibración que se propaga por la Tierra llevando consigo la energía liberada durante un terremoto. (págs. 327, 368)

seismograph/sismógrafo Aparato que registra los movimientos que producen en el suelo las ondas sísmicas al desplazarse por la Tierra. (pág. 370)

selective breeding/apareamiento dirigido Proceso de seleccionar algunos organismos con rasgos deseables para usarlos como progenitores de la siguiente generación. (pág. 151)

selectively permeable/selectivamente permeable Propiedad de la membrana celular que permite el paso de ciertas sustancias e impide el paso de otras. (pág. 158)

sexual reproduction/reproducción sexual Proceso en el que se combina el material genético de dos progenitores para originar un nuevo organismo diferente a ambos. (pág. 150)

shearing/cizallamiento Tipo de esfuerzo que empuja una masa rocosa en sentidos opuestos. (pág. 359)

shield volcano/volcán en escudo Montaña ancha, de pendiente suave y compuesta por capas de lava procedentes de erupciones no explosivas. (pág. 388)

silica/sílice Material compuesto de dos elementos, silicio y oxígeno; se encuentra en el magma. (pág. 377)

sill/reborde Bloque de rocas volcánicas que se forma al introducirse el magma entre las capas rocosas. (pág. 387)

solar energy/energía solar Energía del Sol. (pág. 299)

solar flare/erupción solar Explosión de gas hidrógeno de la superficie del Sol que ocurre al unirse repentinamente arcos de las regiones con manchas solares. (pág. 542)

solar system/sistema solar Gran sistema planetario que consta de la combinación de muchos objetos y sistemas planetarios más pequeños. (pág. 534)

solar wind/viento solar Corriente de partículas cargadas eléctricamente, producida por la corona del Sol. (pág. 540)

solid/sólido Estado de la materia que tiene volumen y forma definidos. (pág. 57)

species/especie Grupo de organismos parecidos cuyos miembros pueden aparearse entre sí y tener descendencia fértil. (pág. 185)

speed/rapidez Distancia que recorre un objeto durante una unidad de tiempo. (pág. 90)

sperm cell/espermatozoide Célula sexual masculina. (pág. 150)

spontaneous generation/generación espontánea Idea errónea de que los seres vivos surgen de fuentes no vivientes. (pág. 125)

spore/espora Célula diminuta capaz de crecer y convertirse en un nuevo organismo. (pág. 201)

spring/manantial Lugar donde el agua subterránea sale a borbotones o emana por las grietas de las rocas. (pág. 414)

stamen/estambre Parte reproductora masculina de las flores. (pág. 209)

stem/tallo Órgano que sostiene las plantas y une las raíces a las hojas. (pág. 208)

stimulus/estímulo Cambio en el entorno del organismo que le hace reaccionar. (pág. 124)

stomata/estomas Pequeños orificios en el envés de la mayoría de las hojas a través de los cuales pueden pasar el oxígeno y el dióxido de carbono. (pág. 205)

storm/tormenta Violenta alteración en la atmósfera. (pág. 503)

storm surge/marejada de tormenta "Bóveda" de agua que se desplaza por la costa donde toca tierra el huracán. (pág. 510)

stratosphere/estratosfera Segunda capa inferior de la atmósfera terrestre; la capa de ozono se encuentra en la estratosfera superior. (pág. 452)

stratus/estratos Nubes en forma de capas planas. (pág. 484)

streak/raya Se aplica al color del polvo de un mineral. (pág. 334)

stress/estrés Reacción que sufre el cuerpo y la mente de una persona ante situaciones de amenaza, desafío e inquietud. (pág. 358)

strike-slip fault/falla transcurrente Tipo de falla donde las rocas de cada lado se desplazan en sentido horizontal, sin apenas movimientos verticales. (pág. 360)

sublimation/sublimación Cambio del estado sólido directamente al gaseoso, sin pasar por el estado líquido. (pág. 78)

substance/sustancia El tipo de materia que presenta propiedades físicas y químicas concretas. (pág. 25)

sunspot/mancha solar Región oscura y menos caliente de la superficie del Sol. (pág. 540)

surface waves/ondas superficiales Tipo de ondas sísmicas que se forman cuando las ondas P y S llegan a la superficie terrestre. (pág. 370)

syncline/sinclinal Pliegue hacia abajo de las rocas debido a la compresión de la corteza terrestre. (pág. 364)

taxonomy/taxonomía Estudio científico de la clasificación de los seres vivos. (pág. 185)

temperature/temperatura Cantidad media de energía de movimiento que hay en las moléculas de una sustancia. (págs. 62, 469)

temperature inversion/inversión térmica Estado en el que una capa de aire templado situada entre dos capas de aire a más temperatura impide que escape el aire cercano a la Tierra. (pág. 442)

tension/tensión Tipo de esfuerzo que estira las rocas de modo que se alarguen en el centro. (pág. 359)

terrestrial planets/planetas telúricos Nombre que se les da a los cuatro planetas interiores: Mercurio, Venus, Tierra y Marte. (pág. 544)

texture/textura Tamaño, forma y patrón de los granos de una roca. (pág. 341)

Theory of Plate Tectonics/Teoría de la tectónica de placas Teoría que expone que los fragmentos de la litosfera terrestre se desplazan de forma constante, impulsados por las corrientes de convección del manto. (pág. 356)

thermal energy/energía térmica Energía total de las partículas de una sustancia debida a sus movimientos o vibraciones; también, energía del movimiento de las moléculas de una sustancia. (págs. 74, 469)

thermometer/termómetro Instrumento usado para medir la temperatura; consta de un delgado tubo de vidrio que tiene en uno de sus extremos una cubeta de líquido, el cual suele ser mercurio o alcohol. (pág. 469)

thermosphere/termosfera Capa exterior de la atmósfera terrestre. (pág. 455)

thorax/tórax Sección media de un insecto a la cual están sujetas las alas y las patas. (pág. 232)

tissue/tejido Grupo de células similares que desempeñan una función determinada en un organismo. (pág. 146)

tornado/tornado Nube con forma de embudo que girando velozmente sale de una nube de tormenta y toca la superficie terrestre, produciendo por lo general una trayectoria destructiva. (pág. 505)

trait/rasgo Característica que un organismo puede transmitir a través de sus genes a su descendencia. (pág. 149)

transpiration/transpiración Proceso por el cual se libera agua a través de las hojas de las plantas. (pág. 398)

tributary/tributario Corriente o río pequeño que desemboca en otra corriente más grande. (pág. 404)

tropical (air mass)/masa de aire tropical Masa de aire templado de baja presión atmosférica que se forma en los trópicos. (pág. 496)

tropism/tropismo Respuesta de crecimiento de las plantas, dirigiéndose hacia un estímulo o alejándose de él. (pág. 210)

troposphere/troposfera Capa inferior de la atmósfera terrestre; zona donde se producen los cambios de tiempo. (pág. 451)

ultraviolet radiation/radiación ultravioleta Forma de energía cuya longitud de onda es más corta que la de la luz visible. (pág. 463)

unbalanced force/fuerza desequilibrada Fuerza neta distinta a cero que cambia el movimiento de un objeto. (pág. 99)

unsaturated zone/zona no saturada Capa de rocas y tierra situada por encima del nivel freático en la que los poros contienen tanto aire como agua. (pág. 413)

vacuole/vacuola Bolsa llena de agua del interior de las células que hace de zona de almacenamiento. (pág. 145)

vaporization/vaporización Paso de la materia del estado líquido al gaseoso. (pág. 76)

vary inversely/varían inversamente Término empleado para describir la relación entre dos variables cuya gráfica forma una curva que se inclina hacia abajo y de izquierda a derecha. (pág. 71)

vascular tissue/tejido vascular En algunas plantas, tejido interno compuesto por estructuras tubulares y dedicado al transporte. (pág. 205)

vein/vena Vaso sanguíneo por donde vuelve la sangre al corazón. (pág. 336)

velocity/velocidad Rapidez en una dirección dada. (pág. 93)

vent/boca Abertura por donde las rocas fundidas y el gas salen del volcán. (pág. 375)

ventricle/ventrículo Cavidad inferior del corazón que bombea sangre a los pulmones y al resto del cuerpo. (pág. 241)

vertebrae/vértebras Huesos que forman la columna vertebral de los animales. (pág. 237)

vertebrate/vertebrado Animal que tiene columna vertebral. (pág. 220)

viscosity/viscosidad Resistencia de un líquido a fluir. (pág. 59)

volcanic neck/cuello volcánico Depósito de magma solidificado en la chimenea de un volcán. (pág. 387)

volume/volumen Cantidad de espacio que ocupa la materia. (pág. 35)

water cycle/ciclo del agua Proceso constante mediante el cual el agua va de la superficie terrestre a la atmósfera y después regresa al suelo, pasando por los componentes vivos o no del medio ambiente. (pág. 398)

water pollution/contaminación del agua Incorporación al agua de cualquier sustancia que tenga efectos negativos para ella o para los seres vivos que de ella dependen. (pág. 424)

water table/nivel freático Parte superior de la zona saturada, o profundidad a la que está el agua subterránea en un acuífero. (pág. 413)

water vapor/vapor de agua Forma gaseosa e invisible del agua. (pág. 437)

watershed/cuenca hidrográfica Extensión de tierra que suministra el agua a un sistema fluvial. (pág. 405)

weather/tiempo Estado de la atmósfera terrestre en un lugar y momento determinados. (pág. 484)

weight/peso Medida de la fuerza de gravedad ejercida sobre un objeto. (pág. 35)

wind/viento Movimiento horizontal del aire desde una zona de presión alta a otra de presión baja. (pág. 472)

wind-chill factor/factor de enfriamiento por viento Incremento del frío causado por el viento. (pág. 473)

zygote/cigoto Óvulo fecundado tras la unión de una célula sexual masculina y otra femenina. (pág. 208)

Index

Index

Index

movements, animal 220
multicellular algae 200
multicellular organisms 123
multistage rockets 567
muscle cells 146

National Aeronautics and Space
   Administration (NASA), 567
National Weather Service 507, 520
   maps, 447, 522, 523
natural gas 297–298
naturally occurring substances 332
Neptune 558
nerve cells 123, 146
nervous system 252
net force 99
neutrons 307, 308
Newton, Isaac 535
nimbostratus clouds 485
nitrates 436
nitrogen bases 176
nitrogen cycle 285
nitrogen fixation 285
nitrogen in atmosphere 435–436
nitrogen oxides 442
nonlinear relationship 105
nonrenewable resources 295
nonvascular plants 205, 206, 208
normal faults 360–361
   mountains formed by, 362–363
nuclear energy 307–311
nuclear fission 307–310
nuclear fusion 310–311, 538–539
nuclear membrane 140
nuclear power plant 308–310
nucleic acids 123
nucleolus 141
nucleus 140–141, 142, 143, 198, 199, 307
   organisms lacking, 145
nymph 233, 234

observation 11, 12, 119, 274, 580
obsidian 377
occluded fronts 501, 523
oceans 396
Ogallala Aquifer 414, 428
oil 296–297
oil spills 193
omnivore 219, 281
operational definition 585
oral groove 199
orders (level of classification), 186
ore 47, 50
organelles 139, 141–145
organic rock 344
organisms 122–130
   cells and, 123, 134–135
   characteristics of, 122–125
   classification of, 184–189
   levels of organization, 123, 146–147
   needs of, 127–129, 402
   responses of. See **responses of**
     organisms
   structure complementing function in,
     123, 146, 186, 202

organs, structure and function of 146
organ systems 238
   structure and function of, 147
osmosis 160
outer core 328, 329, 545
outer planets 552–559
   characteristics of, 552–553
   Jupiter, 554–555
   Neptune, 558
   Pluto and Charon, 559
   Saturn, 555–556
   Uranus, 557
ovary 209, 210
ovule 209, 210
oxbow lake 110, 111, 410
oxygen
   as abiotic factor in ecosystem, 268
   in the atmosphere, 165, 436, 544
   cellular respiration and, 166
   delivery to cells. See **circulatory system;**
     respiratory system
   diffusion into cells, 159
   photosynthesis and production of, 164,
     165
oxygen cycle 285
ozone 436
ozone layer 452, 453, 463

pahoehoe 378
Pangaea 355
panning for gold 47
paramecium 198, 199
parasites 199
passive solar system 301
passive transport 161
Pasteur, Louis 126, 127
pellicle 199
percent 128, 181
perennials 211
permeability, selective 158
pesticides 152
petri dish 17, 194–195, 212, 224
petrochemicals 297
petroleum 296–297
photochemical smog 442
photosphere 539, 541
photosynthesis 163–165, 167, 169, 205,
   268, 281, 285, 402
phyla 186
physical change 30, 32
physical property 26
   classifying substances by, 25, 26, 39
   density as, 38–39
physical science 18
Piccard, Auguste 455
pipe in volcano 375, 376
pistils 209
placenta 255
planarians 225
planets 533, 534, 536–537, 544–561
   distance from sun and period of
     revolution, 560–561
   gravitational force and, 101
   inner (terrestrial), 544–551

   orbit of, 535–536
   outer, 552–559
plant cell 139, 142, 148, 173
plantlike protists 200
plants 189, 204–212
   characteristics shared by, 205–208
   kingdom, 189
   life cycle of, 183
   nonvascular, 205, 206, 208
   photosynthesis by, 163–165, 167, 169,
     205, 268, 281, 285, 402
   vascular, 205, 207, 208–210
plastic 58
plateaus 365
   lava, 388
plate boundaries 356–357
   faults along, 360
plates 354
plate tectonics 354–357
   mountain building and, 362–365
Pluto 559
polar air masses 496
   continental, 498
   maritime, 497, 498
polar easterlies 479, 480
poles, magnetic 101
pollen 209, 441
pollutants 440, 442
pollution
   air, 296, 298, 440–443, 444
   water, 298
ponds 407, 408–409
population 147, 269
   limiting factors for, 277–278
   structure and function in, 269
population density 273
population size 274–276, 279
population statement 276
pores
   in sponge, 223
   underground, 413
position of object
   changes in, 87–88
   direction of motion and, 88, 103
   force and, 99
   speed and, 87, 102, 103
power plants 293
   energy transformations and, 293
   hydroelectric, 302, 304, 306
   nuclear, 308–310
   solar, 300, 304
   wind, 303
precipitation 412, 487–490
   acid rain, 443
   controlling, 490
   measuring, 489
   water cycle and, 398–399
predators 219
prediction 580
pressure 63, 445
   air, 77, 445–450, 501–502
   of gas, 63
   temperature and, 64–65
   volume and, 63–64, 70–71

Index

Acknowledgments

Staff Credits

The people who made up the *Texas Science Explorer* team—representing design services, editorial, editorial services, electronic publishing technology, manufacturing & inventory planning, market research, marketing services, online services & multimedia development, planning & budgeting, product planning, production services, project office, and publishing processes—are listed below. Bold type denotes the core team members.

Scott Andrews, **Carolyn Belanger,** Barbara A. Bertell, Suzanne Biron, **Peggy Bliss,** Kristen Braghi, Dan Breslin, Jonathan Cheney, **Lisa J. Clark,** Robin Clark, Ed Cordero, Bob Craton, Christine Cuccio, **Patricia Cully,** Gabriella Della Corte, Kathleen J. Dempsey, Emily Ellen, Barnard Gage, Jane P. Gardner, **Julie Gecha,** Adam Goldberg, Kerri Hoar, Joanne Hudson, Alan Hull, Anne Jones, Toby Klang, Carolyn Langley, Carolyn Lock, Diahanne Lucas, Don Manning, Jeanne Y. Maurand, **Tim McDonald,** Carolyn McGuire, Karen McHugh, Natania Mlawer, Paul Murphy, Judi Pinkham, **Robin L. Santel,** Suzanne Schineller, **Diane Walsh,** Jane Willan, Pat Williams, Char Lyn Yeakley, Helen Young

Illustrations

AccuWeather: 524, 525
Sally Bensusen: 233
Suzanne Biron: 130,148
Peter Brooks: 35, 48, 72, 80, 431, 543, 560
Patrice Rossi Calkin: 111,198, 199, 244
Warren Cutler: 249, 408–409, 420–421
Kathleen Dempsey: 366, 384
John Edwards & Associates: 205, 283, 284, 293, 301, 303, 309, 329, 356–357, 450, 464, 476, 501, 509, 536, 545, 553
Julia Gecha: 526
Andrea Golden: 229, 403, 414
Biruta Hansen: 270
Keith Kasnot: 141,142, 143,144, 200
MapQuest.com, Inc.: 321, 355, 362, 373, 405, 422, 508, 511, 512, 523
Martucci Studio: 68, 69, 70, 71, 78, 94, 105, 166, 313, 397, 435, 463, 523, 543
Matt Mayerchak: 51, 113,153, 174, 429, 457
Fran Milner: 147, 232, 240, 242
Morgan Cain & Associates: 49, 57, 57, 58, 60, 63, 64, 69, 70, 123, 126, 127, 136, 155, 159, 161, 169, 174, 215, 256, 262, 289, 294, 297, 308, 310, 312, 343, 364, 369, 370, 376, 387, 389, 442, 448, 447, 448, 459, 465, 468, 470, 474, 477, 479, 487, 489, 493, 541, 545, 563, 566, 567, 573, 600–601
Ortelius Design Inc.: 3, 7, 36, 37, 355, 380, 381, 400, 401, 428, 437, 476, 502, 506, 507, 529, 606
Matthew Pippin: 110, 302, 369, 399, 413, 431, 446, 453, 481, 485, 516
John Sanderson: 498
Walter Stuart: 202
Cynthia Turner: 208
Roberta Warshaw: 40, 171, 285, 287, 349, 601tr
J/B Woolsey Associates: 53, 117, 119, 124, 164, 200, 209, 212, 215, 226, 231, 239, 241, 248, 276, 285, 332, 351, 393, 484, 517, 600–601

Photography

Cover Design: Studio Montage

Cover Image: NASA

Front Matter
Page i, NASA; **ii,** NASA; **iii l,** Courtesy of Michael J. Padilla, Ph.D; **iii r,** Courtesy of Martha Cyr, Ph.D. and Ioannis Miaoulis, Ph.D; **viii t,** Ken Lucas/Visuals Unlimited; **viii b,** John Kelly/Image Bank; **ix l,** M. Abbey/Visuals Unlimited; **ix m,** Dr. David Scott/CNRI/Phototake; **ix r,** Dr. Dennis Kunkel/Phototake; **x t,** Bas van Beek/Leo de Wys; **x m,** Patti Murray/Animals Animals; **x b,** Stone/Richard A Cooke III; **xi t,** Superstock; **xi top inset,** Wernher Krutein/Liaison Agency; **xi bl,** Ralph A. Clevenger/Corbis Westlight; **xi bm,** Calvin Larsen/Photo Researchers, Inc.; **xi br,** Tim Olive/SharpShooters; **xii t,** Biophoto Associates/Photo Researchers, Inc.; **xii bl,** NASA/Photo Researchers, Inc.; **xii br,** Steve Vidler/Superstock; **xiii tl,** Dan Sudia/Photo Researchers, Inc.; **xiii tr,** NASA Goddard Laboratory for Atmospheres; **xiii bl,** Russ Lappa; **xiii br,** NOAA; **xiv t,** Richard Haynes; **xiv m,** Renee Lynn/Photo Researchers;

xiv b, Paul Rezendes; **xv t,** Richard Haynes; **xv b,** Superstock; **xvi t,** A. T. Willet/Image Bank; **xvi b,** Doug Martin/Photo Researchers, Inc.; **xvii t,** Robert Maier/Animals Animals; **xvii b,** Richard Haynes; **xviii t,** NASA; **xviii b,** Stone/Mark Lewis; **xix l,** Norbert Rosing/Animals Animals/Earth Scenes; **xix r,** PhotoDisc, Inc.; **xx tl,** Richard Megna/Fundamental Photographs; **xx tml,** Goivaux Communication/Phototake; **xx tmr,** Charles D. Winters/Photo Researchers, Inc.; **xx tr,** Ken Lucas/Visuals Unlimited; **xx bl,** Marc Romanelli/Image Bank; **xx br,** Tim DeFrisco/Allsport; **xxi,** Richard Haynes.

Texas Field Trip
Pages 2 tl, Courtesy of Rosenberg Library, Galveston, Texas; **2 tr,** National Oceanic and Atmospheric Administration/Department of Commerce; **2 bl, 2 br,** Courtesy of Rosenberg Library, Galveston, Texas; **2–3,** NOAA/Science Photo Library/Photo Researchers; **3 t,** Mark Perlstein/Black Star; **4 l,** National Oceanic and Atmospheric Administration/Department of Commerce; **4 m,** Gamma Liaison; **4 r,** AP Photo/David J. Phillip; **5 both,** Courtesy of Wind Engineering Research Center, Texas Tech University.

Nature of Science
Page 6 m, Courtesy of Wind Engineering Research Center, Texas Tech University; **6–7,** Annie Griffiths Belt/National Geographic; **7 t, 7 b, 8, 9 all,** Courtesy of Wind Engineering Research Center, Texas Tech University.

What Is Science?
Page 10 t, Stone/Dave Bjorn; **10 b,** Nancy Sheehan Photography; **11,** Manfred Gottschalk/Tom Stack & Associates; **15,** Tsado/NCDC/NOAA/Tom Stack & Associates; **16, 17,** Richard Haynes; **18 l,** Paula Lerner/Index Stock Imagery; **18 r,** Peter Menzel/Stock Boston; **19 t,** Frank Pederick/The Image Works; **19 b,** Kim Steele/PhotoDisc; **20,** Tsado/NCDC/NOAA/Tom Stack & Associates.

Chapter 1
Pages 22–23, Superstock; **24 both,** Russ Lappa; **25,** Thomas H. Ives/The Stock Market; **26,** PhotoDisc, Inc.; **27 l,** Stone/Cathlyn Melloan; **27 m,** Bernard Roussel/The Image Bank; **27 r,** Bob Firth/International Stock; **28 l,** Ken Lucas/Visuals Unlimited; **28 r,** Yoav Levy/Phototake; **29 t,** David D. Keaton/The Stock Market; **29 tl,** Michael Fogden/DRK Photo; **29 tr,** Glenn M. Oliver/Visuals Unlimited; **29 bl,** Richard Megna/Fundamental Photographs; **29 bml,** Goivaux Communication/PhotoTake; **29 bmr,** Charles D. Winters/Photo Researchers, Inc.; **29 br,** Ken Lucas/Visuals Unlimited; **30 t,** Micheal P Gadomski/Photo Researchers, Inc.; **30 b,** Stone/Lawrence Migdale; **31,** John M. Roberts/The Stock Market; **32,** Stone/Alan R Moller; **33 t,** James Dwyer/Stock Boston; **33 b,** Tony Freeman/PhotoEdit; **34 t,** Richard Haynes; **34 b,** SuperStock; **35 l,** Russ Lappa; **35 r,** Richard Haynes; **36, 37 t,** Corbis-Bettmann; **37 b,** The Granger Collection, NY; **38,** The Art Institute of Chicago; **41 both,** 1998, The Art Institute of Chicago; **42,** Rich Treptow/Visuals Unlimited; **43,** Chuck Feil/Uniphoto; **44,** SCI-VU-IBMRL/Visuals Unlimited; **45,** Ken Eward/Science Source/Photo Researchers, Inc.; **46 t,** Russ Lappa; **46 b,** Corbis-Bettmann; **47 t,** Helga Lade/Peter Arnold, Inc.; **47 bl,** E. R. Degginger/Animals Animals/Earth Scenes; **47 br,** Charles D. Winters/Photo Researchers, Inc.; **48,** Aron Haupt/ David R. Frazier Photo Library; **50,** Heine Schneebeli/Science Photo Library/Photo Researchers, Inc.; **51,** Corbis-Bettmann.

Chapter 2
Pages 54–55, Milton Rand/Tom Stack & Associates; **56 t,** Richard Haynes; **56 b,** Shambroom/Photo Researchers, Inc.; **57,** Stone/Darryl Torckler; **58 t,** Rivera Collection/Superstock; **58 b,** Russ Lappa; **59,** Tsutomu Nakayama/Uniphoto; **60,** Tomas Muscionoco/The Stock Market; **61,** A. Ramey/Stock Boston; **62,** John D. Cunningham/Visuals Unlimited; **63, 64,** Richard Haynes; **65,** Ken Ross/FPG International; **67 both,** Ken Karp; **72,** Russ Lappa; **73, 74 t,** Richard Haynes; **74 b,** Russ Lappa; **75,** Doug Martin/Photo Researchers, Inc.; **76,** The Granger Collection, NY; **77,** Martin Dohrn/Science Photo Library/Photo Researchers, Inc.; **79,** Charles D. Winters/Photo Researchers, Inc.; **80,** Russ Lappa; **81,** Stone/Darryl Torckler.

Chapter 3
Pages 84–85, Frans Lanting/Minden Pictures; **86 t,** Richard Haynes; **86 b,** Roy Morsch/The Stock Market; **87 t,** D. Roundtree/Image Bank; **87 b,** Steve Maslowski/Photo Researchers, Inc.; **88,** NASA; **89 l,** Chuck Zsymanski/International Stock; **89 r,** Robert Maier/Animals Animals; **90,** Mike Agliolo/International Stock; **91,** John Kelly/Image Bank; **92,** National Motor Museum, Beaulieu, England; **93 t,** Topham/The Image Works; **93 b,** David Barnes/The Stock Market; **94,** Marc Romanelli/Image Bank; **95,** A.T. Willet/Image Bank; **97, 98 t,** Richard Haynes; **98 b,** Mike Hewitt/Allsport; **99 t,** Russ Lappa; **99 b,** The Stock Market; **100,** Bob Daemmrich/The Image Works; **101 bl,** Mark C. Burnett/Photo Researchers, Inc.; **101 br,** Tony Freeman/PhotoEdit; **102 t,** Yann Guichaoua/Agence Vandystadt/Allsport; **102 m,** Tim DeFrisco/Allsport; **102 b,** Tracy Frankel/Image Bank; **103,** Addison Geary/Stock Boston; **104,** Corel Corp.; **106,** Richard Haynes; **107,** Lou Jones/Image Bank; **108,** Russ Lappa; **109,** Stone/Jacques Jangoux; **112,** Bill Gillette/Liaison Agency; **112 inset,** Gregory Foster/Liaison Agency; **116,** Brian Smale/Discover Magazine; **117,** Stephen G.

Maka/DRK Photo; **118,** Brian Smale/Discover Magazine; **118 inset,** Helen Ghiradella/Discover Magazine.

Chapter 4

Pages 120–121, Joe McDonald/DRK Photo; **122 t,** Russ Lappa; **122 b,** Beatty/Visuals Unlimited; **123,** John Pontier/Animals Animals; **125,** Michael Quinton/Minden Pictures; **126, 127,** The Granger Collection, NY; **128 l,** James Dell/Science Source/Photo Researchers, Inc.; **128 r,** Zig Leszczynski/Animals Animals; **129,** Jim Brandenburg/Minden Pictures; **131 t,** Richard Haynes; **131 b,** John Coletti/Stock Boston; **131 inset,** Joseph Nettis/Photo Researchers, Inc.; **132, 133 l,** The Granger Collection, NY; **133 r,** Caroline Biological Supply Company/Phototake; **134 both,** The Granger Collection, NY; **135 t,** H. R. Bramaz/Peter Arnold, Inc.; **135 bl,** Corbis-Bettmann; **135 br,** Lawrence Migdale/Stock Boston; **137,** CNRI/Science Photo Library/Photo Researchers, Inc.; **138 t,** Runk/Schoenberger/Grant Heilman Photography; **138 b,** Doug Wilson/Corbis Westlight; **139 l,** M. Abbey/Visuals Unlimited; **139 r,** Runk/Schoenberger/Grant Heilman Photography; **140,** Dr. Dennis Kunkel/Phototake; **141,** Bill Longcore/Photo Researchers, Inc.; **144,** K. G. Murtis/Visuals Unlimited; **145,** Stone/John Cardamone; **146 l,** Dr. David Scott/CNRI/Phototake; **146 r,** Dr. Dennis Kunkel/Phototake; **148,** Runk/Schoenberger/Grant Heilman Photography; **149 both,** Richard Haynes; **150 t,** Stephen J. Krasemann/DRK Photo; **150 m,** PhotoDisc, Inc.; **150 bl,** Stone/Andrew Olney; **150 br,** Brian Parker/Tom Stack & Associates; **151,** Stone/Gary Bumgarner; **152,** Santa Gertudis Association.

Chapter 5

Pages 156–157, Julie Habel/Corbis Westlight; **158,** NASA; **160 l,** Stanley Flegler/Visuals Unlimited; **160 m,** David M. Phillips/Visuals Unlimited; **160 r,** David M. Phillips/Visuals Unlimited; **162,** M. Abbey/Visuals Unlimited; **163 t,** Russ Lappa; **163 bl,** Stone/Cosmo Condina; **163 br,** Biophoto Associates/Photo Researchers, Inc.; **165 l,** Frans Lanting/Minden Pictures; **165 r,** Tom J. Ulrich/Visuals Unlimited; **166 l,** Stephen Dalton/Photo Researchers, Inc.; **166 r,** Phil Dotson/Photo Researchers, Inc.; **167,** Mark Newman/Visuals Unlimited; **168,** Terje Rakke/Image Bank; **170 t,** David Scharf/Peter Arnold, Inc.; **170 b,** Larry Lefever/Grant Heilman Photography; **171,** Stone/Art Wolfe; **172,** Biophoto Associates/Science Source/Photo Researchers, Inc.; **174, 175 all,** M. Abbey/Photo Researchers, Inc.; **178,** Robert Knauft/Biology Media.

Chapter 6

Pages 182–183, J. Lotter Gurling/Tom Stack & Associates; **184 t** Russ Lappa; **184 b,** Inga Spence/The Picture Cube; **185 l,** Gerard Lacz/Animals Animals **185 m,** Tom Brakefield/DRK Photo; **185 r,** Ron Kimball; **186–187,** Thomas Kitchin/Tom Stack & Associates; **188 t,** Alan L. Detrick/Photo Researchers; **188 bl,** Oliver Meckes/Photo Researchers; **188 br,** David M. Phillips/Visuals Unlimited; **189,** Ray Coleman/Photo Researchers; **190 t,** Richard Haynes; **190 b,** Science Photo Library/Photo Researchers; **191,** Dr. Rony Brain/Science Photo Library/Photo Researchers; **192 bl,** Dr. K. S Kim/Peter Arnold; **192 br,** Dr. Ennis Kunkel/Phototake; **193 l,** Stone/Ben Osborne; **193 r,** Michael Abbey/Photo Researchers; **195,** Richard Haynes; **196 t,** Science VU/Visuals Unlimited; **196 b,** Jan Hinsch/Science Photo Library/Photo Researchers; **197 tl,** O.S.F./Animals Animals; **197 tr,** A. Le Toquin/Photo Researchers; **197 b,** Gregory G. Dimijian/Photo Researchers; **198,** Astrid & Hanns-Frieder Michler/Science Photo Library/Photo Researchers; **199,** Eric Grave/Science Source/Photo Researchers; **200,** Sinclair Stammers Oxford Scientific Films; **201 t,** Dwight R. Kuhn; **201 b,** Michael Fogden/Animals Animals; **202,** Fred Unverhau/Animals Animals/Earth Scenes; **203,** David Scharf/Peter Arnold; **204,** Joanne Lotter/Tom Stack & Associates; **206 tl,** Runk/Schoenberger/Grant Heilman Photography; **206 tr, 206 bl,** Runk/Schoenberger/Grant Heilman Photography, Inc.; **206 br,** Rod Planck/Tom Stack & Associates; **207 l,** Runk/Schoenberger/Grant Heilman Photography; **207 inset,** Breck P. Kent; **207 ml,** Thomas Kitchin/Tom Stack & Associates; **207 mr,** David Forbert/Superstock; **209,** E. R. Degginger; **210,** Porterfield-Chickering/Photo Researchers; **211 tl,** E. R. Degginger; **211 tr,** Mark E. Gibson/The Stock Market; **211 b,** Larry Lefever/Grant Heilman Photography.

Chapter 7

Pages 216–217, Norbert Wu/DRK Photo; **218 t,** Richard Haynes; **218 b,** Leonard Lee Rue III/Animals Animals/Earth Scenes; **219 l,** Stone/Oliver Strewe; **219 r,** Frans Lanting/Minden Pictures; **220 l,** Dave B. Fleetham/Visuals Unlimited; **220 r,** Stone/David Tipling; **221,** Corel Corp.; **222,** William C Jorgensen/Visuals Unlimited; **223 t,** Russ Lappa; **223 b,** Gregory Ochocki/Photo Researchers, Inc.; **224 l,** Stone/Charles Seaborn; **224 r,** Biophoto Associates/Photo Researchers, Inc.; **225,** David M. Dennis/Tom Stack & Associates; **226,** Sinclair Stammers/Science Photo Library/Photo Researchers, Inc.; **228 l,** Stone/Kevin & Cat Sweeney; **228 r,** Bruce Watkins/Animals Animals; **230 t,** Richard Haynes; **230 b,** Patti Murray/Animals Animals; **231 l,** John Gerlach/Tom Stack & Associates; **231 r,** Donald Specker/Animals Animals; **232,** CNRI/Science Photo Library/Photo Researchers, Inc.; **234,** The G. R. 'Dick' Roberts Photo Library; **235 tl,** Simon D. Pollard/Photo Researchers, Inc.; **235 tr,** Stone/Tim Flach; **235 b,** Stone/Christoph Burki; **236 l,** Brian Parker/Tom Stack & Associates; **236 m,** Stone/Darryl Torckler **236 r,** Fred Whitehead/Animals Animals; **237 t,** Russ Lappa; **237**

b, Phil Dotson/Photo Researchers, Inc.; **238 l,** Larry Lipsky/DRK Photo; **238 r,** John d. Cummingham/Visuals Unlimited; **239 l,** Jeff Rotman; **239 r,** Herve Berthoule Jacana/Photo Researchers, Inc.; **241,** Suzanne L. Collins & Joseph T. Collins/Photo Researchers, Inc.; **243,** Tom Stack and Associates; **244,** Zig Leszczynski/Animals Animals; **245 l,** Brian Kenney/Natural Selection; **245 r,** M. C. Chamberlain/DRK Photo; **246,** Colin Milkins/Animals Animals; **247 t,** Richard Haynes; **247 b,** Wayne Lankinen/DRK Photo; **248,** Stephen Krasemann/DRK Photo; **250,** Stone/Manfred Danegger; **251 l,** Henry Ausloos/Animals Animals/Earth Scenes; **251 r,** Stone/Art Wolfe; **252 t,** Hilary Pooley/Animals Animals; **252–253 b,** Michael Fogden/DRK Photo; **253 t,** Johnny Johnson/DRK Photo; **254 l,** Tom McHugh/Photo Researchers, Inc.; **254 r,** Jack Dermid; **255 t,** Roger Aitkenhead/Animals Animals; **255 b,** Stone/Chuck Davis; **260,** Courtesy of Lydia Villa-Komaroff; **261,** Courtesy of Lydia Villa-Komaroff; **262 t,** Biophoto Associates/Science Source/Photo Researchers, Inc.; **262 b,** Howard Sochurek/The Stock Market; **263,** Will & Deni McIntyre/Photo Researchers, Inc.

Chapter 8

Pages 264–265, Stone/Tony Craddock; **266 t,** Richard Haynes; **266-267 b,** Shin Yoshino/Minden Pictures; **267 t,** Carr Clifton/Minden Pictures; **267 t inset,** Corel Corp.; **267 b inset,** S. Nielsen/DRK Photo; **268,** John Cancalosi/Tom Stack & Associates; **269,** Patti Murray/Animals Animals; **273 t,** Richard Haynes; **273 b,** Michlo Hoshino/Minden Pictures; **274,** C. Allan Morgan/DRK Photo; **275 t,** Rob Simpson/Visuals Unlimited; **275 b,** Bas van Beek/Leo de Wys; **277,** Mitsuaki Iwago/Minden Pictures; **278 t,** Dan Budnick/Woodfin Camp & Associates; **278 b,** Russ Lappa; **280,** The Stock Market; **281,** Stone/Frans Lanting; **282 tl,** David Davis/Index Stock; **282 tr,** Gail Shumway/FPG International; **282 b,** Nobel Proctor/Science Source/Photo Researchers, Inc.; **286,** Larry Lefever/Grant Heilman Photography.

Chapter 9

Pages 290–291, Stone/Yamada Toshiro; **292,** M. L. Sinibaldi/The Stock Market; **295,** Stone/Richard A Cooke III; **296,** Stone/Keith Wood; **298,** Stone/Mike Abrahams; **299,** Chad Ehlers/International Stock; **300,** Stone/Nadia MacKenzie; **302,** Robert K. Grubbs/Photo Network; **304,** NASA; **305,** Richard Haynes; **306,** Herb Swanson; **307 t,** Russ Lappa; **307 b,** Photograph by Johan Hagemeyer, courtesy AIP Emilio Segre Visual Archives; **310,** Y. Arthus-Bertrand/Peter Arnold, Inc.; **311,** U.S. Dept. of Energy/Science Photo Library/Photo Researchers, Inc.; **313,** Richard Haynes; **314 t,** Stone/Mitch Kezar; **314 b,** Leonard Lessin/Peter Arnold, Inc.; **315,** Stone/Yves Marcoux; **316,** Wolf/Monkmeyer; **317,** Stone/Nadia MacKenzie; **320 t,** Jeff Foott/Tom Stack & Associates; **320 b,** Courtesy of Elroy Masters; **321 t,** Courtesy of Elroy Masters; **321 b,** Pat O'Hara/DRK Photo; **322–323 b,** M. Collier/DRK Photo; **322 t inset,** Vireo; **322 b inset,** Jeff Foott/Tom Stack & Associates; **323 t,** Gilbert Grant/Photo Researchers, Inc.

Chapter 10

Pages 324–325, Hubertus Kanus/Superstock; **326,** ESA/PLI/The Stock Market; **327 l,** Peter Arnold, Inc.; **327 r,** Stone/G. Brad Lewis; **328,** John Eastcott/Yva Momatiuk/The Image Works; **330 t,** Richard Haynes; **330 b,** Barry L. Runk/Grant Heilman Photography; **331 l,** Mark A. Schneider/Visuals Unlimited; **331 m, 331 r, 332 l,** Breck P. Kent; **332 r,** E.R. Degginger; **334 tl,** Paul Silverman/Fundamental Photographs; **334 tr,** Breck P. Kent; **334 bl,** Charles D. Winters/Photo Researchers, Inc; **334 bm,** Runk/Schoenberger/Grant Heilman Photography; **334 br,** William Ferguson; **335 l,** Runk/Schoenberger/Grant Heilman Photography; **335 r,** Paul Silverman/Fundamental Photographs; **336 t,** Runk/Schoenberger/Grant Heilman Photography; **336 b,** Gemological Institute of America; **337 tl,** Bill Pierce/Rainbow; **337 tr,** Pearson Education/PH College/Prentice Hall; **337 m,** Laurence Parent; **337 b,** Michael Newman/PhotoEdit; **339,** Richard Haynes; **340,** Tom Bean; **341 tl,** E. R. Degginger; **341 tm, 341 tr, 341 m, 341 b, 342 r,** Breck P. Kent; **342 l,** E.R. Degginger; **343,** Breck P. Kent; **344 t,** David Welling/Animals Animals/Earth Scenes; **344 m,** Barry Runk/Grant Heilman Photography; **344 b,** PhotoDisc, Inc.; **345 tl,** Barry L. Runk/Grant Heilman Photography; **345 tr,** Andrew J. Martinez/Photo Researchers, Inc.; **345 m,** Jeff Scovil; **345 b,** Jeff Scovil; **346,** David Muench Photography.

Chapter 11

Pages 352–353, Soames Summerhays/Photo Researchers, Inc.; **354 t,** Russ Lappa; **354 b,** Simon Fraser/Science Photo Library/Photo Reseachers, Inc.; **358,** Ben S. Kwiatkowski/Fundamental Photographs; **360 t,** David Parker/Science Photo Library/Photo Researchers, Inc.; **360 b,** David Muench Photography; **361,** Sharon Gerig/Tom Stack & Associates; **362,** Stone/Stan Osolinski; **363,** Phillips Petroleum; **364, 365,** Tom Bean; **367 both, 368, 370 t,** Richard Haynes; **370 b,** Russell D. Curtis/Photo Researchers, Inc.; **371,** AP Photo/Leonetto Medici; **372,** EERC/Berkeley; **374 t, 374 b,** Breck P. Kent; **374 m, 375, 377 b,** E. R. Degginger; **377 t,** Ed Reschke/Peter Arnold, Inc.; **378 t,** William Felger/Grant Heilman Photography; **378 b,** Dave B. Fleetham/Tom Stack & Associates; **379 all,** Alberto Garcia/Saba Press; **380, tl,** North Wind Picture Archives; **380 tr,** Kim Heacox/Peter Arnold, Inc.; **380 b,** Robert Fried Photography; **381,** Alberto Garcia/Saba Press; **382,** Norbert Rosing/Animals Animals/Earth Scenes; **383 l,** AP Photo/Pat Roqua; **383 r,** Antonio Emerito/Sipa Press; **385, 386 t,** Richard Haynes; **386 b,** Brownie Harris/The Stock Market; **387 l,** Tom

Bean/DRK Photo; **387 r,** David Hosking/Photo Researchers, Inc.; **388,** Betty Crowell/Faraway Places; **389 t,** Picture Perfect; **389 m,** Manfred Gottschalk/Tom Stack & Associates; **389 b,** Chris Hamilton/The Stock Market; **390,** Greg Vaughn/Tom Stack & Associates.

Chapter 12
Pages 394–395, Randy Linchs/Sharpshooters; **396,** Richard Haynes; **400 t,** O. Louis Mazzatenta/National Geographic Image Collection; **400 b,** Liba Taylor/Corbis; **401 t,** Stone/Tom Bean; **401 b,** Gianni Dagli Orti/Corbis; **404 t,** Russ Lappa; **404 b,** Superstock; **404 inset,** Wernher Krutein/Liaison Agency; **406,** Les Stone/Corbis Sygma; **407,** Stone/Doug McKay; **410 l,** David L. Brown/The Stock Market; **410 r,** John Shaw/Tom Stack & Associates; **411,** Ralph A. Clevenger/Corbis Westlight; **412 t,** Richard Haynes; **412 b,** Tim Olive/SharpShooters; **417,** Mark Thayer; **418 t,** Russ Lappa; **418 b,** Greg Vaughn/Tom Stack & Associates; **419 l,** PhotoDisc, Inc.; **419 r,** Breck P. Kent/Animals Animals/Earth Scenes; **423 t,** Russ Lappa; **423 b,** Laura Sikes/Corbis Sygma; **424,** Calvin Larsen/Photo Researchers, Inc.; **426,** Russ Lappa; **427 t,** Peter Skinner/Photo Researchers, Inc.; **427 b,** Russ Lappa.

Chapter 13
Pages 432–433, Stone/Jay Simon; **434 t,** Russ Lappa; **434 b,** NASA/Photo Researchers, Inc.; **436 t,** Richard Haynes; **436 b,** Russ Lappa; **437,** George G. Dimijian/Photo Researchers, Inc; **438,** Eric Horan/Liaison Agency; **439,** Richard Haynes; **440 t,** Russ Lappa; **440 b,** Aaron Haupt/Photo Researchers, Inc.; **441 t,** Biophoto Associates/Photo Researchers, Inc.; **441 b,** Paul Lowe/Magnum Photos; **443,** Will McIntyre/Photo Researchers, Inc.; **444,** Steve Casimiro/Liaison Agency; **445 t,** Russ Lappa; **445 b,** Eric A. Kessler; **447,** Ivan Bucher/Photo Researchers, Inc.; **449, 451 t,** Russ Lappa; **451 b,** Steve Vidler/Superstock; **452,** Mark C. Burnett/Photo Researchers, Inc.; **454 t,** The Granger Collection, NY; **454 b,** Corbis-Bettmann; **455 t,** The National Archives/Corbis; **455 b,** NASA; **456;** Jack Finch/Science Photo Library/Photo Researchers, Inc.

Chapter 14
Pages 460–461, William Johnson/Stock Boston; **462–463,** Photo Researchers, Inc.; **467,** Richard Haynes; **468, 469, 472 t,** Russ Lappa; **472 b,** Victoria Hurst/Tom Stack & Associates; **473 t,** Richard Haynes; **473 b,** Gary Retherford/Photo Researchers, Inc.; **475,** Richard Haynes; **476,** Steve McCurry/Magnum Photos; **478,** Scala/Art Resource, NY; **480,** Stone/Ken McVey; **481,** Russ Lappa; **482,** E.J. Tarbuck; **483,** Peter Arnold, Inc.; **485 t,** Michael Gadomski/GADOM/Bruce Coleman; **485 tm,** Phil Degginger/Bruce Coleman, Inc.; **485 bm,** E.R. Degginger; **485 b,** John Shaw/Bruce Coleman, Inc.; **486,** Wendy Shattil/Bob Rozinski/Tom Stack & Associates; **487,** Richard Haynes; **488 t,** AP/Wide World Photos; **488 inset,** Stone/Gerben Oppermans Stone; **488 b,** Nuridsany et Perennou/Photo Researchers, Inc.; **490,** Stone/Bill Frantz; **491,** Stone/Gerben Oppermans.

Chapter 15
Pages 494–495, Pete Turner/Image Bank; **496 both,** Russ Lappa; **497,** Stone/Jim Corwin; **503 t,** Russ Lappa; **503 b,** Dirck Halstead/Liaison Agency; **504,** Dan Sudia/Photo Researchers, Inc.; **505,** Schuster Catalog/Superstock; **506 both,** The Granger Collection, NY; **507,** North Wind Picture Archives; **508,** Sheila Beougher/Liaison Agency; **509,** NASA Goddard Laboratory for Atmospheres; **510,** Clore Collection, Tate Gallery, London/Art Resource, NY; **512,** NOAA; **514,** Tony Freeman/PhotoEdit; **515 t,** Richard Haynes; **515 bl,** Keith Kent/Science Photo Library/Photo Researchers, Inc.; **515 br,** Grant V. Faint/Image Bank; **518,** AP Photos/David J. Phillip; **519 t,** Larry Lawfer, **519 b,** Corel Corp.; **520,** AP Photo/David Umberger; **521,** NOAA; **527,** Schuster Catalog/Superstock.

Chapter 16
Pages 530–531, NASA; **532 t,** Russ Lappa; **532 b,** Anglo-Australian Observatory, photograph by David Malin; **533, 534,** The Granger Collection, NY; **535 t,** Richard Haynes; **535 b,** The Granger Collection, NY; **538,** Richard Haynes; **539,** Digital Vision; **540,** National Solar Observatory; **540 inset,** Space Telescope Science Institute; **542 t,** Space Telescope Science Institute; **542 b,** National Solar Observatory; **546,** NASA; **546 inset,** A.S.P./Science Source/Photo Researchers, Inc.; **547,** Digital Vision; **548,** Digital Vision; **549,** NASA; **550,** Jet Propulsion Laboratory; **551 both,** NASA; **552,** Stone; **554 both,** NASA; **555, 556 t,** Jet Propulsion Laboratory; **556 inset,** Digital Vision; **556 b, 557, 558 both, 559,** NASA; **560, 561, 562 t,** Richard Haynes; **562 b,** Space Telescope Science Institute; **564,** Jet Propulsion Laboratory; **565 l,** U.S. Geological Survey; **565 r,** Jerry Schad/Photo Researchers, Inc.; **566,** Richard Haynes; **567,** NASA/Roger Ressmeyer/CORBIS; **568, 569,** NASA; **570, 571 t,** Jet Propulsion Laboratory; **571 b, 575 t,** The Granger Collection, NY; **575 m,** 1998 North Wind Picture Archives; **575 b,** Hippolyte Sebron (born France 1801–1879) Giant Steamboats on the Levee at New Orleans, 1853. Oil on canvas, Tulane. University Art Collection, Gift of D. H. Holmes Company.; **577,** Richard Pasley/Liaison Agency; **578,** National Portrait Gallery, Smithsonian Institution/Art Resource, NY; **579 t,** 1998 North Wind Picture Archives; **579 b,** Chromo Sohm/Sohm/Photo Researchers, Inc.

Skills Handbook
Page 580, Mike Moreland/Photo Network; **581 t,** FoodPix; **581 m,** Richard Haynes; **581 b,** Russ Lappa; **584,** Richard Haynes; **586,** Ron Kimball; **587,** Renee Lynn/Photo Researchers; **592,** Paul Rezendes.

Appendix
Page 600, 601 both, 602 both, Russ Lappa.